DÉCLIC
Vous allez aimer lire

Sindbâd, le marin
Histoire du pêcheur

Traduction d'Antoine Galland
Adaptation par Camille Page

Dossier par Camille Cohen
Certifiée de lettres modernes

Belin
ÉDUCATION

Sommaire

Retenir l'essentiel

Prolonger la lecture

À la découverte
des *Mille et Une Nuits*

Des contes aux origines lointaines et variées

• Les histoires regroupées dans *Les Mille et Une Nuits* sont issues de **diverses légendes diffusées à travers le monde :** certaines proviennent d'Inde, d'autres de Grèce, de Chine ou de Perse.

• ***Les Mille et Une Nuits*** regroupent donc des **récits anonymes,** souvent diffusés oralement, et qui se sont étoffés au fil du temps. C'est **Antoine Galland** qui permet la découverte de cette œuvre en Europe. Sa traduction connaît, dès sa parution au début du XVIIIe siècle, un **vif succès,** lié au goût du public de l'époque pour le conte et sa fascination pour l'Orient.

Auteur

Antoine Galland
(1646-1715)

est un **diplomate** français. Grâce à ses **voyages à travers l'Orient,** il apprend le turc, le persan et l'arabe, ce qui lui permet de traduire des contes orientaux à partir de 1704.

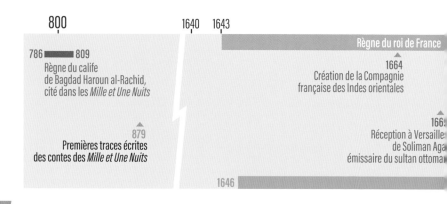

800   1640   1643

Règne du roi de France

786 ■■■ 809
Règne du calife
de Bagdad Haroun al-Rachid,
cité dans les *Mille et Une Nuits*

▲
1664
Création de la Compagnie
française des Indes orientales

▲
879
Premières traces écrites
des contes des *Mille et Une Nuits*

▲
166:
Réception à Versaille:
de Soliman Aga
émissaire du sultan ottoma

1646

Schéhérazade, une conteuse aux mille et une histoires

• Les histoires qui forment le recueil des *Mille et Une Nuits* sont encadrées par le récit de **Schéhérazade.**

• Celui-ci raconte qu'**un cruel sultan, Shahriar,** pour se venger de sa première femme qui lui avait été infidèle, épousait chaque jour une femme et la tuait le lendemain. Fille du grand vizir, **Schéhérazade** se porta volontaire pour l'épouser. Chaque nuit, **elle contait une partie d'une histoire** et ne s'arrêtait qu'au petit matin. **Le sultan devait attendre la nuit suivante** pour en connaître la suite. Par cette ruse, elle put ainsi mettre fin au massacre.

Léon Carré, illustration pour *Les Mille et Une Nuits*, 1931, lithographie.

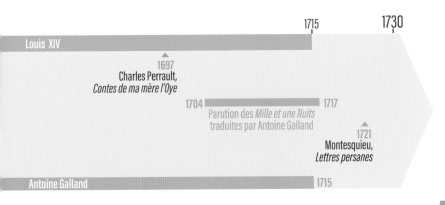

1715

1730

Louis XIV

1697
Charles Perrault,
Contes de ma mère l'Oye

1704   1717
Parution des *Mille et une Nuits*
traduites par Antoine Galland

1721
Montesquieu,
Lettres persanes

Antoine Galland   1715

La mer, entre danger et fascination

Illustrations de Léon Carré pour *Les Mille et Une Nuits*, 1931, lithographie.

Découvrez la mer et ses dangers

1 Observez le document 1. Quels éléments font référence à l'Orient ?

2 Décrivez et comparez les embarcations des deux documents.

3 Choisissez un adjectif dans la liste suivante pour qualifier la mer sur ces deux images. Justifiez votre choix à l'oral.

Belle	Dangereuse	Déchaînée

Imprévisible	Merveilleuse

À vous de jouer !

Imaginez et mettez en scène un dialogue

Par groupes de deux élèves, imaginez que l'homme du document 2 arrive sur une île. Il rencontre un habitant et lui raconte ses aventures.

Étape 1 Imaginez les aventures de l'homme sur le bateau, ainsi que l'échange avec l'habitant de l'île.

Étape 2 Ajoutez des précisions scéniques à votre texte (posture, voix, gestes...).

Étape 3 Entraînez-vous à lire en respectant les intonations et les gestes choisis. Apprenez ensuite votre texte par cœur.

Étape 4 Préparez un décor et des costumes.

Étape 5 Après vous être entraînés, présentez votre scène à la classe.

Lire les textes

NOTE SUR L'ADAPTATION

Cette édition propose une adaptation de deux contes
des *Mille et Une Nuits* à partir de la traduction d'Antoine Galland.
«Sindbâd, le marin» présente l'ensemble des sept voyages
en se concentrant sur les principales péripéties du héros.
«Histoire du pêcheur» met aussi l'accent sur les aventures
du personnage principal.
La syntaxe, la ponctuation et certains mots de vocabulaire ont
fait l'objet de modifications pour faciliter l'accès au texte tout
en veillant à conserver les qualités littéraires de la traduction
d'Antoine Galland.

Sindbâd, le marin

Edmond Dulac, illustration
pour *Sindbâd le Marin*, 1907.

1

Il y avait à Bagdad[1] un pauvre porteur[2] qui se nommait Hindbâd. Un jour qu'il faisait une chaleur excessive, il portait une charge très lourde. Comme il était fatigué du chemin qu'il avait déjà fait, il arriva dans une rue où régnait un doux

5 zéphyr[3]. Ne pouvant désirer un vent plus favorable pour se reposer, il posa sa charge à terre et s'assit dessus près d'une grande maison.

À cet endroit, son odorat fut agréablement frappé d'un parfum exquis qui sortait par les fenêtres. Le porteur

10 entendit à l'intérieur un concert de divers instruments. Cette gracieuse mélodie et la fumée de plusieurs sortes de viandes qui se faisaient sentir lui firent juger qu'il y avait là quelque festin. Il voulut savoir qui demeurait en cette maison et s'approcha de domestiques magnifiquement

15 habillés. Il demanda à l'un d'entre eux comment s'appelait le maître de ce lieu.

« Eh quoi, lui répondit le domestique, vous demeurez à Bagdad, et vous ignorez que c'est ici la demeure du seigneur Sindbâd le marin, ce fameux voyageur qui a parcouru toutes

20 les mers que le soleil éclaire ? »

....

1. **Bagdad**: voir carte, p. 110.
2. **Porteur**: personne dont le métier consiste à porter de lourdes charges.
3. **Zéphyr**: vent léger.

13

Le porteur, qui avait entendu parler des richesses de Sindbâd, ne put s'empêcher d'envier un homme dont la condition lui paraissait aussi heureuse qu'il trouvait la sienne déplorable. Il leva les yeux au ciel, et dit assez haut pour
25 être entendu :

« Puissant créateur de toutes choses, considérez la différence qu'il y a entre Sindbâd et moi. Je souffre tous les jours mille fatigues et mille maux[1]. J'ai bien de la peine à me nourrir pendant que l'heureux Sindbâd dépense avec
30 profusion[2] d'immenses richesses et mène une vie pleine de délices. Qu'a-t-il fait pour obtenir de vous une destinée[3] si agréable ? Qu'ai-je fait pour en mériter une si rigoureuse ? »

Il était encore occupé de ses tristes pensées, lorsqu'il vit sortir de la maison un valet qui vint à lui et qui lui dit :
35 « Venez, suivez-moi, le seigneur Sindbâd veut vous parler. »

Hindbâd fut surpris de l'honneur qu'on lui faisait. Après son discours, il craignait que Sindbâd ne l'envoyât chercher pour lui faire quelque mauvais traitement.
40 Le valet l'introduisit dans une grande salle où il y avait un bon nombre de personnes autour d'une table couverte de toutes sortes de mets[4] délicats. On voyait à la place

....

1. **Maux :** souffrances.
2. **Profusion :** abondance.
3. **Destinée :** sort.
4. **Mets :** aliments.

d'honneur un personnage grave, bien fait et vénérable par une longue barbe blanche. Ce personnage était Sindbâd.

45 Le porteur salua la compagnie en tremblant. Sindbâd lui dit de s'approcher, et après l'avoir fait asseoir à sa droite, il lui servit à manger lui-même, et lui fit donner à boire d'un excellent vin.

Sur la fin du repas, Sindbâd prit la parole. Il s'adressa à 50 Hindbâd et lui demanda comment il se nommait, et quelle était sa profession.

«Seigneur, lui répondit-il, je m'appelle Hindbâd.

– Je suis bien aise[1] de vous voir, reprit Sindbâd. Mais je souhaiterais apprendre de vous-même ce que vous disiez 55 tantôt dans la rue.»

Sindbâd, avant de se mettre à table, avait entendu tout son discours par la fenêtre.

À cette demande, Hindbâd, plein de confusion, baissa la tête, et répondit :

60 «Seigneur, je vous avoue que ma lassitude[2] m'avait mis en mauvaise humeur, et il m'est échappé quelques paroles indiscrètes[3] que je vous supplie de me pardonner.

– Oh ne croyez pas, reprit Sindbâd, que je sois assez injuste pour en conserver du ressentiment[4]. Mais il faut que

....

1. **Bien aise :** ravi.
2. **Lassitude :** découragement.
3. **Paroles indiscrètes :** propos déplacés.
4. **Ressentiment :** colère, rancœur.

65 je vous tire d'une erreur où vous me paraissez être. Vous vous imaginez, sans doute, que j'ai acquis sans peine et sans travail toutes les commodités et le repos dont vous voyez que je jouis. Détrompez-vous. Je ne suis parvenu à un état si heureux qu'après avoir souffert durant plusieurs années 70 tous les travaux du corps et de l'esprit que l'imagination peut concevoir. Oui, seigneurs, ajouta-t-il en s'adressant à toute la compagnie, je puis vous assurer que ces travaux sont si extraordinaires, qu'ils sont capables d'ôter aux hommes les plus avides de richesses l'envie fatale de traverser les 75 mers pour en acquérir. Vous n'avez peut-être entendu parler que de manière confuse de mes étranges aventures, et des dangers que j'ai courus sur mer dans les sept voyages que j'ai faits. Puisque l'occasion s'en présente, je vais vous en faire un rapport fidèle. »

Premier voyage

« J'avais hérité de ma famille des biens considérables, j'en dissipai[1] la meilleure partie dans les débauches de ma jeunesse. Mais je revins de mon aveuglement et je compris que les richesses étaient périssables, et qu'on en voyait bientôt la fin.

Frappé de toutes ces réflexions, je vendis à l'encan[2] en plein marché tout ce que j'avais de meubles. Je me liai ensuite avec quelques marchands qui négociaient par mer. Enfin, je me rendis à Balsora[3] où je m'embarquai avec plusieurs marchands sur un vaisseau.

Nous mîmes à la voile et prîmes la route des Indes orientales par le golfe Persique[4]. Je fus d'abord incommodé de ce qu'on appelle le mal de mer. Mais ma santé se rétablit bientôt, et depuis ce temps-là, je n'ai plus été sujet à cette maladie.

Au cours de notre navigation, nous abordâmes plusieurs îles, et nous y vendîmes ou échangeâmes nos marchandises.

....

1. Dissipai : gaspillai.
2. À l'encan : aux enchères.
3. Balsora : aujourd'hui, Bassora, ville située en Irak (voir carte, p. 110).
4. Golfe Persique : voir carte, p. 110.

Un jour, le calme nous prit face à une petite île qui ressemblait à une prairie par sa verdure. Le capitaine fit plier
20 les voiles et permit de prendre terre à l'équipage. Je fus du nombre de ceux qui y débarquèrent. Mais, alors que nous nous divertissions à boire et à manger, l'île trembla tout à coup et nous donna une rude secousse.

On s'aperçut du tremblement de l'île dans le vaisseau
25 d'où l'on nous cria de nous rembarquer promptement[1]. Nous allions tous périr[2], car ce que nous prenions pour une île était le dos d'une baleine.

Les plus diligents[3] se sauvèrent dans la chaloupe[4], d'autres se jetèrent à la nage. Pour moi, j'étais encore sur
30 l'île, ou plutôt sur la baleine, lorsqu'elle plongea dans la mer. Le capitaine, après avoir reçu sur son bord les gens qui étaient dans la chaloupe et recueilli quelques-uns de ceux qui nageaient, voulut profiter d'un vent frais et favorable qui s'était élevé. Il fit hisser les voiles, et m'ôta l'espérance de
35 regagner le vaisseau.

Je demeurai donc à la merci des flots, poussé tantôt d'un côté, et tantôt d'un autre. Je disputai contre eux ma vie tout le reste du jour et de la nuit suivante. Je n'avais plus de force le lendemain, et je désespérais d'éviter la mort, lorsqu'une

....

1. **Promptement :** rapidement.
2. **Périr :** mourir.
3. **Diligents :** rapides.
4. **Chaloupe :** petite embarcation de sauvetage.

Léon Carré, illustration pour *Les Mille et Une Nuits*,
1931, lithographie.

40 vague me jeta heureusement contre une île. Je m'étendis
sur la terre où je demeurai à demi mort.

Puis, même si j'étais très faible, je cherchai des herbes
bonnes à manger. J'en trouvai quelques-unes et j'eus le bonheur de rencontrer une source d'eau excellente. Les forces

45 m'étant revenues, je m'avançai dans l'île. J'entrai dans une
belle plaine où j'aperçus de loin un cheval qui paissait¹. Je
portai mes pas de ce côté-là. Je remarquai en approchant
que c'était une cavale² attachée à un piquet. Sa beauté attira
mon attention, mais pendant que je la regardais, j'entendis

50 la voix d'un homme qui parlait sous terre. Un moment après,
cet homme parut, vint à moi, et me demanda qui j'étais. Je
lui racontai mon aventure. Après quoi, il me fit entrer dans
une grotte où il y avait d'autres personnes.

Je mangeai de quelques mets qu'ils me présentèrent
55 puis, leur demandai ce qu'ils faisaient dans ce lieu ; ils répon-
dirent qu'ils étaient palefreniers³ du roi Mihrage, souverain
de cette île. Chaque année, à la même saison, ils avaient
coutume d'y amener les cavales du roi qu'ils attachaient
pour les faire s'accoupler avec un cheval marin qui sortait

60 de la mer. Une fois l'accouplement terminé, le cheval marin
se mettait en état de les dévorer, mais les palefreniers l'en
empêchaient par leurs cris, et l'obligeaient à rentrer dans la

1. **Paissait :** mangeait.
2. **Cavale :** jument.
3. **Palefreniers :** personnes qui s'occupent des chevaux.

mer. Quand les cavales étaient pleines, ils les ramenaient, et les chevaux qui en naissaient étaient destinés pour le roi
65 et appelés chevaux marins.

Tandis qu'ils m'entretenaient ainsi, le cheval marin sortit de la mer, se jeta sur la cavale, s'accoupla avec elle et voulut ensuite la dévorer. Mais, au grand bruit que firent les palefreniers, il lâcha prise et alla se replonger dans la mer.

70 Le lendemain, ils reprirent le chemin de la capitale de l'île avec les cavales, et je les accompagnai. À notre arrivée, le roi Mihrage me demanda qui j'étais, et par quelle aventure je me trouvais dans ses états. Après avoir pleinement satisfait sa curiosité, il me témoigna qu'il prenait beaucoup de part[1]
75 à mon malheur. En même temps, il ordonna d'avoir soin de moi, et de me fournir toutes les choses dont j'aurais besoin.

Comme j'étais marchand, je fréquentai les gens de ma profession. Je recherchais particulièrement ceux qui étaient étrangers, tant pour apprendre d'eux des nouvelles
80 de Bagdad que pour trouver quelqu'un avec qui y retourner.

Un jour que j'étais sur le port, un navire y vint aborder. Dès qu'il fut à l'ancre[2], on commença à décharger les marchandises. En jetant les yeux sur quelques ballots, je vis mon nom dessus. C'étaient ceux que j'avais fait charger sur
85 le vaisseau où je m'étais embarqué à Balsora. Je reconnus

....

1. **Prenait beaucoup de part :** s'intéressait beaucoup.
2. **À l'ancre :** immobile, car ayant jeté l'ancre.

même le capitaine. Mais comme j'étais persuadé qu'il me croyait mort, je l'abordai, et lui demandai à qui appartenaient les ballots :

"J'avais sur mon bord, me répondit-il, un marchand de
90 Bagdad, qui se nommait Sindbâd. Un jour, il mit pied à terre avec plusieurs passagers sur une île prétendue qui n'était autre chose qu'une baleine, d'une grosseur énorme, qui s'était endormie à fleur d'eau. Aussitôt échauffée par le feu qu'on avait allumé sur son dos pour faire la cuisine,
95 elle commença à se mouvoir[1] et à s'enfoncer dans la mer. La plupart des personnes qui étaient dessus se noyèrent, et le malheureux Sindbâd fut de ce nombre. Ces ballots étaient à lui.

— Capitaine, lui dis-je alors, je suis ce Sindbâd que vous
100 croyez mort et qui ne l'est pas : ces ballots sont mon bien et ma marchandise."

Je lui racontai alors de quelle manière je m'étais sauvé, et par quelle aventure j'avais rencontré les palefreniers du roi Mihrage.

105 Il se sentit ébranlé de[2] mon discours et il fut bientôt persuadé que je n'étais pas un imposteur, car arrivèrent des gens de son navire qui me reconnurent et me firent de grands compliments. Enfin, il me reconnut aussi lui-même :

....

1. **Se mouvoir :** bouger.
2. **Ébranlé de :** troublé par.

"Dieu soit loué, me dit-il, vous vous êtes heureusement
échappé d'un si grand danger. Voilà votre bien, prenez-le, il
est à vous : faites-en ce qu'il vous plaira."

Je le remerciai et je louai sa probité[1]. Je choisis ce qu'il
y avait de plus précieux dans mes ballots et j'en fis présent
au roi Mihrage qui accepta mon présent et m'en fit de
beaucoup plus considérables. Après cela, je me rembarquai sur le même vaisseau. Mais, avant, j'échangeai les
marchandises qui me restaient contre d'autres du pays.
J'emportai avec moi du bois d'aloès, de santal, du camphre, de la muscade, du clou de girofle, du poivre, et du
gingembre. Nous passâmes par plusieurs îles et abordâmes
enfin à Balsora, d'où j'arrivai en cette ville avec la valeur
d'environ cent mille sequins[2]. Ma famille me reçut et je la
revis avec tous les transports[3] que peut causer une amitié
vive et sincère. J'achetai des esclaves, de belles terres et
je fis une grosse maison. Ce fut ainsi que je m'établis,
résolu d'oublier les maux dont j'avais souffert et de jouir
des plaisirs de la vie. »

Sindbâd s'étant arrêté, il ordonna aux joueurs d'instruments de recommencer leurs concerts. On continua jusqu'au
soir de boire et de manger. Lorsqu'il fut temps de se retirer,

....

1. Probité : grande honnêteté.
2. Sequins : ancienne monnaie venant de Venise.
3. Les transports : la grande émotion.

Sindbâd se fit apporter une bourse de cent sequins, et la donnant au porteur :

« Prenez, Hindbâd, lui dit-il, retournez chez vous, et revenez demain entendre la suite de mes aventures. »

135 Le porteur se retira fort confus de l'honneur et du présent qu'il venait de recevoir.

Hindbâd s'habilla le lendemain plus proprement que le jour précédent et retourna chez le voyageur. Une fois que les conviés furent tous arrivés, on servit et l'on tint table très 140 longtemps. Le repas fini, Sindbâd prit la parole :

« Seigneurs, dit-il, je vous prie de me donner audience[1], et de vouloir bien écouter les aventures de mon second voyage. Elles sont plus dignes de votre attention que celles du premier. »

----

1. **Donner audience :** laisser la parole.

Second voyage

« J' avais résolu, après mon premier voyage, de passer tranquillement le reste de mes jours à Bagdad. Mais l'envie de voyager et de négocier par mer me reprit : j'achetai des marchandises et je partis une seconde fois avec d'autres marchands.

Nous allions d'îles en îles, et nous y faisions des trocs[1] très avantageux. Un jour nous descendîmes dans une de ces îles, couverte de plusieurs sortes d'arbres fruitiers, mais déserte.

Pendant que les uns se divertissaient à cueillir des fleurs et les autres des fruits, je pris mes provisions et du vin, et je m'assis près d'une eau coulante. Je fis un assez bon repas de ce que j'avais. Après quoi, le sommeil vint. Quand je me réveillai, je ne vis plus le navire à l'ancre.

Je me levai, je regardai de toutes parts, et je ne vis pas un des marchands qui étaient descendus dans l'île avec moi. J'aperçus seulement le navire à la voile, mais si éloigné que je le perdis de vue peu de temps après.

....

1. **Trocs :** échanges.

Je poussai des cris épouvantables, je me frappai la tête,
20 et me jetai par terre. Je me reprochai cent fois de ne m'être
pas contenté de mon premier voyage. Mais tous mes regrets
étaient inutiles.

Sans savoir ce que je deviendrais, je montai au haut d'un
grand arbre d'où je regardai de tous côtés. Ayant aperçu
25 quelque chose de blanc, je descendis de l'arbre. Je marchai
vers cette blancheur qui était si éloignée que je ne pouvais
pas bien distinguer ce que c'était.

Lorsque j'en fus à une distance raisonnable, je remarquai que c'était une boule blanche d'une hauteur et d'une
30 grosseur prodigieuse. Dès que j'en fus près, je la touchai,
et la trouvai fort douce.

Le soleil alors était prêt à se coucher. L'air s'obscurcit
tout à coup, comme s'il était couvert d'un nuage épais. Je
m'aperçus que ce qui causait cette obscurité était un oiseau
35 d'une grandeur et d'une grosseur extraordinaire. Je me sou-
vins d'un oiseau appelé Roc dont j'avais souvent entendu
parler, et je conçus[1] que la grosse boule que j'avais tant
admirée devait être un œuf de cet oiseau. En effet, l'oiseau
s'abattit et se posa dessus, comme pour le couver. En le
40 voyant venir, je m'étais serré près de l'œuf, de sorte que
j'eus devant moi un des pieds de l'oiseau ; il était aussi gros
qu'un gros tronc d'arbre. Je m'y attachai fortement avec

---

1. **Conçus :** compris.

En savoir plus sur cette légende

la toile de mon turban, dans l'espérance que le Roc, lorsqu'il
reprendrait son vol, m'emporterait hors de cette île déserte.

45 Effectivement, dès qu'il fit jour l'oiseau s'envola et m'enleva
si haut que je ne voyais plus la terre. Puis, il descendit tout
à coup avec rapidité. Lorsque le Roc fut posé, et que je
me vis à terre, je déliai rapidement le nœud qui me tenait

attaché à son pied. J'avais à peine achevé de me détacher
50 qu'il donna du bec sur un serpent d'une longueur inouïe. Il
le prit et s'envola aussitôt.

Le lieu où il me laissa était une vallée très profonde,
environnée de toutes parts de montagnes si hautes qu'elles
se perdaient dans les nuages, et tellement escarpées[1] qu'il
55 n'y avait aucun chemin par où monter.

En marchant dans cette vallée, je remarquai qu'elle était
parsemée de diamants d'une grosseur surprenante. Mais
j'aperçus bientôt un grand nombre de serpents si gros et si
longs qu'ils pouvaient engloutir un éléphant. Ils se retiraient
60 pendant le jour dans leurs antres où ils se cachaient à cause
du Roc, leur ennemi, et ils n'en sortaient que la nuit.

À la tombée de la nuit, je me retirai dans une grotte où
je jugeai que je serais en sûreté. Je soupai d'une partie de
mes provisions, au bruit des serpents qui commencèrent à
65 paraître. Leurs affreux sifflements me causèrent une frayeur
extrême et ne me permirent pas de passer la nuit tranquillement. Le jour étant venu, les serpents se retirèrent. Alors, je
sortis de ma grotte en tremblant, et je marchai longtemps sur
les diamants. À la fin, je m'assis et, malgré l'inquiétude dont
70 j'étais agité, je m'endormis après avoir fait encore un repas
de mes provisions. J'étais à peine assoupi que quelque chose
tomba près de moi avec grand bruit et me réveilla. C'était

---

1. **Escarpées :** en pente.

Léon Carré, illustration pour *Les Mille et Une Nuits*, 1931, lithographie.

une grosse pièce de viande fraîche et, au même moment, j'en vis rouler plusieurs autres du haut des rochers.

75 J'avais toujours tenu pour un conte[1] ce que j'avais entendu dire plusieurs fois au sujet de la vallée des diamants, et de la ruse dont se servaient quelques marchands pour en tirer ces pierres précieuses. On m'avait dit la vérité. En effet, ces marchands se rendent près de cette vallée au moment
80 où les aigles ont des petits. Ils découpent de la viande et la jettent par grosses pièces dans la vallée. Les diamants, sur la pointe desquels elles tombent, s'y attachent. Les aigles fondent sur ces pièces de viande, et les emportent dans leurs nids au haut des rochers pour servir de pâture à leurs
85 aiglons. Alors les marchands courant aux nids obligent, par leurs cris, les aigles à s'éloigner, et prennent les diamants qu'ils trouvent attachés aux pièces de viande. Ils se servent de cette ruse parce qu'il n'y a pas d'autre moyen de tirer les diamants de cette vallée.

90 J'avais cru jusque-là qu'il ne me serait pas possible de sortir de cet abyme[2] que je regardais comme mon tombeau. Mais je changeai de sentiment. Ce que je venais de voir me permis d'imaginer un moyen de rester en vie.

Je commençai par amasser les plus gros diamants qui
95 se présentèrent à mes yeux, et j'en remplis le sac de cuir

....

1. **Tenu pour conte :** cru faux.
2. **Abyme :** gouffre.

qui m'avait servi à mettre mes provisions. Je pris ensuite la pièce de viande qui me parut la plus longue, je l'attachai fortement autour de moi avec la toile de mon turban, et je me couchai le ventre contre terre, la bourse de cuir attachée à ma ceinture.

Je ne fus pas plutôt en cette situation que les aigles vinrent chacun se saisir d'une pièce de viande qu'ils emportèrent. Un des plus puissants aigles m'enleva avec le morceau de viande dont j'étais enveloppé, et me porta au haut de la montagne jusque dans son nid. Les marchands ne manquèrent pas alors de crier pour épouvanter les aigles. Lorsqu'ils les eurent obligés à quitter leur proie, un d'entre eux s'approcha de moi et commença à me quereller[1] en me demandant pourquoi je lui ravissais[2] son bien.

"Consolez-vous, lui dis-je, j'ai des diamants pour vous et pour moi plus que n'en peuvent avoir tous les autres marchands ensemble."

En disant cela, je les lui montrai. Je n'avais pas achevé de parler que les autres marchands qui m'aperçurent s'attroupèrent autour de moi fort étonnés de me voir, et j'augmentai leur surprise par le récit de mon histoire.

Ils m'emmenèrent dans leur logement et là, ayant ouvert ma bourse en leur présence, la grosseur de mes diamants

....

1. **Quereller :** disputer.
2. **Ravissais :** volais.

les surprit. Je priai le marchand à qui appartenait le nid où
j'avais été transporté (car chaque marchand avait le sien) d'en
choisir autant qu'il en voudrait. Il se contenta d'en prendre
un seul. Comme je le pressais d'[1]en recevoir d'autres :
"Non, me dit-il, je suis fort satisfait de celui-ci, qui est
assez précieux pour m'épargner la peine de faire désormais
d'autres voyages pour l'établissement de ma petite fortune."
Je passai la nuit avec ces marchands. Comme chacun
d'eux paraissait content des diamants qui lui étaient échus[2],
nous partîmes le lendemain tous ensemble. Nous gagnâmes
le premier port d'où nous passâmes à l'île de Roha. J'y échangeai quelques-uns de mes diamants contre de bonnes marchandises. De là, nous allâmes à d'autres îles. Enfin, nous
abordâmes à Balsora d'où je me rendis à Bagdad. J'y fis
d'abord de grandes aumônes[3] aux pauvres, et je jouis hono-
rablement du reste de mes richesses immenses que j'avais
apportées et gagnées avec tant de fatigues.»

Ce fut ainsi que Sindbâd raconta son second voyage. Il
fit donner encore cent sequins à Hindbâd qu'il invita à venir
le lendemain entendre le récit du troisième. Les conviés
revinrent le jour suivant à la même heure, de même que le
porteur qui avait déjà presque oublié sa misère passée. Après
le repas, Sindbâd fit ainsi le détail de son troisième voyage.

....

1. **Le pressais de :** l'encourageais à.
2. **Échus :** donnés en partage.
3. **Aumônes :** dons aux plus pauvres. L'aumône est un des cinq piliers de l'islam.

Troisième voyage

« Très vite je m'ennuyai de vivre dans le repos et je partis de Bagdad avec de riches marchandises du pays que je fis transporter à Balsora. Là, je m'embarquai avec d'autres marchands.

Un jour que nous étions en pleine mer, nous fûmes battus d'une tempête horrible qui nous fit perdre notre route. La tempête continua plusieurs jours et nous poussa devant le port d'une île où nous fûmes obligés d'aller mouiller. Lorsqu'on eut plié les voiles, le capitaine nous dit :

"Cette île, et quelques autres voisines, sont habitées par des sauvages tous velus qui vont venir nous assaillir. Quoique ce soit des nains, ne résistons pas, parce qu'ils sont en plus grand nombre que les sauterelles, et que s'il nous arrivait d'en tuer un, ils se jetteraient tous sur nous et nous assommeraient."

Le discours du capitaine mit tout l'équipage dans une grande consternation. Nous vîmes paraître une multitude innombrable[1] de sauvages hideux, couverts par tout le corps d'un poil roux, et hauts seulement de deux pieds.

....

1. Innombrable : qu'on ne peut pas compter.

Gaël Lannurien, illustration pour
Les Sept Voyages de Sindbâd, le Marin, Neofelis éditions, 2011.

20 Ils se jetèrent à la nage et environnèrent en peu de temps notre vaisseau. Ils s'agrippèrent aux bords et aux cordages du navire, et grimpèrent de tous côtés.

Nous les vîmes faire cette manœuvre avec la frayeur que vous pouvez vous imaginer, sans oser nous défendre. Ils 25 déplièrent les voiles et coupèrent le câble de l'ancre. Après avoir fait approcher de terre le vaisseau, ils nous firent tous débarquer.

En nous avançant dans l'île, nous nous attendions tous à une mort certaine. Nous aperçûmes alors un grand édifice : 30 un palais bien bâti et très élevé qui avait une porte d'ébène[1] à deux battants. Nous entrâmes dans la cour et nous vîmes en face un vaste appartement où il y avait d'un côté un monceau[2] d'ossements humains et, de l'autre, une infinité de broches à rôtir. Nous tremblâmes à ce spectacle et nous 35 tombâmes par terre, saisis d'une frayeur mortelle.

Le soleil se couchait et la porte de l'appartement s'ouvrit avec beaucoup de bruit. Aussitôt, nous en vîmes sortir une horrible figure d'homme noir, de la hauteur d'un grand palmier. Il avait au milieu du front un seul œil rouge et 40 ardent comme un charbon allumé. Les dents de devant, qu'il avait très longues et très aiguës, lui sortaient de la bouche, et la lèvre inférieure lui descendait sur la poitrine.

....

1. Ébène : bois très sombre et d'une grande dureté.
2. Monceau : grand tas.

Ses oreilles ressemblaient à celles d'un éléphant, et lui couvraient les épaules. Il avait les ongles crochus et longs
45 comme des griffes. Quand il nous eut bien considérés, il s'avança vers nous. Il étendit la main sur moi, me prit par la nuque du cou, et me tourna de tous côtés comme un boucher qui manie une tête de mouton. Voyant que j'étais si maigre, que je n'avais que
50 la peau et les os, il me lâcha. Il prit les autres tour à tour, les examina de la même manière. Comme le capitaine était le plus gras de tout l'équipage, le géant le tint d'une main et lui passa une broche au travers du corps. Ayant ensuite allumé un grand feu, il le fit rôtir et le mangea à son souper. Ce repas
55 achevé, il se coucha et s'endormit en ronflant d'une manière plus bruyante que le tonnerre. Pour nous, il ne nous fut pas possible de goûter la douceur du repos. Le jour étant venu, le géant se réveilla, se leva, sortit, et nous laissa dans le palais.

Notre condition nous parut si affreuse que plusieurs de
60 nos camarades furent sur le point d'aller se précipiter dans la mer, plutôt que d'attendre une mort si étrange. Mais un de la compagnie prit alors la parole :

"Il nous est défendu, dit-il, de nous donner nous-mêmes la mort. N'est-il pas plus raisonnable que nous songions au
65 moyen de nous défaire du barbare qui nous destine à un trépas si funeste[1] ?"

....

1. **Un trépas si funeste :** une mort si tragique.

Comme il m'était venu à l'esprit une idée, je la communiquai à mes camarades qui l'approuvèrent.

"Mes frères, ajoutai-je, construisons plusieurs radeaux
70 qui puissent nous porter. Lorsqu'ils seront achevés, nous les laisserons sur la côte jusqu'à ce que nous jugions à propos de nous en servir. Cependant, nous exécuterons le dessein[1] que je vous ai proposé pour nous délivrer du géant : s'il réussit, nous pourrons attendre ici avec patience qu'il
75 passe quelque vaisseau ; si au contraire nous manquons notre coup, nous gagnerons nos radeaux, et nous nous mettrons en mer."

Mon avis fut approuvé de tout le monde, et nous construisîmes des radeaux.

80 Nous retournâmes au palais vers la fin du jour, et le géant y arriva peu de temps après nous. Il fallut encore nous résoudre à voir rôtir un de nos camarades. Mais, enfin, nous nous vengeâmes de la cruauté du géant. Après avoir achevé son détestable souper, il se coucha et s'endormit.

85 Neuf des plus hardis d'entre nous, et moi, nous prîmes chacun une broche, nous en mîmes la pointe dans le feu pour la faire rougir, et ensuite nous la lui enfonçâmes dans l'œil en même temps.

Le géant poussa un cri effroyable. Il se leva brusquement,
90 et étendit les mains de tous côtés pour se saisir de quelqu'un

....

1. **Dessein :** projet.

afin de le sacrifier à sa rage. Mais nous eûmes le temps de nous éloigner de lui. Après nous avoir cherchés vainement, il trouva la porte à tâtons[1] et sortit avec des hurlements épouvantables.

95 Nous sortîmes du palais après le géant et nous nous rendîmes au bord de la mer dans l'endroit où étaient nos radeaux. Nous les mîmes d'abord à l'eau, et nous attendîmes qu'il fît jour pour nous jeter dessus. C'est alors que nous aperçûmes notre cruel ennemi, accompagné de deux géants

100 à peu près de sa grandeur qui le conduisaient.

Nous nous jetâmes sur nos radeaux, et nous commençâmes à nous éloigner du rivage. Les géants se munirent de grosses pierres, accoururent sur la rive, entrèrent même dans l'eau jusqu'à la moitié du corps, et nous les jetèrent si

105 adroitement, qu'à l'exception du radeau sur lequel j'étais, tous les autres furent brisés, et les hommes qui étaient dessus se noyèrent. Pour moi, comme je ramais de toutes mes forces, je me trouvai hors de la portée des pierres.

Quand je fus en pleine mer, je devins le jouet du vent

110 et des flots qui nous jetaient tantôt d'un côté et tantôt d'un autre. Le lendemain, j'aperçus un navire. Je criai de toute mes forces pour me faire entendre. Tout l'équipage m'aperçut, et le capitaine m'envoya la chaloupe. Quand je fus à bord, les marchands et les matelots me demandèrent par quelle

---

1. **À tâtons :** doucement, avec hésitation.

Charles Folkard, *Le Troisième Voyage de Sindbâd, le Marin*, 1917, lithographie.

115 aventure je m'étais trouvé dans cette île déserte. Après leur avoir raconté tout ce qui m'était arrivé, les plus anciens me dirent qu'ils avaient bien de la joie de me voir échappé à tant de périls[1]. Ils s'empressèrent de me régaler de ce qu'ils avaient de meilleur et le capitaine, remarquant que
120 mon habit était tout en lambeaux, eut la générosité de me donner un des siens.

Nous naviguâmes quelque temps et nous abordâmes enfin à l'île de Salahat où nous entrâmes dans le port. Les marchands commencèrent à faire débarquer leurs
125 marchandises pour les vendre ou les échanger. De l'île de Salahat, nous allâmes à une autre, où je me fournis de clous de girofle, de cannelle et d'autres épices. Après une longue navigation, j'arrivai à Balsora et de là je revins en cette ville de Bagdad avec tant de richesses que j'en ignorais la quan-
130 tité. J'en donnai encore aux pauvres une partie considérable, et j'ajoutai d'autres grandes terres à celles que j'avais déjà acquises.»

Sindbâd acheva ainsi l'histoire de son troisième voyage. Il fit donner cent autres sequins à Hindbâd, en l'invitant au
135 repas du lendemain et au récit du quatrième voyage.

....

1. **Périls:** dangers.

Quatrième voyage

« Les plaisirs et les divertissements que je pris après mon troisième voyage n'eurent pas des charmes assez puissants pour me déterminer à ne pas voyager davantage. Je mis donc de l'ordre dans mes affaires et je partis. Je pris la route de la Perse[1] et j'arrivai à un port de mer où je m'embarquai.

Un jour, nous fûmes surpris d'un coup de vent qui obligea le capitaine à faire amener[2] les voiles et à donner tous les ordres nécessaires pour prévenir le danger dont nous étions menacés. Mais toutes nos précautions furent inutiles. Le vaisseau, ne pouvant plus être gouverné, donna sur des récifs[3] et se brisa de manière qu'un grand nombre de marchands et de matelots se noya, et que la charge périt.

J'eus le bonheur de m'agripper à une planche et fus emporté par un courant vers une île qui était devant moi. J'y trouvai des fruits et de l'eau de source qui servirent à rétablir mes forces.

Le jour suivant, je m'éloignai du rivage. Avançant dans l'île, j'aperçus des gens occupés à cueillir du poivre.

....

1. Perse : voir carte, p. 110.
2. Amener : ici, abaisser.
3. Donna sur des récifs : s'échoua sur des rochers.

Gaël Lannurien, illustration pour
Les Sept Voyages de Sindbâd, le Marin, Neofelis éditions, 2011.

Ils vinrent au-devant de moi et me demandèrent en arabe qui j'étais, et d'où je venais. Ravi de les entendre parler comme moi, je leur racontai de quelle manière j'avais fait naufrage.

Je demeurai avec eux jusqu'à ce qu'ils eussent amassé la quantité de poivre qu'ils voulurent. Après quoi, ils me firent embarquer sur leur navire, et nous nous rendîmes dans une autre île d'où ils étaient venus. Ils me présentèrent à leur roi qui était un bon prince. Il eut la patience d'écouter le récit de mon aventure. Il me fit donner ensuite des habits, et ordonna qu'on prenne soin de moi.

L'île où je me trouvais était fort peuplée et abondante en toutes sortes de choses. Cet agréable asile[1] commença à me consoler de mon malheur, et les bontés que ce généreux prince avait pour moi achevèrent de me rendre content.

Comme je faisais ma cour au roi, il me dit un jour :

"Sindbâd, je t'aime, et je sais que tous mes sujets qui te connaissent te chérissent à mon exemple. J'ai une prière à te faire. Je veux te marier, afin que le mariage t'arrête en mes états, et que tu ne songes plus à ta patrie."

Comme je n'osais résister à la volonté du prince, il me donna pour femme une dame de sa cour, noble, belle, sage et riche. Après les cérémonies des noces, je m'établis chez la dame avec laquelle je vécus quelque temps dans une union parfaite.

....

1. **Asile :** refuge.

Un jour, la femme d'un de mes voisins tomba malade et mourut. J'allai chez lui pour le consoler :

"Dieu vous conserve, lui dis-je, et vous donne une longue vie.

45 — Hélas, je n'ai plus qu'une heure à vivre.

— Oh, ne vous mettez pas dans l'esprit une pensée si funeste. J'espère que cela n'arrivera pas.

— Je souhaite que votre vie soit de longue durée. Pour ce qui est de moi, je vous apprends que l'on m'enterre

50 aujourd'hui avec ma femme. Telle est la coutume que nos ancêtres ont établie dans cette île : le mari vivant est enterré avec la femme morte, et la femme vivante avec le mari mort. Rien ne peut me sauver."

Pendant qu'il m'entretenait de cette étrange barbarie, les

55 parents, les amis et les voisins arrivèrent pour assister aux funérailles. On revêtit le cadavre de la femme de ses habits les plus riches et on la para¹ de tous ses joyaux.

On l'enleva ensuite dans une bière² découverte et le convoi se mit en marche. Le mari était à la tête du deuil et suivait le

60 corps de sa femme. On prit le chemin d'une haute montagne. Lorsqu'on y fut arrivé, on leva une grosse pierre qui couvrait l'ouverture d'un puits profond, et l'on y descendit le cadavre. Après cela, le mari embrassa ses parents et ses amis, et se laissa mettre sans résistance dans une bière, avec un pot d'eau

65 et sept petits pains auprès de lui. Puis on le descendit de la

1. **La para :** l'habilla.
2. **Bière :** ici, cercueil.

José Tapiro y Baro, *Préparatifs de mariage de la fille du sultan à Tanger*, 1870, aquarelle, collection privée.

même manière qu'on avait descendu sa femme. La cérémonie achevée, on remit la pierre sur l'ouverture.

Je ne pus m'empêcher de dire au roi ce que je pensais là-dessus.

70 "Sire, lui dis-je, je ne saurais assez m'étonner de l'étrange coutume qu'on a dans vos états[1], d'enterrer les vivants et les morts ! J'ai bien voyagé, j'ai fréquenté des gens d'une infinité de nations, et je n'ai jamais entendu parler d'une loi si cruelle.

– Que veux-tu, Sindbâd, me répondit le roi, c'est une loi

75 commune, et j'y suis soumis moi-même : je serai enterré vivant avec la reine mon épouse, si elle meurt la première.

– Mais, Sire, oserais-je demander à votre majesté si les étrangers sont obligés d'observer cette coutume ?

– Sans doute. Ils ne font pas exception lorsqu'ils sont

80 mariés dans cette île."

Je m'en retournai tristement au logis avec cette réponse. La crainte que ma femme ne mourût la première me faisait faire des réflexions mortifiantes. Je tremblais à la moindre indisposition[2] que je voyais à ma femme. Mais, hélas, j'eus

85 bientôt la frayeur toute entière ! Elle tomba véritablement malade, et mourut en peu de jours.

Le roi, accompagné de toute sa cour, voulut honorer de sa présence le convoi. Les personnes les plus considérables de la ville me firent aussi l'honneur d'assister à mon enterrement.

----

1. **Dans vos états :** sur vos terres.
2. **À la moindre indisposition :** au moindre signe de maladie.

90 Lorsque tout fut prêt pour la cérémonie, on posa le corps de ma femme dans une bière avec tous ses joyaux et ses plus magnifiques habits. On commença la marche. Avant d'arriver à la montagne, je suppliai le roi et ceux qui se trouvèrent autour d'avoir compassion envers moi.

95 Mais personne ne fut attendri. On se hâta de descendre le corps de ma femme dans le puits et l'on m'y descendit un moment après dans une autre bière découverte, avec un vase rempli d'eau et sept pains. Enfin, on remit la pierre sur l'ouverture du puits, en dépit de l'excès de ma douleur 100 et de mes cris pitoyables.

À mesure que j'approchais du fond, je découvrais, à la faveur du peu de lumière qui venait d'en haut, ce lieu souterrain. C'était une grotte très vaste. Je sentis bientôt une puanteur insupportable qui sortait d'une infinité de cadavres que je 105 voyais à droite et à gauche. Lorsque je fus en bas, je me jetai par terre où je demeurai longtemps plongé dans les pleurs.

Néanmoins, au lieu d'appeler la mort à mon secours, l'amour de la vie me porta à prolonger mes jours. J'allai à tâtons, et en me bouchant le nez, prendre le pain et l'eau 110 qui étaient dans ma bière et j'en mangeai.

Je vécus quelques jours de mon pain et de mon eau, mais enfin, n'en ayant plus, je me préparai à mourir.

Je n'attendais plus que la mort lorsque j'entendis lever la pierre. On descendit un cadavre et une personne vivante. Le 115 mort était un homme. Pendant qu'on descendait la femme, je m'approchai de l'endroit où sa bière devait être posée. Je donnai sur la tête de la malheureuse deux ou trois grands coups d'un gros os dont je m'étais saisi. Je l'assommai. Je ne faisais cette action inhumaine que pour profiter du pain

120 et de l'eau qui étaient dans la bière, j'eus des provisions pour quelques jours. Au bout de ce temps-là, on descendit encore une femme morte et un homme vivant, je tuai l'homme de la même manière.

Un jour que je venais de tuer encore une femme, j'enten-

125 dis souffler et marcher. J'avançai du côté d'où partait le bruit et il me parut entrevoir quelque chose qui prenait la fuite. Je suivis cette espèce d'ombre qui soufflait toujours en fuyant à mesure que j'en approchais. Je la poursuivis si longtemps, et j'allai si loin que j'aperçus enfin une lumière. Je continuai

130 de marcher vers cette lumière. À la fin, je découvris qu'elle venait par une ouverture du rocher assez large pour y passer.

Je m'avançai jusqu'à l'ouverture, j'y passai, et me trouvai sur le bord de la mer. Imaginez-vous l'excès de ma joie ! Il fut tel que j'eus de la peine à me persuader que ce n'était pas

135 une imagination. Lorsque je fus convaincu que c'était une chose réelle, je compris que la chose que j'avais suivie était un animal sorti de la mer, qui avait coutume d'entrer dans la grotte pour s'y repaître[1] de corps morts.

Je retournai dans la grotte et j'allai ramasser dans les

140 bières tous les diamants, les rubis, les perles, les bracelets

....

1. **Repaître**: nourrir.

d'or, et enfin toutes les riches étoffes que je trouvai sous ma main. Je portai tout cela sur le bord de la mer.

Au bout de deux ou trois jours, j'aperçus un navire qui vint passer près de l'endroit où j'étais. Je fis signe de la toile de mon turban et je criai de toute ma force pour me faire entendre. On m'entendit et l'on détacha la chaloupe pour venir me chercher. À la demande que les matelots me firent, par quelle disgrâce[1] je me trouvais en ce lieu, je répondis que je m'étais sauvé d'un naufrage depuis deux jours avec les marchandises qu'ils voyaient. Heureusement pour moi, ces gens se contentèrent de ma réponse et m'emmenèrent avec mes ballots.

Nous passâmes devant plusieurs îles et, enfin, j'arrivai à Bagdad avec des richesses infinies. Pour rendre grâce à Dieu des faveurs qu'il m'avait faites, je fis de grandes aumônes, tant pour l'entretien de plusieurs mosquées, que pour la subsistance des pauvres, et me donnai tout entier à mes parents et à mes amis, en me divertissant et en faisant bonne chère[2] avec eux. »

Sindbâd finit ainsi le récit de son quatrième voyage. Il fit un nouveau présent de cent sequins à Hindbâd qu'il pria comme les autres de revenir le jour suivant à la même heure pour dîner chez lui. Le lendemain, à la fin du repas, Sindbâd commença de cette sorte le récit de son cinquième voyage.

....

1. Disgrâce : malheur.
2. En faisant bonne chère : en mangeant bien.

H. J. Ford, *Deux Rocs détruisant le navire de Sindbâd lors de son cinquième voyage*, 1898, gravure.

Cinquième voyage

« Les plaisirs eurent encore assez de charmes pour effacer de ma mémoire toutes les peines et les maux que j'avais soufferts, sans pouvoir m'ôter l'envie de faire de nouveaux voyages. C'est pourquoi j'achetai des marchandises et je partis avec elles pour me rendre au premier port de mer. Là, je fis construire un navire et l'équipai à mes frais. Dès qu'il fut achevé, je le fis charger et m'embarquai dessus. Je reçus plusieurs marchands de différentes nations avec leurs marchandises.

Nous fîmes voile au premier bon vent, et prîmes le large. Après une longue navigation, nous abordâmes sur une île déserte où nous trouvâmes l'œuf d'un Roc d'une grosseur pareille à celui dont vous m'avez entendu parler. L'œuf renfermait un petit Roc prêt à éclore dont le bec commençait à paraître.

Les marchands, qui étaient descendus à terre avec moi, cassèrent l'œuf à grands coups de haches, firent une ouverture par où ils tirèrent le petit Roc par morceaux, puis le firent rôtir. Je les avais avertis de ne pas toucher à l'œuf. Mais ils ne voulurent pas m'écouter.

Ils eurent à peine achevé ce régal, qu'apparurent en l'air deux gros nuages. Le capitaine s'écria que c'étaient le père et la mère du petit Roc. Il nous pressa tous de nous rembarquer au plus vite. Nous suivîmes son conseil avec empressement, et nous remîmes à la voile.

Cependant les deux Rocs approchèrent en poussant des cris effroyables qu'ils redoublèrent quand ils eurent vu l'état où l'on avait mis l'œuf, et que leur petit n'y était plus. Pour se venger, ils reprirent leur vol du côté d'où ils étaient venus, et disparurent quelque temps.

Ils revinrent, et nous remarquâmes qu'ils tenaient entre leurs griffes chacun un morceau de rocher énorme. Lorsqu'ils furent précisément au-dessus de mon vaisseau, ils s'arrêtèrent, et, se soutenant en l'air, l'un lâcha la pièce de rocher qu'il tenait. Mais, par l'adresse du timonier[1] qui détourna le navire d'un coup de timon, elle ne tomba pas dessus : elle tomba à côté, dans la mer. L'autre oiseau laissa tomber sa roche si justement au milieu du vaisseau qu'elle le rompit et le brisa en mille pièces. Les matelots et les passagers furent tous écrasés, ou submergés. Je fus submergé moi-même. Mais j'eus le bonheur de m'agripper à une pièce du débris. Ainsi, en m'aidant tantôt d'une main, tantôt de l'autre, j'arrivai enfin sur une île.

----

1. Timonier : celui qui tient le timon (le gouvernail), donc qui conduit le navire.

Je m'assis sur l'herbe pour me remettre un peu de ma
45 fatigue. Après quoi, je me levai et m'avançai dans l'île. Il
me sembla que j'étais dans un jardin délicieux. Je voyais
partout des arbres chargés de fruits, les uns verts, les autres
mûrs, et des ruisseaux d'une eau douce et claire qui faisaient
d'agréables détours. Je mangeai de ces fruits que je trouvai
50 excellents, et je bus cette eau.

Lorsque je me fus avancé dans l'île, j'aperçus un vieillard qui me parut fort cassé[1]. Il était assis sur le bord d'un
ruisseau. Je m'imaginai d'abord que c'était quelqu'un qui
avait fait naufrage comme moi. Je m'approchai de lui, je le
55 saluai, et il me fit seulement une inclination de tête. Je lui
demandai ce qu'il faisait là. Mais au lieu de me répondre, il
me fit signe de le charger sur mes épaules, et de le passer
au-delà du ruisseau.

Je crus qu'il avait besoin que je lui rende service. C'est
60 pourquoi, l'ayant chargé sur mon dos, je passai le ruisseau.

"Descendez", lui dis-je alors en me baissant pour faciliter
sa descente.

Mais au lieu de se laisser aller à terre (j'en ris encore
toutes les fois que j'y pense), ce vieillard, qui m'avait paru
65 décrépit[2], passa légèrement autour de mon cou ses deux
jambes et se mit à califourchon sur mes épaules en me

....

1. **Cassé :** en mauvaise santé.
2. **Décrépit :** en très mauvaise condition physique.

serrant si fortement la gorge qu'il semblait vouloir m'étrangler. La frayeur me saisit en ce moment, et je tombai évanoui.

70 Malgré mon évanouissement, le vieillard demeura toujours attaché à mon cou. Lorsque j'eus repris mes esprits, il m'appuya fortement contre l'estomac un de ses pieds, et de l'autre, me frappant rudement le côté, il m'obligea de me relever malgré moi. Étant debout, il me fit marcher sous

75 des arbres. Il me forçait de m'arrêter pour cueillir et manger les fruits que nous rencontrions. Il ne quittait point prise pendant le jour. Et quand je voulais me reposer la nuit, il s'étendait par terre avec moi, toujours attaché à mon cou.

Un jour que je trouvai en mon chemin plusieurs calebasses[1] sèches, j'en pris une assez grosse et j'y mis le jus

80 de plusieurs grappes de raisins. Lorsque j'en eus rempli la calebasse, je la posai dans un endroit où j'eus l'adresse de me faire conduire par le vieillard plusieurs jours après. Là, je pris la calebasse, et la portant à ma bouche, je bus

85 d'un excellent vin qui me fit oublier pour quelque temps le chagrin mortel dont j'étais accablé. Cela me donna de la vigueur. J'en fus même si réjoui que je me mis à chanter et à sauter en marchant.

Le vieillard, qui s'aperçut de l'effet que cette boisson

90 avait produit en moi, me fit signe de lui en donner à boire :

....

1. **Calebasses :** récipients fabriqués avec les fruits du calebassier.

je lui présentai la calebasse, il la prit. Comme la liqueur lui parut agréable, il l'avala jusqu'à la dernière goutte. Il y en avait assez pour l'eni-vrer. Bientôt la fumée du vin lui montant à la tête, il commença à chanter à sa manière, et à se trémous-ser sur mes épaules. Ses jambes se relâchèrent peu à peu ; de sorte que voyant qu'il ne me serrait plus, je le jetai par terre où il demeura sans mouvement. Alors je pris une grosse pierre, et je lui écrasai la tête.

Walter Stanley Paget, illustration pour *Les Mille et Une Nuits,* vers 1895.

Je sentis une grande joie de m'être délivré pour jamais de ce maudit vieillard, et je marchai vers le bord de la mer, où je rencontrai des gens d'un navire qui venait de mouiller[1] là. Ils furent extrêmement étonnés de me voir, et d'entendre le détail de mon aventure.

----

1. **Mouiller :** jeter l'ancre du bateau pour s'arrêter.

"Vous étiez tombé, me dirent-ils, entre les mains du vieillard de la mer, et vous êtes le premier qu'il n'ait pas étranglé. Il n'a jamais abandonné ceux dont il s'était rendu maître qu'après les avoir étouffés."

Après m'avoir informé de ces choses, ils m'emmenèrent avec eux dans leur navire. Le capitaine remit la voile ; et après quelques jours de navigation, nous abordâmes au port d'une grande ville.

Un des marchands du vaisseau qui m'avait pris en amitié, m'obligea à l'accompagner, et me conduisit dans un logement destiné à servir de retraite aux marchands étrangers. Il me donna un grand sac. Ensuite, il me recommanda à quelques gens de la ville et les pria de me mener avec eux amasser des noix de coco.

Au fil des jours, je fis un si grand amas de noix de coco que j'en avais pour une somme considérable.

Le vaisseau sur lequel j'étais venu avait fait voile avec des marchands qui l'avaient chargé de noix de coco qu'ils avaient achetées. J'attendis l'arrivée d'un autre qui aborda bientôt au port de la ville pour faire un pareil chargement. Je fis embarquer dessus toutes les noix de coco qui m'appartenaient.

Nous mîmes à la voile, et prîmes la route de l'île où le poivre croît[1] en plus grande abondance. De là,

---

1. Croît : pousse.

nous gagnâmes l'île de Comari[1] qui porte la meilleure espèce de bois d'aloès. J'échangeai mes noix de coco dans ces deux îles contre du poivre et du bois d'aloès, et me rendis, avec
140 d'autres marchands, à la pêche des perles. Je me remis en mer avec joie sur un vaisseau qui arriva heureusement à Balsora. De là, je revins à Bagdad où je fis de très grosses sommes d'argent du poivre, du bois d'aloès, et des perles que j'avais apportés. Je distribuai en aumônes la dixième
145 partie de mon gain et je cherchai à me délasser[2] de mes fatigues dans toutes sortes de divertissements.»

Ayant achevé ces paroles, Sindbâd fit donner cent sequins à Hindbâd qui se retira avec tous les autres convives. Le lendemain, la même compagnie se trouva chez le riche Sindbâd
150 qui, après l'avoir régalée comme les jours précédents, demanda audience, et fit le récit de son sixième voyage.

---

1. **Île de Comari:** aujourd'hui, la Grande Comore, île de l'archipel des Comores (voir carte, p. 110).
2. **Délasser:** reposer.

Gustave Doré, *Naufrage de Sindbâd et de ses compagnons*,
xixe siècle, gravure colorisée.

Sixième voyage

« Vous êtes sans doute en peine de savoir comment, après avoir fait cinq naufrages et avoir essuyé[1] tant de périls, je pus me résoudre encore à tenter la fortune. J'en suis étonné moi-même quand j'y pense. Quoi qu'il en soit, au bout d'une année de repos, je me préparai à faire un sixième voyage.

J'arrivai à un port de mer où je m'embarquai sur un bon navire. Mais le capitaine et le pilote perdirent leur route, de manière qu'ils ignoraient où nous étions. Quand ils la reconnurent enfin, le capitaine quitta son poste en poussant des cris. Il jeta son turban par terre, s'arracha la barbe, et se frappa la tête :

"Je vous annonce, nous dit-il, que nous sommes dans l'endroit le plus dangereux de toute la mer. Un courant très rapide emporte le navire et nous allons tous périr dans moins d'un quart d'heure."

À ces mots, il ordonna de faire ranger les voiles. Mais les cordages se rompirent dans la manœuvre, et le navire

....

1. **Essuyé :** ici, affronté.

fut emporté par le courant au pied d'une montagne où il échoua et se brisa.

20

La montagne, au pied de laquelle nous étions, faisait la côte d'une île très longue et très vaste. Cette côte était toute couverte de débris de vaisseaux qui y avaient fait naufrage ; et par une infinité d'ossements qu'on rencontrait, nous jugeâmes qu'il s'y était perdu bien du monde. C'est aussi une chose presque incroyable que la quantité de marchandises et de richesses qui se présentaient à nos yeux de toutes parts.

25

Ici, au lieu que[1] partout ailleurs les rivières sortent de leur lit pour se jeter dans la mer, tout au contraire une grosse rivière d'eau douce s'éloigne de la mer et pénètre dans la côte au travers d'une grotte obscure dont l'ouverture est extrêmement haute et large. Ce qu'il y a de remarquable dans ce lieu, c'est que les pierres de la montagne sont de cristal, de rubis, ou d'autres pierres précieuses.

30

Pour achever la description de cet endroit qu'on peut appeler un gouffre, puisque jamais rien n'en revient, il n'est pas possible que les navires puissent s'en écarter ; et il n'est pas possible de gagner le sommet de la montagne, ni de se sauver par aucun endroit.

35

Nous demeurâmes sur le rivage comme des gens qui ont perdu l'esprit et nous attendions la mort de jour en jour. D'abord nous avions partagé nos vivres à part égale.

40

1. **Au lieu que :** tandis que.

Ainsi, chacun vécut plus ou moins longtemps que les autres, selon son tempérament et suivant l'usage qu'il fit de ses provisions.

Ceux qui moururent les premiers furent enterrés par les autres. Pour moi, je rendis les derniers devoirs[1] à tous mes compagnons. Lorsque j'enterrai le dernier, il me restait si peu de vivres que je jugeai que je ne pourrais pas aller loin ; de sorte que je creusai moi-même mon tombeau, résolu à me jeter dedans, puisqu'il ne restait plus personne pour m'enterrer.

Mais Dieu eut encore pitié de moi et m'inspira la pensée d'aller jusqu'à la rivière qui se perdait sous la voûte de la grotte. Là, après avoir examiné la rivière avec beaucoup d'attention, je me dis :

"Cette rivière qui se cache ainsi sous la terre doit sortir par quelque endroit. En construisant un radeau, et m'abandonnant dessus au courant de l'eau, j'arriverai à une terre habitée ou je périrai. Si je péris, je n'aurai fait que changer de genre de mort, si je sors au contraire de ce lieu fatal, non seulement j'éviterai la triste destinée de mes camarades, et je trouverai peut-être une nouvelle occasion de m'enrichir."

Je n'hésitai pas à travailler au radeau après ce raisonnement. Quand il fut achevé, je le chargeai de quelques ballots

....

1. **Je rendis les derniers devoirs** : j'enterrai.

de rubis, d'émeraudes, d'ambre gris, de cristal de roche, et d'étoffes précieuses. Puis je m'embarquai sur le radeau avec deux petites rames, et me laissant aller au cours de la rivière.

70   Sitôt que je fus sous la voûte, je ne vis plus de lumière, et le fil de l'eau m'entraîna. Je voguai quelques jours dans cette obscurité, sans jamais apercevoir le moindre rayon de lumière. Pendant ce temps-là, j'achevai de consommer mes provisions. Alors, sans pouvoir m'en défendre, un doux

75   sommeil vint saisir mes sens. En me réveillant, je me vis avec surprise dans une vaste campagne au bord d'une rivière où mon radeau était attaché, et au milieu d'un grand nombre de noirs[1]. Je me levai dès que je les aperçus, et je les saluai. Ils me parlèrent, mais je ne comprenais pas leur langage.

80   À ce moment, je me sentis si transporté de joie que je ne savais si je devais me croire éveillé. Étant persuadé que je ne dormais pas, je m'écriai, et récitai des vers arabes.

Un des noirs, qui comprenait l'arabe, m'ayant entendu parler ainsi, s'avança et prit la parole :

85   "Mon frère, ne soyez pas surpris de nous voir. Nous habitons la campagne que vous voyez, et nous sommes venus arroser aujourd'hui nos champs de l'eau de ce fleuve qui sort de la montagne voisine. Nous avons remarqué que l'eau emportait quelque chose, nous sommes vite accourus

---

1. Noirs : Sindbâd découvre des peuples inconnus et les décrit.

90 pour voir ce que c'était, et nous avons trouvé ce radeau. Nous vous supplions de nous raconter votre histoire qui doit être

95 extraordinaire."

Je leur fis un rapport fidèle de tout ce qui m'était arrivé, ce qu'ils parurent écouter avec

100 admiration.

"Voilà, me dirent-ils par la bouche de l'interprète, une histoire des

Lucien Laforge, illustration pour *Sindbâd, le marin*, 1912.

plus surprenantes. Il faut que vous veniez en informer le

105 roi vous-même."

Je leur répondis que j'étais prêt à faire ce qu'ils voudraient.

Les noirs envoyèrent aussitôt chercher un cheval que l'on amena peu de temps après. Ils me firent monter dessus. Nous marchâmes tous ensemble jusqu'à la ville de

110 Serendib[1], car c'était dans cette île que je me trouvais. Les noirs me présentèrent à leur roi. Je m'approchai de son trône où il était assis, et le saluai. Ce prince me fit relever et il me fit avancer et prendre place auprès de lui. Il me demanda

---

1. Serendib : aujourd'hui, Sri Lanka (voir carte, p. 110).

premièrement comment je m'appelais : lui ayant répondu
115   que je me nommais Sindbâd, surnommé le Marin à cause
de plusieurs voyages que j'avais fait par mer, j'ajoutai que
j'étais habitant de la ville de Bagdad.

"Mais, reprit-il, comment vous trouvez-vous dans mes
états, et par où y êtes-vous venu ?"

120   Je ne cachai rien au roi, je lui fis le même récit que vous
venez d'entendre. Il en fut si surpris et si charmé qu'il commanda qu'on écrivit mon aventure en lettres d'or pour être
conservée dans les archives de son royaume.

Puis, il chargea un de ses officiers d'avoir soin de moi,
125   et me fit donner des gens pour me servir.

Mais je suppliai le roi de me permettre de retourner
en mon pays, ce qu'il m'accorda. Il m'obligea à recevoir
un riche présent[1], puis lorsque j'allai prendre congé de lui,
il me chargea d'un autre présent bien plus considérable,
130   et en même temps d'une lettre pour le Commandeur des
croyants[2], notre souverain seigneur, en me disant :

"Je vous prie de présenter de ma part ce présent et cette
lettre au calife Haroun Alraschid, et de l'assurer de mon
amitié."

135   Je pris le présent et la lettre avec respect, en promettant
à sa majesté d'exécuter ses ordres.

....

1. **Présent :** cadeau.
2. **Commandeur des croyants :** nom donné au calife, chef des musulmans.

La lettre du roi de Serendib était écrite sur la peau d'un animal très précieux à cause de sa rareté, et dont la couleur tire sur le jaune. Les caractères de cette lettre étaient d'azur[1].

140 Voici ce qu'elle contenait en langue indienne :

LE ROI DES INDES, DEVANT QUI MARCHENT

MILLE ÉLÉPHANTS, QUI DEMEURE DANS UN

PALAIS DONT LE TOIT BRILLE DE L'ÉCLAT

DE CENT MILLE RUBIS, ET

145 QUI POSSÈDE EN SON TRÉSOR

VINGT MILLE COURONNES

ENRICHIES DE

DIAMANTS ; AU

CALIFE HAROUN

150 ALRASCHID.

Le présent consistait premièrement en un vase d'un seul rubis, creusé, rempli de perles très rondes ; deuxièmement, en une peau de serpent qui avait des écailles grandes comme une pièce de monnaie d'or, et dont la propriété était de préserver

155 de maladie ceux qui couchaient dessus ; troisièmement, en cinquante mille drachmes[2] de bois d'aloès le plus exquis, avec trente grains de camphre de la grosseur d'une pistache. Tout cela était accompagné d'une esclave d'une beauté ravissante, et dont les habillements étaient couverts de pierreries.

....

1. **D'azur :** bleue.
2. **Drachme :** ancienne mesure de masse grecque, équivalant à 4,3 grammes environ.

160 Ayant pris congé, je me remis en route. Après une longue et heureuse navigation, j'abordai à Balsora d'où je me rendis à Bagdad. La première chose que je fis après mon arrivée fut de m'acquitter de la commission[1] dont j'étais chargé. Je pris la lettre du roi de Serendib et j'allai me présenter

165 à la porte du Commandeur des croyants. On me conduisit devant le trône du calife. Je lui fis la révérence et je lui présentai la lettre et le présent. Le calife me demanda s'il était vrai que ce prince était aussi puissant et aussi riche qu'il le marquait par sa lettre.

170 "Commandeur des croyants, lui répondis-je, je puis assurer votre majesté qu'il n'exagère pas ses richesses et sa grandeur. J'en suis témoin.

– La sagesse de ce roi, dit-il, paraît en sa lettre, et après ce que vous venez de me dire, il faut avouer que sa sagesse

175 est digne de ses peuples, et ses peuples dignes d'elle."

À ces mots, il me congédia[2] et me renvoya avec un riche présent.»

Sindbâd s'arrêta de parler, et ses auditeurs se retirèrent. Mais Hindbâd reçut auparavant cent sequins. Ils revinrent

180 encore le jour suivant chez Sindbâd qui leur raconta son septième et dernier voyage dans ces termes.

....

1. M'acquitter de la commission : accomplir la tâche.
2. Il me congédia : il m'invita à m'en aller.

Septième et dernier voyage

« Au retour de mon sixième voyage, j'abandonnai absolument la pensée d'en faire jamais d'autres. Mais un jour, un de mes gens vint m'avertir qu'un officier du calife me demandait.

Je suivis au palais l'officier qui me présenta au prince.

"Sindbâd, me dit-il, j'ai besoin de vous. Allez porter ma réponse et mes présents au roi de Serendib, il est juste que je lui rende la civilité qu'il m'a faite.

– Commandeur des croyants, lui dis-je, je suis prêt à exécuter tout ce que m'ordonnera votre Majesté. Toutefois, je la supplie de songer que je suis rebuté[1] des fatigues incroyables que j'ai souffertes. J'ai même fait vœu de ne plus jamais sortir de Bagdad."

De là, je lui fis un long détail de toutes mes aventures.

"J'avoue, dit-il, que voilà des événements bien extraordinaires. Pourtant il ne faut pas qu'ils vous empêchent de faire ce voyage. Il ne s'agit que d'aller à l'île de Serendib vous acquitter de la commission que je vous donne. Après cela, vous serez libre de revenir."

....

1. **Rebuté :** dégoûté.

20   Comme je vis que le calife exigeait absolument cela de moi, je lui témoignai que j'étais prêt à lui obéir.

Je me préparai en peu de jours à mon départ. Je pris la route de Balsora où je m'embarquai. Arrivé à l'île de Serendib, j'exposai aux ministres la commission dont j'étais chargé, 25 et l'on me conduisit au palais avec honneur. J'y saluai le roi en me prosternant selon la coutume.

Le prince me reconnut et me témoigna une joie toute particulière de me revoir.

"Ah, Sindbâd, me dit-il, soyez le bienvenu ! Je vous jure 30 que j'ai songé à vous très souvent depuis votre départ."

Je lui fis mon compliment et je lui présentai la lettre et le présent du calife.

Le roi de Serendib eut un grand plaisir de voir que le calife répondait à l'amitié qu'il lui avait témoignée. Peu de 35 temps après cette audience, je sollicitai mon congé. Le roi me fit un présent considérable. Je me rembarquai aussitôt dans le dessein de retourner à Bagdad. Mais je n'eus pas le bonheur d'y arriver comme je l'espérais.

Trois ou quatre jours après notre départ, nous fûmes atta-40 qués par des corsaires[1]. Quelques personnes de l'équipage voulurent faire résistance, mais il leur en coûta la vie. Pour moi et tous ceux qui eurent la prudence de ne pas s'opposer aux corsaires, nous fûmes faits esclaves.

....

1. **Corsaires :** marins navigant sur des navires rapides, dont le but est de capturer et de piller les bateaux étrangers qu'ils croisent.

Les corsaires nous emmenèrent dans une grande île très
éloignée où ils nous vendirent.

Je tombai entre les mains d'un riche marchand qui me
mena chez lui où il me fit bien manger et habiller en esclave.
Quelques jours après, il me demanda si je ne savais pas
quelque métier. Je lui répondis que je n'étais pas un artisan,
mais un marchand de profession, et que les corsaires qui
m'avaient vendu m'avaient enlevé tout ce que j'avais.

"Mais, dites-moi, reprit-il, ne pourriez-vous pas tirer à
l'arc?"

Je lui répondis que c'était un des exercices de ma jeunesse,
et que je ne l'avais pas oublié depuis. Alors il me donna un
arc et des flèches, et m'ayant fait monter derrière lui sur un
éléphant, il me mena dans une forêt éloignée de la ville.

Là, il me montra un grand arbre :

"Montez sur cet arbre et tirez sur les éléphants que vous
verrez passer. Car il y en a une quantité prodigieuse dans
cette forêt."

Après m'avoir dit cela, il me laissa des vivres, reprit le
chemin de la ville, et je demeurai sur l'arbre à l'affût[1] pendant toute la nuit.

Je n'aperçus aucun éléphant pendant tout ce temps-là.
Cependant, le lendemain, j'en vis paraître un grand nombre.

....

1. **À l'affût :** en train de guetter.

Je tirai dessus plusieurs flèches. Enfin, il en tomba un par
terre. Les autres se retirèrent aussitôt et me laissèrent la
70   liberté d'aller avertir mon patron qui me régala d'un bon
repas et loua mon adresse. Puis, nous allâmes ensemble
à la forêt où nous creusâmes une fosse dans laquelle nous
enterrâmes l'éléphant que j'avais tué. Mon patron se pro-
posait de revenir lorsque l'animal serait pourri, et d'enlever
75   les dents pour en faire commerce.

Je continuai cette chasse pendant deux mois. Un matin,
les éléphants vinrent à moi avec un horrible bruit et en si
grand nombre que la terre tremblait sous leurs pas. Ils s'approchèrent de l'arbre où j'étais monté et l'environnèrent[1]
80   tous, la trompe étendue et les yeux attachés sur moi. À ce
spectacle étonnant, je restai immobile et saisi d'une telle
frayeur que mon arc et mes flèches me tombèrent des mains.

Alors, un des plus gros éléphants embrassa[2] l'arbre avec
sa trompe et fit un si puissant effort qu'il le déracina et le
85   renversa par terre. Je tombai avec l'arbre. L'animal me prit
avec sa trompe et me chargea sur son dos. Il se mit ensuite
à la tête de tous les autres et me porta jusqu'à un endroit
où m'ayant posé à terre, il se retira avec tous ceux qui
l'accompagnaient. Après avoir été quelque temps étendu sur
90   la place, je me levai. Je remarquai que j'étais sur une colline

....

1. Environnèrent: entourèrent.
2. Embrassa: serra avec force.

Sindbâd en péril parmi les éléphants,
XIXᵉ **siècle, gravure.**

assez longue et assez large, toute couverte d'ossements et de dents d'éléphants. Je ne doutai point que c'était là leur cimetière et qu'ils m'avaient amené exprès ici pour me l'enseigner, afin que je cesse de les persécuter. Je tournai
95 mes pas vers la ville et j'arrivai chez mon patron.

"Ah, pauvre Sindbâd, me dit-il, j'étais dans une grande peine! J'ai été à la forêt, j'y ai trouvé un arbre déraciné, un arc et des flèches par terre. Et après t'avoir inutilement cherché, je désespérais de jamais te revoir. Raconte-moi ce
100 qui t'est arrivé."

Je satisfis sa curiosité. Le lendemain, étant allés tous deux à la colline, il reconnut avec une extrême joie la vérité de ce que je lui avais dit. Nous chargeâmes l'éléphant sur lequel nous étions venus de tout ce qu'il pouvait porter de
105 dents. Au retour, il me dit:

"Mon frère, que Dieu vous comble de toutes sortes de biens et de prospérités! Je déclare devant lui que je vous donne la liberté. Voilà toute notre ville enrichie par votre moyen.

– Patron, Dieu vous conserve! Pour toute récompense
110 je ne vous demande que la permission de retourner en mon pays.

– Hé bien, répliqua-t-il, le Moçon[1] nous amènera bientôt des navires qui viendront charger de l'ivoire[2]. Je vous

....

1. **Moçon:** vent saisonnier qui souffle de la mer vers la terre.
2. **Ivoire:** matière résistante dont sont constituées les défenses des éléphants.

renverrai alors, et vous donnerai de quoi vous conduire
chez vous.''

Je demeurai chez lui en attendant le Moçon. Pendant ce
temps-là, nous fîmes tant de voyages à la colline que nous
remplîmes ses magasins d'ivoire.

Les navires arrivèrent enfin. Mon patron ayant choisi
lui-même celui sur lequel je devais m'embarquer le chargea
d'ivoire. Après l'avoir remercié, je m'embarquai.

En mer, nous nous arrêtâmes dans quelques îles pour
y prendre des rafraîchissements. Mais, pour éviter les dangers de la mer jusqu'à Balsora, je fis débarquer l'ivoire qui
m'appartenait, résolu de continuer mon voyage par terre.
Je demeurai longtemps en chemin, et je souffris beaucoup.
Je souffrais avec patience : je n'avais plus à craindre ni les
tempêtes, ni les corsaires, ni les serpents, ni tous les autres
périls que j'avais courus.

Toutes ces fatigues finirent enfin : j'arrivai heureusement
à Bagdad. J'allai d'abord me présenter au calife. Le prince
me dit que la longueur de mon voyage lui avait causé de
l'inquiétude. Quand je lui appris l'aventure des éléphants,
il en parut fort surpris. Il trouva cette histoire et les autres
que je lui racontai si curieuses qu'il chargea un de ses secré-
taires de les écrire en caractères d'or pour être conservées
dans son trésor. Je me retirai très content de l'honneur et
des présents qu'il me fit, puis je me donnai tout entier à ma
famille, à mes parents et à mes amis. »

140   Ce fut ainsi que Sindbâd acheva le récit de son septième et dernier voyage. Il s'adressa ensuite à Hindbâd :

« Hé bien, mon ami, avez-vous jamais entendu dire que quelqu'un ait souffert autant que moi ? N'est-il pas juste qu'après tant de travaux, je jouisse d'une vie agréable et
145   tranquille ?

– Il faut avouer, Seigneur, répondit Hindbâd, que vous avez essuyé d'effroyables périls. Mes peines ne sont pas comparables aux vôtres. Vous méritez non seulement une vie tranquille, vous êtes digne encore de tous les biens que
150   vous possédez, puisque vous en faites un si bon usage, et que vous êtes si généreux. Continuez donc de vivre dans la joie jusqu'à l'heure de votre mort. »

Sindbâd lui fit donner encore cent sequins, le reçut au nombre de ses amis, lui dit de quitter sa profession de por-
155   teur, de continuer à venir manger chez lui ; et qu'il aurait lieu de se souvenir toute sa vie de Sindbâd le marin.

Alain Thomas, *Le Retour de Sindbâd*,
2005, huile sur bois, collection privée.

Charles William Bartlett, *Pêcheur avec un filet*, 1920, illustration.

Histoire du pêcheur

Lincoln Seligman, *Pêcheur solitaire*,
2019, acrylique sur toile.

Il y avait autrefois un pêcheur très âgé, et si pauvre qu'à peine pouvait-il gagner de quoi nourrir sa femme et ses trois enfants. Il allait tous les jours à la pêche et, chaque jour, il s'était fait une loi de ne jeter ses filets que quatre fois seulement.

Il partit un matin, se rendit au bord de la mer et jeta ses filets. Comme il les tirait vers le rivage, il sentit d'abord de la résistance. Il crut avoir fait une bonne pêche. Mais, un moment après, il s'aperçut qu'il n'y avait dans ses filets que la carcasse d'un âne.

Le pêcheur, affligé[1], jeta ses filets une seconde fois. En les tirant, il sentit encore beaucoup de résistance, ce qui lui fit croire qu'ils étaient remplis de poisson. Mais il n'y trouva qu'un grand panier plein de gravier et de fange[2].

« Ô fortune[3], s'écria le pêcheur, cesse d'être en colère contre moi ! Je suis parti de ma maison pour venir ici chercher ma vie, et tu m'annonces ma mort. Je n'ai pas d'autre

....

1. **Affligé :** accablé.
2. **Fange :** boue.
3. **Fortune :** ici, au sens latin de « sort, hasard ».

métier que celui-ci pour subsister[1], et malgré tous les soins que j'y apporte, je peux à peine fournir aux plus pressants besoins de ma famille.»

20 En achevant ces plaintes, il jeta pour la troisième fois ses filets. Mais il n'amena que des pierres, des coquilles et des ordures. Son désespoir fut tel qu'il faillit en perdre la tête.

25 Après avoir fini sa prière du matin, le pêcheur jeta ses filets pour la quatrième fois. Quand il jugea qu'il devait y avoir du poisson, il les tira comme auparavant avec peine. Il n'y avait pourtant pas de poissons. Mais il trouva un vase de cuivre jaune qui lui parut contenir quelque chose. Il remar-

30 qua qu'il était fermé et scellé[2] de plomb, avec l'empreinte d'un sceau[3].

Il examina le vase de tous côtés, le secoua, mais n'entendit rien. Le pêcheur prit alors son couteau et l'ouvrit. Il pencha aussitôt l'ouverture contre terre, mais rien n'en

35 sortit. Il le posa devant lui, et une fumée très épaisse s'en échappa. Cette fumée s'éleva jusqu'aux nues[4] et, s'étendant sur la mer et sur le rivage, forma un gros brouillard. Lorsque la fumée fut toute hors du vase, elle se réunit et prit

....

1. Subsister: vivre.
2. Scellé: fermé.
3. Sceau: objet qui permet de sceller en gravant un symbole avec du plomb ou de la cire.
4. Nues: nuages.

Edward Frederick Brewtnall, *Le Pêcheur*,
fin du XIXe siècle, aquarelle, Londres.

la forme d'un génie[1] deux fois aussi haut que le plus grand
40 de tous les géants. À l'aspect de ce monstre d'une grandeur
si démesurée, le pêcheur voulut prendre la fuite. Mais il était
si troublé et si effrayé qu'il ne put marcher.

« Salomon[2], s'écria d'abord le génie, Salomon, grand
prophète de Dieu, pardon, pardon ! Jamais je ne m'oppose-
45 rai à vos volontés. J'obéirai à tous vos commandements. »

À ces paroles, le pêcheur se rassura et lui dit :

« Esprit superbe[3], que dites-vous ? Il y a plus de dix-huit
cents ans que Salomon, le prophète de Dieu, est mort.
Apprenez-moi votre histoire, et pour quelle raison vous étiez
50 renfermé dans ce vase. »

Le génie regarda le pêcheur d'un air fier et lui répondit :

« Parle-moi plus civilement[4]. Tu es bien hardi[5] de m'appeler esprit superbe.

— Hé bien, répondit le pêcheur, vous parlerai-je avec plus
55 de civilité, en vous appelant hibou du bonheur ?

— Je te dis, reprit le génie, de me parler plus civilement
avant que je te tue.

— Pourquoi me tueriez-vous ? répliqua le pêcheur. Je viens
de vous mettre en liberté. L'avez-vous déjà oublié ?

....

1. **Génie :** être surnaturel que l'on retrouve souvent dans les contes orientaux.
2. **Salomon :** personnage de la Bible, roi d'Israël et prophète pour les juifs comme pour les musulmans.
3. **Superbe :** admirable, grandiose.
4. **Civilement :** convenablement.
5. **Hardi :** audacieux.

60 — Non, je m'en souviens, répondit le génie, mais cela ne m'empêchera pas de te faire mourir. Je n'ai qu'une seule grâce à t'accorder. C'est de te laisser choisir de quelle manière tu veux que je te tue.

— Mais en quoi vous ai-je offensé ? reprit le pêcheur.
65 Est-ce ainsi que vous voulez me récompenser du bien que je vous ai fait ?

— Je ne peux pas te traiter autrement, dit le génie. Écoute mon histoire. Je suis un de ces esprits rebelles qui se sont opposés à la volonté de Dieu. Tous les autres génies reconn-
70 nurent le grand Salomon et se soumirent à lui. Pour se venger, Salomon chargea Assaf, fils de Barakhia, de venir me prendre. Assaf s'empara de moi, et me mena devant le trône du roi. Salomon me commanda de quitter mon genre de vie, de reconnaître son pouvoir, et de me soumettre à
75 ses commandements. Je refusai de lui obéir et de lui prêter serment[1] de fidélité et de soumission. Pour me punir, il m'enferma dans ce vase de cuivre. Afin que je ne puisse pas m'échapper de ma prison, il imprima lui-même, sur le couvercle de plomb, son sceau où le grand nom de Dieu
80 était gravé. Cela fait, il mit le vase entre les mains d'un des génies qui lui obéissaient, avec ordre de me jeter à la mer. Durant le premier siècle de ma prison, je jurai que si quelqu'un m'en délivrait avant les cent ans achevés, je le

....

1. **Serment :** promesse.

85 rendrais riche. Mais le siècle s'écoula, et personne ne me rendit ce bon office[1]. Pendant le second siècle, je fis serment d'ouvrir tous les trésors de la terre à quiconque me mettrait en liberté. Mais je ne fus pas plus heureux. Dans le troisième, je promis de faire puissant monarque mon libérateur. Mais ce siècle se passa comme les deux autres. Enfin, enragé de
90 me voir prisonnier si longtemps, je jurai que si quelqu'un me délivrait dans la suite, je le tuerais impitoyablement et ne lui accorderais pas d'autre grâce que de choisir la façon de le tuer. Puisque tu es venu ici aujourd'hui, et que tu m'as délivré, choisis donc comment tu veux que je te tue.»
95 Ce discours affligea fort le pêcheur.

«Je suis bien malheureux, s'écria-t-il, d'être venu en cet endroit rendre un si grand service à un ingrat[2]. Considérez votre injustice, et révoquez[3] un serment si peu raisonnable.

– Non, ta mort est certaine», dit le génie.

100 Le pêcheur, voyant le génie décidé à le tuer, tâcha encore de l'apaiser :

«Hélas! reprit-il, daignez avoir pitié de moi, en considération[4] de ce que j'ai fait pour vous.

– Je te l'ai déjà dit, dit à nouveau le génie, c'est justement
105 pour cette raison que je suis obligé de t'ôter la vie.

....

1. **Office :** ici, service.
2. **Ingrat :** égoïste, sans aucune reconnaissance.
3. **Révoquez :** annulez.
4. **Considération :** reconnaissance.

Edmond Dulac, illustration
pour *Les Mille et Une Nuits*, 1907, collection privée.

– Cela est étrange, répliqua le pêcheur, que vous vouliez absolument rendre le mal pour le bien.

– Ne perdons pas de temps, interrompit le génie. Tous tes raisonnements ne sauraient me détourner de mon dessein[1]. Hâte-toi de dire comment tu souhaites que je te tue.»

La nécessité donne de l'esprit. Le pêcheur s'avisa d'un stratagème.

«Puisque je ne saurais éviter la mort, dit-il au génie, je me soumets donc à la volonté de Dieu. Mais avant, je vous conjure de me dire la vérité sur une question que j'ai à vous faire.

– Demande-moi ce que tu voudras.

– Je voudrais savoir si, effectivement, vous étiez dans ce vase. Oseriez-vous en jurer par le grand nom de Dieu ?

– Oui, répondit le génie, je jure par ce grand nom que j'y étais.

– Je ne peux pas vous croire, répliqua le pêcheur. Ce vase ne pourrait pas seulement contenir un de vos pieds. Comment se peut-il que votre corps y ait été renfermé tout entier ?

– Je te jure pourtant, répondit le génie, que j'y étais tel que tu me vois. Est-ce que tu ne me crois pas ?

– Non vraiment, dit le pêcheur. Et je ne vous croirai point, à moins que vous ne me fassiez voir la chose.»

....

1. Dessein : projet

Alors le corps du génie se mit à se dissoudre, et le génie,
se changeant en fumée et se rassemblant ensuite, commença à rentrer dans le vase et continua jusqu'à ce que
plus rien ne reste au-dehors. Aussitôt, il sortit du vase une
voix qui dit au pêcheur:

« Hé bien, incrédule[1] pêcheur, me voici dans le vase. Tu
me crois à présent? »

Le pêcheur, au lieu de répondre au génie, prit le couvercle
de plomb, et ferma promptement[2] le vase:

« Génie, lui cria-t-il, demande-moi grâce à ton tour, et
choisis de quelle mort tu veux que je te fasse mourir. Mais
non, il vaut mieux que je te rejette à la mer, dans le même
endroit d'où je t'ai tiré. Puis, je ferai bâtir une maison sur
ce rivage, où je demeurerai, pour avertir tous les pêcheurs
qui viendront y jeter leurs filets, de bien prendre garde de
repêcher un méchant génie comme toi, qui as fait serment
de tuer celui qui te mettra en liberté. »

Le génie irrité[3] fit tous ses efforts pour sortir du vase.
Mais ce ne fut pas possible, car l'empreinte du sceau du
prophète Salomon l'en empêchait.

« Ô génie, dit le pêcheur, toi qui étais le plus grand et qui
es à cette heure le plus petit de tous les génies, tu retourneras
à la mer. Tu as persisté dans la volonté de me tuer, je dois

1. Incrédule: sceptique, qui ne croit pas ce qu'on lui dit
2. Promptement: rapidement
3. Irrité: agacé.

à mon tour être impitoyable[1]. Je vais, en te laissant dans ce vase et en te rejetant à la mer, t'ôter l'usage de la vie jusqu'à la fin des temps : c'est ma vengeance. »

155 — Pêcheur, mon ami, répondit le génie, je te conjure[2] de ne pas faire une si cruelle action. Songe[3] qu'il n'est pas honnête de se venger, et qu'au contraire il est louable[4] de rendre le bien pour le mal.

— Non, dit le pêcheur, je ne te délivrerai pas.

160 — Encore un mot, pêcheur, s'écria le génie. Je te promets de ne te faire aucun mal ; je t'enseignerai un moyen de devenir puissamment riche. »

L'espérance de se tirer de la pauvreté désarma le pêcheur.

« Jure-moi, dit-il, par le grand nom de Dieu, que tu feras 165 ce que tu dis, et je vais t'ouvrir le vase. »

Le génie le fit, et le pêcheur ôta[5] aussitôt le couvercle du vase. Il en sortit à l'instant de la fumée, et la première chose que fit le génie après avoir repris sa forme fut de jeter le vase dans la mer. Cette action effraya le pêcheur :

170 « Génie, dit-il, qu'est-ce que cela signifie ? Ne voulez-vous pas garder le serment que vous venez de faire ? »

La crainte du pêcheur fit rire le génie qui lui répondit :

....

1. Impitoyable : sans aucune pitié.
2. Conjure : supplie.
3. Songe : pense.
4. Louable : honnête, juste.
5. Ôta : enleva.

« Non, pêcheur, rassure-toi. Je n'ai jeté le vase que pour me divertir et voir si tu en serais alarmé. Pour te persuader que je veux tenir parole, prends tes filets et suis-moi. »

Le génie se mit à marcher devant le pêcheur qui le suivit avec une certaine défiance[1]. Ils montèrent au haut d'une montagne d'où ils descendirent vers un étang situé entre quatre collines.

Lorsqu'ils furent arrivés au bord de l'étang, le génie dit au pêcheur :

« Jette tes filets, et prends du poisson. »

Le pêcheur fut rassuré car il en vit une grande quantité dans l'étang. Mais ce qui le surprit beaucoup, c'est qu'il y en avait de quatre couleurs différentes : des blancs, des rouges, des bleus, et des jaunes. Il jeta ses filets et en amena quatre, dont chacun était d'une de ces couleurs. Comme il n'en avait jamais vu de pareils, il ne pouvait se lasser de les admirer. Jugeant qu'il en pourrait tirer une somme assez considérable, il était très heureux.

« Emporte ces poissons, lui dit le génie, et va les présenter à ton sultan. Il t'en donnera plus d'argent que tu n'en as manié[2] en toute ta vie. Tu pourras venir tous les jours pêcher en cet étang. Mais je t'avertis de ne jeter tes filets qu'une fois chaque jour. Autrement il t'arrivera malheur, prends-y garde. »

....

1. Défiance : méfiance.
2. Manié : eu entre les mains.

En disant cela, il frappa du pied la terre qui s'ouvrit et se referma après l'avoir englouti[1].

Le pêcheur, résolu[2] à suivre les conseils du génie, se garda bien de jeter une seconde fois ses filets. Il reprit le chemin de la ville se faisant mille réflexions sur son aventure. Il alla droit au palais du sultan pour lui présenter ses poissons.

Le sultan fut très surpris lorsqu'il vit les quatre poissons. Il les prit l'un après l'autre pour les considérer avec attention. «Prenez ces poissons, dit-il à son premier vizir, et portez-les à la cuisinière. J'imagine qu'ils ne seront pas moins bons qu'ils ne sont beaux.»

Après s'être acquitté de cette commission[3], le vizir retourna vers le sultan qui le chargea de donner au pêcheur quatre cents pièces d'or. Le pêcheur concevait à peine son bonheur et le regardait comme un songe[4]. Mais il reconnut, par la suite, que ce bonheur était réel par le bon usage qu'il en fit, en l'employant aux besoins de sa famille.

....

1. Englouti: avalé.
2. Résolu: déterminé.
3. S'être acquitté de cette commission: avoir exécuté cette tâche.
4. Songe: ici, rêve.

Comprendre les textes

Vérifier sa compréhension des textes

Répondez aux questions suivantes.

Sindbâd, le marin

1 Quel est le métier de Hindbâd ?

2 Comment rencontre-t-il Sindbâd ?

3 Qui lui raconte les aventures de Sindbâd ?

4 Replacez les péripéties suivantes dans l'ordre chronologique.

a. La vallée aux diamants   **b.** La chasse aux éléphants

c. Le mariage de Sindbâd   **d.** Le vieillard étrangleur

e. L'île de la baleine   **f.** Le géant cannibale

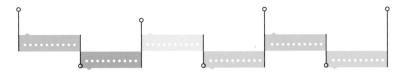

Histoire du pêcheur

1 Quelle règle le pêcheur s'est-il fixée ?

2 Au bout de combien d'essais remonte-t-il le vase du génie ?

3 Quelle ruse emploie-t-il pour se débarrasser du génie ?

Donner ses impressions de lecture

1 Avez-vous préféré l'histoire de *Sindbâd, le marin* ou l'*Histoire du pêcheur* ? Expliquez votre choix.

2 Parmi les adjectifs suivants, lequel décrit le mieux votre conte favori ?

Captivant   Drôle   Effrayant

Merveilleux   Passionnant

3 Si vous deviez ajouter une morale à la fin des deux contes, quelle serait-elle ?

4 Rédigez l'acrostiche de Sindbâd.

S
I
N
D
B
Â
D

Repère littéraire

Pour rédiger un **acrostiche**, utilisez les lettres du nom proposé pour former des mots qualifiant le personnage.

5 Écrivez votre portrait chinois en complétant les phrases suivantes.

Si j'étais un voyage de Sindbâd, je serais

Si j'étais un adversaire de Sindbâd, je serais

Si j'étais une qualité de Sindbâd, je serais

Si j'étais un défaut de Sindbâd, je serais

Si j'étais un personnage de ces contes, je serais

Si j'étais un lieu de ces contes, je serais

Si j'étais un objet de ces contes, je serais

Sindbâd, le marin

Extrait 1 Deux hommes aux vies opposées
(p. 13-16, l. 1-79)

→ **Comment la rencontre entre Sindbâd et Hindbâd introduit-elle le récit ?**

1 Reliez les adjectifs aux personnages qu'ils caractérisent.

Désespéré •
Généreux •   • Sindbâd
Jaloux •
Pauvre •   • Hindbâd
Riche •

2 Quelle figure de style est utilisée dans cette phrase : « Je souffre tous les jours mille fatigues et mille maux » (p. 14, l. 27-28) ? Selon vous, quel effet produit-elle ?

Coup de pouce Une **figure de style** peut servir à amplifier ou diminuer des éléments, à les comparer ou encore à jouer avec les sons.

3 **LANGUE** Complétez le tableau ci-dessous en relevant le vocabulaire des sens que l'on retrouve dans la description du palais, avant l'entrée de Hindbâd (p. 13, l. 8-15).

Vue 👁	Ouïe 👂	Odorat 👃	Goût 👅

4 À quoi le palais de Sindbâd peut-il bien ressembler ? Sur Internet ou au CDI, faites des recherches sur les palais orientaux, puis choisissez celui qui vous semble le plus proche de celui de Sindbâd. Justifiez votre choix à l'oral.

5 D'après les explications de Sindbâd, quel est le but de son récit ?

Extrait 2 L'affrontement du héros avec un monstre (p. 35-38, l. 28-109)

→ **En quoi Sindbâd apparaît-il comme un véritable héros ?**

1 Relevez les comparaisons employées par Sindbâd pour décrire le monstre. Dans quel but a-t-il recours à ces images ?

2 _✐ À partir de votre relevé, dessinez l'adversaire de Sindbâd.

3 Pourquoi le cannibale s'en prend-il d'abord aux compagnons du marin ?

4 Reconstituez, dans l'ordre chronologique, les étapes de la stratégie de Sindbâd face au géant.

5 Quelles qualités du marin sont mises en avant dans cet épisode ? Entourez les bonnes réponses.

Courage   Force   Gentillesse

Patience   Ruse   Sang-froid

6 Regardez la vidéo proposée ci-contre, puis expliquez les points communs entre Ulysse, héros de *L'Odyssée*, et Sindbâd.

En savoir plus sur le cyclope

Repère littéraire

L'Odyssée, épopée écrite par le poète grec Homère (VIIIe siècle av. J.-C.), raconte le difficile retour d'**Ulysse** dans sa patrie d'Ithaque après la guerre de Troie. Il traverse les mers pour rentrer chez lui et rencontre des monstres effrayants, comme le **cyclope Polyphème**.

Extrait 3 La dernière mission de Sindbâd

(p. 67-74, l. 1-156)

→ **Comment le récit du dernier voyage de Sindbâd annonce-t-il la morale du conte ?**

1 **a.** Pourquoi Sindbâd doit-il repartir en voyage ?

b. En avait-il envie ? Quels arguments avance-t-il ?

2 **a.** Avec qui Sindbâd échange-t-il dans cet extrait ?

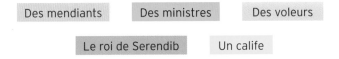

Des mendiants   Des ministres   Des voleurs

Le roi de Serendib   Un calife

b. Que constatez-vous sur le statut de ces personnages ?

c. Quelle place Sindbâd occupe-t-il désormais dans la société ?

3 Hindbâd a-t-il changé d'avis sur Sindbâd à la suite de son récit ? Comprenez-vous sa position ?

4 **LANGUE** Hindbâd conclut ainsi :

« Continuez donc de vivre dans la joie
jusqu'à l'heure de votre mort. » (p. 74, l. 151-152)

a. Relevez le verbe conjugué. Quels sont les temps et mode employés ?

b. Quel est l'effet produit ?

5 Selon vous, le sort de Sindbâd est-il enviable ?

Histoire du pêcheur

Extrait 4 L'apparition d'un être merveilleux (p. 80-86, l. 25-115)

→ **Comment le merveilleux se manifeste-t-il dans ce conte ?**

1 Comment le génie apparaît-il ?

2 **a.** Sa description est-elle précise ? Relevez les adjectifs qui le décrivent. Que remarquez-vous ?
b. Correspond-il à la représentation qui en est faite page 85 ?

3 **LANGUE** Choisissez l'un des parcours suivants et répondez aux questions permettant d'étudier le mot « génie ».

Parcours 1 ★

Trouvez un adjectif de la même famille que « génie ».

Parcours 2 ★★

a. Recherchez l'étymologie du mot « génie ».
b. Trouvez ensuite un mot de la même famille, puis employez-le dans une phrase qui en éclairera le sens.

Parcours 3 ★★★

a. Recherchez l'étymologie du mot « génie ».
b. Cette étymologie correspond-elle au sens qu'on donne à ce mot dans le texte ?

4 Relevez les éléments qui font du génie un être merveilleux.

Des contes orientaux traditionnels

1 Recopiez les formules par lesquelles débutent les deux contes.

2 **a.** Relisez la première phrase de *Sindbâd, le marin*. Sait-on dans quelle région du monde l'action va se passer ?

b. Sait-on à quelle époque elle se passe ? À votre avis, pourquoi ?

3 Placez les étiquettes suivantes en fonction du rôle des personnages dans le schéma actanciel du conte.

> **Coup de pouce**
>
> Le **schéma actanciel** permet d'identifier les rôles des différents personnages d'une histoire : le **héros** doit accomplir une **quête** ; pour cela, il est aidé par des **adjuvants**, tandis que des **opposants** sèment des embuches sur son chemin.

| Le capitaine *(1ᵉʳ voyage)* | Le géant cannibale |

Le capitaine (1er voyage) | Le géant cannibale

Le roi de Serendib | Le vieillard étrangleur

S'enrichir | Sindbâd | Voyager

Adjuvants
....
....

Héros
....

Quête
....
....

Opposants
....
....

4 Sindbâd raconte ses aventures en distinguant plusieurs voyages.

a. Dans quelles circonstances les conte-t-il ?

b. Comment marque-t-il la fin du récit de chaque voyage ?

Des créatures merveilleuses redoutables

5 Quel point commun trouve-t-on entre le physique du cannibale, celui du Roc (*Sindbâd, le marin*) et celui du génie (*Histoire du pêcheur*) ?

6 « Lorsque la fumée fut toute hors du vase, elle se réunit et prit la forme d'un génie deux fois aussi haut que le plus grand de tous les géants. » (p. 80-82, l. 37-40)

a. Quel procédé d'écriture est utilisé dans cette description ?
b. Que souligne-t-il ?

7 Trouvez l'intrus dans cette liste de personnages des deux contes. Justifiez votre réponse.

Géant cannibale	Génie	Roi de Serendib

Vieillard étrangleur

Des héros chanceux et rusés

8 Complétez le tableau ci-dessous en indiquant les passages où les personnages ont eu recours à la ruse et ceux où ils ont été chanceux.

	Chance	Ruse
Sindbâd, le marin		
Histoire du pêcheur		

9 Pourquoi les deux personnages doivent-ils parfois utiliser la ruse, et non la force ?

S'exprimer à l'oral et à l'écrit

Vocabulaire

1 Classez les mots suivants dans le tableau ci-dessous.

Aloès   Camphre   Cèdre   Cristal de roche

Émeraude   Noix de coco   Rubis

Pierres précieuses	Végétaux

2 Reliez ces expressions en lien avec la mer à leur signification.

Arriver à bon port. ●   ● Atteindre l'endroit ou l'objectif voulu.

Avoir le vent en poupe. ●   ● Avoir de la chance, de la réussite.

Ce n'est pas la mer à boire ! ●   ● Être dans une mauvaise situation.

Être au creux de la vague. ●   ● Faire croire des bêtises à quelqu'un.

Mener quelqu'un en bateau. ●   ● Ce n'est pas compliqué.

Mettre les voiles. ●   ● Partir.

3 Classez chacun des adjectifs suivants, en lien avec la ruse, dans l'encadré qui convient.

Astucieux   Dégourdi   Hypocrite   Intelligent

Malin   Perfide   Sournois   Subtil

Qualités	Défauts
....	....
....	....
....	....

Activités orales 🗨️

4 Par groupes de trois élèves, jouez la rencontre entre Hindbâd et Sindbâd.

- Relisez le début du texte (p. 13 à 16).
- Répartissez-vous les rôles : l'un(e) d'entre vous sera le metteur en scène, l'autre jouera Sindbâd et le/la dernier(ère) jouera Hindbâd.
- Réécrivez les passages au discours direct en les raccourcissant.
- Pendant que les comédiens répètent leur texte, le metteur en scène les dirige : il indique les gestes, les intonations et peut également prévoir un décor et des costumes.
- Répétez votre texte en veillant à parler suffisamment fort et à occuper l'espace en vous déplaçant.
- Jouez la scène devant vos camarades.

5 À la manière de Sindbâd, vous racontez vos aventures. Dans votre récit, vous décrivez l'animal le plus incroyable que vous ayez croisé lors d'un voyage. Toutefois, vous ne devez pas le nommer : il faut donc le dépeindre avec beaucoup de précision !

- Faites d'abord quelques recherches sur l'animal choisi.
- N'hésitez pas à ajouter des commentaires pour montrer combien il est impressionnant. Utilisez des phrases exclamatives.
- Entraînez-vous à lire votre texte plusieurs fois en insistant sur les termes qui soulignent la particularité de votre animal, puis lisez-le à vos camarades.
- Interrogez-les : ont-ils trouvé de quel animal il s'agit ?

Méthode Pensez à utiliser des **comparaisons**. Par exemple : «Cet animal est encore plus gros qu'un éléphant».

6 Échangez vos avis sur la question suivante : selon vous, lequel des voyages de Sindbâd a été le plus effrayant ?

- Répartissez-vous en binômes en choisissant un camarade qui ne partage pas le même avis que vous.
- Notez chacun sur une feuille le voyage qui vous a semblé le plus effrayant.
- Faites la liste des éléments marquants (monstres, habitants, voyage lointain...), puis rédigez votre argumentaire.
- Entraînez-vous à lire votre texte. Pensez à accentuer les mots effrayants ou à faire des gestes.
- Face à la classe, discutez avec votre camarade pour échanger vos points de vue.
- La classe votera pour l'élève qui a le mieux justifié son choix.

> **Méthode** Vous pouvez rédiger votre argumentaire en commençant par : « Selon moi, le voyage le plus effrayant est le..., car... ».

7 Imaginez que le pêcheur rentre chez lui et raconte à sa femme ce qui lui est arrivé. Par groupes de deux élèves, improvisez la discussion entre le mari et sa femme.

- Réfléchissez aux intentions et aux émotions de votre personnage (colère, surprise, joie...). N'hésitez pas à utiliser des phrases interrogatives ou exclamatives pour les mettre en valeur.
- Pensez aux gestes que le pêcheur et sa femme pourraient faire.
- Vous prendrez soin d'insister sur le caractère extraordinaire de cette aventure.

Activités écrites _ ✎

8 Sindbâd décide de reprendre la mer : imaginez son huitième et dernier voyage.

- Sindbâd ne comptait pas reprendre la mer. Trouvez ce qui a pu le pousser à le faire.
- Racontez son voyage : fut-il long ou court ? La mer était-elle calme ou agitée ?
- Détaillez ses impressions à la vue de l'île sur laquelle il est arrivé : joie, peur, émerveillement...
- Imaginez les dangers auxquels il a dû faire face, puis expliquez enfin comment il a réussi à s'en sortir : ruse, aide, combat...

9 Rédigez à votre tour un conte oriental à la manière des *Mille et Une Nuits*.

- Rendez-vous à l'adresse suivante : **http://expositions.bnf. fr/1001nuits/pedago/page1.htm**.
- Sélectionnez le héros ou l'héroïne de votre conte dans la liste proposée, puis choisissez chaque élément (décor, lieu, etc.) en cliquant sur les mots en orange.
- Lisez ensuite votre conte, puis ajoutez les détails qui vous semblent importants.
- Imprimez votre conte et présentez-le à la classe.

10 Créez un abécédaire illustré.

- Par groupes de dix élèves, choisissez dix épices et plantes aromatiques, puis organisez-les par ordre alphabétique.
- Décrivez chacun un élément et décorez-le en vous inspirant de récits de voyages. Vous pouvez même vous procurer certaines plantes et les coller dans votre abécédaire !

Histoire des arts

Lecture d'images 📷

Observez attentivement les images des pages 12, 45 et 75, puis répondez aux questions suivantes.

Les merveilles de l'Orient

1 **a.** Sur l'image page 12, où se trouve Sindbâd ?

b. Quels éléments montrent que Sindbâd est un hôte de qualité ?

2 Remplissez le tableau suivant avec les éléments qui font référence à l'Orient sur les trois images (vêtements, objets, décor, couleurs...).

Image 1 (p. 12)	Image 2 (p. 45)	Image 3 (p. 75)

3 Observez la forme de l'image page 75. Que remarquez-vous ? Pourquoi avoir choisi cette forme selon vous ?

À vous de jouer !

> **Faites découvrir des images avec un podcast**
>
> Vous allez enregistrer un podcast afin de présenter une des images et de donner envie de la découvrir.
>
> **Étape 1** Préparez un court texte structuré en trois parties : présentation de l'image (artiste, date...) ; description (couleurs, personnages) ; éléments faisant référence à l'Orient.
>
> **Étape 2** Entraînez-vous à lire votre texte. Lisez de façon expressive afin de donner envie à ceux qui vous écouteront d'aller découvrir votre image.
>
> **Étape 3** Enregistrez-vous à l'aide d'un smartphone, d'une tablette ou d'un ordinateur. Lorsqu'un enregistrement vous convient, sauvegardez-le. Vos productions pourront être postées sur le site de votre collège.

Atelier cinéma

L'Odyssée de Pi
d'Ang Lee

Année de sortie : 2012
Images : couleur
Genre : aventure
Principaux interprètes : Suraj Sharma (Pi adolescent), Irrfan Khan (Pi adulte), Tabu (la mère de Pi) et Adil Hussain (le père de Pi)

Le réalisateur

Ang Lee est né en 1954 à **Taïwan**. Il est à la fois **réalisateur, producteur et scénariste.** Il est considéré comme l'un des plus grands réalisateurs contemporains et a reçu de nombreux prix, dont l'**Oscar du meilleur réalisateur** pour le film *Brokeback Moutain* (2006).

Le film

L'action de *L'Odyssée de Pi* débute à **Pondichéry, en Inde**. Les parents de Pi tiennent un **zoo** et décident de partir à l'étranger avec leurs animaux. Le bateau fait **naufrage**, le jeune homme se retrouve sur un **canot**, accompagné d'un dangereux prédateur...

Visionnez la bande-annonce

1. Quelle image de la mer est donnée dans cet extrait ?

2. Quels éléments renvoient à la rêverie ?

3. De quelles qualités Pi semble-t-il faire preuve ?

Retenir l'essentiel

Les personnages

Des héros rusés et chanceux

SINDBÂD

Sindbâd est le **héros** du conte. Il vit dans un **magnifique palais** acquis grâce aux richesses amassées lors de ses **sept voyages**. Il se plaît à **raconter ses aventures** et les dangers auxquels il a échappé à Hindbâd et à ses invités, autour d'un bon repas. Étant maintenant **âgé**, il aspire à une **vie paisible**, à l'opposé de celle qu'il a menée jusqu'alors.

HINDBÂD

Hindbâd est un **porteur très pauvre**, qui mène une existence difficile. Un jour, il tombe par chance sur le luxueux **palais de Sindbâd**. Il se révolte d'abord contre l'**injustice de la vie**. Mais ses sentiments changent lorsqu'il rencontre Sindbâd, qui lui fait chaque jour le **récit de ses aventures** et le paie pour l'écouter.

LE PÊCHEUR

Cet homme **très âgé et très pauvre** a une femme et trois enfants. Il s'est fixé la règle de ne jeter **ses filets de pêche** que **quatre fois par jour**. Lors de sa rencontre avec le génie, il utilise la **ruse** afin d'échapper à la mort. Pris au piège, ce dernier lui confie le **secret qui lui permettra de ne plus souffrir de la pauvreté**.

Des créatures effrayantes

DES ANIMAUX ET CRÉATURES MERVEILLEUSES

Sindbâd décrit plusieurs **animaux** auxquels il a été confronté lors de ses voyages. Parmi les plus dangereux, on retrouve l'**oiseau Roc**, d'une taille démesurée, et des **serpents** gigantesques qui gardent des diamants. Sindbâd rencontre également une **créature géante à un seul œil**, à laquelle il parvient à échapper en l'aveuglant.

DES PERSONNAGES HOSTILES

Lorsqu'il accoste une île, le **marin** ne rencontre **pas toujours des peuples amicaux**. Ainsi, lors de son cinquième voyage, **Sindbâd** croise un **vieillard** qu'il porte sur ses épaules pour l'aider, sans se douter que celui-ci a tué tous les hommes qui l'ont porté auparavant...

LE GÉNIE

Sorti d'un **vase de cuivre jaune**, cet **être surnaturel** est d'une taille démesurée. **Esprit rebelle**, il a refusé d'obéir au roi Salomon 1 800 ans auparavant : celui-ci l'a alors **enfermé** dans un vase pour le punir. Il s'est juré au fil des siècles de **tuer celui qui le libèrerait**.

L'Orient et la mer au cœur des récits

LES VOYAGES DE SINDBÂD

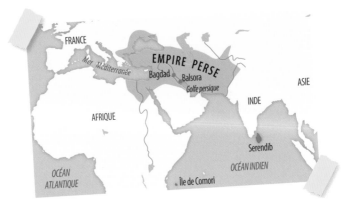

FRANCE

Mer Méditerranée

EMPIRE PERSE

Bagdad Balsora

Golfe persique

ASIE

INDE

AFRIQUE

Serendib

OCÉAN INDIEN

OCÉAN ATLANTIQUE

Île de Comori

BAGDAD

Bagdad est une **très grande ville de l'Empire perse** située en actuel Irak, dans laquelle se trouve le somptueux **palais de Sindbâd**. Il y revient après chaque voyage. C'est ici qu'il raconte son histoire à Hindbâd.

BALSORA

Balsora est le **port** à partir duquel **Sindbâd part à l'aventure**. C'est également là qu'il revient avant de pouvoir rentrer chez lui à Bagdad.

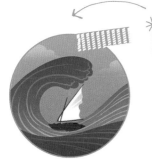

✳ LA MER

La mer occupe une place primordiale **dans les deux contes. Sindbâd** passe son temps à naviguer d'île en île, en étant toujours soumis aux courants marins. Le **pêcheur**, quant à lui, jette ses filets quatre fois par jour au bord de la mer, jusqu'à rencontrer le génie. Dans ces deux contes, la mer est donc **source de richesses**, mais aussi de **grands dangers**.

✳ LES ÎLES

À travers ses voyages, Sindbâd découvre de nombreuses îles. Il y trouve des **richesses** (épices, diamants, bois…), mais aussi des **créatures** toutes plus **effrayantes** les unes que les autres (cyclope, animaux sauvages, populations hostiles…).

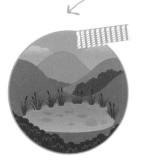

✳ L'ÉTANG ENTRE QUATRE COLLINES

Le génie conduit le pêcheur vers cet étang **exceptionnellement riche en poissons**, de quatre couleurs différentes. La seule règle donnée par le génie est de n'y jeter ses filets qu'une fois par jour.

Des voyages merveilleux qui font grandir

LE VOYAGE

Le voyage est un **thème majeur** dans *Sindbâd, le marin*. Il ne s'agit pas simplement d'aller d'un point à un autre, mais de **traverser le monde au péril de sa vie** et de **découvrir des peuples**, des coutumes, des plantes exotiques et des animaux extraordinaires. Le voyage, **symbole de liberté et de danger**, fait grandir Sindbâd : le jeune marin, qui ne voyait que le profit, devient un **vieil homme qui a gagné en sagesse** et qui comprend le bien précieux qu'est une vie en sécurité. En racontant son histoire à Hindbâd, il revit par la même occasion ses aventures.

LA RICHESSE ET LA PAUVRETÉ

Les **personnages** que l'on rencontre en premier dans ces deux contes sont **très pauvres**. Que ce soit le pêcheur ou Hindbâd, tous deux peinent à nourrir leur famille. La **grande pauvreté de Hindbâd** est en opposition avec l'**immense richesse de Sindbâd**. Mais Hindbâd, d'abord jaloux, comprend à la fin du conte que cette **richesse** est **méritée**. Dans le deuxième conte, le génie montre au pêcheur le chemin d'un coin de pêche qui lui permet de **ne plus jamais se soucier de l'argent**.

LE MERVEILLEUX

Dans le conte du pêcheur, le **merveilleux** s'exprime au travers du **personnage du génie** : un être surnaturel emprisonné dans un vase. **Sindbâd** rencontre lui aussi des **créatures merveilleuses**, comme le géant à un seul œil ou l'oiseau Roc. Ces créatures sont **dangereuses** et poussent les héros à **ruser** pour s'en sortir.

LA RUSE

Pour se sortir des dangers qu'ils affrontent, Sindbâd et le pêcheur doivent ruser, car ils se retrouvent face à des **monstres physiquement plus puissants qu'eux**. Le génie, être surnaturel, est bien plus fort que le vieux **pêcheur**. Ce dernier lui **joue** alors **un tour** : il affirme que le génie n'est pas capable de rentrer dans le vase ; piqué dans son orgueil, celui-ci souhaite montrer ce qu'il peut faire et se retrouve enfermé. **Sindbâd** utilise lui aussi son **intelligence**, notamment face au géant, à qui il crève l'unique œil, ou lorsqu'il arrive à se sortir de la vallée de diamants.

Des contes orientaux riches

❶ Des contes orientaux

a. Un Orient atemporel

Aucun des contes n'est situé dans le temps. Dans l'*Histoire du pêcheur*, les **lieux** semblent **magiques**, tandis que l'action de *Sindbâd, le marin* est basée en **Orient**. Des éléments (décor, paysages...) renvoient dans les deux contes à cette partie du monde, qui n'est **pas toujours bien délimitée** dans l'espace.

b. Un schéma narratif respecté

Ces deux contes suivent les différentes **étapes du schéma narratif** : situation initiale, élément perturbateur, péripéties, élément de résolution et situation finale.

c. Une fin heureuse

Tout est bien qui finit bien : les deux personnages finissent **riches**, **heureux** et surtout **à l'abri des dangers**.

→ Activité 1, p. 116

❷ Des héros types

a. Des personnages aux destins fabuleux

Le pêcheur peinait à nourrir sa famille **avant de rencontrer le génie**. Sindbâd, avait connu la richesse, mais l'avait dilapidée **avant de la retrouver grâce à ses voyages**.

b. Deux hommes aux nombreuses qualités

Le pêcheur, comme Sindbâd, fait preuve de **courage** en affrontant des ennemis puissants. Les deux héros montrent aussi leur **intelligence** et leur **bonté**.

→ Activité 3, p. 117

en rebondissements

③ Des aventures pleines de dangers

a. De nombreuses péripéties
Dans ces deux contes, **les événements s'enchaînent.** Les **voyages** de Sindbâd, surtout, sont riches en action : chacun comporte plusieurs **péripéties.**

b. Des adversaires redoutables
Les héros des deux contes font face à des **adversaires** bien plus **puissants** qu'eux : **animaux sauvages gigantesques** pour Sindbâd, **génie** surnaturel démesuré pour le pêcheur...

c. Des dangers insoupçonnés
Certains adversaires de Sindbâd ne semblent pas effrayants. Ainsi, **le vieillard «étrangleur»** rencontré lors de son cinquième voyage, ou encore son **mariage**, qui ne présentaient *a priori* aucun danger, se sont avérés redoutables.

➜ Activité 2, p. 116

④ Les leçons du conte

a. Des leçons à tirer
Dans ces deux contes, la **bravoure**, la **ruse**, mais aussi la **clémence** des héros sont **récompensées** : elles les mettent pour toujours à l'abri du besoin. Cela permet de donner une leçon au lecteur.

b. Le changement d'avis de Hindbâd
Hindbâd tire une leçon après avoir écouté le récit du marin : il a parlé trop vite en affirmant que Sindbâd n'avait pas mérité sa situation et a compris qu'**on ne peut juger de la vie de quelqu'un sans la connaître.**

➜ Activité 4, p. 117

Bilan

À vous de jouer !

Activité 1 ▸ Reliez chaque étape du schéma narratif de l'*Histoire du pêcheur* au moment de l'intrigue auquel il correspond.

1. Situation initiale ●

2. Élément déclencheur ●

3. Péripétie ●

4. Élément de résolution ●

5. Situation finale ●

● **a.** Le génie conduit le vieil homme vers un étang magique.

● **b.** Le pêcheur pêche de quoi vivre aisément.

● **c.** Le pêcheur remonte un vase fermé par un sceau.

● **d.** Un génie sort du vase et menace le pêcheur de le tuer.

● **e.** Un pauvre pêcheur a l'habitude de jeter ses filets quatre fois par jour.

Activité 2 ▸ Retrouvez les créatures rencontrées par Sindbâd et le pêcheur dans cette grille de mots mêlés.

Baleine   Éléphants   Géant

Génie   Roc   Serpents

M	W	F	G	E	A	N	T	X	P
E	L	E	P	H	A	N	T	S	B
S	R	F	F	C	K	T	U	E	A
L	G	E	N	I	E	Y	K	R	L
K	Q	G	G	H	M	A	Z	P	E
S	Y	X	R	P	U	W	Z	E	I
E	T	Z	L	M	G	N	Z	N	N
L	S	S	X	F	N	O	P	T	E
U	R	S	P	Y	C	O	I	S	K
L	G	R	O	C	W	F	R	T	Q

À vous de jouer !

Activité 3 ▶ Décodez le message de Sindbâd grâce à ce rébus.

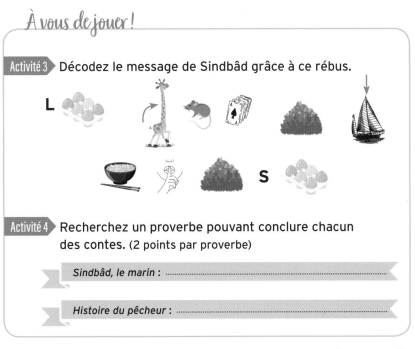

L   S

Activité 4 ▶ Recherchez un proverbe pouvant conclure chacun des contes. (2 points par proverbe)

Sindbâd, le marin : ....

Histoire du pêcheur : ....

Réponses 3. Le courage est ma richesse.

Évaluez-vous !

Comptez 1 point par bonne réponse et gravissez les marches du podium. Jusqu'où irez-vous ?

Prolonger la lecture

Un tour du monde des lieux merveilleux

Un palais à couper le souffle

Marco Polo, *Le Livre des Merveilles*

Le Livre des Merveilles est le récit des voyages du grand explorateur italien Marco Polo (1254-1324). Ici, il décrit le palais éblouissant de Koubilaï Khan, empereur de Chine, qui a d'ailleurs fait de lui son ambassadeur.

Sachez que le Grand Khan demeure dans la capitale du Catay, nommée Pékin, trois mois par an : décembre, janvier et février. C'est dans cette ville qu'il a son palais, que je vais maintenant vous décrire. [...]

5 C'est le plus grand qu'on ait jamais vu. Il n'a pas d'étage mais le pavement[1] est bien dix paumes[2] plus élevé que le sol alentour et le toit est très haut. Les murs des salles et des chambres sont tous couverts d'or et d'argent et on y a peint des dragons, des bêtes, des oiseaux, des chevaliers, et toutes sortes d'animaux. Le plafond est ainsi fait que

10 l'on n'y aperçoit rien d'autre que de l'or et des peintures. La salle est si vaste que six mille hommes pourraient bien y prendre leurs repas. Les chambres sont si nombreuses que c'est un spectacle extraordinaire. Ce palais est si grand et superbe que personne ne pourrait en concevoir un qui soit mieux fait. Les tuiles du toit sont toutes vermeilles[3], vertes,

15 bleues, jaunes et de toutes les couleurs. Elles sont si bien vernissées[4] qu'elles resplendissent comme du cristal, de sorte qu'on les voit briller de très loin à la ronde ; et sachez que cette toiture est si solide et résistante qu'elle dure beaucoup d'années.

Marco Polo, *Le Livre des Merveilles ou le Devisement du monde*,
LXXXIV [1298], trad. par Violette d'Aignan © Gallimard,
« La Bibliothèque Gallimard », 1998.

....

1. **Pavement :** sol constitué de pierres taillées.
2. **Paumes :** ancienne unité de longueur correspondant à 7 centimètres environ.
3. **Vermeilles :** d'un rouge vif.
4. **Vernissées :** brillantes, car recouvertes de vernis.

Une île qui enchante les sens

Les Mille et Une Nuits, « Histoire du prince Zeyn Alasnam et du roi des génies »

Le prince Zeyn, après avoir gaspillé beaucoup de richesses, a vu en songe un vieillard lui indiquant d'aller au Caire, car beaucoup de richesses l'y attendent. Avec Mobarec, ancien esclave de son père, ils sont récupérés par un bateau magique afin de s'y rendre pour rapporter une statue extrêmement précieuse. La seule règle est de ne prononcer aucun mot pendant le voyage. Voici les premières paroles de Mobarec à leur arrivée.

« Nous pouvons présentement parler, dit Mobarec. L'île où nous sommes, est celle du roi des Génies ; il n'y en a point de semblable dans le reste du monde. Regardez de tous côtés, prince, est-il un plus charmant séjour[1] ? C'est sans doute une véritable image de ce
5   lieu ravissant que Dieu destine aux fidèles observateurs de notre loi. Voyez les champs parés de fleurs et de toutes sortes d'herbes odorantes. Admirez ces beaux arbres, dont les fruits délicieux font plier les branches jusqu'à terre. Goûtez le plaisir que doivent causer ces chants harmonieux que forment dans les airs mille oiseaux de
10   mille espèces inconnues dans les autres pays. » Zeyn ne pouvait se lasser de considérer la beauté des choses qui l'environnaient ; et il en remarquait de nouvelles à mesure qu'il s'avançait dans l'île.

Enfin, ils arrivèrent devant un palais de fines émeraudes, entouré d'un large fossé, sur les bords duquel, d'espace en espace, étaient
15   plantés des arbres si hauts qu'ils couvraient de leur ombrage tout le palais. Vis-à-vis la porte qui était d'or massif, il y avait un pont fait d'une seule écaille de poisson, quoiqu'il eût pour le moins six toises[2] de long et trois de large. On voyait à la tête du pont une troupe de Génies d'une hauteur démesurée, qui défendaient l'entrée du château
20   avec de grosses massues d'acier de la Chine.

Les Mille et Une Nuits, d'après la traduction
d'Antoine Galland, Gallimard, « Folio Classique », 1991.

....

1. Séjour : ici, lieu.
2. Toises : ancienne unité de longueur correspondant à 1,9 mètre.

Les vestiges d'une cité incroyable

Jules Verne, *Vingt Mille Lieues sous les mers*

Dans ce roman de Jules Verne (1828-1905), le professeur Aronnax, accompagné du capitaine Nemo, découvre l'Atlantide, une cité enfouie sous l'océan.

Quel était ce monde exorbitant que je ne connaissais pas encore ? [...]

En effet, là, sous mes yeux, ruinée, abîmée, jetée bas, apparaissait une ville détruite, ses toits effondrés, ses temples abattus, ses arcs
5 disloqués[1], ses colonnes gisant à terre, où l'on sentait encore les solides proportions d'une sorte d'architecture toscane[2] ; plus loin, quelques restes d'un gigantesque aqueduc ; ici l'exhaussement[3] empâté d'une acropole, avec les formes flottantes d'un Parthénon ; là, des vestiges de quai, comme si quelque antique port eût abrité
10 jadis sur les bords d'un océan disparu les vaisseaux marchands et les trirèmes[4] de guerre ; plus loin encore, de longues lignes de murailles écroulées, de larges rues désertes, toute une Pompéi[5] enfouie sous les eaux, que le capitaine Nemo ressuscitait à mes regards !

Où étais-je ? Où étais-je ? Je voulais le savoir à tout prix, je voulais
15 parler, je voulais arracher la sphère de cuivre qui emprisonnait ma tête.

Mais le capitaine Nemo vint à moi et m'arrêta d'un geste. Puis, ramassant un morceau de pierre crayeuse, il s'avança vers un roc de basalte noire et traça ce seul mot
20 ATLANTIDE.

Jules Verne, *Vingt Mille Lieues sous les mers*,
[1870], Le Livre de Poche, 2001.

....

1. Disloqués : qui ne tiennent plus en un seul bloc.
2. Toscane : qui vient de Toscane, une région d'Italie.
3. Exhaussement : surélévation.
4. Trirèmes : bateaux de combat, dans l'Antiquité.
5. Pompéi : cité antique ensevelie par l'éruption du Vésuve.

Livres

Gilles Baraqué,
Au ventre du monde
L'École des Loisirs, 2012

Ce roman raconte l'histoire de Pahoétama, une petite fille qui a été faite garçon par son grand-père pour qu'elle puisse pêcher, car cela est interdit aux femmes de cette île. Elle devra affronter bien des dangers au cours de ses aventures.

Lucas Rufi,
L'Incroyable Île Fourmite
2020

Embarquez avec deux marins pour une aventure qui vous fera découvrir un environnement splendide.

Ali Baba
Belin-Éducation, 2020

Ce conte des Mille et Une Nuits raconte l'histoire d'Ali Baba :

un homme pauvre et misérable qui trouve un jour un trésor qui appartient à quarante voleurs. Va-t-il réussir à leur échapper ?

Films

Tim Johnson et Patrick Gilmore, *Sinbad : la légende des sept mers,*
2002

Suivez Sinbad dans de trépidantes aventures à la recherche du Livre de la Paix.

Ang Lee, *L'Odyssée de Pi,*
2012

Pi est, avec un tigre du Bengale, le seul rescapé du naufrage de son cargo dans l'océan Pacifique. Comment va-t-il parvenir à survivre sur une mer hostile avec une bête féroce ?

Sites Internet

http://expositions.bnf.fr/1001nuits/albums/1001/index.htm
Rendez-vous à cette adresse pour découvrir les magnifiques illustrations de différents contes des Mille et Une Nuits par Léon Carré.

https://www.youtube.com/watch?v=OZoZd7ALCZU
Visitez l'Institut du monde arabe à travers cette vidéo. Les objets présentés prennent vie grâce aux histoires contées.

Dans la même collection

3 nouvelles engagées (anthologie)
3 nouvelles de science-fiction (anthologie)
4 histoires de sorcières (anthologie)
4 nouvelles de fantômes (anthologie)
30 poèmes pour célébrer le monde (anthologie)
30 poèmes pour dire l'amour (anthologie)
30 poèmes engagés (anthologie)
Ali Baba
Le Chevalier dans tous ses états (anthologie)
Merlin l'Enchanteur
Sindbâd, le marin, Histoire du pêcheur
Alexandrine Civard-Racinais, Les Robinsons de l'île Tromelin
Pierre Corneille, Le Cid
Jean-Claude Grumberg, La plus précieuse des marchandises
Homère, L'Odyssée
Sid Jacobson et Ernie Colón La Vie d'Anne Frank en bande dessinée
Maurice Leblanc, L'Évasion d'Arsène Lupin
Mme Leprince de Beaumont, La Belle et la Bête
Jack London, L'Appel de la forêt
Guy de Maupassant, La Parure et autres nouvelles sur les apparences
Molière, Les Fourberies de Scapin
Molière, Le Médecin malgré lui

Crédits iconographiques

Couverture: Radosveta Zhelyazkova; **p. 4:** Bridgeman Images/Granger; **p. 5:** Kharbine-Tapabor/ Coll. Grob; **p. 6h et 6b:** Kharbine-Tapabor/Coll. Grob; **p. 9-58:** © Neofelis éditions; **p. 12-91:** AKG-Images/UIG/Universal History Archive/© Adagp, Paris 2021; **p. 19:** Kharbine-Tapabor/Coll. Grob; **p. 27:** Bridgeman Images/Look and Learn; **p. 29:** Kharbine-Tapabor/Coll. Grob; **p. 34:** © Neofelis éditions; **p. 39:** AKG-Images/UIG/Universal History Archive; **p. 45-107:** Photo12/Alamy/Artefact; **p. 50:** Bridgeman Images/Granger; **p. 55:** Bridgeman Images/Look and Learn; **p. 58:** AKG-Images/ North Wind Pictures; **p. 63:** Kharbine-Tapabor/DR; **p. 71:** AKG-Images/North Wind Pictures; **p. 75-119:** La Collection/Alain Thomas 2005; **p. 76:** Bridgeman Images/MEPL; **p. 78:** Bridgeman Images/ Lincoln Seligman; **p. 81:** Bridgeman Images/Royal Watercolour Society; **p. 85:** Kharbine-Tapabor/ © Adagp, Paris 2021; **p. 91:** AKG-Images/UIG/Universal History Archive/© Adagp, Paris 2021; **p. 105-123bd:** Aurimages/AllPix_SunsetBox/Dune Entertainment/Fox 2000 Pictures; **p. 123hg:** © L'École des loisirs; **p. 123mg:** Lucas Rufi; **p. 123bg:** © Humensis/Belin Éducation; **p. 123hd:** Aurimages/ BBQ_DFY/Dreamworks; Éléments graphiques: Istock.

Création couverture: SAJE.
Maquette intérieure et direction artistique: Studio Graphique Humensis.
Mise en pages: Ariane Aubert.
Illustrations (p. 108-113): Emmanuelle Pioli.
Carte et frise: Coredoc.
Iconographie: Geoffroy Mauzé.
Suivi éditorial: Mirna Bousser.

© Belin Éducation / Humensis, 2021 pour l'adaptation, les notes et le dossier pédagogique.
170 bis, boulevard du Montparnasse, 75680 Paris cedex 14

 IMPRIM'VERT®

La pâte à papier utilisée pour la fabrication du papier de cet ouvrage provient de forêts certifiées et gérées durablement.

Imprimé en France par Estimprim – 25110 Autechaux
Dépôt légal : août 2021 – N° d'édition : 03581883-01
ISBN 979-10-358-1883-8

Weekending
In New England

By Betsy Wittemann and Nancy Woodworth

Wood Pond Press
365 Ridgewood Road
West Hartford, CT. 06107

Readers should bear in mind that prices, especially in restaurants and lodgings, change seasonally and with inflation. Prices quoted in this book were correct at presstime. They are offered as a relative guide, rather than an absolute.

Lodging rates quoted are for peak periods; weekdays and off-season dates may be lower.

The authors have personally visited and evaluated the places recommended in this book. Unlike some guidebooks, there is no charge levied for inclusion.

The authors invite readers' comments and suggestions.

Cover design by Robert Smith.

Cover photo by Jim McElholm/Newport County Convention & Visitors Bureau: Harborside dining in Newport, R.I.

Graphics by Jay Woodworth.

Copyright © 1997, 1993, 1988, 1984 and 1980 by Betsy Wittemann and Nancy Woodworth

Library of Congress Catalog No. 80-80817

ISBN No. 0-934260-81-8

Published in the United States of America
Fifth Edition.

Contents

About the Authors

Betsy Wittemann is a freelance journalist and travel writer and a former reporter and editor for daily newspapers in Rochester, N.Y., and Hartford, Conn. She is the co-author of several travel guidebooks, including *Daytripping & Dining in Southern New England* and *Waterside Escapes in the Northeast,* both co-authored with Nancy Webster Woodworth. With her husband, Ross Wittemann, she wrote *The Fireside Guide to New England Inns and Restaurants..* A native of Bridgeport, Conn., she has lived in Athens, Greece, and San Juan, Puerto Rico, where she was associate editor of a Caribbean travel magazine. Her travel articles have appeared in major newspapers in the Northeast. She and her husband reside in Glastonbury, Conn.

Nancy Webster Woodworth and her family are such inveterate travelers that when they moved to Connecticut, they spent their first weekend exploring New York City while others would have been unpacking. A native of Montreal, she traveled extensively in Canada and hitchhiked through Europe on $3 a day before her marriage to an American newspaper editor. In the 1970s, she started writing her "Roaming the Restaurants" column for the West Hartford News, which led to the other half of the *Daytripping & Dining in New England* series. She and her husband, Richard Woodworth, are co-authors of *Getaways for Gourmets in the Northeast,* two editions of *Inn Spots & Special Places,* one for New England and one for New York and the Mid-Atlantic, and *The Restaurants of New England.* She and her husband live in West Hartford.

Books by Betsy Wittemann and Nancy Webster Woodworth

Daytripping & Dining in Southern New England
Weekending in New England
Daytripping & Dining 2 in New England
The Best of Daytripping & Dining in Southern New England and Nearby New York
Waterside Escapes in the Northeast

To Our Readers

Americans are weekenders. We head out after work on Friday for a needed break in our daily routine.

Such a trip is an ideal break. A short or long weekend away refreshes and relaxes, returning us to our regular activities with a new outlook. And, because it doesn't draw on too many vacation days for those of us with limited holiday time, we can enjoy a weekend away every now and then.

New England is the perfect place for the weekender. Distances are short and diversions many. Hop in your car and you can reach most weekend destinations within a few hours.

We recognized this years ago, publishing the first weekending guide in 1980. We continue to update and revise, seeking out the best destinations in the region for each season. What all of these choices have in common are a good selection of accommodations, dining options, and things to see and do. Some are relaxing, others invigorating. All are delightful in their own way and are favorite places of ours. We hope you'll make them your favorites, too.

A word about our research methods. We do not rely on questionnaires or telephone calls to determine whether an inn, a restaurant or a tourist attraction is up to par. We visit in person, talk to the owners, inspect rooms, sample foods. We try to bring you the best and latest information available so that your trip will be successful. We cherish our reputation for credibility and tell it like it is. No one can buy their way into our books.

In this new fifth edition, we have made extra efforts to find especially good values in lodging and dining – to help you have a wonderful weekend without breaking the bank.

Please know that we welcome your suggestions and comments. Write to us at Wood Pond Press, 365 Ridgewood Road, West Hartford, CT 06107, or E-mail us at woodpond@pop.ntplx.net.

Now, we invite you to share in our discoveries.

Betsy Wittemann and Nancy Woodworth

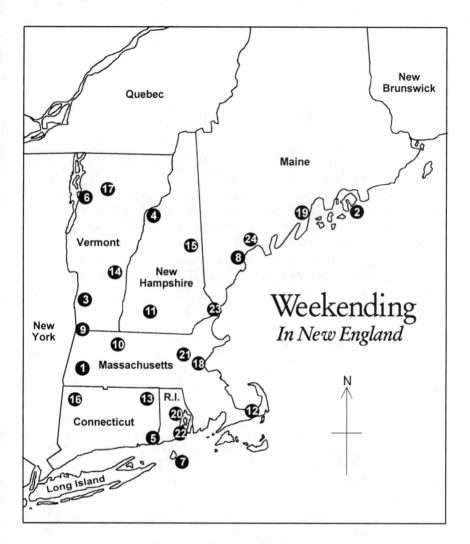

Weekending Destinations

1. Southern Berkshires, MA
2. Mount Desert Island, ME
3. Manchester, VT
4. Franconia-Bethlehem, NH
5. Southeast Connecticut
6. Burlington / Champlain Islands, VT
7. Block Island, RI
8. Portland, ME
9. Bennington, VT - Williamstown, MA
10. Pioneer Valley, MA
11. Monadnock Region, NH
12. Cape Cod, MA
13. Northeastern Connecticut
14. Woodstock, VT
15. Mount Washington Valley, NH
16. Northwest Corner, CT
17. Stowe, VT
18. Boston, MA
19. Camden, ME
20. Providence, RI
21. Concord / Lexington, MA
22. Newport, RI
23. Portsmouth, NH
24. Freeport / The Harpswells, ME

1  Summer

Music lovers relax on lawn outside Shed at Tanglewood.

A Sophisticated Summer Sojourn
The Southern Berkshires, Mass.

Ah, the Berkshires! The word conjures up thoughts of New England to anyone west of the Hudson River, of Tanglewood to the knowledgeable music lover, of quaint villages and country inns to generations of travelers, of sylvan retreats that have inspired the artists and authors who have called the Berkshires home.

And ah, the greens! When grass is dry and hay-colored and the summer humidity oppressive, the soft emerald lawns of the Berkshires delight the eye, with the contrast of wooded hills and dark evergreen forests refreshing, verdant and cooling at every glance.

The Berkshires means different things to different people: at least three mountains worthy of the name, lakes and streams, fall foliage tours, culture and arts, ski areas and hiking trails, classic New England villages, historic homes, and places and names associated with the best of Americana.

For the summer visitor, the number of attractions is mind-boggling – enough to keep one busy for a week, if not longer. And yet the lesser known, unexpected discoveries in almost every nook and cranny of the mountain mosaic that is the Berkshires account for much of their unfolding appeal, even to those who know them well.

Summer simply wouldn't be summer in New England without a Sunday afternoon at Tanglewood. We have often made it a day-long outing, stopping for a morning swim in a secluded stream and then spreading our blanket on the lawn outside the music shed for a picnic (usually gazpacho, chicken salad and chardonnay) and an afternoon with the Boston Symphony, Beethoven and the New York Times.

And New England simply wouldn't be New England without a visit to picturesque Stockbridge and the southern Berkshires countryside. This is the inland route we take with visitors who want to see and sense New England in a short tour. For purposes of this guide, we've focused on the southern Berkshires and three inter-related themes: the arts, history and nature.

The arts are centered in Lenox and Stockbridge, which attracted literati of such name and number in the mid-1800s that the area became known as "America's Lake Country." Herman Melville, Nathaniel Hawthorne, Henry Adams, Edith Wharton and Henry Wadsworth Longfellow all lived here. Today, the Berkshires are unrivaled as America's summer cultural center with the foremost in music, dance and theater festivals.

Lenox remains an architectural showplace with vestiges of its days as "the inland Newport." For some of America's 400 who built palatial villas there around the turn of the century, the mountains were the summer equal of sand and surf or an autumnal transition between shore and city. "The well-regulated society person," according to an 1893 magazine quoted in an exhibition at Chesterwood, "can no more neglect a visit to Lenox during some part of the season than he can to observe Lent or to speak French at dinner."

Stockbridge is the storybook village whose scenes and residents were depicted by the late resident artist Norman Rockwell. Its New England-perfect nature is epitomized by its train depot: In 1892, townspeople were upset over the railroad's plans and commissioned architect Stanford White instead. And in the 1960s, villagers fought over the presence of Alice's Restaurant, memorialized by Arlo Guthrie after it was run out of town. Recently, the town experienced something of a battle over plans for expansion of the Norman Rockwell Museum.

The sophistication of Lenox and Stockbridge stands in startling contrast with the Berkshires of yesteryear, much of which still slumbers off the beaten path a few miles away.

Pages from the past are West Stockbridge with a vaguely Old West air, the lovely community of South Egremont, the covered bridges and tree-lined green of Sheffield, the remnants of the Shaker community still visible at Tyringham, and tiny towns like New Marlboro and Sandisfield, the forested settlement where Edmund Sears wrote the Christmas carol, "It Came Upon a Midnight Clear."

The natural beauty prompted Oliver Wendell Holmes's quote: "There's no tonic like the Housatonic," a reference to the river that snakes through the southern Berkshires. Waterfalls, ponds and hidden lakes abound. The flora of Bartholomew's Cobble, the Berkshire Botanical Garden and even the Tanglewood grounds vie with the foliage for visitors' attention.

History and nature focus in a place like Mount Washington, the old "town among the clouds," whose 60 or so permanent residents used to cast the first votes in presidential elections. Now, blueberrying is the chief occupation in the Bay State's least populated and highest town. Near the top, sky-high Guilder Pond is flanked by the Berkshires' best show of flowering mountain laurel in June. Beyond the meandering roads and old buildings is the summit of Mount Everett, the state's second highest peak, with a three-state view of the Berkshires, the Catskills and the Litchfield Hills.

The views are sublime – and so are the Berkshires.

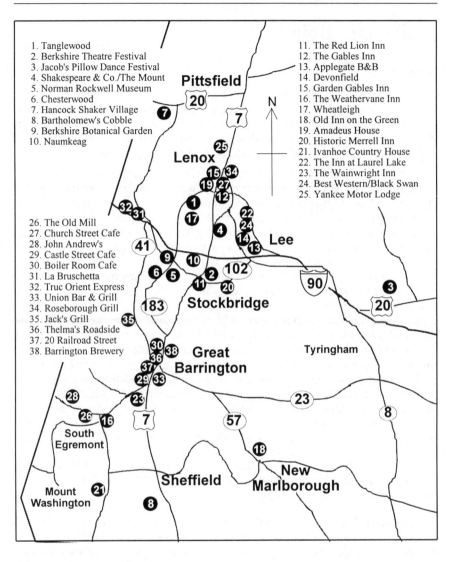

1. Tanglewood
2. Berkshire Theatre Festival
3. Jacob's Pillow Dance Festival
4. Shakespeare & Co./The Mount
5. Norman Rockwell Museum
6. Chesterwood
7. Hancock Shaker Village
8. Bartholomew's Cobble
9. Berkshire Botanical Garden
10. Naumkeag

11. The Red Lion Inn
12. The Gables Inn
13. Applegate B&B
14. Devonfield
15. Garden Gables Inn
16. The Weathervane Inn
17. Wheatleigh
18. Old Inn on the Green
19. Amadeus House
20. Historic Merrell Inn
21. Ivanhoe Country House
22. The Inn at Laurel Lake
23. The Wainwright Inn
24. Best Western/Black Swan
25. Yankee Motor Lodge

26. The Old Mill
27. Church Street Cafe
28. John Andrew's
29. Castle Street Cafe
30. Boiler Room Cafe
31. La Bruschetta
32. Truc Orient Express
33. Union Bar & Grill
34. Roseborough Grill
35. Jack's Grill
36. Thelma's Roadside
37. 20 Railroad Street
38. Barrington Brewery

Getting There

The Berkshires present unfolding panoramas on both sides of the Massachusetts Turnpike (Interstate 90), which connects with the New York Thruway at West Stockbridge and heads east to Springfield and Boston. U.S. Route 20 and State Route 9 are other east-west roads. U.S. Route 7 is the principal north-south highway; the locals call State Route 41 the "Scenic Route."

Bonanza Bus Lines, Greyhound Lines and Peter Pan Bus Lines provide frequent bus service to and through the region, especially to Pittsfield, the major city.

Limited train service is provided by Amtrak from Boston and the west.

Albany Airport and Bradley International (Springfield-Hartford) serve the area.

Seeing and Doing

The Arts

Nowhere else is so much music, arts and theatrical activity concentrated in one area every summer (in fact, Lenox recently became the site of the National Music Foundation's new national music center). People come from near and far for one or more performances; serious students and noted performers are in residence the entire season, which is roughly the last week of June to Labor Day.

Among the offerings:

Tanglewood. The summer home of the Boston Symphony Orchestra and its Berkshire Music Center programs, Tanglewood is synonymous with music and the Berkshires. The 210-acre estate, with the waters of Stockbridge Bowl shimmering in the distance, is a perfect setting for the BSO, which started presenting nine weekends of concerts each summer back in 1936. The acoustically excellent, open-air shed seats 6,000 and is the place for the connoisseur who wants to see or be seen. Up to 10,000 more find spots under the sun or stars outside on the lawn, where you can't see but can hear just fine. We like to arrive when the gates open two hours prior to the performance and pick a spot under the biggest tree just outside the shed. Some of the picnics with wicker baskets, checkered tablecloths and candelabra are as elaborate as the football tailgating parties at the Yale Bowl. A new cafeteria doles out food and wine; the adjacent gift shop specializes in music, naturally. The grounds are made for strolling, and you can view the replica of Nathaniel Hawthorne's house across Hawthorne Road from the Friends of Tanglewood tent. Come early and stay late to avoid the traffic which, despite the volume, moves quite expeditiously. Special events feature visiting performers many weekdays in season in the Shed or in the new Seiji Ozawa Concert Hall. The open rehearsal ($12.50) every Saturday morning at 10:30 is an excellent and intimate way for budget-watchers to get up close.

West Street (Route 183), Lenox. (413) 637-5165. Concerts Friday at 8:30 (with 6 o'clock preludes in Ozawa Hall), Saturday at 8:30 and Sunday at 2:30. Tickets, $14 to $63; admission to lawn, generally $12.50.

Berkshire Theatre Festival. This summer institution has been described by the New York Times as "one of the most adventurous and exciting theaters in the country." Dedicated exclusively to the American repertoire, the festival brings top talent and four shows each summer to the 440-seat playhouse. An apprentice company performs children's plays by young playwrights Wednesday-Saturday at noon under the tent. A new Unicorn Theatre was inaugurated in 1996. The Mainstage Playhouse, designed in 1886 by Stanford White as the Stockbridge casino, was the social center of the community until it became the nation's second summer theater in 1928.

Main Street, Stockbridge. (413) 298-5576. Mainstage performances, Monday-Saturday at 8, matinees Thursday at 2 and Saturday at 3. Tickets, $25 to $34.

Jacob's Pillow Dance Festival. The oldest and foremost summer dance festival in America, the "Pillow" offers everything from classic ballet to folkdancing and is known for its 300 world premieres. The rustic 100-acre wooded setting (upgraded in 1992 for the 60th anniversary season) includes several restored 18th-century barns. One is named for founder Ted Shawn, who launched the full-fledged festival in 1942 after ten experimental summers. A nine-week season is presented Tuesday-Saturday at 8:30; Saturday matinees at 2. You can bring your own food for a picnic on the lawn prior to the performance, or buy food here. A corollary series is presented Thursday-Sunday in the Studio/Theatre; tickets, $12 to $15. *George Carter Road off Route 20, Becket. (413) 243-0745. Tickets, $27 to $43.*

Shakespeare & Company. The evening sky and the gardens of The Mount, Edith Wharton's former estate above Laurel Lake, yield a natural amphitheater for classical Shakespearean theater. Twelve productions were staged in 1996 in four theaters, including the newly renovated Stables Theatre and the outdoor Oxford Court Theatre, tucked in a quiet glen that was once a grass tennis court. The Mainstage headliner in 1996, presented outdoors for six weeks, was "The Merry Wives of Windsor." *Route 7 at Plunkett Street, Lenox. (413) 637-3353. Mainstage, Friday-Sunday and Tuesday at 8., Tickets, $19.50 to $29.50.*

MORE ENTERTAINMENT: The **Aston Magna Festival,** considered the mecca of baroque, presents five concerts Saturdays at 6 from early July to early August in St. James Church, Great Barrington. Chamber music emanates to national notice from a barn-like shed on a wooded slope off Route 7 south of Pittsfield during **South Mountain Concerts,** scheduled five Sundays at 3 in September and early October. The **Berkshire Opera Company** presents two operas each summer at Monument Mountain Regional High School south of Stockbridge. The **Berkshire Choral Festival** pairs a 200-voice chorus with the Springfield Symphony Orchestra for summer concerts Saturday at 8 in its concert shed at the Berkshire School in Sheffield. There are dinner performances in the **Stockbridge Summer Music Series** at the Seven Hills Inn & Restaurant in Lenox and **Stockbridge Cabaret** musical productions at the DeSisto Estate, Stockbridge. In 1996, the Berkshire Performing Arts Theatre presented its first summer concert series to mixed reviews in the 1,200-seat concert hall at the new **National Music Center** at 70 Kemble St., Lenox.

Norman Rockwell Museum at Stockbridge. The world's largest collection of original art by America's favorite illustrator is on display in the new and expanded Norman Rockwell Museum. The museum moved from the Old Corner House in town to a sparkling $5 million building on the 36-acre Linwood estate along the Housatonic River in the Glendale section. Nine galleries display more than 500 original paintings and drawings by the artist, who lived his last 25 years in town and made its scenes and people his subjects. Guided tours are scheduled, or you can go on your own. The artist's studio was moved to the site from the center of Stockbridge and was re-created as he left it. The museum also includes changing exhibits of Stockbridge memorabilia and a gift shop that does a land-office business, including the sale of some 30,000 reproductions annually of Rockwell's painting of Stockbridge's Main Street at Christmas. *Route 183, Stockbridge. (413) 298-4100. Daily 10 to 5, May-October; Monday-Friday 11 to 4 and weekends 10 to 5, rest of year. Adults $8, children $2.*

Chesterwood. The secluded estate of sculptor Daniel Chester French, famed for the Minute Man in Concord and the Seated Lincoln in Washington, has been open to the public since his daughter donated it in 1969 to the National Trust for Historic Preservation. Visitors start at a gallery in the old cow barn, where many of French's sculptures are shown. But the house and studio are the gems of Chesterwood. The 30-room Colonial revival built in 1900 is where French spent six months a year until he died there in 1931. Gracious rooms flank the wonderfully wide, full-length hall in which a summer breeze cools the visitor. One interesting item among many is a rose from Lincoln's casket. In the 22-foot-high studio you can see French's plaster-cast models of the Seated Lincoln and a graceful Andromeda, which he was working on at his death. It's placed on a flatcar on a 40-foot-long railroad track and wheeled outdoors occasionally so schoolchildren can see, as French did, how a sculpture looks in natural light. The front of the studio with a corner fireplace, couch and piano is where he entertained frequent guests; in back is a piazza with wisteria vines and concord grapes framing a view of Monument Mountain. Chesterwood's gift shop is worth a visit; you also may stroll along easy trails in a hemlock forest carpeted with needles. A picnic area overlooks a large cutting garden.

Route 183, Stockbridge. (413) 298-3579. Daily 10 to 5, May-October. Adults $6.50, children $1.

Tyringham Art Galleries. It's worth a detour just to view the outside of this fantastic place, once the studio of Sir Henry Kitson, sculptor of the Minute Man in Lexington. Called the Gingerbread House and looking as if it's straight from Hansel and Gretel, it is certainly the most unusual gallery in an area that has many. The roof, fashioned to resemble an English thatched roof, is itself a sculpture, weighing 80 tons and resting on a frame of chestnut beams. Do go inside – you'll marvel at the stained-glass windows, stone floors and some very interesting art. Out back, you can wander around a sculpture garden with surprises at every turn; sit beside an idyllic pond and admire the wildflowers and birds.

Tyringham Road, Tyringham. (413) 243-3260. Daily 10 to 5, Memorial Day to Columbus Day. Adults, $1.

Berkshire Center for Contemporary Glass. You can see glass-blowers at work in this large new co-op studio and gallery, the centerpiece of what is billed as the premier working artists' community in the Berkshires. Watch up close as artists form hot molten glass into whimsical vases, sculptures, elegant perfume bottles and more. The beautiful products are artfully displayed in a gallery, where we were amused by a platter of glass donuts. Classes in making paperweights and the like are offered to the public. Nearby, contemporary sculptures stand outside the **Waterside Gallery.** A brochure detailing "The Art of West Stockbridge" guides visitors to various studios.

6 Harris St., West Stockbridge. (413) 232-4666. Daily, 10 to 6.

The History

History reveals itself everywhere in the Berkshires. Perhaps it's not so "old" nor so prominent as in more historic areas to the east, but for certain people and periods of Americana this area is supreme.

Hancock Shaker Village. Nowhere is the Shaker way of life better depicted than at this 1,200-acre site, the third of eighteen Shaker communities established in the United States. The Shakers called this "The City of Peace" and lived here from 1790 to 1960. Twenty restored buildings, including a round stone barn, are furnished with Shaker-made furniture and local artifacts. Village craftspeople make furniture, brooms, tinware, baskets and other 19th-century Shaker products. Shaker foods are available in the Village Cafe.

Route 20 at Route 41, Pittsfield. (413) 443-0188. Daily 9:30 to 5, Memorial Day to late October; 10 to 3, April-May and November. Adults $10, children $5.

The Mount. With four theaters, lush gardens and guided tours, the 50-acre estate built by writer Edith Wharton in 1902 offers a day's worth of activities for the visitor. The Shakespeare & Company productions are foremost, but those with an interest in Wharton will enjoy tours of her Neo-Georgian home, which is very much a restoration in progress. Only a few rooms on the first floor are fully restored. The tour guides' information about the writer is more interesting and complete than are the rooms of her house. Her niece, landscape architect Beatrix Farrand, designed the lawns, woodlands and formal gardens.

Plunkett Street at Route 7, Lenox. (413) 637-1899. Daily, 9 to 3, Memorial Day through October and weekends in May. Adults $6, students $4.50.

Colonel John Ashley House. The oldest house in the Berkshires (1735), this restored beauty off by itself in a meadow looks up to Mount Everett. Colonel Ashley was a judge and legislator; because of his position, our guide pointed out, the structure was somewhat elaborate for its day. In the lovely meeting room on the second floor (note the original paneling and built-in cupboard), the Sheffield Declaration of Independence was signed three years before the country's. Early furnishings and the pottery collection make this a good companion to the tour of nearby Bartholomew's Cobble (see Nature).

Cooper Hill Road, west of Route 7A, Ashley Falls. (413) 229-8600. Guided tours, Wednesday-Sunday and holidays 1 to 5, late June to Labor Day; weekends only, Memorial Day to late June and Labor Day to Columbus Day. Adults $5, children $2.

STOCKBRIDGE'S MAIN STREET is an historic area in its own right. West of the famed **Red Lion Inn,** built in 1773 as a small tavern, is the **Mission House,** the town's first house and moved to the site in 1927 from Prospect Hill. Built in 1739 by the Rev. John Sergeant, the first missionary to the Stockbridge Indians, it is full of American furnishings prior to 1740. The rear of the house was Sergeant's domain, where the Indians visited. His wealthy wife Abigail entertained in front. The landscaped gardens are notable for herbs and plants of the period. Open daily 10 to 5, Memorial Day to Columbus Day. Adults $5, children $2.

Across the street is the **Merwin House** ("Tranquility"), built about 1825 and shown by the Society for the Preservation of New England Antiquities. Furnishings reflect the elegant life of its wealthy Victorian-era residents. Open Tuesday, Thursday and weekends noon to 5, June to mid-October; adults $4, children $2). Near the end of Main Street is First Congregational Church, a striking, deep-red brick edifice built in 1824 and once the pulpit for Calvinist Jonathan Edwards. It's fronted by the stone **Children's Chimes Tower,** erected by town father David

Dudley Field for his grandchildren and still rung from 5:30 to 6 every afternoon, per his directions, "from apple blossom time until frost." Just beyond are the Village Cemetery, where the epitaphs tell the story of early Stockbridge, and the Ancient Indian Burial Ground.

The Nature

The wealth of the Southern Berkshires is not all in its arts or its moneyed past. Residents and summer-home owners know it best, perhaps, for its beautiful and varied natural attractions, which range from wildlife preserves to mountain vistas, from waterfalls to secluded lakes. A sampling:

Bartholomew's Cobble. A cobble is an old Yankee word for a limestone outcropping above a meadow and this National Natural Landmark nestles close by the Housatonic River. The peaceful setting of meadow and woods offers 200 acres of rock garden, where no fewer than 500 species of wildflowers, 100 species of trees, shrubs and vines, and 40 species of ferns have been catalogued. All over the cobble you can follow clearly marked trails and rest on rustic benches; although there are no tables, you can spread your picnic blanket and drink in a goodly portion of nature with your repast. The small Bailey Museum of Natural History displays local flora and fauna, plus a few Indian artifacts.
Rannape Road off Route 7A, Ashley Falls. (413) 229-8600. Museum daily 9 to 5, April 15 to November; grounds open year-round. Adults $3, children $1.

Berkshire Botanical Garden. Wonderful aromas fill the herb garden at this fifteen-acre, mostly outdoor botanical showplace with a pond, shrubs, trees, perennial borders, wildflowers, annuals, experimental plantings and more. A busy program is provided for members and children, but visitors may stroll the gardens from dawn to dusk. The solar greenhouse attracts special attention, and we loved the maple syrup house, the magnificent rose garden and the prolific vegetable garden with its own weather station. Inside are a small library and gift shop, both with a stress on things botanical. Picnickers are welcome on the grounds. The Herb Associates sell their wares in an outdoor shed for the benefit of the non-profit center, which stages a popular Summer Festival in August and a Harvest Festival the first weekend in October.
Junction of Routes 102 and 183, Stockbridge. (413) 298-3926. Daily 10 to 5, May-October. Adults $5.

Naumkeag. Many admire the interior of this 26-room, Norman-style gabled mansion built in 1885 by Stanford White for Joseph H. Choate, lawyer for the Rockefeller family and ambassador to the Court of St. James. But we like it best for the lavish hillside landscaping and gardens fashioned by Choate's daughter Mabel, who devoted her life to philanthropy, collecting art and nurturing Naumkeag. Here she produced a private world of terraces, walkways, sculpted topiary, fountains and even a Chinese pagoda. In a cool Venetian garden, water trickles from a tiny fountain; a stream cascades beside the steps in a grove of birch trees. The sculpture in the gardens befits Miss Choate's interest in the arts.
Prospect Hill, Stockbridge. (413) 298-3239. Tours, Tuesday-Sunday 10 to 4:15, Memorial Day to Labor Day, weekends only to Columbus Day. Admission $6.50; gardens only, $5; children, $2.50.

SWIMMING. What's a summer day without a swim? Despite all the water, the pickings for the public seem rather slim – or is it simply that most visitors are too busy to stop for a dip? Pittsfield folks crowd the beaches of Pontoosuc Lake at Lanesboro. We prefer out-of-the-way spots like York Lake in New Marlborough, Spectacle Pond in Sandisfield, Benedict Pond in Beartown State Park near Great Barrington, Prospect Lake in North Egremont and tiny Lake Mansfield, with its interesting playground and hidden beach tucked away at the northwest edge of Great Barrington. Wahconah Falls State Park east of Dalton comes highly recommended, and the natives may guide you to their secret swimming holes.

— *Get Away from It All* —

Mount Washington. Rising above the picturesque, historic community of South Egremont is the town of Mount Washington, which occupies Mount Everett, the second highest mountain in Massachusetts. The town is a veritable treasure of scenery acknowledged by few other than its 60 or so year-round residents. Start at the junction of Routes 23 and 41 next to **Smiley Pond,** a busy bird refuge and wildlife preserve. Following signs for Bash Bish Falls, you begin the climb, passing an occasional house or an abandoned inn. Eight miles up is **Mount Everett Reservation,** with Guilder Pond and its showy June display of mountain laurel, which blooms all over the mountain; it takes fifteen minutes to hike to the summit from the upper parking lot. Continue past the 1876 Town Hall and the 1874 Church of Christ down a road through a 400-foot-deep gorge to **Bash Bish Falls,** a 50-foot plunge that is the Berkshires' most dramatic. A good trail leads from a parking lot to the top of the falls. Cable fences on both sides of the crystal-clear creek keep one from seeing much of the falls, but the view through the gorge toward the Catskills is rewarding. Farther down the road, just before the New York State line, is a short road leading to the base of the falls. Several other waterfalls and mountain peaks in Massachusetts's southwesternmost town make it a haven for lovers of the wild and remote. The high-bush blueberries that make Blueberry Hill Farm the town's commercial livelihood sometimes go begging for lack of pickers.

New Marlborough-Monterey-Tyringham. These sparsely populated towns offer scenery and history in a choice package. Poke along back roads or follow a Circle Tour map provided by the Berkshire Visitors Bureau. We enjoyed the abandoned mills in the Mill River area and the Bucks County look of the Clayton area. Umpachene Falls, if you persevere long enough to find it, has a lovely park and a falling stream that you'll likely have to yourself. York Lake in Sandisfield State Forest offers delightful picnic groves on both sides of a small beach. The hamlets of Southfield, New Marlborough and Monterey are particularly quaint. An enchanting valley cutting between hills in Tyringham reminds some of the Austrian Tyrol. Mark Twain and Grover Cleveland summered here, and Sir Henry Kitson built his fantastic "Gingerbread House" in the valley. We like not only the Tyringham Main Road but the parallel side road along the hillside past Shaker Pond and beside some colorful old Shaker buildings, the last remnants of the once-thriving Shaker community overlooking Tyringham Cobble. These really are back roads – some of them dirt and most bumpy. Don't go without a detailed map.

Shopping

Obviously there are too many shops in this sophisticated, far-flung area for us to give a comprehensive guide. Here are some of our favorites.

Lenox has probably the area's most exclusive shops. The small branch of **Talbots** on Walker Street has timeless fashions. Nearby is **Evviva!** for contemporary designer clothing. **Mary Stuart Collections** at 81 Church St. purveys exquisite accessories for bed and bath, fine china and glass, plus gifts and children's things. For handknits, English cashmeres and imported yarns, visit **Tanglewool;** for contemporary crafts, the **Hoadley Gallery.** Handsome weavings, from pillows to coats, are displayed at **Weaver's Fancy.** Head to **Bev's Homemade Ice Cream** for an ice-cream fix. **Moore Fine Food,** 62 Church St., is a catering service and prepared-foods store where you can pick up the makings for a super Tanglewood picnic.

In Stockbridge, don't miss the small shops in the Mews, a skip over from the Red Lion Inn. Adorable clothes for children, including hand-smocked dresses, are to be found at **Hodge Podge,** as are frilly nightgowns for grownup ladies, sportswear and nifty gifts. We can't even begin to tell you the things in **Williams & Sons Country Store** just around the corner on Main Street. It's a true, jumbled-up country store operating since 1795 – amble in and enjoy the aromas. Nearby is the **1884 House,** an unusual Flemish-style building that once housed the town records and now stocks imports for men and women from the British Isles. We are enchanted by the **Dolphin Studio** on Main Street west of the Mission House; here are the home and studios of Primm and John ffrench, with a colorful melange of ceramic villages, batik pillows, silk-screened cards, hanging birdmobiles and fanciful necklaces. Primm knits all kinds of sweaters to order, and John will make a small ceramic reproduction of your house for about $300.

Great Barrington is where much of the interesting shopping action has focused of late, especially along Railroad Street. Expect to find surprises from **Byzantium Crystal Essence** to **Gatsby's,** an old-time department store. We admired the cute quilted jackets depicting rabbits for toddlers in the windows of **M. Lacey Linen & Layette.** Billing itself as "Provence in the Berkshires," **Mistral's** offers an attractive selection of bed and bath accessories, perfumes and kitchenware. Along Main Street are **Evergreen,** where we were struck by the flamingo birdhouses among all the neat American pottery, clothing and gifts, and **T.P. Saddle Blanket,** the most colorful store we've been in recently, stocking rugged mountain and western apparel, turquoise jewelry, hot sauces, rugs and even furniture on two fascinating floors.

A mile north of Great Barrington on Route 7 is the **Jenifer House Commons,** home to varied enterprises from **Olde,** an antiques market with 75 dealers on three floors, to **DeWoolfson Down,** claiming America's largest collection of duvet covers and imported bed linens, along with comforters, pillows and featherbeds from its own workshop. The new **Berkshire Art Gallery and Art Center** features paintings of the natural surroundings of this corner of the world. **The European Ladies Fashion Outlet** offers a large selection and some good bargains, especially upstairs.

Great Barrington Pottery, actually on Route 41 in Housatonic but with a small new store at 999 South Main St. (Route 7), is worth a visit to see the Richard Bennett pottery that merges East and West, the first authentic Japanese woodburning kiln built in the United States, and a collection of beautiful silk flowers that can be custom-arranged. Tea is served daily from 1 to 4 in a ceremonial tea house amid formal Japanese gardens. Toward West Stockbridge on Route 41 is the fascinating **Undermountain Weavers** workshop and showroom. Dutch and Anne Pinkston design and make cloth on century-old looms, using fine wools from the Shetland Islands and rare Chinese cashmere. Jackets, scarves, ponchos, vests, hats and blankets are displayed.

Started as an outlet center for the sweaters of ex-New York designer Neuma Agins, **The Buggy Whip Factory** in out-of-the-way Southfield evolved into a specialty outlet, crafts and antiques center claiming 85 dealers. With occasional entertainment, train rides, a duck pond, pushcarts in a farmers' market, the **Cottage Cafe** and about twelve shops in the restored factory and outbuildings, it's the kind of place where you go for an hour – and may end up spending the afternoon.

ANTIQUING is big business in the Berkshires, and all the Berkshires towns contain antiques stores. The biggest concentration is around Sheffield, where every second house seems to have an antiques sign in front of it. One place not to miss is **Twin Fires** on Berkshire School Road at Route 41, Sheffield. Seemingly more antiques than are carried by all the rest of the dealers around are grouped in two barn structures with three floors each. One section is a recreated arcade with shops from 18th-century London. More shops are clustered along Route 23 in South Egremont, where we were impressed by **The Splendid Peasant.**

Where to Stay

Large and small country inns, motels, B&Bs and resorts (and even the luxurious spa, Canyon Ranch in the Berkshires) are dotted across the area. Many are booked months to a year in advance for the Tanglewood season. Many require stays of three or four nights on peak weekends, and some insist on prepayment of the entire bill. Rates vary widely, highest on summer and foliage weekends, often lower weekdays and much lower out of season. Because the Berkshires inns are so special, we concentrate on them here.

Inns and B&Bs

The Red Lion Inn. The granddaddy of them all, this big white wood structure immortalized by Norman Rockwell in his painting of Stockbridge's Main Street is the essence of a New England inn. The site has held an inn since 1773; the present building, erected in 1897, was enlarged in the 1960s. Summer guests sit and rock on the front porch, which seems a block long, and watch the activity all around. The spacious public rooms are filled with collections of antiques, and the **Pink Kitty** gift shop in the corner has a fine selection for impulse buyers and doting grandparents. Also here is **Country Curtains,** the original in the retail chain launched by Jane Fitzpatrick, who took over the inn in the late 1960s with her state-senator husband and has restored it with taste. Rates for the 111 rooms and suites (most with color TV and 80 with private bath) vary widely, depending on the season and day of the week. The Red Lion also offers a two-bedroom apartment called **Meadowlark,** sculptor Daniel Chester French's summer studio at Chesterwood, a special experience for $350 a night, May-October. The dining room is enormously popular with visitors and pleasant in an old hotel kind of a way; we prefer the adjacent **Widow Bingham Tavern** for its cozy, rustic atmosphere. Dinner entrées go from $17.50 for chicken breast stuffed with Monterey chèvre to $26 for filet mignon with a peppered madeira sauce. In warm weather, the verdant, impatiens-bedecked patio behind the inn is fine for a drink or lunch, perhaps a turkey club sandwich, baked Boston scrod or creamed chicken and biscuit ($8.75 to $14.50). Light food is available until midnight in the downstairs **Lion's Den** lounge.

Main Street, Stockbridge 01262. (413) 298-5545. Fax (413) 298-5130. Doubles, $94 to $159, EP; suites, $350.

The Gables Inn. One of the original Berkshires cottages built in 1885, this was the home of the mother-in-law of Edith Wharton, the writer who lived here while her own cottage, The Mount, was under construction. These days the Queen Anne Victorian has been grandly upgraded and expanded by Frank and Mary Newton, who offer some of Lenox's most lavish accommodations among their eighteen guest rooms and suites. Particularly stunning are the Jockey Club Suite and two new cathedral-ceilinged suites in a second-floor addition. Frank likes to show guests the eight-sided library where Edith Wharton wrote some of her short stories and the Show Business Room, full of signed photos of old stars and shelves of showbiz volumes with which to curl up on the chintz loveseat in front of the fireplace. Ever-improving, the Newtons have added a tennis court and an enclosed, solar-heated swimming pool with a jacuzzi in the back yard. Continental breakfast is served in the morning. In summer, Mary pampers B&B guests in six more rooms at their home down the street, known as **The Summer White House.**

103 Walker St., Lenox 01240. (413) 637-3416 or (800) 382-9401. Doubles, $90 to $160; suites, $210.

Applegate Bed & Breakfast. Six tranquil acres bearing apple trees, rose gardens and a swimming pool beckon sophisticates to this pillared Georgian Colonial, built by a New York surgeon in the 1920s as a weekend retreat. Today, airline pilot Rick Cannata and his wife Nancy, a former flight attendant, share it as an elegant B&B. The main floor holds a large living room, an enclosed sun porch used for reading and TV, a dining room with breakfast tables set for four, and a screened back porch facing the pool and rose gardens. A carved staircase leads to the six guest rooms, each with private bath. The master suite comes with a kingsize poster bed, working fireplace, sitting area and a great steam shower. Other rooms, slightly less grand in scale, hold queensize beds. Even the smallest is a delight, done up in Victorian style with an antique bed, marble-topped dresser and a hat rack holding granny hats. A two-bedroom, condo-style apartment is available for $330 a night (three-night minimum) in the rear carriage house. The continental-plus breakfast includes cereal and yogurt. Cheese and wine are put out in the afternoon and brandy and chocolates are in the bedrooms at night.

279 West Park St., RR 1, Box 576, Lee 01238. (413) 243-4451 or (800) 691-9012. Doubles, $110 to $195.

Devonfield. This was the former summer home of George Westinghouse Jr. and later a World War II refuge of Queen Wilhelmina of the Netherlands. Now it's a comfortable, traditional New England-style B&B. New owners Ben and Sally Schenck are upgrading the old Haus Andreas, which they purchased from Gerhard

Schmid, former chef-owner of the Gateways Inn in Lenox. They offer six rooms and three suites, all with private baths and queen or king beds. A pool-side guest house includes a kingsize bedroom, a kitchenette/living room with a pullout sofa facing a corner fireplace, a jacuzzi tub and not one but two patios. A house-party atmosphere prevails weekends on Devonfield's main floor, which includes a large living room, a cozy television room, a huge side porch and a guest pantry. Breakfast in the dining room is a mix of buffet items and a hot entrée like eggs or blueberry pancakes.

85 Stockbridge Road, Lee 01238. (413) 243-3298 or (800) 664-0880. Fax (413) 243-1360. Doubles, $155 to $195; suites and cottage, $205 to $260.

Garden Gables Inn. Mario and Lynn Mekinda from Toronto have upgraded this triple-gabled house run since 1951 as a homey little inn of the old school. They've added private baths for each of the eleven original guest rooms, a few of them rather small but cozy and clean. More luxurious are a new king bedroom with jacuzzi bath and two new cathedral-ceilinged suites above the inn's expanded dining room, each with kingsize canopy bed, sitting area in front of the corner fireplace, whirlpool bath and private balcony. Four more suites with TV/VCR, fireplaces and queensize Eldred Wheeler canopy beds occupy a new detached front cottage, which continues the gabled dormer theme. The eighteen rooms offer quite a range in size and price. But everyone enjoys sherry from the decanter in the entry parlor and a substantial breakfast buffet offered in a charming dining room, which has been expanded by opening onto a new wraparound screened porch. A 72-foot-long swimming pool and prolific gardens also are attractions at this verdant, five-acre oasis in the heart of Lenox.

135 Main St., Box 52, Lenox 01240. (413) 637-0193. Fax (413) 637-4554. Doubles, $120 to $175; suites and cottages, $225.

The Weathervane Inn. This venerable inn has been much upgraded by innkeepers Anne and Vincent Murphy, she a former Long Island school teacher and he a private detective who loves to chat. The 1785 farmhouse with a Greek Revival addition has eight rooms, ranging from Colonial to contemporary, all with private baths; two more rooms are available in a coach house in back near the pool. The inn's serene, many-windowed dining room is graced by a large and striking mural of the inn and its neighbors, lovingly rendered by a Connecticut artist. This is the setting for elegant dinners prepared by Anne, who changes her menu nightly. Entrées range from $16 to $20 for the likes of shrimp scampi, pork tenderloin dijonnaise, roast duckling with orange-raisin sauce and steak kabobs. Many are detailed in her cookbook, *There's Always Another Meal at the Weathervane Inn.*

Route 23, Box 23, South Egremont 01258. (413) 528-9580 or (800) 528-9580. Fax (413) 528-1713. Dinner by reservation, Friday and Saturday 5:30 to 8:30 in summer, from 6:30 rest of year. Doubles, weekends $175 to $200, MAP; weekdays $95 to $130, B&B.

Wheatleigh. Tired of country inns? If you'd like to stay in an Italian palazzo, this one in Lenox may be for you and, added bonus, you can walk to Tanglewood. Built in 1893 for the Countess de Heredia, Wheatleigh is romantic, dramatic and ornate. From the moment you drive up to the imposing entrance of the honey-

1893 Italian palazzo that houses Wheatleigh reflects grand style of Berkshire "cottages."

colored brick building framed in wrought iron, you are in a different world. The seventeen guest rooms vary widely. Some have terraces and fireplaces and are huge; others were former maids' quarters and are sized accordingly. Caring owners Susan and Linwood Simon are continually improving, enhancing the furnishings, hanging prized artworks and adding TV/VCRs and portable telephones. Facilities include a state-of-the-art fitness room, a tennis court and a heated swimming pool hidden away in a glade on the 22-acre property. Chef Peter Platt oversees the exceptional new American cuisine served in a gracious dining room and a large enclosed porch. Dinner is prix-fixe, $68 for three courses from regular, low-fat and vegetarian menus that change nightly and from which you can mix and match; a special tasting menu allows a sampling of more dishes for $90. The popular new Grill Room in the old library dining room offers less lofty fare à la carte, from $16.50 for an exotic vegetarian pasta dish to $24.50 for black angus beef tenderloin with crispy polenta. For the clientele here amid surroundings that the Berkshires' most lavish resort brochure understates as of "noble proportions," price is no object.

West Hawthorne Road, Lenox 01240. (413) 637-0610. Fax (413) 637-4507. Lunch in summer, Tuesday-Saturday noon to 1:30; dinner nightly by reservation, 6 to 9; Grill Room, 5 to 9, July and August only; Sunday brunch in summer, 10:30 to 1:30. Doubles, $195 to $535, EP.

High Style in the Country

The Old Inn on the Green & Gedney Farm. Known for inspired dining by candlelight, this rural, 1760 stagecoach inn has been attracting well-heeled overnight guests lately. That's due mainly to the addition of luxury accommodations in a huge Normandy-style barn called Gedney Farm down the street. Beneath the barn's soaring 30-foot-high ceiling is a lineup of three rooms and eight two-level suites, their second floors fashioned from the old hayloft and reached by private staircases. Most come with fireplaced sitting rooms and double whirlpool tubs. Rooms are decorated simply but with panache in motifs from Moroccan to French provincial. Upstairs in the main inn are six rather spare bedrooms, two with private baths. A continental breakfast is served in the stenciled dining rooms. The prix-fixe dinners ($48) are a Saturday tradition worth driving miles for. A short and with-it à la carte menu is offered other nights on the canopied, candlelit terrace or inside the tavern beside the hearth. Dine casually on interesting appetizers, pastas and entrées priced from $17.50 to $22.50. The **Gallery Cafe** in the Gedney Farm Gallery offers lunch seasonally on weekends from 11 to 3, inside amid artworks or outside overlooking fields and sculptures.

Route 57, New Marlboro 01230. (413) 229-3131 or (800) 286-3139. Fax (413) 229-2053. Dinner by reservation, Sunday-Friday 5:30 to 9 (closed Tuesday, also Monday-Wednesday in winter); Saturday, 5:30 to 9. Doubles, $120 to $160 in inn; $175 to $285 at Gedney Farm.

Good Values

Amadeus House. The theme is music at this B&B, nicely restored by classical music buffs John Felton, a former foreign editor of National Public Radio, and his wife Marty Gottron, a freelance editor. John, now a confirmed Lenox booster as head of the Chamber of Commerce, promotes theirs as eight unusually varied accommodations, from the deluxe ground-floor Mozart Room to two small bedrooms that share a bath. A two-bedroom, third-floor apartment is rented by the week. The Mozart Room has a queensize tiger maple bed, a wicker sitting area facing a wood stove and a private porch. On the second floor are two spacious rooms with queensize beds and private baths, one with an extra twin bed. Two mid-size rooms with private baths constitute the "Tanglewood wing." Two small bedrooms sharing a bath in the rear may be the best B&B values in Lenox. The heart of the house is the cozy parlor/music room, where selections from a collection of 500 classical CDs are played throughout the day and the walls are hung with music-themed posters. Hearty breakfasts – perhaps mushroom quiche, omelets or orange waffles – are served in a dining room open to Marty's country kitchen. Afternoon tea is offered on the wraparound porch.

15 Cliffwood St., Lenox 01240. (413) 637-4770 or (800) 205-4770. Doubles, $85 to $175; two-bedroom suite, $900 weekly for two, $1,000 for four.

Historic Merrell Inn. Unheard of for the Berkshires, the owners of this beautifully restored 1800 tavern actually lowered their price structure lately in a successful effort to raise their over-all occupancy rate. No wonder the place is often full on slow days, when others' rooms are going begging. One of the first properties in the Berkshires to be listed in the National Register of Historic Places, the impressive building was saved by Mabel Choate of Naumkeag in Stockbridge, who eventually donated it to the Society for the Preservation of New England Antiquities. Faith and Charles Reynolds restored its ten guest rooms on three floors, all furnished with canopy or four-poster beds and antiques they've collected over 30 years. Guests register in the old tap room at the only circular Colonial bar still intact. A grandfather's clock from 1800 graces the central hallway; the upper stairway retains its original smoke painting, an imitation of marble. Charles delights in showing the building's prized possessions. Despite its age, this inn is elegant and comfortable. Common rooms have oriental rugs and guest rooms are carpeted; some have fireplaces and all have new plumbing. The old keeping room with an enormous beehive oven has been converted into a parlor. Guests are served a full breakfast and have the run of the grounds, which stretch past a screened gazebo back to the Housatonic River.

Route 102, South Lee 01260. (413) 243-1794 or (800) 243-1794. Fax (413) 243-2669. Doubles, $125 to $145 weekends, $85 to $105 weekdays.

A Budget Choice

Ivanhoe Country House. Literally under the mountain along Undermountain Road is this attractive 220-year-old guest house, white with black shutters and a red door. Carole and Dick Marghery raise golden retrievers and shelter guests in nine spacious and nicely decorated, pastel-pretty rooms, all with private baths and refrigerators. One suite of two bedrooms shares the deepest bathtub imaginable – "you can really soak your cares away," says Carole. She delivers guests their breakfast (coffee or cocoa and muffins) via tray to their door. "I wouldn't want to drink my first cup of coffee in the morning with perfect strangers," she explains, "and I don't expect my guests to." If they want to mingle, they can use the large game room paneled in chestnut with fireplace, library, television and piano, or a pool out back.

254 South Undermountain Road (Route 41), Sheffield 01257. (413) 229-2143. Doubles, $85 to $110; suite, $175.

Family Finds

The Inn at Laurel Lake. We never really noticed this 1900 inn that had seen better days. Just as well, for young new owners Tom and Heidi Fusco faced a monumental task when they bought the decaying place in 1996. They purchased new mattresses for the beds in their nineteen guest rooms, changed four to kingsize and three to queens, and started adding private baths. They had thirteen private baths at our visit, with two more on the way. Decor ranged from tired to homey, but was being freshened with new wallpaper. The best attributes involve the two-acre property, the only one with access to Laurel Lake. A grass "beach," dock and rope swing entice children, and chairs and picnic tables are scattered about the lawn and woods. A swing set is placed beside a tennis court. The Fuscos, who have youngsters of their own, welcome families and require only two-night minimums on weekends. They serve a continental-plus breakfast in the dining room on the main floor, which also offers a game room and music room.

615 Laurel St. (Route 20), Lee 01238. (413) 243-1436. Doubles, $120 to $195.

The Wainwright Inn. This substantial white brick house was built as a Tory tavern and inn in 1766 and carries considerable history. It was once the home of the inventor of the Pope automobile and a co-inventor with Thomas Edison, who visited here. Until lately a five-unit apartment house, it was reopened in 1993 by Anne and David Rolland and their teenagers. Their eight guest rooms range from the front-corner Federal Room with poster bed, single jacuzzi, private porch and working fireplace to two rooms with shared bath and a third-floor suite with queen bed, skylit bath and a kitchen that attests to its past. The place conveys a homey, lived-in look, from the TV playing in the living room the afternoon we stopped by to the family pictures in one of the bedrooms and the old Wainwright Hall sign posted along the staircase. David runs the inn, while Anne is responsible for the gardens. He provides a buffet breakfast plus pancakes or french toast cooked to order. He also offers a five-course dinner for guests on Saturday evenings ($25 each, BYOB). Children are welcome, and cribs and cots are available.

518 S. Main St., Great Barrington 01230. (413) 528-2062. Doubles, $100 to $150; efficiency, $175.

Motels

Best Western Black Swan Inn. You might think this is just a motel beside Laurel Lake, but with the addition of a twelve-room wing, it's considerably more. Half of the 52 rooms face the lake and have private decks. Nine new rooms come with fireplaces and cast-marble hydrotubs, some have queen or king four-poster beds, and all are smartly decorated, most with two velvet armchairs. Some contain refrigerators, and the Lincoln Room has a log cabin quilt and a framed copy of the Gettysburg Address on the wall. In this wing is a handsome lounge/bar with a fireplace and an old English service bar the owners found in New Hampshire, as well as an exercise room and a Finnish sauna. The original motel rooms are nice, too, with cable TV, telephones and full baths. The glamorous dusky rose dining room known as **Cygnets Lakeside** has large solarium windows that make you feel you're almost on the water. The wide-ranging dinner menu, priced from $15.95 to $21.95, retains specialties of one of the owners, who was a Hungarian freedom fighter. Although there is no beach at this part of the lake, the Black Swan has a swimming pool, and pontoon and paddle boats to take out; it's obviously a favorite with families (no children in the new wing, however).
Route 20, Lee 01238. (413) 243-2700 or (800) 876-7926. Fax (413) 243-2700. Doubles, $150 to $205.

Yankee Motor Lodge. Best of the motels scattered along the Pittsfield Road north of town is this 61-room charmer, solid in red brick and lovingly tended for three generations by the Trombly family. Rooms vary from spacious to cozy. Nicely decorated in the Colonial style, they are spread out in three buildings, away from the road and facing broad lawns. A hit in the summer is the pool, flanked by a waterfall cascading through evergreens down a mound of rocks. In other seasons, the draw is the twelve rooms with wood-burning fireplaces. You can determine which they are by the stacks of firewood outside their doors. These rooms come with one queen or two double beds. We lucked into one of these during a family ski trip some years back.
Routes 7 & 20, Lenox 01240. (413) 499-3700. Fax (413) 499-3634. Doubles, $133 to $173.

Where to Eat

The Berkshires have their share of smart and expensive restaurants – a few, we feel, rather pretentious. As with lodging, you should reserve well ahead, especially on weekends. There also are casual and reasonable spots that are fun (and good), and more seem to pop up every year.

Classy Dining

The Old Mill. This restored 18th-century grist mill, which opened as a restaurant in 1979, is one of our favorites anywhere. The atmosphere is a cross between a simple Colonial tavern and a European country inn – homespun and friendly, yet sophisticated – a happy combination created by owners Terry and Juliet Moore. Most entrées, which always include the freshest of fish, are priced in the high teens. The sautéed calves liver with Irish bacon is a masterpiece. We also liked the oven-roasted poussin with garlic and the roast duck with poached pears and port sauce. If black bean soup is on the menu, try it, but save room for the mocha torte. The house salad is better than most. An addition to the smaller of two dining rooms provides large windows looking over Hubbard Brook in back. No reservations are accepted except for parties of five or more, so arrive before 7 on weekends if you don't want to wait. The excellent food and relative value make the Old Mill very popular.

Route 23, South Egremont. (413) 528-1421. Entrées, $17 to $24. Dinner nightly, 5 to 9:30 or 10:30. Closed Monday or Tuesday in off-season.

Church Street Cafe. This early (1981) "American bistro" that preceded the trend seems to be everybody's favorite in Lenox. Owners Linda Forman and Clayton Hambrick, once Ethel Kennedy's chef, specialize in fresh, light cafe food served inside amid artworks and ficus trees and outside on a canopied deck. Dinner might bring grilled swordfish with an olive-caper pesto, sautéed Maine crab cakes with homemade dill tartar sauce and grilled lamb loin with a cabernet sauce. An appetizer of grilled fried corncake with chipotle chile sauce and an entrée of grilled Jamaican jerk chicken with tropical fruit salsa attest to Clayton's range. His chocolate mousse loaf was written up in the first issue of Chocolatier magazine, but we're partial to the chilled cranberry soufflé topped with whipped cream. Our latest lunch ($7.50 to $9.50) included a super black bean tostada with three salsas and the colorful Church Street salad laden with goat cheese and chick peas.

69 Church St., Lenox. (413) 637-2745. Entrées, $16.95 to $24.95. Lunch, Monday-Saturday 11 to 2; dinner nightly, 5:30 to 9; Sunday brunch in summer. Closed Monday and Tuesday in winter.

John Andrew's. We don't know which is more appealing: the inspired cooking and presentation at affordable prices, or the expansive rear dining porch, overlooking deck, lawn and woods. We'd eat there any time the weather cooperated, although the mod interior in Roman red and green with a tiled fireplace entices, too. These are perfect settings for chef-owner Dan Smith, who pairs grilled salmon with crisp potatoes and a compote of roast tomatoes and basil, roast cod with lemongrass chile broth and coconut rice, garlicky roast pork with a fondue of onions and a straw potato pancake, and spiced leg of lamb with a pilaf of dried cherries and sweet corn. Every accompaniment is different. We'd start with bruschetta of Tuscan white bean puree, charred tomatoes and arugula or one of the exotic salads, and finish with a chocolate-hazelnut torte or espresso ice cream. Pizzas and pastas are priced from $9 to $13.

Route 23, South Egremont. (413) 528-3469. Entrées, $16.50 to $19.50. Dinner nightly, 5 to 10; Sunday brunch, 11:30 to 3.

Castle Street Cafe. Chef-owner Michael Ballon has attracted quite a following since returning to the Berkshires after several years at upscale restaurants in New York. The storefront space next to a theater is the perfect setting for his gutsy cooking, perhaps sautéed shrimp with black bean and ginger sauce, grilled cornish game hen marinated in lemon and garlic or grilled veal chop with roasted garlic sauce. Try a pasta dish like fettuccine with smoked salmon or an appetizer of fried shrimp dumplings. Or simply sup on a half-pound burger with straw potatoes, a menu fixture for $9. Save room for the world's best chocolate mousse cake (as

rated by New York Newsday), frozen lemon soufflé or a selection of homemade ice creams and sorbets.
10 Castle St., Great Barrington. (413) 528-5244. Entrées, $16 to $22. Dinner, Wednesday-Monday 5 to 9:30 or 10:30.

Boiler Room Cafe. Caterer Michele Miller, once a chef at the late Alice's Restaurant of Arlo Guthrie fame near here, moved her restaurant and catering service from an old boiler room at the Buggy Whip Factory outlet and antique center in Southfield into a farmhouse along busy Route 7. Three intimate dining rooms on the main floor and a larger one upstairs hold mismatched chairs at white-clothed tables. Her kitchen caters some of the Berkshires' best parties, but also prepares an interesting dinner menu billed as "cuisine locale." Instead of being categorized, everything is lumped together in roughly the sequence you would order. You might start with spicy pumpkin soup ($4) or a Mediterranean plate of grilled lamb sausage and portobellos, eggplant pâté, black olive focaccia and local roasted garlic ($15). Or try a corn pizza with yukon gold potatoes, grilled portobellos and roquefort ($9) or roast rack of lamb. The wood grill yields Virginia-style baby back ribs, cedar-smoked salmon and moulard duck breast. For dessert we'd choose Michele's superb dacquoise, although the blueberry-lemon tart and the apple-blackberry crumb pie sound good, too.
405 Stockbridge Road (Route 7), Great Barrington. (413) 528-4280. Entrées, $15 to $22. Dinner, Tuesday-Saturday from 5:30.

La Bruschetta Ristorante. The place where Truc Orient Express got its start gave way in 1992 to this upscale Italian eatery, opened by Steven and Catherine Taub, he the former executive chef and she the pastry chef at Blantyre and Wheatleigh. The fare is robust, the cooking exciting and the prices relatively down to earth. Pastas are in the $14.50 to $16 range (except $17.50 for a straw and hay masterpiece with a sauté of rock shrimp, asparagus and tomatoes). Typical entrées are pan-roasted organic salmon with lemon-basil sauce, roasted organic pork tenderloin encrusted in toasted fennel, a grilled sausage sampler, and grilled New York strip steak with gorgonzola polenta. Start with the Venetian crab ravioli or antipasto for two. Finish with one of Catherine's delectable desserts, perhaps chocolate-hazelnut cake or tirami su. Except for artworks on the walls, the decor in two small rooms remains the same as when it was Trúc's, from whom the Taubs obtained the space when the Vietnamese restaurant moved to larger quarters next door.
1 Harris St., West Stockbridge. (413) 232-7141. Entrées, $15.50 to $17.50. Dinner nightly except Wednesday, 6 to 8:30 or 9, Sunday 5:30 to 8:30.

Trúc Orient Express. This engaging restaurant was started in 1979 by Trai Thi Duong, who is from Vietnam by way of Hartford, where she used to run Trúc's Restaurant. It features patio and indoor dining on two elegant floors amid oriental rugs, well-spaced tables set with white damask linens, sleek modern chairs with upholstered seats, gorgeous screens and huge black vases inlaid with mother of pearl. Haunting Vietnamese music plays in the background, and haunting aromas based on garlic waft from the kitchen. Dishes are perfectly prepared and the prices relatively high for Vietnamese food (most in the $9 range at lunch, to $17 at dinner).

Try the Vietnamese egg rolls, sweet and sour fish, duck with lemongrass, singing chicken or shaking beef. Our favorite is the happy pancake.
Harris Street, West Stockbridge. (413) 232-4204. Entrées, $11.50 to $17. Lunch daily, 11 to 3; dinner, 5:30 to 9 or 10. Closed Monday in winter.

Casual Dining

Union Bar & Grill. This fun place was opened in 1996 by Dan and Susan Smith of John Andrew's restaurant in South Egremont and three partners. They created what Susan called a light industrial look in purple, silver and black, with a bar along one side partitioned from dining areas along the other. The all-day menu is perfect for those who like to mix and match. You might start with shredded barbecued duck in a blue corn tortilla, a tempura of vegetables with cilantro chutney or smoked fish terrine with blini and pickled vegetable salad. Sandwiches range from grilled asiago cheese with roasted chiles to grilled portobello mushroom, prosciutto and fontina on sourdough. The pizza with smoked salmon and mascarpone sounds sensational. Dinner dishes include grilled calamari, lacquered salmon with vegetable spring rolls and garlic flank steak with tomatillo salsa and sweet potato fries.
293 Main St., Great Barrington. (413) 528-8226. Entrées, $11 to $13. Open daily except Wednesday, 11:30 to 11.

Roseborough Grill. Chef Laura Shack Willnauer, a former New York caterer and student of James Beard, has upgraded the old Cheesecake Charlie's space into an antiquey, country-style grill and bar. There's seating for a total of 140 in the bar-lounge, in two dining rooms (one country casual and the other elegant in pink and green), and outside on front and back porches. The front porch was where our party decided to eat on a late-summer evening, most selecting from the special, three-course dinner menu for a bargain $14.95 prix-fixe. The homemade soups of the night, pea and vegetable, proved quite robust and the salad of organic greens dressed with a shallot vinaigrette was outstanding. The sirloin stir-fry with vegetables and rice seemed a bit paltry, but the grilled whole cornish game hen was so ample that half went home for lunch the next day. The Santa Fe shrimp cakes with chipotle rémoulade and the linguini with clams were good choices from the wide-ranging à la carte menu. For lunch ($6.95 to $8.95), expect things like a grilled eggplant or shrimp cake sandwich, caesar salad with grilled portobello mushroom and salade niçoise. The house dessert is roseberry pie, combining blackberries, blueberries, raspberries and strawberries. Most of us were too sated for anything but the pear sorbet.
83 Church St., Lenox. (413) 637-2700. Entrées, $9.95 to $21.95. Lunch daily, 11:30 to 3:30; dinner, 5 to 9 or 10; Sunday brunch, 11:30 to 3:30.

Reminders of the Past

Jack's Grill. The little hamlet of Housatonic, where Alice of Alice's Restaurant fame had her second restaurant, is home to this unusual eatery fashioned from an old hardware store and now operated as "a footloose subsidiary of the Red Lion Inn." An ancient green truck bearing the name is parked out front. An electric train runs around the ceiling, enlivening the prevailing expanse of wood tables and floors. The original store shelves at either end display artifacts like old lunch boxes, cookie jars, toys and china dolls. The menu is a mixed bag, modestly priced and ranging widely from a hamburger for $5.95 to grilled salmon fillet with a lentil ragoût and sweet onion jam. Other possibilities run from linguini with grilled chicken and pot roast like your grandmother used to make to seared potato-crusted hake and grilled flank steak with horseradish mashed potatoes and zucchini fries. Starters could be nachos or crispy salmon cake. Desserts are out of the past: a root-beer float, tollhouse cookies and jello or chocolate pudding.

Main Street, Housatonic. (413) 274-1000. Entrées, $10.95 to $14.95. Dinner, Tuesday-Sunday from 5, Sunday brunch 11 to 2. Closed November-May.

Thelma's Roadside. "Not your ordinary diner," advertises this new establishment designed to look like, well, a 1950s diner. Owner Bruce Firger named the former steakhouse for his mother. It's quite a bit larger than a diner and its food is a cut above, thanks to French chef Jean Claude Vierne. Specials like escargots bourguignonne, onion tarts, steamed mussels in wine, seafood risotto and grilled salmon raifort are interspersed with predictable diner fare and blue-plate specials ($7.86). The brunch menu might yield blueberry crêpes and eggs en cocotte. The soda fountain dispenses Berkshire Ice Cream.

107 Stockbridge Road, Great Barrington. (413) 528-0880. Entrées, $6 to $15. Weekdays, noon to 9 or 10, weekends from 8.

A Good Value

20 Railroad Street. Great for children as well as adults (both babies and grandmothers were much in evidence each time we lunched there) is this convivial storefront space featuring a stunning mahogany bar acquired from the old Commodore Hotel in New York City. Soups, salads, sandwiches and burgers are the all-day fare. We enjoyed a "hap hazard," pita bread full of chili and bacon and topped with melted cheese, filling and really delicious. A perfect broccoli and cheese omelet was accompanied by a decent little salad. Another time we had a chicken salad plate and a crabmeat puff, each accompanied by enough slices of fresh melon, strawberries and grapes that we skipped dessert. Nightly dinner specials are under $11, be they yankee pot roast, chicken and shrimp scampi atop linguini, lamb loin filet or steak au poivre. Housemade desserts include chocolate cake, coconut-custard pie, and apple crisp with ice cream. The tables are covered with collages of old pictures, walls are brick or barn red, and overhead fans add to a casual, relaxed feeling.

20 Railroad St., Great Barrington. (413) 528-9345. Entrées, $4.95 to $10.95. Open daily, noon to 10; Sunday brunch, 11:30 to 2.

Special Interests/Budget Prices

Barrington Brewery & Restaurant. Ensconced in one of the red barns at Jenifer House Commons, this cheerful new brew pub with outdoor seating is an adjunct of a small brewery operation. Any of the six local ales goes well with the food on the wine-ranging menu. Try the brewer's snack (hot pretzels and celery sticks for dipping into a cheese spread made with amber beer and spices), a ploughman's lunch of sausage and brie, an open-faced steak and stout sandwich or a smoked turkey reuben. Prices are in the $5 to $8 range, but a few simple entrées like chicken quesadillas, shepherd's pie and New York strip steak are added at night.

Stockbridge Road (Route 7), Great Barrington, (413) 528-8282. Entrées, $8.95 to $13.95. Open daily, 11:30 to 10.

Blue Heaven Rotisserie. The old Blue Heaven Turkey Farm took on a new incarnation in 1996 as the "home of the best turkey sandwich." Turkey is cooked on the rotisserie and offered in seven kinds of turkey sandwich ($3.75 to $4.25), paired with pesto, roasted red peppers, hummus and such. This is a good place to pick up a prepared picnic for two ($22.50), and locals order whole turkeys, chicken roasters and stuffed duck to go for easy dinner parties. More sandwiches plus a variety of side dishes associated with the traditional Thanksgiving meal are offered in the off-season.

30 Church St., Lenox. (413) 637-3204. Open daily, 11 to 7 or 8.

Martin's Restaurant. At the top of the most offbeat retail street in the Berkshires stands this storefront proclaiming "breakfast served all day." Martin Lewis, formerly a chef at the Waldorf-Astoria, packs them in with potato omelets, corned-beef hash with poached eggs and toast and a "tower of bagel," at $6 the priciest item and loaded with smoked salmon, cream cheese, tomato and bermuda onion. The lunch menu adds a few salads and sandwiches in the $2.50 to $5.50 range.

49 Railroad St., Great Barrington. (413) 528-5455. Breakfast daily from 6; lunch, 11:30 to 3.

FOR MORE INFORMATION: Berkshire Visitors Bureau, The Berkshire Common, Pittsfield 01201, (413) 443-9186 or (800) 237-5747. Individual chambers of commerce have information booths in Lenox, Stockbridge and Great Barrington.

2 ✵ Summer

Famed Bass Rocks lighthouse hugs rockbound shore at tip of Mount Desert Island.

The Cadillac of Islands
Mount Desert and Bar Harbor, Maine

It's August, and the city pavements and the dried-up lawns begin to seem mighty unenticing. The mind wanders to the eastern shores of Maine – memories of misty fogs and sparkling blue waters, noble rocks, thundering surf, and succulent lobsters to be eaten on a wharf.

The epitome of this vision for us is Mount Desert (pronounced "dessert") Island. Although seemingly a long way from just about anywhere, the trip is worth the effort – for a long weekend or a week (the four million who come annually make Acadia National Park the nation's second most visited national park). Mount Desert has just about everything we love in Maine. It is the kind of place where you can be as active or as idle as you like.

Families camp, millionaires summer in their "cottages," and trippers can find a hundred motels, inns and B&Bs. Palatial yachts and cruisers dot the inland harbor. Older folks relax on benches and watch the activity.

Bar Harbor is the largest, best-known town on Mount Desert Island and is its focal point. But it is of strollable size, with many shops and restaurants to investigate. In August, however, it's crammed with tourists.

More rewarding for a feel of old Maine are visits to the towns of Seal Harbor, Northeast Harbor, Southwest Harbor, Manset, Bass Harbor and Somesville, one of the prettiest New England villages and the island's first settlement. With an unrivaled location at the head of Somes Sound, the Eastern Seaboard''s only natural fjord, Somesville is a joy – the whites of its houses enhanced by petunias, geraniums and morning glories spilling from flower boxes that line the street.

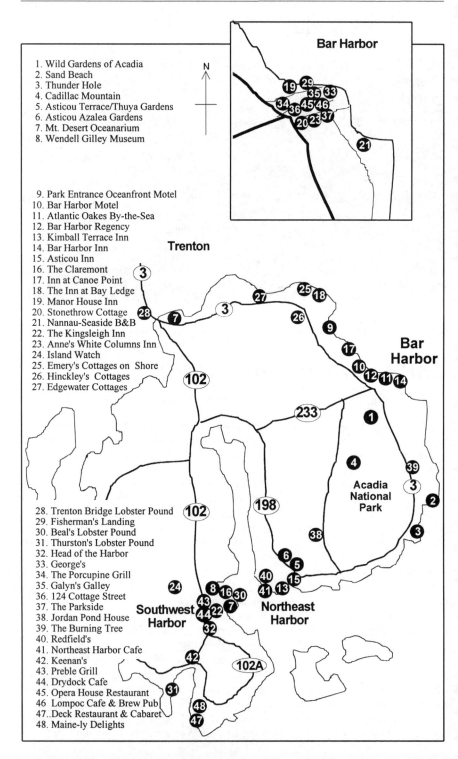

1. Wild Gardens of Acadia
2. Sand Beach
3. Thunder Hole
4. Cadillac Mountain
5. Asticou Terrace/Thuya Gardens
6. Asticou Azalea Gardens
7. Mt. Desert Oceanarium
8. Wendell Gilley Museum

9. Park Entrance Oceanfront Motel
10. Bar Harbor Motel
11. Atlantic Oakes By-the-Sea
12. Bar Harbor Regency
13. Kimball Terrace Inn
14. Bar Harbor Inn
15. Asticou Inn
16. The Claremont
17. Inn at Canoe Point
18. The Inn at Bay Ledge
19. Manor House Inn
20. Stonethrow Cottage
21. Nannau-Seaside B&B
22. The Kingsleigh Inn
23. Anne's White Columns Inn
24. Island Watch
25. Emery's Cottages on Shore
26. Hinckley's Cottages
27. Edgewater Cottages

28. Trenton Bridge Lobster Pound
29. Fisherman's Landing
30. Beal's Lobster Pound
31. Thurston's Lobster Pound
32. Head of the Harbor
33. George's
34. The Porcupine Grill
35. Galyn's Galley
36. 124 Cottage Street
37. The Parkside
38. Jordan Pond House
39. The Burning Tree
40. Redfield's
41. Northeast Harbor Cafe
42. Keenan's
43. Preble Grill
44. Drydock Cafe
45. Opera House Restaurant
46. Lompoc Cafe & Brew Pub
47. Deck Restaurant & Cabaret
48. Maine-ly Delights

The draw for most island visitors is Acadia, the first national park established east of the Mississippi. Situated where northern and temperate zones overlap, the park has an amazing variety of flora and fauna – including plants of the Arctic tundra – on its 40,000 acres of unspoiled beauty. Most of the park is on Mount Desert, but a section is to the northeast on Schoodic Peninsula and another part offshore on Isle au Haut and other islands.

Just about everyone travels the Park Loop Road, twenty miles covering the park's major points of interest. Most visitors also consider a drive to the summit of Cadillac Mountain a must. Park rangers sometimes lead a 4 a.m. hike to the 1,530-foot-high summit, the highest point on the Atlantic coast; those keen enough to participate can be among the first in the United States to see the rising sun.

The park offers guided walks, self-guided nature trails, carriage roads, cruises, campground talks, scenic spots, beaches and picnic areas. It's hard to find time to take advantage of everything available. And don't think that because Mount Desert is a fairly small island, it's easy to explore. Roads are convoluted, driving times between towns are longer than you might think, and there is much to see along the way.

Whether you stick to the main roads of the park and Bar Harbor, or strike off to the less crowded side of the island, Mount Desert Island offers rewards to those of all ages and inclinations.

Getting There

Most people arrive by car via U.S. Route 1 through Ellsworth, the entry point for Mount Desert Island, or by ferry from Nova Scotia. The small Bar Harbor/ Hancock County Airport in Trenton, just off the island, is served by Colgan Air. Delta, Continental and Northwest airlines fly into Bangor International Airport, 45 miles away. During summer, Greyhound/Vermont Transit serves Bar Harbor.

Incidentally, the **M.V. Bluenose,** (800) 341-7981, leaves Bar Harbor for Yarmouth, N.S., at 8 a.m. and returns at 9:30 p.m. daily from late June to mid-September (three times a week, rest of year). The one-way trip takes six hours and saves hundreds of miles for those visiting Canada's Maritime Provinces. The ferry carries 1,100 passengers and 250 vehicles, has a duty-free shop, a bar and slot machines, and costs $55 per auto, $39.95 per adult and $19.95 for children, each way. We recommend taking a dramamine before this trip, for it can be quite rough; the last time we crossed, we did not envy those on the daytrip package ($49.95, with two meals) who had to face the return trip after getting seasick on the way over.

In 1997, the Bluenose ferry service was taken over by Northumberland Ferries of Charlottetown, P.E.I., (902) 485-6580. Rates and schedules were undetermined.

Seeing and Doing

Acadia National Park

Your first stop should be the main Visitor Center, three miles northwest of Bar Harbor at Hulls Cove and open daily from 8 to 4:30, May-October. Atop a rather long stairway, the center has a huge picture window overlooking Frenchman Bay – a stunning view, except that on several visits we were unable to see much but fog, a frequent hazard here. Watch the fifteen-minute film "Search for Acadia," shown on the half hour, which gives the flavor of the area.

Pick up the folder on the naturalist programs – you will discover a marvelous variety. Sea cruises, nature walks (some at dusk or at night), mountain hikes, bike trips, orienteering and astronomy watches are among the offerings. Our family chose a sunset program at the outdoor amphitheater of the Seawall Campground where the ranger, a geology professor in Kentucky, gave an informative, slide-illustrated talk on how a glacier shaped the island two million years ago. A full moon rose over the shed that housed the screen as he talked, and afterward, campers with flashlights trekked quietly through the woods back to their tents.

New national park fees took effect in 1997, and nominal charges were planned for some naturalist programs.

Admission to the Park Loop Road costs $5 daily per car for all occupants, $10 for a four-day pass, or $3 per person for pedestrians or cyclists, good for four days. An annual local pass also is available for $20.

The Park Loop Road

Starting at the Visitor Center, this 27-mile loop winding through the eastern half of the island can take three hours or a day, depending on the number and duration of stops, is mostly one-way and may be entered and exited at several locations. The first two overlooks provide good views of Frenchman Bay, Bar Harbor and the area burned by a disastrous 1947 fire.

One of our favorite stops is **Sieur de Monts Spring,** named after the first French governor here and covered by a small octagonal structure. You can drink its waters from a fountain in the adjacent nature center. The **Abbe Museum,** a short stroll up a hill, tells most of what you could want to know of the area's history, especially of the Indians (adults $2, children 50 cents). The **Wild Gardens of Acadia** maintained by the Bar Harbor Garden Club are a special treat. All the native plants of the forests, bogs, mountains and shores are labeled and grouped in thirteen different areas, from deciduous weeds to dry heath and bog. Beautifully maintained gravel paths lead from horned bladderwort to grass pink to baked-appleberry to pickerel weed to fragrant waterlily, with benches for relaxation along the way.

The Champlain Mountain overlook offers the steep, 1.4-mile **Precipice Trail** up the side of the mountain, which the intrepid members of our family climbed, picking wild blueberries for sustenance along the way. They reported it took an hour and a half to get up, forty minutes to come down and there were two tunnels and countless firemen-type ladders to traverse, with sheer drops to contemplate. The trail has been closed lately when peregrine falcons were nesting in its ledges.

After the climb, you may be hot enough to brave the waters below (usually 55 degrees at their warmest) at **Sand Beach,** the only saltwater beach in the park. Changing rooms are provided, the surf is fun and you'll feel exhilarated if not numb after a dip. By the way, the sand is really crushed stone and seashells, which give it a gray tint. For the non-swimmers, an easy 1.8-mile trail, **Ocean Path,** goes alongside the water here. A short hike inland heads to **The Beehive,** a 520-foot mountain with a honeycombed face sculpted by glaciers.

Youngsters love **Thunder Hole,** where the waves rush into a small cave and roar out with a sound of distant thunder if tides and surf are right. A small gift shop here has all kinds of Maine memorabilia, including calendars, cookbooks, aprons decorated with lobsters, T-shirts and pine sachets.

From **Otter Cliffs,** look out to sea from the highest headlands on the East Coast. At **Otter Point,** take your cooler and walk down through the evergreens to the rocks for a picnic enhanced by the crashing surf, hundreds of colorful lobster buoys and the occasional bold seagull looking for a handout.

Near Seal Harbor, the Park Loop Road turns inland toward the venerable Jordan Pond House, a good restaurant and an island tradition for its service of tea and popovers on the lawn. Stop and enjoy the fine view of **Jordan Pond** and the two rounded mountains known as the Bubbles (named by a summer youth for the bosom of his amour).

High at the end of Jordan Pond is a huge boulder (you can climb up to it, and rangers lead groups up) called a glacial erratic, which looks as though it will topple off at any moment. Then you pass beautiful deep-blue **Eagle Lake** and on your way up **Cadillac Mountain** you keep seeing it below, getting smaller and bluer.

Even the ashen-faced Annie in our group doesn't flinch on the road up Cadillac – it is so well designed that you hardly know you're on a mountain. The view from the top is stupendous in all directions; at dusk, watch the sunset from the Sunset parking area. At any time, take the short trail at the summit with interpretive signs and maps. There are also a gift shop and restrooms.

Hiking, Walking and Biking

Besides the Park Loop Road tour, there are many other drives and cycling routes on the island. Take **Sargent Drive,** which borders the fjord-like Somes Sound, out of Northeast Harbor to Somesville for some of the best views. Across the sound is **Echo Lake,** with a fine beach and changing rooms, and water far warmer for swimming than the ocean. Head down the west side of Echo Lake for a short hike up to **Beech Cliff,** which has a great view down to the lake below (yes, you can hear your echo).

The park's **Carriage Roads** rate special mention. Fifty miles of winding gravel paths were built early in the century by philanthropist John D. Rockefeller Jr., a summer resident of Seal Harbor, who sought to preserve the horse and carriage lifestyle in the face of automobile encroachment. The remarkably designed roads, complete with seventeen granite and cobblestone bridges, take walkers, bicyclists and horseback riders past dazzling scenery. **Wildwood Stables,** located on the Park Loop Road near Jordan Pond, (207) 276-3622, no longer has horseback rides but does offer six carriage rides a day in open carriages drawn by sturdy draft horses. One of the best is a sunset ride to the summit of Day Mountain.

Take a Hike. Besides the carriage paths, 120 miles of hiking trails await the hiker. They vary from mountain climbs (naturalists lead hikes up Acadia and Gorham and Huguenot Head) to self-guided walks for casual strollers – the Jordan Pond nature path and the Ships Harbor nature trail.

Walk the Bar. For two hours on either side of low tide, you can walk across the water on a sand bar from Bar Harbor to Bar Island, where there are trails and shoreline to explore and the clear water is considerably warmer than at Sand Beach. Bring a bathing suit (change in the woods) and a picnic, but don't stay too long or you'll have to swim back across the current. The bar surfaces at the foot of Bridge Street. If the tide's in, settle for a walk along the quarter-mile-long **Shore Path** from the Town Pier to Hancock Street, passing shorefront mansions from the Golden Age.

BIKING. Although the terrain is hilly, biking opportunities abound throughout Acadia National Park and Mount Desert Island. The park visitor center offers detailed maps of roads and trails through the park. Cyclists can take the same routes as listed above on the Park Loop and other drives. They can get away from cars and trailers on the park's carriage paths. The Eagle Lake-Witch Hole Loop is a five-hour carriage park ride with spectacular views of lakes, mountains and ocean. For shore-viewing, bike the road to Seawall and Wonderland. Bicycles may be rented at **Bar Harbor Bicycle Shop,** 141 Cottage St.; **Acadia Outfitters,** 106 Cottage St., and **Acadia Bike & Canoe,** 48 Cottage St. and at **Southwest Cycle,** Main Street, Southwest Harbor.

Garden Treats

Asticou Terraces and Thuya Gardens. It's a ten-minute hike up a steep but well-maintained switchback trail to the gardens surrounding Thuya Lodge, former home of landscape artist Joseph Henry Curtis. The intrepid are rewarded with a spectacular hilltop spread of annuals, plus hardy laurel and rhododendron that you don't expect to see so far north. Other attractions are a gazebo, a free-form freshwater pond, a shelter with pillowed seats and deck chairs in the shade – just as you'd find in the gardens of a private estate, which this once was. A plaque relates that Curtis left this "for the quiet recreation of the people of this town and their summer guests."
Route 3, Northeast Harbor. (207) 276-3344. Open daily, 7 to 7, July and August. Free.

Asticou Azalea Gardens. You can walk amid azaleas in early summer here. Twenty species were moved from the former Rief Point gardens of Beatrix Farrand in Bar Harbor, while new varieties are added each year in this showplace funded by John D. Rockefeller Jr. Around a free-form pond are azaleas and rhododendron at their remarkable best in June, a Sand Garden with an arrangement of sand and stones as in Kyoto, Japanese-style evergreens and bonsai. There are gravel paths raked into lovely patterns to walk and stone benches for contemplation in this, one of the most perfect gardens we've seen.
Junction of Routes 3 and 198, Northeast Harbor. Open daily, 7 a.m. to 9 p.m., April-October. Free.

On the Water

The possibilities are endless, ranging from a Bluenose ferry trip to Nova Scotia for a long day at the slot machines, to a sunset dinner cruise to the Cranberry Islands. Sightseeing boat tours and deep-sea fishing expeditions leave from Bar Harbor, Northeast Harbor, Southwest Harbor and Bass Harbor; the mailboat rides out to the Cranberry Islands from Bass Harbor are cheaper.

Lobster fishing and whale-watch expeditions are popular. Among a number of whale-watch outfits, the **Bar Harbor Whale Watch Co.,** (207) 288-2386 or (800) 942-5374, offers a three-hour excursion aboard Maine's only jet-powered catamaran, a new $3 million whale-watcher, departing from the Bluenose Ferry Terminal two to three times daily for $30. A sign posts the previous day's count – five whales and hundreds of dolphins when we were there.

Sea Princess Cruises, Northeast Harbor, (207) 276-5352. Under park auspices, naturalist sea cruises leave daily at 9:45 a.m. and 1 p.m.. May-October, for excursions of nearly three hours through Somes Sound and the Cranberry Isles to Little Cranberry Island, with a stop at the village of Islesford (adults $13, children $9). The Sea Princess also offers a 90-minute Somes Sound fjord cruise and a three-hour sunset dinner cruise.

Naturalists also narrate a 4.5-hour cruise from Northeast Harbor to Baker Island, where you hike with a park ranger (adults $15, children $9), and a two-hour nature cruise from Bar Harbor through Frenchman Bay ($14 and $10).

CANOEING AND KAYAKING. The lakes of Mount Desert Island are paradise for canoeists and kayakers. Locals recommend Long Pond, the island's largest with three access points; secluded Seal Cove Pond, Echo Lake, Eagle Lake and Jordan Pond. Tidal currents in Somes Sound are dangerous for light craft; you also might be surprised by frolicking porpoises. Canoeing the Bass Harbor Marsh at high tide is quite an experience, especially on a moonlit night when you may hear and see herons, owls, beavers and deer. Canoes may be rented from **Acadia Bike & Canoe,** 48 Cottage St., or **Acadia Outfitters** at 106 Cottage St. in Bar Harbor or **National Park Canoe Rental** at Pond's End in Somesville (mornings, $20; afternoons, $22, and full day, $30). Acadia Outfitters, **Coastal Kayaking Tours** at 48 Cottage St. and **National Park Sea Kayak Tours,** 137 Cottage St., also offer sea kayak tours. Typical are National Park's half-day guided tours for six tandem kayaks, $43 per person.

Music and Theater

Acadia Repertory Theatre, Masonic Hall, Route 102, Somesville, (207) 244-7260. This island institution celebrates its 25th summer season in 1997. Four or five plays are presented in two-week cycles each Tuesday-Sunday at 8:15 and Sunday at 2. Tickets, $10 to $14.

Arcady Music Festival, Box 780, Bar Harbor, (207) 288-3151 or 288-2141. The Arcady Music Society sponsors guest artists in seven concerts Monday evenings at College of the Atlantic in Bar Harbor. Tickets, $12.

The **Bar Harbor Town Band** gives old-fashioned band concerts on the Village Green on Monday and Thursday nights at 8.

For 30 seasons, the **Bar Harbor Music Festival,** (207) 288-5744, has presented a month of classical and pops concerts ranging from piano recitals and brass quintets at the Congregational Church to a tea concert at the Breakwater 1904 B&B, a string orchestra concert at the Blackwoods campground amphitheater and a pops concert finale at Kebo Valley Golf Club.

The annual **Mount Desert Festival of Chamber Music** offers concerts on five Tuesday nights in Northeast Harbor.

Museums

Mount Desert Oceanarium. Everything you want to know about lobsters and other sea life is available at the Mount Desert Oceanarium, now at three locations on the island. The original is in a former Southwest Harbor ship's chandlery, where there are twenty tanks, exhibits on tides, sea water and weather and a commercial fishing room. Harbor seals, Maine lobsters and a marsh walk are featured at the newest and largest Oceanarium site along Route 3 near the entrance to the island. In the Lobster Room you can touch a lobster and talk with a lobsterman.

Nearly 10,000 tiny lobsters as small as your fingernail are on display in the Oceanarium's Lobster Hatchery, beside the municipal pier in Bar Harbor.
Clark Point Road, Southwest Harbor. (207) 244-7330. Admission varies from $3.50 at the Hatchery to $5.50 at the original oceanarium to $5.95 at the new Oceanarium. Combination tickets for all are $9.75 adults, $6.75 children. Each open Monday-Saturday 9 to 5, mid-May to mid-October.

Wendell Gilley Museum. Housed in a solar-heated building, the museum shows more than 200 of the late local woodcarver's birds and decoys ranging in size from a two-inch woodcock to a life-size bald eagle, daily films on natural history and special exhibitions.
Main Street, Southwest Harbor. (207) 244-7555. Open Tuesday-Sunday 10 to 4, May-December. Adults $3, children $1.

Natural History Museum. Located in a turreted stone mansion facing Frenchman Bay at the College of the Atlantic, more than 60 exhibits depict animal and plant life on Mount Desert Island. Mounted mammals and birds are shown in life-like scenes.
Route 3, Bar Harbor. (207) 288-5015. Open daily 9 to 5, June to Labor Day, 10 to 4 to Columbus Day. Adults $2.50, children $1.

Bar Harbor Historical Society Museum. In the basement of the Jesup Memorial Library you will find a large collection of early photographs, hotel registers and a fascinating scrapbook of the 1947 fire.
34 Mount Desert St., Bar Harbor. (207) 288-3838. Open Monday-Saturday 1 to 4, mid-June to October. Free.

Great Harbor Collection at the Old Firehouse Museum. The 1917 Town Hall/Fire Station is now a museum. Artifacts from fire trucks to forks, toys to tools and sewing machines to sleighs reflect the heritage of Northeast, Southwest and Seal harbors.
Main Street, Northeast Harbor. (207) 276-5262. Open Monday-Saturday 10 to 5, late June to Columbus Day. Donation.

Shopping

Bar Harbor stores range from traditional to tacky. Many are crafts shops, some of which change from year to year. First on our agenda in any town is a look at the latest local guides in the bookstores; **Sherman's** at 56 Main St. (also in Northeast Harbor) has books, maps, nautical charts, records and stationery. It has competition from the new **Port in a Storm Bookstore** in Somesville, a two-story treasure converted from a general store. Two cats, a sofa and a pair of binoculars occupy a reading area in back beside the water. The upstairs looks like a mezzanine gallery with works of local artists, huge windows onto Somes Sound and illuminated display shelves around an atrium.

Don't miss **Island Artisans** at 99 Main St., Bar Harbor. It's a co-op, owned by the artists who are represented in the handsome shop by their quilts, pillows and napkins done in hand-screened prints, lamps, stained and blown glass, weavings and much more. The **Acadia Shops** at 85 Main St. (and at locations in the park) feature gifts, crafts and foods of Maine. The elegant grocery store, **J.H. Butterfield**

Co., has been on Main Street forever with a fine supply of gourmet foods, chocolates, picnic items and luscious fruits, plus a good selection of wines and beers. **Window Panes** offers round candles that looked like balls of stained glass, as well as a trellised patio full of patio accessories. More Main Street shops include **Cool as a Moose,** with zillions of T-shirts and bathing suits; the **Driven Woman** for clothes and cards; **Bowl and Board** for cedar planters and birdhouses, and **The Blue Heron** for darling children's clothes and Maine-oriented gifts. **The Dancing Deer** on Mount Desert Street sells cards, Salt Marsh Pottery and all kinds of miniatures. Nearby are the **Eclipse Gallery** for fine American crafts and **Birdsnest Gallery** for mainly bird pictures and sculptures. Master gem cutter Sean Sweeney matches fine gemstones to gold settings as well as showing works of Maine artist Anne Kilham at his **Spruce Grove Gallery,** 43 Cottage St.

Northeast Harbor has one of our favorite gift shops, the fine **Kimball Shop** on Main Street, with room after room full of pretty china, furniture, Cuisinart supplies and everything else that's "in." Its **Boutique** a couple of doors down the street offers zippy summer clothing. **Beals Classics,** an offshoot of the fine Beals clothing and gift store in Ellsworth, stocks very nice gifts and pottery, Godiva chocolates and choice wines. We were taken by the colorful champagne glasses handpainted with lilies, until we saw the $260 price tag for a set of six. **Anne Fairbanks Ltd.** (winter address: Boca Grande, Fla.) offers suave clothes. Another winterer in Boca Grande, Wini Smart, shows her evocative paintings of Maine at **Smart Studio and Art Gallery.** New in 1996 was her garden shop around the corner, **Wini Smart's Garden Gallery.** Everything a Northeast Harborer would want in a summer home is shown at **The Romantic Room,** where we admired the smart sayings on pillows, the painted furniture and the quilts. We like the jewelry at **Fourteen Carrots** and the remarkable wooden sculptures of birds at **Redfield Artisans Gallery.** **Local Color** offers handpainted woven clothing, soft and elegant in jewel-like colors, and fabulous rugs starting at about $975 for a tiny one.

In Southwest Harbor, **Hot Flash Anny's** has fantastic stained-glass pieces (you can watch works in progress at the studio). **Mayan Designs** imports hand-crafted jewelry from Thailand, Greece and Mexico, among other countries.

Hungry or need a rest from shopping? Stop in Southwest Harbor at **Mrs. McVety's Ice Cream and Sandwich Shop,** where school teacher Judy McVety in summer offers heath bar and cappuccino frozen yogurt, many flavors of ice cream and good sandwiches. **Jumpin' Java Espresso Cafe Bar** purveys all kinds of coffees, as well as sandwiches made with Boar's Head meats, salads, bagels and the like. The new **Little Notch Cafe** and retail outlet sells baked goods, sandwiches and some of the superb breads from the Little Notch Bakery based in The Shops at Hinckley Great Harbor Marina.

Where to Stay

It seems as if hundreds of motels and cottage colonies line Route 3 into Bar Harbor. With all the accommodations, you wouldn't think you'd need reservations – and we've always been able to find something – but in season (July to Labor Day and especially August) the good motels fill up fast with people reserving for arrival on the Bluenose Ferry from Nova Scotia in the evening or planning to board the next morning. It's wise to book for at least the first night; you can always look elsewhere the next day if you aren't satisfied.

In Bar Harbor itself are plenty of inns, motels and B&Bs, and on the other side of the island, more of the same plus a couple of grand old hotels – the kind to which rich widows used to come for the entire summer.

Motels and Cottages

Park Entrance Oceanfront Motel. Sequestered in a quiet location across from the National Park Visitor Center, the 57 rooms here overlook manicured lawns leading down to a quarter-mile shoreline along Frenchman Bay. Each has a kingsize or two double beds and a terrace or balcony with chairs to lounge on. Some have a view of the heated swimming pool and jacuzzi. At the foot of the grounds are a picnic area, mooring facilities, rowboats, a small pebble beach and so many mussels on the rocks for the digging that one of our party thought he was in seafood heaven. There's no extra charge for up to four people in a room.
Route 3, Bar Harbor 04609. (207) 288-9703 or (800) 288-9703. Fax (207) 288-9703. Doubles, $149 to $170. Open May-October.

Bar Harbor Motel. Reasonably priced family units, a location near the Blue-nose ferry terminal and within long-walking distance of town, and a heated pool as warm as bath water (great for tired bones and chilly days) make this a good bet. Much upgraded since our first stay here in budget quarters, the 70 rooms are spread out in buildings of four units each up the side of a hill; set back from the road, it's quiet until the Bluenose horn blows rather early in the morning. Tucked away in the woods at the top is the refurbished "patio section," where tall windows in our spacious room looked onto a shady common patio and the back yard was Acadia National Park. Two-bedroom family units go for $128 in high season. Complimentary coffee is served in the attractive lobby.
100 Eden St., Bar Harbor 04609. (207) 288-3453 or (800) 388-3453. Doubles, $98 to $108. Open mid-May to mid-October.

Atlantic Oakes By-the-Sea. Right beside the ferry terminal on the estate that belonged to Sir Harry Oakes is this good-looking 151-unit motel, which includes 43 oceanview units in a four-story addition. We're partial to the older, low-slung units closest to Frenchman Bay, their balconies or patios enjoying privacy as well as peace and quiet. The restored Harry Oakes mansion, operated as a B&B, offers eight rooms and a suite (doubles, $125 to $237). The ten-acre complex has an indoor and a heated outdoor pool, five tennis courts, a pebbly beach and a pier where you can rent boats.
100 Eden St., Bar Harbor 04609. (207) 288-3453 or (800) 388-3453. Doubles, $128 to $162.

Bar Harbor Regency/Holiday Inn/Sunspree Resort & Marina. Erected in 1986 by Ocean Properties of Florida, the luxury Regency structure was taken over by the Holiday Inn in 1990 and later made a Sunspree resort, which accounts for the long-winded name. Its four floors contain 180 rooms, all rather sophisticated for Down East Maine (there's even a glass-enclosed elevator from which to view Frenchman Bay). The grounds include tennis courts, a walking path, a small pool, two hot tubs and a sauna. There's a **Tiki Bar** in a gazebo by the pool overlooking the bay. The **Edenfield** dining room has windows onto the ocean and offers a standard seafood menu. A lobster pound beside the marina features a New England clambake.

123 Eden St., Bar Harbor 04609. (207) 288-9723 or (800) 234-6835. Doubles, $149 to $199. Open mid-May to mid-October.

Kimball Terrace Inn. This modern, three-story motel contains 70 rooms, 50 with balconies looking across a small pool to the busy marina and harbor across the way. The rest offer what euphemistically are called "forest views." Our large room was notable for a separate vanity area and a private balcony, which helped compensate for towels that were as thin as the walls and floors between the units. Off to one side are a cocktail lounge and the **Main Sail Restaurant** serving three meals a day in three dining rooms.

Huntington Road, Northeast Harbor 04662. (207) 276-3383 or (800) 454-6225. Fax (207) 276-4102. Doubles, $110 to $125. Open April-October.

Inns and Resorts

Bar Harbor Inn. Right in town and right on the water by the town pier, this seven-acre compound is a convenient and attractive place in which to stay. It offers 51 elegant rooms in the main inn and 64 more in a luxurious oceanfront lodge erected on the site of the inn's former waterside motel, part of whose modest facility was moved uphill and used for a few years before being razed for a new building with 38 deluxe rooms in 1994. The grandest accommodations are those in the new lodge, where spacious rooms on two floors offer private decks or balconies with a stunning view of rocks, water and islands. Deep green draperies that match the dust ruffles on the beds, moiré wallpaper, rose carpeting, good art and big bathrooms with pink fixtures and fluffy towels characterize these rooms. We didn't know there was such a pleasant public Shore Path around the point along Frenchman Bay until we stayed here. Wicker sedan chairs and flourishing impatiens in ceramic pots greet guests at the pillared entrance of the main inn. In the elegant, semi-circular **Reading Room** restaurant, you can order dinners from $15.95 for roasted chicken stuffed with boursin cheese and asparagus to $21.95 for loin of lamb. Meals and drinks are served at the colorful **Waterfront Terrace** beside the pier. A lounge offers entertainment and a pool overlooks the harbor. A complimentary continental breakfast is offered in the morning. The Sunday champagne brunch buffet ($14.95) features live entertainment along with sumptuous breakfasty treats.

Newport Drive, Box 7, Bar Harbor 04609. (207) 288-3351 or (800) 248-3351. Fax (207) 288-5296. Doubles, $139 to $265 in inn, $149 to $169 in motel, $235 to $265 in lodge. Lodge open year-round.

Asticou Inn. A wonderful old resort hotel popular with those who prefer to be away from the hustle and bustle of Bar Harbor is the Asticou, which dates to 1883 but is kept thoroughly up to date and elegant. Cheerful, pleasant common rooms with oriental rugs and wingback chairs welcome guests, some of whom seem to have been coming here for extended stays for the last fifty years. They stay in the inn's 50 simple rooms or in seventeen outlying rooms in Cranberry Lodge, guest houses or the circular Topsider cottages. The setting high above the harbor is exceptional with well-tended gardens and a swimming pool. The lounge, deck and cheerfully muraled dining room offer spectacular views. The elaborate dinner menu, offered to the public as well as guests, is priced from $17.95 for citrus chicken to $32.95 for lobster grand marnier served over puff pastry or rack of lamb with a minted glace di viande. Meals in the off-season are served at Cranberry Lodge. The traditional Thursday buffet dinner-dances were discontinued in 1996 in favor of live entertainment by a pianist or harpist at dinner nightly and more special events throughout the week. Lately, the Asticou has extended its season, dropped its MAP requirement for "country view rooms" (EP, $150 to $180) and keeps the cottages open year-round.

Route 3, Northeast Harbor 04662. (207) 276-3344 or (800) 258-3373. Doubles, $250 to $297, MAP; suites, $269 to $356, MAP. Asticou open May 10 to Oct. 15; cottages year-round.

The Claremont. A landmark for more than a century, the Claremont is the island's oldest hotel and is on the National Register of Historic Places. The gracious dining room, in which every table has a view of Somes Sound, is highly recommended by locals. Guests can have cocktails at the boathouse, on the porch or beside the fireplace, before adjourning for dinner where main dishes ($14 to $19) might include chicken provençal, roasted pork loin and chargrilled rack of lamb. There are 24 recently renovated rooms in the main yellow wooden building, all with private full baths. Two substantial guest houses provide six more rooms and two suites, a couple with fireplaces. Available for longer stays are twelve housekeeping cottages with living rooms, decks and franklin or stone fireplaces. Croquet, boating and tennis are offered, and the hardy can swim from the dock in Somes Sound.

Clark Point Road, Box 136, Southwest Harbor 04679. (207) 244-5036 or (800) 244-5036. Fax (207) 3512. Doubles, $120 to $150 B&B, $162 to $192 MAP; cottages, $150 to $180, EP. Hotel open mid-June to mid-October; cottages and guest houses, late May to late October.

B&Bs

The Inn at Canoe Point. One of Mount Desert Island's few small B&Bs right on the ocean, this is a stunner of a place that's booked months, even a year, in advance. One look at the wooded waterfront location and you'll realize why. When Nancy and Tom Cervelli, formerly of the Kingsleigh Inn in Southwest Harbor, bought the B&B in May 1996, it already was basically full for the season. The Cervellis had only to fine-tune, adding a fireplace and remodeling bathrooms – "upgrading one room at a time," in Nancy's words. All six guest rooms have private baths, good views and are decorated in exquisite taste. Guests partake of a full breakfast in the waterfront Ocean Room; they also luxuriate in front of the fireplace in the living room or outside on what has to be the nicest waterside deck on the island.

Route 3, Box 216, Bar Harbor 04609. (207) 288-9511. Doubles, $135 to $245.

The Inn at Bay Ledge. This inn has been upscaled by new owners Jack and Jeani Ochtera, formerly of the Holbrook House in Bar Harbor. They offer king or queen canopy and four-poster beds in seven guest rooms with private baths, two with jacuzzis. All have picture windows affording splendid vistas of Frenchman Bay, and balconies were added to three upstairs rooms in 1996. Rolling lawns and gardens lead to a sheer cliff, where a steep staircase descends to the stony beach

Lawn chairs at The Claremont face Somes Sound near Southwest Harbor.

and a cave. An expansive deck stretches along the front of the inn; here are umbrellaed tables and twig chairs where you may read and relax at this, a truly relaxing place. A small swimming pool and whirlpool are on a lower level of the deck. The inn's main floor contains a sauna and steam shower, as well as a breakfast room where Jeani offers blueberry buckle or cheese strata. Farewell boxes of Bay Ledge candies are given to guests upon departure. The inn also offers three cottages hidden in the trees across the road.

1385 Sand Point Rd., Bar Harbor 04609. (207) 288-4204. Fax (207) 288-5573. Doubles, $150 to $250 in inn; cottages, $130 to $150. Open May-October.

Breakwater 1904. Taped classical music plays inside this impressive 1904 English Tudor mansion, grandly reborn from dereliction in 1992 on four acres beside Frenchman Bay. Guests enjoy two elegant parlors, a second-floor sitting room with a rooftop deck beside, six fireplaced guest rooms with private baths, a library-game room with a billiards table, and a long piazza furnished in chintz and wicker, facing the Shore Path and Bald Porcupine Island out in Frenchman Bay. Resident innkeeper Margaret Eden serves breakfast at a table big enough for twenty in the formal dining room. The main course might be vegetable omelet, blueberry stuffed french toast or lemon pancakes with raspberry sauce. Afternoon tea is taken by the fireplace beneath a large portrait of owners Tom and Bonnie Sawyer of Bangor, who decorated the inn as a showcase for Drexel-Heritage furniture and Country Inns magazine. The Breakwater has a full liquor license, and complimentary hors d'oeuvres are put out in the late afternoon. A pair of new two-bedroom townhouse units in a side carriage house rent for $1,200 weekly.

45 Hancock St., Bar Harbor 04609. (207) 288-2313 or (800) 238-6309. Fax (207) 288-2377. Doubles, $195 to $335. Open mid-April to mid-November.

Manor House Inn. Listed on the National Register, this striking mustard yellow house with green trim occupies a prime residential location across from the old Bar Harbor Club. Innkeepers Mac Noyes and James Dennison, who took over in 1989, offer nine comfortable guest rooms and suites in the main house, three in a rear chauffeur's cottage and two in little gingerbread cottages at the side of the property. All have private baths and queen or kingsize beds. The main house is outfitted with colorful Victorian wallpapers, period antiques and a decidedly Victorian theme. Each of the romantic, rustically elegant cottages with bow windows has rattan furniture, a corner gas fireplace, TV and front deck. A full buffet break-fast, including a main dish like quiche or a eggs florentine, is offered in the formal dining room. Guests enjoy a fireplaced parlor and a wraparound porch with a neat wicker swing on the side, overlooking an acre of elaborately landscaped grounds.

106 West St., Bar Harbor 04609. (207) 288-3759 or (800) 437-0088. Fax (207) 288-2974. Doubles, $85 to $145; cottages, $135 and $145; suites $165 and $175. Open mid-April to mid-November.

Stonethrow Cottage. Bar Harbor natives Peggy and Ed Douglas bought this charming cottage with dormers and turret in 1991 from a friend of her grand-mother and took four years to restore it into the beauty it is today. They offer seven guest rooms, all with queen beds, private baths and whirlpool tubs. The showy bathrooms are each uniquely tiled and their washbasins handpainted in different motifs; the fixtures are gold, even the whirlpool jets, and the towel bars are made of brass. Goose down pillows and comforters and colorful florals enhance the bedrooms, which are outfitted with antiques, chintz and lace. Everyone raves about Peggy's spinach quiche with scallions and red peppers, a favorite main dish at breakfast served at two tables for six in the fireplaced dining room. The ebullient innkeepers offer wine and cheese in the afternoon. There's a curved window seat in the corner turret of the living room. A lovely rear porch, furnished in wicker, looks onto a long and shady back yard so secluded you don't realize you're in the heart of town – just a stone's throw away.

67 Mount Desert St., Bar Harbor 04609. (207) 288-3668 or (800) 769-3668. Doubles, $135; turret suite, $175.

Nannau-Seaside Bed & Breakfast. Value-conscious travelers and families like this unassuming 1904 mansion in the Shingle Style on four wooded acres a mile south of town. Listed on the National Register, the sprawling house harbors three guest rooms with sitting areas, fireplaces, queensize beds, down comforters and distant ocean views. Original William Morris-designed wallpapers and fab-rics decorate most rooms. A third-floor bedroom can connect with a twin-bedded room to form a two-bedroom suite. Guests may use two enormous parlors and a great side porch. Outside are tables and chairs on a grassy terrace, perennial beds and a croquet lawn. A trail leads to a small sand beach at Compass Harbor, where a few neighbors were swimming in water in the low 60s at our visit. Owners Ron and Vikki Evers serve lavish breakfasts in the formal dining room.

Lower Main Street, Box 710, Bar Harbor 04609. (207) 288-5575. Doubles, $95 to $135; suite, $155. Open May-October and occasionally in winter.

The Kingsleigh Inn. A wraparound porch full of wicker and colorful pillows embellishes this B&B with glimpses of water in the distance. Inside are winning common rooms and eight guest rooms with private baths. Queensize beds, Waverly wall coverings and fabrics, and country accents lend character to each room. One room offers a new balcony overlooking the harbor. Check the view from the tele-scope placed between two wicker chairs in the prized Turret Suite. Innkeepers Ken and Cyd Collins serve breakfast by candlelight at tables for two in an elegant dining room. Their repertoire includes eggs florentine, waffles with fruits and lemon french toast with blueberry drizzle.

100 Main St., Southwest Harbor 04679. (207) 244-5302. Doubles, $90 to $125; turret suite, $175.

Budget Choices

Anne's White Columns Inn. Bar Harbor's early "guest house row" acquired yet another when a Christian Science church was converted into as contemporary a Victorian B&B as you could find. The ten spacious guest rooms have modern baths, queensize beds and cable TVs; three on the second floor come with private balconies. Wine and cheese are served in the fireplaced parlor, where a buffet breakfast including three kinds of cereal is put out in the morning. Owner Anne Bahr blends her own hazelnut coffee. She and her husband Bob, general manager of the Bangor Symphony Orchestra, have added lots of colorful landscaping to the property lately.

57 Mount Desert St., Bar Harbor 04609. (207) 288-5357 or (800) 321-6379. Doubles, $75 to $110. Open mid-May to mid-October.

Island Watch. Floor-to-ceiling windows and a couple of spacious decks take full advantage of the panoramic view of islands and water at this contemporary ranch house atop a high ridge east of town. Maxine Clark rents six homey guest rooms (one a single) with private baths, plus an efficiency suite in a separate building. Guests enjoy TV and stereo in the spacious living/dining room, where a full breakfast is served in the morning. We managed to rouse ourselves from the great rear deck long enough to enjoy Maxine's french toast with ricotta stuffing and strawberry-raspberry sauce at a festive table in the dining room. Since our visit, Maxine has added a greenhouse at the end of the dining room so folks may enjoy both breakfast and plants with an island view.

Freeman Ridge Road, Box 1359, Southwest Harbor 04679. (207) 244-7229. Doubles, $75; efficiency, $85.

Variety Beside the Shore

The Moorings Inn & Cottages. Calling itself the "Little Norway of America," the Moorings claims perhaps the island's most dazzling location at the entrance to Somes Sound in Manset, not far from Southwest Harbor. It's a delightful small, down-home, off-the-beaten-path inn with ten rooms, all named for sailing ships built in Maine. There also are three rooms with decks, refrigerators and microwaves in a motel wing and six efficiency units in three white cottages and a garden apartment. Some of the upstairs inn rooms have new waterfront balconies. We called our room the Agatha Christie, as several of her paperbacks were on the bureau; a nice touch was a candle in a china holder beside the bed. Towels are large and fluffy and the beds have colorful patterned sheets. The fireplace glows on cool summer mornings in the inn's living room, which has a color TV and a clutter of books and magazines. The coffee pot is on all day in the adjacent office, where complimentary orange juice and donuts are served every morning. Owners Betty and Leslie King provide charcoal for the grills beside the shore, a spectacular place to cook your steak or seafood dinner, and you can rent canoes, rowboats and sailboats, and borrow clamming equipment. The beach is stony; the water cold but swimmable. We're obviously fond of the Moorings – it's most unpretentious and the prices are, too.

Shore Road, Box 744, Southwest Harbor 04679. (207) 244-5523 or 244-3210. Doubles, $65 to $80; cottages, $80 to $100.

Cottage Colonies

Mount Desert Island has more old-fashioned cabins and cottages than you probably knew still existed. Some of our favorites:

Emery's Cottages on the Shore. Of all the cottage complexes, we like this the best. It has fourteen housekeeping and seven sleeping cottages, the latter closest to the water. All have electric heat, cable TV and private baths, most with tub-shower combinations. The sleeping cottages come with a queensize bed and a refrigerator; some of the efficiencies have kingsize beds. A pleasant lawn leads to a gravel beach; lawn chairs, picnic tables and grills are provided.
Sand Point Road, Box 172, Bar Harbor 04609. (207) 288-3432. Weekly rates, non-housekeeping $440 to $470; efficiencies, $565 to $700; daily rates off-season and when available. Open May to late October.

Hinckley's Dreamwood Cottages. Cabins in a grove of high pines, some with screened porches and fireplaces, and a heated, keyhole-shaped pool make this an appealing place. Three two-bedroom cottages, twelve efficiency cabins and eight motel units all have TVs and wall-to-wall carpeting. Two four-bedroom units are available for large families ($121 to $225).
Route 3, RD 1, Box 1180, Bar Harbor 04609. (207) 288-3510 or (800) 678-2224. Fax (207) 288-3510. Doubles, $59 to $109. Open mid-May to mid-October.

Edgewater Motel and Cottages. A cove-front location well off the highway commends this 23-unit mix of efficiency cottages and a two-story motel, four of whose spacious, paneled rooms have fireplaces, kitchens and kingsize beds. Each cottage has its own deck facing the water.
Salisbury Cove, Box 566, Bar Harbor 04609. (207) 288-3491. Doubles, $485 to $650 weekly; motel, $77 to $100. Open mid-April to mid-November.

Camping

The national park operates two campgrounds, **Blackwoods,** five miles south of Bar Harbor on Route 3, and **Seawall,** two miles south of Southwest Harbor on Route 102A. Both are in wooded areas near the ocean. From mid-June to mid-September, Blackwoods camping is by reservation only for $13 a night. Reservations are accepted no earlier than eight weeks before arrival date through Mistix at (800) 365-2267. Camping is free at the 300 Blackwoods sites in the off-season, mid-October to mid-May. The 200-plus campsites at Seawall are on a first-come, first-served basis. Camping here is $11 a night, or $8 for a walk-in site.

Privately owned campgrounds abound in the area, and we stayed at one near Ellsworth when Seawall was sold out. **Bar Harbor Campground** at Salisbury Cove is the closest to Bar Harbor. **Mount Desert Narrows Campground** is the only one on the ocean. Rates from $15 to $20 for a family of four are typical.

Where to Eat

When you think of Maine, you think of lobsters. And the prices are reasonable, as low as $7.95 for a lobster supper at recent visits. But Bar Harbor isn't all lobster, nor are all the restaurants in Bar Harbor.

Lobster Pounds

The cheapest lobsters are at the tiny shacks lining Route 3 on the way onto the island from Ellsworth. Large signs tell what the going price is, and most have picnic tables where you can dig in. Considered the best is **Trenton Bridge Lobster Pound,** (207) 667-2977, a rustic, family-owned affair with dining inside and out beside the Narrows between Frenchman and Western bays. Lobster, usually $5.50 a pound or less, is served here daily from 8:30 to 8, May to mid-October.

Fisherman's Landing, 27 West St., Bar Harbor, (207) 288-4632. With a convenient and picturesque setting, this is the one to which we head on the first night of most trips to Bar Harbor. You place your order in a cookhouse shack, find a picnic table on the wharf, under a pavilion or on an upstairs deck, get a beer or a carafe of wine from the adjacent bar and wait for the most succulent lobster ever to be boiled ($7.25 to $8.25 a pound, last we knew). The french fries are terrific, and you can get hamburgers, lobster and crab rolls, and other items as well. It's cool and quiet beside the water, and you may get to watch the brilliantly lighted Bluenose ferry glide by about 9:15. Open daily, noon to 9, June-September.

Beal's Lobster Pier, Clark Point Road, Southwest Harbor, (207) 244-3202. Things are more rustic here beside the Coast Guard Station, and the feeling is rather commercial. You can eat on the pier at picnic tables, and lobsters, mussels and steamers are sold inside. Lobsters are about $6.95 to $7.95 a pound boiled, but boiling often ends early, between 6:30 and 8. At the casual **Captain's Galley** out front, they had plenty of dessert pastries but were strangely out of most flavors of ice cream the last time we were there. Open daily in season, 9 to 8.

Thurston's Lobster Pound, Steamboat Wharf Road, Bernard, (207) 244-7600. From the canopied upstairs deck on Steamboat Wharf, you can look below and see where the lobstermen keep their traps. This is a real working lobster wharf. And if you couldn't tell from all the pickup trucks parked along the road, one taste of the lobster will convince you. You can get a lobster roll for $6.95 or a lobster dinner for $6.75 to $7.75 a pound, plus $3.75 for the extras. Pick out one of the twelve square tables for four on the covered deck and dig in. Beer and wine are available. Open daily, 11 to 8:30, Memorial Day through September.

Head of the Harbor, Route 102, Southwest Harbor, (207) 244-3508. Lobsters are steaming and steaks are grilling outside at the entrance as you place your order at a side window. Waitresses deliver meals to picnic tables on the expansive deck looking down toward Somes Sound or a screened porch adjacent. Fish chowder and onion rings and a crab roll ($7.95) made a good lunch. At another visit, we enjoyed a sunset dinner by citronella candlelight: stuffed shrimp with potato salad and sautéed scallops with french fries and three-bean salad (both $12.95), accompanied by a Napa Ridge chardonnay for $11.95 and followed by fresh raspberry pie. The lobster here is $8.95 a pound; add $2 for a complete dinner. Open from noon to 9 or later, Memorial Day to early October.

In-Town Choices

George's. This is a bit hard to find in a Southern-style house behind the First National Bank, but it offers some of the island's more imaginative food. Local history teacher George Demas has parlayed his original Greek theme into a glamorous restaurant with an ambitious menu. The menu is unusual in that all appetizers are $8; all grazers, $12, and all entrées, $23. You can graze or order a prix-fixe meal (appetizer, main course and dessert) for $32. At one dinner, hot crusty French bread and the best little Greek salads ever preceded the entrées: distinctive smoked scallops on fettuccine and a special of shrimp on a fresh tomato sauce with feta cheese, rice pilaf and New Zealand spinach with orange juice and orange zest. Most recently, we loved the appetizer of salmon quesadilla and a special of elk medallions, but found the night's lamb dish overdone and the medley of sorbets rather paltry. Desserts are usually first-rate, from chilled champagne sabayon with figs to fresh peach crème brûlée and, one night, an irresistible fresh blueberry and peach meringue.

7 Stevens Lane, Bar Harbor. (207) 288-4505. Dinner nightly, 5:30 to 11. Open mid-June through October.

The Porcupine Grill. The name comes from the nearby Porcupine Islands, and owner Tom Marinke's local antiques business provided the furnishings for this trendy grill. Downstairs is crowded and cafe-like; the small upstairs rooms are fancier and quieter. Start with the signature caesar salad topped with garlic-fried clams ($7.95), a local goat cheese and green onion tart served warm with grapes and blueberry compote, or smoked salmon and caviar with lemon-corn madeleines and fennel cream. Among entrées we liked the sautéed shrimp and peas in a garlic cream sauce over fresh egg noodles and the grilled chicken with ginger-peach chutney. Pork tenderloin with plum chutney and grilled salmon with Caribbean marinade and mango and papaya salsa are other possibilities. Finish with the sublime peach ice cream and ginger shortbread if they're on the docket.

123 Cottage St., Bar Harbor. (207) 288-3884. Entrées, $16.95 to $19.95. Dinner nightly from 5:30; winter, Friday-Sunday from 6.

Galyn's Galley. Popular locally is this year-round establishment in an old boarding house sandwiched between storefronts near the pier. You can watch the sidewalk parade from the tiny front porch or catch a view of the harbor from the glassed-in upstairs room in the rear. Fresh seafood is the specialty, outside or in several nautical dining rooms, and lunch is said to be particularly good here. The food is a cut above most restaurants of its ilk: fresh fish specials, garlic shrimp over rice, sautéed scallops with scallions and garlic, jambalaya, peppercorn chicken, filet mignon and prime rib. Most entrées are under $12.95; filet mignon and rack of lamb go up to $22.95. Lobster bisque, stuffed mushrooms and shrimp cocktail are among starters. Finish with Indian pudding, chocolate mousse or blueberry-apple crisp. Light fare is offered at the mahogany bar in the **Galley Lounge.**

17 Main St., Bar Harbor. (207) 288-9706. Entrées, $8.95 tyo $22.95. Daily, 11 to 10 or 11. Closed in January.

124 Cottage Street. "Downeast fare, creatively prepared" is the theme of this house-like restaurant, one of Bar Harbor's most popular and seemingly always jammed. The crowded scene and the 45-item gourmet salad bar attract many; you'll likely wait for seats in the rear courtyard or the enclosed front porch, even on weeknights. The extensive, something-for-everyone menu specializes in seafood (including bouillabaisse and four versions of shrimp), pastas and house favorites like Bombay chicken and New York sirloin. Sweet finales include double chocolate fudge cake, varying cheesecakes and strawberry pound cake.

124 Cottage St., Bar Harbor. (207) 288-4383. Entrées, $13.50 to $20.95. Dinner nightly, 5 to 10. Open May-October.

The Parkside. Seemingly every table gets a window view and every diner seems to be on display to passersby at this aptly named restaurant across from the village green. There are outside patios, tables by full-length windows inside and, at our latest visit, a new second-story deck. Come here for lunch, when burgers start at $4.50 and a lobster roll goes for $10.95. Assorted lobster dinners were featured for $9.95 to $12.95 the noontime we stopped by. The dinner menu gets a bit more adventurous: it's priced from $14.95 for Haitian crab cakes or roasted pork tenderloin to $18.95 for bouillabaisse.

185 Main St., Bar Harbor. (207) 288-3700. Daily, 11 a.m. to midnight, May-October.

Around the Island

Jordan Pond House. Tea on the lawn at this landmark in the national park is a Bar Harbor tradition. Green lawns sloping down to Jordan Pond and the Bubbles mountains in the background are the spectacular backdrop for a steady stream of visitors who start arriving at 2:30 for tea (two popovers with butter and strawberry preserves, $5.50) and, more recently, cappuccino or espresso with popovers ($6.50). The restaurant is contemporary, with cathedral ceilings, huge windows and open porches onto the lawn. The menu is fairly standard; lobster, seafood, chicken and steak at night. For lunch on the porch, the seafood pasta and curried chicken salad are fine. Don't try to fill up on the popover – it's huge, but hollow.

Park Loop Road, Acadia National Park. (207) 276-3316. Entrées, $11 to $18. Lunch, 11:30 to 2:30; tea, 2:30 to 5:30; dinner 5:30 to 8 or 9. Open mid-May to mid-October.

The Burning Tree. This summery place is one of our island favorites, off the beaten path between Bar Harbor and Northeast Harbor. Those in the know beat a path to the screened front porch and two interior dining rooms for what the chef-owners call gourmet seafood with organic produce and a vegetarian sideline. Our party of four enjoyed a delicious vegetarian sushi, grilled scallops and chilled mussels with mustard sauce for starters. Then we delved into grilled monkfish with tomato coulis, a spicy cioppino, grilled trout with basil and fennel, and cajun lobster and shrimp au gratin. The vegetable accompaniments were outstanding, as were the desserts, among them fresh strawberry pie and nectarine mousse cake. Prices are down to earth: $4.50 to $6.50 for most appetizers, under $17.50 for entrées. The good little wine list harbored a Chilean sauvignon blanc for $11.

Route 3, Otter Creek. (207) 288-9331. Entrées, $12.50 to $17.50 Dinner nightly except Tuesday, 5 to 10. Open June to mid-October.

Redfield's. Widely considered the best on the island, this small restaurant is run by Maureen and Scott Redfield. Located next to the family's Redfield Artisans showroom, it would be quite at home in the Hamptons or on Nantucket,

although the prices and lack of pretensions are refreshingly Down East. The decor is simple yet sophisticated. Tiny lamps hanging from long cords over most tables illuminate some large and summery impressionist-type paintings and make the two adjoining rooms rather bright. We staved off hunger with Maureen's fabulous foccacia topped with tomatoes and goat cheese, exquisite house salads and a shared appetizer of venison carpaccio, as we nursed the house La Veille Ferme wine. Lemon sorbet in a lotus dish preceded the entrées. Sesame-seared tuna with wasabi-scented coconut-ginger compote and grilled swordfish with gingered tomato-tamari sauce were among chef Scott's choices. Our sliced breast of duck with fresh chutney and the marinated loin of lamb with goat cheese and black olives were superb. Chocolate-almond mint tart and strawberry sorbet ended a memorable meal.
Main Street, Northeast Harbor. (207) 276-5283. Entrees, $17.95 to $22.95. Dinner, Monday-Saturday 6:30 to 8:30; weekends in off-season.

Northeast Harbor Cafe. Bold and flavorful American cuisine is the theme at this pleasant little cafe and bar done up in white and dark green, down to the cafe curtains. The menu is extensive, no fewer than eight salads and twenty sandwiches for lunch, and these with a twist: grilled portobello salad and Maine shrimp quesadilla, for instance. For dinner, start with jalapeño cheddar biscuits with sherried Maine crabmeat or grilled polenta with sautéed spinach and roasted red pepper coulis. Main courses range from herb-crusted chicken on grilled ratatouille to seafood sauté served over spinach and egg pasta. Dessert could be Maui wowee pie (coconut and pineapple with a nut crust) or mixed berry shortcake. Delectable squares, muffins and cookies are available for takeout.
Main Street, Northeast Harbor. (207) 276-4151. Entrées, $13.50 to $21.95. Open daily, 11 to 8, mid-May through October.

Preble Grille. When the landlord razed the building that housed Terry Preble's summery **Fin Back** restaurant in Bar Harbor after the 1996 season, his fans did not lose all. He already had opened this Southwest Harbor outpost in the space formerly occupied by the Clark Point Cafe, and now he could concentrate his considerable cooking talents here. The grill had suffered somewhat in comparison with the original during its first two years, and the Fin Back closing may have been the shot in the arm it needed. The menu here – "regional cuisine with Mediterranean pizzazz" – is similar but simpler. Appetizers range from three kinds of quesadillas to grilled Thai shrimp with a spicy peanut sauce, grilled polenta with local chèvre, and Maine crab cakes with sweet and sour lime sauce. The smoked chicken with dried apricots, spinach, walnuts and romano cheese over farfalle is a stellar pasta dish. Expect entrées like cioppino, saffron risotto with shrimp, grilled pork chop with beer-mustard-honey sauce and grilled angus strip steak topped with gorgonzola and roasted garlic. Dessert might be chocolate-raspberry tart or homemade sorbet.
14 Clark Point Road, Southwest Harbor. (207) 244-3034. Entrées, $13.75 to $17.95. Dinner nightly, 5:30 to 10. Closed Tuesday and Wednesday in off-season.

Drydock Cafe & Inn. The Drydock has expanded and upgraded its decor and prices since we first visited, but the extensive international menu is nicely varied and the prices easy on the pocketbook. For dinner you can order anything from blackened swordfish and chicken boursin to broiled seafood platter and filet wellington with crabmeat. Lighter fare includes Mexican dishes like nachos, vegetarian quesadilla and a super tostada salad. For lunch, try one of the burgers served on bulky rolls – the Maine comes with cheddar and bacon – with chips and salad. There's a full bar, a fairly good wine list and a large selection of beers. Upstairs are two guest rooms and three larger units with kitchenettes, all with private baths and cable TV, for $65 to $90.

108 Main St., Southwest Harbor. (207) 244-3886. Entrées, $11.95 to $17.95. Lunch, 11:30 to 3:30; dinner, 5 to 10. Shorter hours in off-season.

Keenan's. With lobster traps perched on the roof and pots of water steaming lobsters out front, this looks like many a seafood shack. But Keenan's has high culinary aspirations. Chef Frank Keenan, of French-Canadian descent, and his wife Liz call their cuisine Acadian, a blend of Cajun and Down East cooking. From the galley-size kitchen come remarkable treats that draw locals-in-the-know: crab cakes, seafood gumbo, shrimp étouffée, blackened swordfish and barbecued back ribs marinated in a mysterious red sauce, the only ingredients known being tomatoes and vinegar. Sandwiches and appetizers like fried clams are in the $3.95 to $8.95 range.

Route 102A, Bass Harbor. (207) 244-3403. Entrées, $6.95 to $12.95. Dinner nightly in summer, from 4:30; fewer days in off-season. No credit cards.

Maine-ly Quaint

Maine-ly Delights. From a van that dispensed hot dogs and crab rolls, Karen Holmes Godbout has expanded over the years to the point where she now has a roof over her head, a room with an open kitchen and an outdoor deck. This is an authentic place, where a hot dog costs only $1.25 and a lobster roll, $6.95. Karen's fryolator is famous for her original Oh-Boy Doughboys, and she still picks the blueberries that go into her muffins and pies. Even with a beer and wine license, she stresses, "I am quaint, not fancy, Down East all the way."

Ferry Road, Bass Harbor. (207) 244-3656. Open daily, 7 a.m. to 9 p.m., June-September.

Dining, Plus...

The Opera House Restaurant and Listening Room. Co-owner April Blair Carlson is a native of New Iberia, La., which accounts for the cajun-accented food and baked goods offered here. She and husband Bruce are also devotees of opera, which accounts for the listening room at the back of the restaurant, in which opera music is played all day. The walls are covered to the last inch with opera memorabilia and pictures of opera singers, and there's a circle of mismatched antique easy chairs where the music is a little louder for those who want to listen. Full of character, the place has a funky bar in the middle and a cheery solarium in front, where breakfast is bargain-priced from 93 cents for a beignet to $2.79 for an egg benedict. This is an "adult dining" spot, with an extensive dinner menu ranging from for chicken piccata to a house original, châteaubriand ponselle, stuffed with lobster tails, served with crabmeat sauce and carved tableside. Blackened halibut, seafood gumbo and crawfish étouffée are other specialties, as are bananas foster and a rum-chocolate mousse dessert developed to honor a Swedish opera singer.

Put a dollar in the milk can at the entrance and take home a loaf of the famous French quartered bread – they sell more than 60 loaves a day.
27 Cottage St., Bar Harbor. (207) 288-3509. Entrées, $16.95 to $25.95. Breakfast and dinner daily, May to mid-October.

The Lompoc Cafe & Brew Pub. The versatile menu and affordable prices appeal at this convivial, intimate cafe with slightly less noisy dining outside in a bocce garden. Lompoc's blueberry ale and four others brewed on premises are featured, as are 20 beers on tap, single-malt scotches, espresso and cappuccino, and what have you. The menu, with a decided international emphasis, ranges widely, from appetizers, sandwiches and salads to exotic pizzas, a ploughman's lunch and a Persian plate. Tempting dinner choices include Mediterranean scallops and pasta, drunken shrimp, Indonesian peanut chicken and a spicy Cuban black bean vegetable stir-fry, served over couscous with cilantro crème fraîche. For dessert, how about fresh fruit crisp or a triple chocolate truffle, or even an international hot chocolate?
36 Rodick St., Bar Harbor. (207) 288-9392. Entrées, $10.95 to $14.95. Daily, noon to 1 a.m., May-October.

The Deck House Restaurant and Cabaret Theater. On a hill overlooking Bass Harbor, just past the Swans Island Ferry, this is something of a local institution, having presented dinner cabaret shows annually since 1975. Dinner starts at 6:30 and at 8:15, the wait staff become players and perform barbershop, show tunes and monologues in the round. Grilled swordfish, cornish game hen, prime rib, boiled lobster and tournedos rossini are all priced at $16.95.
Ferry Road, Bass Harbor. (207) 244-5044. Dinner shows nightly in season.

Picnicking

Picnic spots are everywhere around Mount Desert Island. Official park areas like Thompson Island, Bear Brook, Seawall and Pretty Marsh officer picnic tables, grills and restrooms. Picnicking is permitted elsewhere in the park, but visitors must observe Acadia's carry-in, carry-out policy.

FOR MORE INFORMATION: Bar Harbor Chamber of Commerce, Box 158, Bar Harbor 04609, (207) 288-5103 or (800) 288-5103. Two good information centers are on Route 3 at the entrance to the island and at the Bluenose Ferry Terminal.

3  Summer

Mount Equinox provides backdrop for the stately Equinox hotel in Manchester Village.

Mountain Greenery

Manchester, Vt.

Manchester was discovered as a summer place well before the Civil War era. A London scholar, J.A. Graham, who traveled in the region in 1797, wrote home to England about the summer season in Manchester with great enthusiasm.

"It is neither too hot nor too cold; and even in July or August, which are the most sultry months of the year, the mountains refresh the weary traveler...." wrote the Englishman, as quoted in Charles Crane's book, *Let Me Show You Vermont.*

Located in the southwestern part of the Green Mountain State, quite close to the border of New York state, are three Manchester postal addresses – the village, the center and the depot. These days all three Manchesters flow into one another without much fanfare, but it was the village that first became a summer resort of note.

Its geographic position was ideal. On the eastern flank of Mount Equinox, the highest mountain of the Taconic Range, the village lies between the Taconics and the Green mountains, with gorgeous views all around. City folk from the East Coast were attracted to these mountains, and hotelier Franklin Orvis courted them by creating the Equinox House in 1849. Today, its descendent is a posh resort hotel with golf course, spa, several dining rooms, and activities galore.

Franklin's brother, Charles, started a business in 1850 stemming from his own interest, fishing. The Orvis Company became the mail-order supplier of note for the sport of fly fishing. Today, Orvis still has its main store in Manchester, where it sells not only fly-fishing equipment, but country clothing for men and women.

By the Civil War era, the Equinox House and other inns were thriving. Mary

Todd Lincoln, wife of the President, brought her two sons to the Equinox House for two weeks in 1863 and 1864 to escape the heat and tensions of Washington, D.C.

Robert Todd Lincoln, a student at Harvard at the time, was so captivated by the area that he returned in 1902 to build a Greek Revival mansion for himself and his family, called Hildene. Nearing retirement from law practice in Chicago, he spent increasingly long periods at Hildene, where he died in 1926 at the age of 83. The estate remained in the Lincoln family until 1975. It is now open to the public.

Hildene is the crowning example of the sort of "summer home" that was built in the Manchester area in the late 19th and early 20th century. The village was recognized as a spa for wealthy visitors and even during the Depression, liveried and white-gloved servants were at the curb of the Equinox House, opening the doors of fancy cars for guests.

The introduction of downhill skiing in America in the 1930s was a boon for the growth of the Manchester area's winter tourism. Nearby Bromley became one of the first developed ski mountains in the country. Later, Stratton blossomed into a full-service ski resort.

But even with the ski trade in winter and the breathtaking fall foliage season, summer remains the most popular time to visit. There is much to see and do in Manchester and its neighboring towns.

Sports enthusiasts can enjoy hiking, biking, camping, canoeing, swimming, fishing, horseback riding, golf, tennis and even falconry. The Appalachian and Long trails wind side by side through the Green Mountains near Manchester, separating once again when they get farther north. The Battenkill River is the ultimate trout fishing stream; canoeists love it, too. Golf courses include the famed Gleneagles course at The Equinox and a fine course at Stratton Mountain.

Those who want culture will find two long-established summer theaters, a thriving music festival, an art center and many art galleries, antiques shops and shows. There are plans to build a civic center that will be home to a symphony orchestra.

Shopping is another draw, especially at the upscale outlet stores in attractive centers near the junction of Routes 11 and 30. We like all the specialty shopping: antiquarian book stores, fine food shops, wood crafts and furniture stores, places to buy restored quilts or one-of-a-kind crafts, an incredible doll store.

The business of innkeeping is well established. There's a good range of options when it comes to accommodations – from clean-as-a-whistle motels and cozy B&Bs to full-service inns and resorts. Restaurants offer similar variety and price ranges.

All these aspects may draw you here and keep you busy, but for us, Manchester's greatest asset is its beauty. The area offers panoramic mountain vistas at virtually every turn, as well as an opportunity to drive to the top of Mount Equinox for the granddaddy of views. While Manchester has become too big and too busy to be the typical quaint Vermont village, nearby Dorset, Danby, Landgrove, Londonderry and Weston – complete with covered bridges and maple syrup stands – qualify.

Getting There

Interstate 87 in New York and Interstate 91 in Vermont provide access to the area, as do U.S. Route 7 and other state highways. Vermont Transit buses serve Manchester Center. There are small airports at Bennington and Rutland. Visitors also may fly into major airports at Albany, N.Y., or Hartford, Conn., and rent a car to drive to Vermont.

Seeing and Doing

The Mountains

Most visitors are drawn to the mountains, one way or the other.

Mount Equinox. Everyone should drive at least once to the top of the highest peak (3,816 feet) in the Taconic Range. The 5.2-mile **Skyline Drive** begins its ascent from Route 7A five miles south of Manchester. The drive up takes about twelve minutes, is quite scenic and not at all scary, as mountain drives go. Several pulloffs allow stopping for photos or a picnic. At the top, you find yourself in a large parking lot next to the rather sorry-looking **Equinox Mountain Inn,** (800) 868-6843, whose dining room is open for lunch and dinner daily except Wednesday. Our latest lunch was slow in coming and not worth the wait, nor was the view. A better bet is to bring a picnic and take the easy half-hour walk along the summit ridge to Lookout Point, from which you get a panoramic 360-degree view. Below is Manchester, and on a clear day you can see as far as New York State, Massachu-

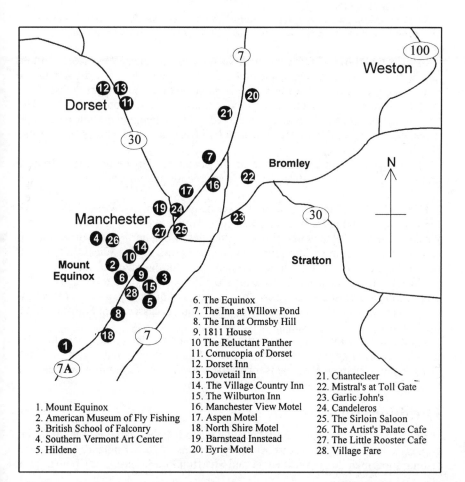

1. Mount Equinox
2. American Museum of Fly Fishing
3. British School of Falconry
4. Southern Vermont Art Center
5. Hildene

6. The Equinox
7. The Inn at WIllow Pond
8. The Inn at Ormsby Hill
9. 1811 House
10 The Reluctant Panther
11. Cornucopia of Dorset
12. Dorset Inn
13. Dovetail Inn
14. The Village Country Inn
15. The Wilburton Inn
16. Manchester View Motel
17. Aspen Motel
18. North Shire Motel
19. Barnstead Innstead
20. Eyrie Motel

21. Chantecleer
22. Mistral's at Toll Gate
23. Garlic John's
24. Candeleros
25. The Sirloin Saloon
26. The Artist's Palate Cafe
27. The Little Rooster Cafe
28. Village Fare

setts and New Hampshire – even (surely the literature exaggerates) as far as Mount Royal in Montreal.

Toll, $6 for car and driver, $2 each additional passenger. Daily 8 a.m. to 10 p.m., May-October.

Bromley. New at this venerable ski resort east of town are DevalKarts, mountain carts with wide wheels that are better known in Europe. You can brake to take your cart down the mountainside as slowly or as fast as you want. Rides are $6, or $16 for a three-ride pack. Bromley also has an Alpine Slide, which celebrated its twentieth anniversary in 1996. A single ride in the sled costs $5; three-ride packs are $13. Bromley offers scenic chairlift rides for $5 each, children $4.

Route 11, Peru. (802) 824-5522. All rides daily 9:30 to 5, Memorial Day to mid-October.

Stratton Mountain. Seventeen miles southeast of Manchester off Route 30 is one of the East's showiest ski resorts and golf complexes. Gondolas take passengers to the summit of Southern Vermont's highest mountain, and you can shop before or after in the Bavarian-style Village Square complex at the base. The ride is great fun on a clear day.

Stratton Mountain Access Road, Stratton. (800) 787-2886. Rides daily, 9:30 to 4:15, late June to mid-October. $8 per person, or $21 for up to six in one gondola.

MOUNTAIN BIKING. Mountain bikers like to haul their bikes on the gondola to the top of Stratton Mountain and then ride down – a fairly wild ride. A network of wooded trails is available for mountain bikers in the Sun Bowl area of Stratton.

Numerous town roads and forest service roads also lure mountain bikers. The Green Peak area in Manchester is considered quite challenging in some parts. You drive out to the actual trailhead on Dorset Hill Road, about two miles from Morse Hill Road, in Manchester.

The Battenkill Sports Cycle Shop, in the center of Manchester where Route 7 and Routes 11/30 meet, (802) 362-2734, has rentals and information.

HIKING. The Manchester area is hiker heaven for many. White blazes mark the two major hiking trails, the Appalachian Trail and the Long Trail, which are virtually the same as they pass through Manchester in a north-south direction and can be accessed from various points, including Routes 11 and 30 east of the town center. Shelters are located about every ten miles for overnight stays.

The Green Mountain Trail, just over six miles long, is rated moderate to difficult. It can be accessed from Forest Road 10 just east of Danby, north of Manchester. An easier trek is the three-mile Greendale Trail, accessed from Forest Road 18 off Route 100 north of Weston.

For directions and hiking trails in the area, consult the pamphlet, "Day Hikes on the Manchester Ranger District of the Green Mountain National Forest." Guided day hikes in the Green Mountains for all hiker levels are offered from Manchester by Highlander Hiking, (800) 429-8268.

Outdoor Activities

FISHING. Anglers come from far and wide to fish the nearby Battenkill River, considered one of the finest trout-fishing streams in New England. Other good fishing spots include the **West River** and **Stratton Pond**. The Orvis Company has maps of the river showing access points. Fly casting and lessons are offered through the **Orvis Fishing Schools,** (800) 235-9763, and **Battenkill Anglers,** (802) 362-3184.

The American Museum of Fly Fishing. This special museum combines history, literature and lore with tributes to great fly fishermen, including Presidents Grover Cleveland, Calvin Coolidge and George Bush, all of whom loved the sport. Did you know that a nun wrote the first description of fly fishing in England back in the 1400s? Or that Charles Orvis of the company here that bears his name designed and patented a perforated fishing reel in 1874? Or that artist Winslow Homer was an avid fly fisherman? The museum also mounts special exhibitions. When we visited, magnificent watercolors by James Prosek, the college student who authored the incredible book, *Trout: An Illustrated History,* were on display.
Route 7A, Manchester. (802) 362-3300. Open daily, 10 to 4, May-October; weekdays only, rest of year. Admission, $3.

SWIMMING AND BOATING. Emerald Lake State Park, just east of Manchester off Route 7 in East Dorset, (802) 362-1655, is a well-maintained, 430-acre park. Swimming, boating and fishing are permitted and there's a marked nature trail. You can rent canoes and paddle boats. Day use, $1.

You also can swim in an abandoned marble quarry off Route 30 south of Dorset.

The Battenkill River is great for canoeing as well as fishing. **Battenkill Canoe Ltd.** in Arlington, south of Manchester, rents canoes for the day ($45).

GOLFING. Golfers are welcome for a fee at the **Equinox Gleneagles Country Club** course at The Equinox resort in Manchester, the **Stratton Mountain Country Club** course in Bondville, and the **Tater Hill Country Club** course between Londonderry and Chester. Prepare at **The Practice Tee** driving range in Manchester.

A Novel Diversion

British School of Falconry. Those who have tried everything might consider the sport of falconry, which dates back at least to 2000 B.C. The first of its kind in the United States, the school is associated with The Equinox resort. Two Englishmen, Rob Waite and Chris Davis, offer lessons in flying Harris hawks. Hawks are used instead of falcons because of the wooded environs around Manchester (falcons are used in open fields and meadows). The hawks must be kept at a careful "flying weight" (usually under two pounds) so that they will be hungry enough to hunt for prey, but not too weak to go after it.

We found the 45-minute introductory lesson fascinating. Any fears were dispelled when we learned how gentle these birds really are. After you're introduced to your bird, you don Wellies and put the heavy falconer's glove on your left hand. Out in the field you're taught how to release the bird from its perch on your finger and to have it return to you (a little meat will do the trick).

After an introductory lesson, you can free fly a hawk during a 90-minute "hawk walk" along scenic trails. You also can go for a full day's hunting session in season or a day of "Country Pursuits," a half day of falconry and a half day of fishing. Call ahead to reserve a time.
River Road, Manchester. (802) 362-4780. Introductory lesson, $65; hawk walk, $130.

Arts and Culture

The Southern Vermont Art Center. A real treasure on a 407-acre estate, this includes a National Historic Trust mansion with ten galleries for exhibiting contemporary and classic art, manicured lawns with sculptures and a pavilion for musical events. There is a botany trail, too. An annual highlight is a summer exhibition by members of the organization, which was founded in 1929. The 350-seat concert and performing arts pavilion is used for theatrical and musical productions of all varieties. **The Artist's Palate Cafe** on the property is good for lunch (see Where to Eat).

West Road, Manchester. (802) 362-1405. Daily except Monday, 10 to 5, Sunday noon to 5, Memorial Day to late October; also Monday-Saturday 10 to 4, December-March. Adults, $3.

ART GALLERIES. Several fine art galleries are located in the Manchester area. They include **Tilting at Windmills,** which claims to be the largest in the state; **Gallery North Star,** the Manchester location for a Grafton-based gallery, and the **Beside Myself Gallery** in Arlington, which specializes in contemporary paintings and sculpture by regional artists.

MUSIC. The **Manchester Music Festival,** (802) 362-1956, is an important summer festival. Classical music programs are scheduled weekly in July and August at the Southern Vermont Art Center pavilion by groups such as the Manhattan String Quartet. Tickets are about $20.

SUMMER THEATER. Two towns close to Manchester, Dorset and Weston, have summer theaters of long standing. The **Dorset Theatre Festival,** (802) 867-5777, mounts half a dozen plays, each for about ten days, in the intimate Dorset Playhouse in the center of the village. We saw an excellent production of Agatha Christie's "Witness for the Prosecution." Performances are nightly at 8, Saturday at 8:30; matinees, Wednesday at 2 and Saturday at 4. The **Weston Playhouse,** (802) 824-5288, celebrated its 60th anniversary season in 1996 with five plays, each running for ten days. Performances are Tuesday-Saturday at 8, Sunday at 7, and Wednesday and Saturday matinees at 3.

Historic Hildene

Hildene. The former home of Robert Todd Lincoln, son of Abraham Lincoln, is a highly recommended stop. The 24-room Georgian Revival mansion was in the Lincoln family until the death in 1975 of the president's great-granddaughter, Mary Lincoln Beckwith, who left it to the Christian Science Church. It was subsequently purchased by the Friends of Hildene, who operate it as a non-profit house museum.

Because the Lincoln family lived for so long in the home and no other family occupied it, it is filled with personal memorabilia and furnishings. These include the ornate, high-backed bed in which Robert Lincoln died in 1926 at the age of 83, the office where he conducted business for his law firm in Chicago, the Aeolian pipe organ that he purchased for his wife Mary (she played; he used player tapes) and can be heard by visitors, even one of Abraham Lincoln's stovepipe hats. The guide during our 90-minute tour was most informative. Afterward, you can explore the beautiful and extensive English-style gardens designed by Robert

Rustic-looking Dorset Playhouse is a longtime summer attraction in area.

Lincoln's daughter, Jesse Beckwith. The grounds are used for special events, including antiques shows. A gift shop in the nearby carriage house is fun to check out.

Route 7A, Manchester. (802) 362-1788. Tours daily on the half hour, 9:30 to 4, mid-May through October. Adults $7, children $2.

Shopping

Were you born to shop? Then you'll like the Manchester area. **Factory stores** with designer fashions lure some. Names like Anne Klein, Burberry's, Brooks Brothers, Calvin Klein, Christian Dior and Giorgio Armani are represented. Most are grouped in centers like Battenkill Plaza or Manchester Square, close to the intersection of Routes 11 and 30.

Antiques stores are numerous, and several antiques shows make Manchester home. On alternating years in July a major show known for the quality of its merchandise takes place in either Dorset or at Hildene.

The **Deeley Gallery** in Manchester specializes in fine 19th and early 20th-century American paintings. Mark Richard Reinfurt at **Equinox Antiques** focuses on 18th and 19th-century American formal furniture and decorative accessories. **Carlson Antiques** on the green in Dorset has eight rooms of fine formal and country furniture and Victorian linens. **Stonewalls Antiques,** also in Dorset, carries early American and country furniture, china, silver, rugs and decorating accessories. The **Danby Antiques Center** in Danby offers a little bit of everything, with several dealers represented.

For readers and writers, two stops hold special appeal. The **Northshire Book Store** in the center of Manchester is one of the largest and liveliest book stores in New England. The children's department is especially good. A marvelous new shop called **Ex Libris** opened in 1995 in Dorset. Edith Miller has provided the feeling of an English library in this small, interestingly arranged space. We found beautiful stationery, bookplates, old and rare books, a selection of new books, antique pens, inkwells, glass fountain pens and other writing necessities. She also sells antique furniture.

Doll and dollhouse lovers can't pass up a visit to **The Enchanted Dollhouse** on Route 7A north of Manchester. Here you'll find dolls, dollhouses, miniature furniture and wallpapers and accessories for furnishing and decorating a dollhouse or a miniature scene, stuffed animals and interesting toys.

If you're moved to paint a watercolor, check out **The Owls Nest Art Center** in Manchester, which has a complete line of artist supplies.

We can never pass by **J. K. Adams Co.** on Route 30 in Dorset without stopping. Here is a factory store (the factory is next door) selling hardwood products for kitchen and home. The revolving wood spice racks for kitchen counter are wonderful and small tables for various rooms and purposes are also useful.

Also in Dorset on Route 30 is **Marie Miller American Quilts,** where two rooms of old quilts have been restored and cleaned.

The **Vermont Country Store** in Weston is fabulous. The catalog comes to our house, but we like to stop in to see the real thing. You'll find men's and women's clothing, items for home and kitchen, regional foods, candy and much more. The store owns **The Bryant House Restaurant** next door, where you can get a good lunch.

Mother Myrick's Confectionery is one of our favorite stops in Manchester Center. The best hot fudge sauce in the world, mouth-watering candy (the buttercrunch is to die for), desserts like lemon lulu cake, ice cream and fine coffees – this is where you can indulge your sweet tooth to heart's content.

Youngsters like the **Jelly Mill,** also on Route 7A in Manchester Center. In this three-story emporium you'll find a little of a lot of things. We enjoy the many flavors of jelly beans – how about cream soda or pistachio? We also like House Works on the second floor, chock full of items for the kitchen, including cookbooks.

Check out the basement at the main **Orvis** store nearby for some real bargains, although you may have to hunt around. Things aren't as well organized as upstairs.

Don't overlook the Village Shops opposite the Equinox resort. This is one of only three places in the state to have an official **Vermont State Craft Center.** We loved the quilts we saw here the last time we poked around. Other attractions include the **Claire Murray Shop** with hand-hooked rugs and needlepoint item by this extraordinary artist and craftswoman, **Irish Too** with handcrafted clothing, jewelry and gifts from Ireland, **Decorative Interiors & Design Studio** with custom furnishings and elegant gifts, and the **Brookside Angler,** a fly shop with instruction, guides and books for the outdoorsman. **Sweaters, Etc.** offers handmade knits.

The **Basket Barn** on Route 7A has lots of baskets and other household items like pot holders, aprons and tablecloths. There is even a **Fuller Brush Store** on Route 11/30 in Manchester.

Where to Stay

Because of Manchester's long history of tourism, there are plenty of accommodations to choose from at all price ranges. No large hotel or motel chains have made inroads. Instead, your selection is from highly individual establishments, each offering its own brand of hospitality.

Resorts and Full-Service Inns

The Equinox. Since its resurrection from a decade of inoperation in 1985, the Equinox has gotten spiffier and spiffier. One of the grand dames of summer resorts, the resort is now open year-round, with elegant lodging and dining. The property was acquired in 1991 by a partnership whose majority owner is Guinness, the spirits company that owns the noted Gleneagles Hotel in Scotland. They even named their championship eighteen-hole golf course here, the Gleneagles. The classic and columned white hotel facing the village green opens into a world of lush comfort, starting with a dramatic, two-story lobby with a view of Mount Equinox. The 141 rooms and suites in the main hotel, furnished in light pine with coordinated bedspreads and draperies, are equipped with modern baths, TVs and telephones. The nearby Equinox Townhouses offer suites of one to three bedrooms.

The **Charles Orvis Inn** is the latest Equinox restoration of the 19th-century home of the founder of the renowned fly-fishing enterprise and its theme is – what else? – fishing. The nine elegant suites (three with one bedroom and the rest with two) are decorated with the ambiance of a British club. All have gas fireplaces, TVs in living room and bedrooms, jacuzzi-style tubs in Vermont marble bathrooms, large dining tables and full cherry kitchens, even though you probably won't be using them. A full breakfast next door at The Equinox is included (or you can have a continental breakfast delivered to your room) and tea is served in the late afternoon. Rates also include access to a well-stocked bar, "The Tying Room," where you can pour your own drinks. Also on the lower level is a billiards room with two playing tables.

The Equinox offers two dining options, the formal **Colonnade** dining room (see Where to Eat) and the more casual **Marsh Tavern** that spreads across part of the front of the hotel with a bar and well-spaced tables flanked by windsor and wing chairs and loveseats, handsome in dark green, red and black. A spa in an adjacent building out back has a pool, steam rooms, an exercise room, massage therapy, aerobics, the works – with spa packages to match. Two pools (one indoor), saunas, tennis courts, an eighteen-hole golf course and the British School of Falconry are other facilities. The whole complex is stately, pricey and refined, although the staff is friendly and accommodating.

Route 7A, Manchester Village 05254. (802) 362-4700 or (800) 362-4747. Fax (802) 362-4861. Doubles in main hotel, $169 to $559; townhouses, $369 to $659; Charles Orvis Inn, $569 to $899.

The Reluctant Panther. This inn is distinctively decorated from the exterior – deep purple with yellow shutters – to the exuberant florals and stripes in sixteen guest rooms in two buildings. Owners Robert and Maye Bachofen, he a Swiss hotelier and she a personable Peruvian, offer first-class dining as well as some of the most sumptuous and comfortable accommodations in town. Goose down duvets cover the beds and guests find a half bottle of wine and two wine glasses awaiting their arrival. Eight rooms have their own fireplaces; one even has a huge fireplace opposite a whirlpool tub in the bathroom. Hearty country breakfasts are served in a pretty room with slate floors and marble-topped tables. The inviting dining room, with a greenhouse at one end, is highly regarded and open to the public by reservation. The changing dinner menu might offer cioppino, grilled veal chop with dijon mustard glaze, and roast rack of lamb with rosemary. The wine list is ambitious.

One of the desserts is the Swiss Treat, a sweet chestnut puree with creme chantilly and meringue.

West Road, Box 678, Manchester Village 05254. (802) 362-2568 or (800) 822-2331. Fax (802) 362-2586. Entrées, $20 to $25. Dinner, Thursday-Monday from 6; weekends only in winter. Doubles, $175 to $350, MAP.

The Inn at Willow Pond. From the lobby in the restored barn with a huge fieldstone fireplace to the 60-foot lap pool tucked behind the main building, this five-building inn spread on a hillside has a certain appeal. The 40 guest rooms and suites (all are listed as suites, but some simply consist of a large room) are decorated in Colonial style with handmade quilts or down comforters, folk art and, in many cases, four-poster beds. Some suites have wood-burning fireplaces. **The Restaurant at Willow Pond** (see Where to Eat) serves northern Italian cuisine in a restored 18th-century house on the property.

Route 7A North, Manchester 05255. (802) 362-4733 or (800) 533-3533. Doubles, $128 to $218.

Bed and Breakfasts

The Inn at Ormsby Hill. Ted and Chris Sprague came from the Newcastle Inn in Maine, where they made a stellar reputation for themselves, to take over this five-room B&B in 1995. They immediately finished off a second-floor wing of the gracious old mansion for five additional bedrooms. The new rooms have gas fireplaces, whirlpool tubs and attractive decor. Our favorite is still the main-floor Library, where we could settle in for several days. It has well-stocked bookshelves, an ample whirlpool tub, a wood-burning fireplace and a queensize four-poster bed with a crewel-embroidered canopy. Chris, an accomplished cook, provides extravagant buffet breakfasts with hot entrées and dessert – sometimes blueberry peach cobbler with vanilla ice cream. She also has added Friday and Saturday evening meals for guests who want them. On Friday, the meal is simple and informal – something like a stew, salad and dessert for $20 a couple. On Saturday, a more elaborate, four-course dinner is $60 for two, BYOB, with a single seating at 7.

Route 7A, Manchester Village 05254. (802) 362-1163 or (800) 670-2841. Doubles, $115 to $205.

1811 House. Marnie and Bruce Duff run this charming B&B in a home formerly occupied by Mary Lincoln Isham, granddaughter of President Abraham Lincoln. The cocoa-colored main house was built in the 1770s; the name reflects the date at which it became an inn. Eleven guest rooms are in the main inn and three more in the Cottage across the parking lot. All have private baths and six have fireplaces. Our favorite Mary Isham Room has one of the original fireplaces, a queen canopy bed with plain white spread, black painted floor with area oriental rugs and a picture-perfect view of the village's main street. The front parlors of the house are beautifully and somewhat formally furnished and have fireplaces. So does the cozy pub, where the innkeepers – both of Scottish ancestry – offer a selection of 43 single-malt scotches to guests in the late afternoon or evening. Marnie, the breakfast cook, may serve eggs benedict, baked pears, scones and fresh orange juice. She also bakes huge chocolate-chip cookies.

Route 7A, Manchester Village 05254. (802) 362-1811 or (800) 432-1811. Doubles, $160 to $200.

Cornucopia of Dorset. Bill and Linda Ley have approached the ten-year mark as innkeepers at this intimate and welcoming B&B with no signs of flagging. The white clapboard, turn-of-the-century home is right in the middle of the delightful village of Dorset. Guests can walk to summer theater at the Dorset Playhouse, as well as to three good restaurants in town. Four comfortable rooms with king or queen beds in the main house plus a rear two-story cottage with living room and loft bedroom – perfect for honeymooners or second honeymooners – comprise the accommodations, all with private baths. Recently, gas stoves have been added to two bedrooms. Our favorite is The Scallop, a cozy front corner room with a canopied queen bed and new handmade quilt, a corner wood-burning fireplace and a large bathroom. The personable Leys are known for their attention to detail, from champagne served at check-in to the piece of Mother Myrick's buttercrunch on the pillow of a bed turned down ever so artistically upon your return from dinner. Linda, a great breakfast cook, loves fussing for her guests. The repast, served in a large dining room, might include baked apple-butter french toast, pecan, sausage and apple crêpes, or a pear-almond breakfast pudding with fresh cream. Other common rooms are a cozy fireplaced library with two recliners, a living room with overstuffed sofas; and an airy sun room. The large lawn out back is also inviting.

Route 30, Box 307, Dorset 05251. (802) 867-5751 or (800) 566-5751. Fax (802) 867-5753. Doubles, $105 to $135; cottage, $205.

Dovetail Inn. This appealing B&B run by Jim and Jean Kingston overlooks the Dorset Green. All eleven guest rooms are in one of the two white, Federal side-by-side houses; breakfast is served in the keeping room of the other house. Decor is Colonial and the guest living room has stenciled wallpaper, wide floorboards, and individual tables with a variety of different-style chairs. Jean bakes every morning, so a fresh yeast bread, muffins or biscuits will come with juice and fruit for breakfast. The bedrooms, all with private baths, vary in size and have doubles, kings and queen beds. One large room in back has a queen bed, kitchenette-wet bar and deck overlooking the back yard and a lovely perennial garden.

Route 30, Dorset 05251. (802) 867-5747. Doubles $75 to $195.

Country-Style Inns

Dorset Inn. Gretchen Schmidt and Sissy Hicks operate what is claimed to be the oldest continually operating country inn in Vermont (since 1796). The big white inn with black shutters overlooks the Dorset green. The living room, to the left of the central hallway, is inviting with a gathering of wing chairs in navy windowpane fabric before the fireplace, and plenty of puzzles and books to keep one entertained. The 29 rooms and two suites on the second and third floors have been upgraded, and more renovations were in the plans for 1997. All sport modern baths, wall-to-wall carpeting, print wallpapers and antique furnishings. Two of the nicest are the third-floor front corner rooms, one of which has twin sleigh beds and Audubon prints on the wall. The inn serves a hearty breakfast (sourdough or fruit pancakes and all sorts of egg dishes) as well as highly rated dinners in the attractive, country-style dining room and a fireplaced tavern room much beloved by the locals (see Where to Eat).

Church and Main Streets, Dorset 05251. (802) 867-5500. Doubles, $200 to $225 MAP; suites, $300 to $325 MAP.

The Village Country Inn. Pale yellow with rose shutters, this large inn, signals romance from the moment you enter the frilly lobby. In fact, innkeepers Anne and Jay Degen aim for a romantic experience, and no children are allowed. Room 106 sets the mood with lace curtains, deep pink and rose decor, and a footed tub on a dais in the bathroom, which also contains an oversize, clear glass shower stall. Room 130 has a king canopied bed, violet-studded wallpaper and a chaise, with purple walls in the adjoining bathroom. Among the 33 rooms are two-room suites and garden rooms with private entrances from the gardens. All have telephones; some have televisions. There's an outdoor pool with a marble terrace. Dinner is served in a French country dining room decorated with white trellises and ivy. In summer, service is also offered on the outdoor terrace.

Route 7A, Box 408, Manchester Village 05254. (802) 362-1792 or (800) 370-0300. Fax (802) 362-7238. Dinner nightly, 6 to 9; Thursday-Sunday, November-May. Doubles, $150 to $250, MAP.

A Country Estate

The Wilburton Inn. This brick tudor inn was originally built as a country home by Albert Gilbert, a wealthy Chicago businessman and good friend of Robert Todd Lincoln, whose estate, Hildene, was close by. Later used as a school, the twenty-acre estate was purchased in 1987 by Connecticut physician Albert Levis and his wife, Georgette, the sister of playwright Wendy Wasserstein. Dr. Levis's interest in contemporary art has resulted in amazing sculptures placed around the property as well as his own version of a Greek temple built on a knoll. The main inn with its burnished cherry woodwork and leaded glass windows contains eleven guest rooms – 24 more are in smaller "cottages" on the property. Room 4 in the main house with a king bed and private entry is usually booked for brides – weddings are a big business here. Rooms on the third floor are somewhat smaller than those on the second, but have better views of the valley. The grounds include a pool and tennis courts, and we can imagine some guests never leaving the property, so restful is the feeling of being away from the world. The inn's dining room, open to the public by reservation, is handsome with dark wood walls, cherry beams and a massive fireplace. Hurricane lamps flicker on tables in the evening. Chef Dave Stoel's dinner fare includes grilled salmon with raspberry gastrique, roast duckling with cointreau-orange sauce and broiled scallops of lamb with garlic-rosemary sauce. A complete dinner for two is offered house guests at $55. Full breakfast is included in the rates.

River Road, Manchester Village 05254. Entrées, $15 to $20. Dinnner nightly, 6 to 9. (802) 362-2500 or (800) 648-4944. Doubles, $140 to $205.

Motels

Manchester View Motel. This is a motel in name only. Crowning a hill off Route 7 north of town with views in all directions, the complex comprises five deep brown buildings with white trim, each of which contains some unusual and individualistic accommodations. Most of the 35 rooms and suites have terrific mountain views and decks to take advantage. About half offer fireplaces. A heated outdoor pool is a summer attraction, as is a well-equipped exercise room. Our favorite guest room is the Ethan Allen, located in part of a converted barn, a huge space with queen canopy bed, antique pine furniture, wood-burning fireplace and a great deck that overlooks the mountains. Seven other accommodations, including spacious "grand suites" with two rooms and one and a half baths, have two-person jacuzzis, 25-inch televisions and gas fireplaces. A few standard queen rooms are on the small side, but cable TV/VCR and refrigerators are pluses. Owners Pat and Tom Barnett have been making improvements here for twenty years. A separate breakfast room offers guests the convenience of fruit, muffins and cereal for $2.50 each.

Route 7A, Manchester Center 05255. (802) 362-2739. Fax (802) 362-2739. Doubles, $74 to $145; suites, $150 to $190.

A Good Value

Eyrie Motel. A bit of a sleeper, this twelve-unit motel is located on a 23-acre bluff back from the highway, which gives it a great deal of privacy. Mia and Valter Utkin are friendly, caring owners who also tend the hanging baskets of flowers and keep the pool in shape. Each room has two queen beds, a full bath, refrigerator, TV, telephone and air conditioning. A complimentary continental breakfast (juice, coffee, and toast or English muffins) is offered in an attractive common room with good views of the mountains.

Route 7A, Box 501, East Dorset 05253. (802) 362-1208. Doubles, $65 to $75.

Aspen Motel. Varied accommodations are offered in this 24-unit, gray-with-burgundy-trim motel on the main drag, which is impeccably cared for by brothers Bruce and Scott Welsh, whose father originally bought the property twenty years ago. The motel stretches out behind a pool and shuffleboard area in the center of the complex. All units are air-conditioned and have in-room coffeemakers; some have refrigerators. Doubles, queen and king beds are available. A Cape Cod-style house, the Birches, with two bedrooms, a large living room, dining area and kitchen is ideal for families or two couples ($150 to $175 a night). Ditto for the Mendham in a separate building with connecting bedrooms, each with a double and twin, full bath and private deck with mountain views.

Box 548, Route 7A, Manchester Center 05255. (802) 362-2450. Doubles, $58 to $90.

North Shire Motel. Some of the best mountain views around are from the fourteen chalet-style guest rooms at this secluded motel on spacious grounds south of Manchester. Each unit has a cathedral ceiling, sliding glass doors, telephone, air conditioning, and two double or a kingsize bed. Outside each is an individual patio. A pool with patio is artfully tucked into the landscape and sited for privacy. A complimentary continental breakfast is offered in the common room.

Route 7A, Box 413, Manchester 05254. (802) 362-2336. Doubles, $75 to $80.

Barnstead Innstead. The name is a bit cumbersome but this is one of the more attractive smaller accommodations in the area, located just west of the center of Manchester on the road to Dorset. A New England hay barn, built in the 1830s, has been converted into a cozy place to stay. A dozen rooms offer private baths, carpeting, cable TV and courtesy coffee. We liked our two-room suite, carpeted in a braided rug look with nice touches like a pierced tin lamp in the hall. Another time we stayed in Room 1, paneled in barnwood with kingsize bed, tiled bath and two old school desks that doubled as chairs and nightstands. Rough pine furniture contributes to a rustic feeling. A secluded swimming pool and patio are much enjoyed by summer guests.

Route 30, Box 988, Manchester Center 05255. (802) 362-1619. Doubles, $75 to $100.

Where to Eat

The Manchester area has a wide range of places to dine – from fine continental fare to more casual spots.

Fine Dining

Chantecleer. Swiss-born chef Michel Baumann turned this converted dairy barn with silo into a renowned restaurant. A serious chef-owner who insists on doing it his way, he serves no more than 50 diners in a two-section dining room, plus a couple of tables tucked in next to the bar (the three tables near the old stone fireplace are reserved first in chilly weather). The rustic interior, with beamed ceiling and lots of wood, has elegant table appointments. Crystal and silverplate gleam in the soft lighting. After fifteen years, certain dishes have become classics. The escargots glazed with hazelnut-garlic butter and a splash of pernod is a house favorite. Other starters ($6 to $9) include baked French onion soup, eggplant and roasted red pepper terrine, and pastrami-cured salmon and Atlantic smoked salmon, served together with a blueberry chutney. Signature entrées are dover sole, herbed rack of lamb and grilled veal chop with madeira wine and morels.

Route 7A, East Dorset. (802) 362-1616. Entrées, $21 to $27.50. Dinner by reservation, nightly except Tuesday from 6.

Mistral's at Toll Gate. Whatever the season, the dining-room tables overlooking the rushing stream out back are the favored ones. The stream is lighted at night and is always fascinating, even when crusted with ice in the dead of winter. A small footbridge across the water is decked out with little white lights. Contemporary lacquered black chairs are at tables covered with bright blue cloths over white. Flickering candles in etched glass holders add a romantic note, and the taped piano music was very relaxing the night we ate here. With large glass windows giving good views of the stream and woods beyond, we almost felt we were in a grotto, although a fancy one. Dana Markey is the chef, while his wife Cheryl handles the front of the house. The dinner menu might start with French onion soup, crab cakes grenobloise, lemon and black pepper smoked trout and a spinach and radicchio salad. For entrées, sautéed native trout stuffed with scallop mousse, roast duckling with strawberry sauce and stuffed breast of chicken marsala are possibilities. Our crispy sweetbreads dijonnaise were excellent. Coupe mistral, the dessert of choice, is coffee ice cream rolled in hazelnuts and topped with hot fudge. Linzertorte and praline cheesecake are also offered.

Toll Gate Road (off Routes 11/30), Manchester. (802) 362-1779 or (800) 279-1779. Entrées, $17 to $22. Dinner nightly except Wednesday, from 6.

The Colonnade at the Equinox. With a stenciled and vaulted ceiling, The Colonnade is suitably formal for those who like to dress up and have a leisurely dinner experience. Located toward the rear of the Equinox hotel, it's the resort's more elegant dining room; casual fare is served up front in the Marsh Tavern. Appetizers include poached mussels with plum tomatoes, oregano, saffron and focaccia, and glazed duck breast with charred sweetbreads in a blackberry vinaigrette. Chilled sweet potato and chive soup and a lobster and roasted red pepper bisque were offered on a summer menu. For main courses, you might try sautéed red snapper with potato and chive crust, poached chicken breast and lobster with asparagus and basil potatoes, or pan-seared veal medallions with chanterelles and shallot risotto. Chocolate grand marnier cake could be on the dessert menu.

Route 7A, Manchester Village. (802) 362-4700. Entrées, $20 to $25. Dinner, Wednesday-Sunday in season, 6 to 9:30; Sunday brunch, 11 to 2:30.

Dorset Inn. We like the comfortable feeling of this classic old inn on the green in Dorset – it really seems like Vermont. Sissy Hicks, co-owner and chef, maintains an inventive menu. The main dining room has dark green walls and white tablecloths with plaid undercloths. Brass chandeliers make it a bit more formal than the adjacent tavern, where the tablecloths are homespun green, the ceiling is pressed tin, and there is a fireplace in the brick wall on one side. The same, unusually varied menu is offered in both rooms. Starters ($5 to $7.50) include yam fritters with maple syrup, grilled polenta with sautéed portobello mushrooms and capers, and spicy turkey chili with yogurt and minced onions. Expect entrées like grilled steak with James Beard's classic sauce, sautéed calves liver with bacon and onions, and crispy duck confit with braised red cabbage, wild rice and plum chutney, plus such vegetarian choices as Moroccan vegetable stew with couscous and harissa, garbanzo croquettes served with sautéed spinach, salsa and sour cream and baked eggplant crêpes. There is always a burger on the menu and you can make a meal of one of the dinner salads, too. The lunch menu, often served in a pretty sunroom, stresses salads and sandwiches.

On the Green, Dorset. (802) 867-5500. Entrées, $9 to $18.50. Lunch daily in summer and fall, 11:30 to 2; dinner nightly, from 5:30.

Inn at West View Farm. Two dining rooms – one the more formal front room with green cloths and bentwood chairs, and the other toward the back called Clancy's Tavern for Clancy the dog – are available at this establishment owned by Dorothy and Heimut Stein. We chose the tavern one Saturday evening, since we had tickets for the Dorset Playhouse and wanted to make sure we could be fed in plenty of time. When one of us ordered the rosemary chicken from the menu at 6:30, we were informed they'd run out of chicken already. Other tavern choices ($10.95 to $12.95) were garlic shrimp with risotto and tagliatelle with pesto and both were fine. We did wish they'd lower the lighting a little, for the room seemed too bright. Entrées in the attractive main dining room, served with house salad, included sautéed Maine crab cakes, grilled cajun-style swordfish, pan-seared veal sweetbreads and rack of lamb. The inn also has ten guest rooms with private baths, for $85 to $125 B&B.

Route 30, Dorset. (802) 867-5717. Entrées, $15 to $20. Dinner nightly except Monday, 6 to 9.

Ethnic Fare

The Restaurant at Willow Pond. Two fireplaced dining rooms with gentle lighting and well-spaced, white-clothed tables are attractive places in which to enjoy northern Italian cuisine. The restaurant, part of the Inn at Willow Pond complex, is in a renovated, 18th-century farmhouse on the property. Typical appetizers are rollatini (grilled eggplant with a three-cheese and spinach stuffing and a tomato and porcini mushroom sauce), polenta topped with a sundried-tomato basil pesto, and grilled tuna on a bed of mesclun greens with red and yellow pepper salsa. Or how about a spinach salad with Vermont chèvre and pancetta tossed in a warmed balsamic vinaigrette? Pasta choices could be linguini alla pesto, seafood diavolo and fettuccine fileto di pomodoro (with a fresh tomato sauce and prosciutto). Veal piccata, chicken scampi and grilled beef filet served with portobello mushrooms and caramelized shallots are among the entrées. The restaurant claims it has the largest selection of fine Italian wines in Vermont. Italian-blend espresso and cappuccino also are available.

Route 7A, Manchester. (802) 362-4733. Entrées, $18 to $22. Dinner nightly, 5:30 to 9:30.

Garlic John's. Here is a fun Italian restaurant, now in its fifteenth year and enlarged to accommodate the crowds over the years. Chianti bottles hang from the ceiling, as they have from the start, and two of the three original owners – Sue Coccomo and Frank Shattuck – are still in charge. There never was a man named John, but they thought it sounded good. Families can come here and be sure the kids will find something to eat, and outdoors enthusiasts can stoke up on energy-building pasta, too. Garlic bread and salad come with entrées. The large selection includes favorites like baked manicotti, lasagna, pasta and meatballs and fettuccine alfredo. But you will also find pasta with garlic and oil (and anchovies if you wish), pasta bolognese and jumbo cheese ravioli. Chicken, veal, beef and seafood come in many guises, including broiled salmon with grilled vegetables, veal or chicken piccata, veal marsala and chicken with sundried tomatoes, rosemary and cream.

Routes 11/30, Manchester Center. (802) 362-9843. Entrées, $12.95 to $17.95. Dinner nightly, 4 to 9:30, Sunday from 3.

Candeleros. This attractive restaurant, serving "authentic Mexican cuisine," opened in 1995 in an old house on Route 7A opposite the small Chamber of Commerce information building. Light wood furniture and colors of the country – terra cotta, yellow, earth tones predominate – set the scene for an ambitious menu for lunch and dinner. Wreaths of dark red chile peppers adorn the walls of the bar/dining room to the left of the entry; there's another dining room on the right. In the summer, this is one of few places in the area where you can dine outdoors – even if you are at wrought-iron tables beside the main drag. Great margaritas made with pomegranate juice are touted, and the tableside guacamole preparation is terrific. It is mashed up before your eyes from avocado, tomato, onion, cilantro and lime. A favorite menu item is the enchiladas de mole poblano (two chicken-filled tortillas in a sauce of ground chiles and nuts with a touch of chocolate). Everything is available for takeout.

Main Street, Manchester. (802) 362-0836. Entrées, $8.50 to $15.95. Open daily, 11:30 to 10.

Hot and Hearty

The Sirloin Saloon. If anything, the Sirloin Saloon only gets bigger, better and more popular. Richly colored Tiffany lamps light the old grist mill, where dining areas feature a fine collection of American Indian art and artifacts. The ornate bar, a conversation piece, was taken from a former speakeasy in Granville, N.Y. The menu suits hearty appetites, starring choice western grain-fed beef; with it come rice or potato and homebaked bread. Prime rib, New York or teriyaki sirloin, wood-grilled shrimp or Atlantic salmon, shrimp scampi, lobster and various combinations are among the choices. A section called "light entrées" offers the salad bar alone for $7.95 and things like petite grilled chicken or petite teriyaki sirloin. Mud pie, New York cheesecake and a variety of ice creams and frozen yogurts are dessert choices.

Routes 11 and 30, Manchester Center. (802) 362-2600. Entrées, $9.95 to $19.95. Dinner nightly, 5 to 10 or 11.

An Artistic Choice

The Artist's Palate Cafe. The kitchen here is run under the aegis of The Equinox resort, and the food is very good indeed. In good weather it's fun to lunch on the patio, overlooking the rolling lawns and sculpture garden. We opted for the Garden Room on the rainy Saturday we visited. Tables are covered with solid cloths in primary colors and napkins are contrasting, making for colorful place settings. The menu is attached to an artist's palette. One of us had the warm ham and cheese croissant, served with grilled apples and fruit salad; the other chose the crab and asparagus melt over a toasted English muffin with a load of fresh tomato chunks. Both were delicious. Other possibilities included soup of the day, garden salad, and entrées like seafood caesar salad (with smoked shrimp and scallops), poached salmon and vermicelli, and char-broiled sirloin burger.

Southern Vermont Art Center, West Road, Manchester. (802) 362-1405. Entrées, $7 to $9.50. Lunch, Tuesday-Saturday 11:30 to 3, Sunday noon to 3.

For Breakfast and Lunch

The Little Rooster Cafe. This nifty little breakfast and lunch spot along a commercial strip is an offshoot of the Chantecleer restaurant. Hub Poelmann, the chef, oversees a creative menu with lots of daily specials. The free-standing building has room for about a dozen light wood tables and the open kitchen is kept humming. For breakfast, "The Rooster" is an English muffin topped with Canadian bacon, creamed spinach and poached eggs, over which is a light mustard sauce with smoked salmon, capers and dill ($6.95). Belgian waffles are served, of course, with Vermont maple syrup and "The Ultimate Corned Beef Hash" is sautéed with potatoes, peppers, onions and rosemary and topped with two poached eggs and a light béchamel sauce. At lunchtime, dig into a grilled tuna niçoise salad, the Rooster Veggie (focaccia bread spread with Vermont goat cheese mousse, roasted peppers, grilled eggplant, tomatoes and watercress) or a leg of lamb sandwich, roasted with rosemary and served with garlic mayonnaise, watercress and tomatoes between focaccia bread. We thought the chicken salad plate was delicious.

Route 7A, Manchester Center. (802) 362-3496. Entrées, $7 to 9. Breakfast daily, 7 to 11:30; lunch, 11:30 to 2:30.

Village Fare. Folks rave about the breakfasts and lunches at this small storefront establishment down the street from The Equinox. Describing itself as a cafe, bakery and coffee house, it also serves Vermont beers and wine and it's a good place to pick up a terrific sandwich for takeout, although there are plenty of tables – and a couple of old green park benches out front – for eating there. On Saturday nights, there's live music.

Union Street, Manchester Village. (802) 362-2544. Open daily except Monday, 6 a.m. to 6 p.m., later on Saturdays when entertainment is scheduled.

Picnicking

Probably the most fun would be to tote your picnic to Lookout Point at the top of Mount Equinox on a clear day. If you don't have time for that, find a spot on the lawns of Hildene, or at Emerald Lake State Park. Or just drive up some glorious mountain road and find your own place. For provisions:

Al Ducci's Italian Pantry, Elm Street, Manchester, (802) 362-4449. Hard to find (off Highland Avenue, which is off Routes 11/30), this Italian deli offers good salads and sandwiches and welcomes call-in orders for takeout. Specialties include Italian meats and cheeses, homemade fresh mozzarella and Italian breads. You also can get pastas and raviolis for dinner. Open daily, 9 to 6.

Pampered Picnics, Manchester. (802) 362-5136. Patricia Houston will make a picnic for you and deliver it anywhere. Among the items she suggests are vegetable terrine, baked chèvre and basil tart, calamari salad, fruit and cheese plate, and sandwiches of mesquite turkey, curried chicken salad and grilled maple-glazed breast of chicken. All sound very good.

Village Fare (see above) also packs box lunches.

FOR MORE INFORMATION: Chamber of Commerce for Manchester and the Mountains, 2 Main St., R.R. 2, Box 3451, Manchester Center, VT 05255. (802) 362-2100.

4 ✿ Summer

Kinsman Range is on view from breakfast table at Bungay Jar B&B

A Notch Above
Franconia-Bethlehem, N.H.

Franconia Notch. Perhaps no name other than Mount Washington better conjures up the essence of the Granite State. Here, receding glaciers from the Ice Age cut an eight-mile-long swath between the Franconia and Kinsman mountain ranges. Their legacies of beauty and adventure have stirred visitors for two centuries.

The Flume, the Old Man of the Mountains, the Basin, Echo Lake, the Cannon Mountain aerial tramway – these are the best-known attractions of New Hampshire's best-known notch, which would be called a gap or a pass in other mountain regions. They make up Franconia Notch State Park, ranked among the nation's best parks by Money magazine.

Many tourists only pause to tour the Flume and get a distant look at the Old Man's profile etched in granite. Then they turn around and head back down south to join the hordes around Lake Winnipesaukee or North Conway.

Too bad. For beyond the notch is a different world, one of spectacular vistas, few people and fewer signs of contemporary civilization. This is the world epitomized by the words of poet Robert Frost: "Two roads diverged in a wood, and I – I took the one less traveled by, and that has made all the difference."

Frost and other literary notables were drawn by the serenity of small-town Franconia (population 800), so named because of its resemblance to the Franconia Alps in Germany. Grand summer hotels proliferated across the hillsides of Franconia and neighboring Sugar Hill in the 19th century. The nation's first ski school was established at Peckett's-on-Sugar Hill in 1929, and soon skiers were riding the nation's first aerial tramway lift to the top of Cannon.

Beyond Franconia and Sugar Hill lies Bethlehem, which claims to be the highest incorporated town east of the Rockies, though we know others that seem higher. Bethlehem occupies a mountain ridge 1,500 feet above sea level. Thousands of hay fever sufferers came here for its pollen-free air in the late 1800s; by the turn of the century the early resort village boasted four railroad stations and 30 hotels. Today it is billed as the nation's smallest town with two PGA-rated golf courses. Its low-key lifestyle has made it a favorite summering place for Hasidic Jews from the New York metropolitan area.

Gone today are the large hotels. The crowds and the condos stop at the south side of Franconia Notch, leaving Franconia, Sugar Hill, Bethlehem and even the "city" of Littleton for those who appreciate them as vestiges of the past.

Mountain scenery, rural and village life, peaceful inns, hiking and other outdoors activities – these are the attributes that draw folks north of the notch. So venture beyond. If you relish tranquillity, you'll be glad you did.

Getting There

The area is reached by I-93, which cuts through Franconia Notch via the scenic Franconia Notch Parkway, one of only two interstate parkways in the country.

Daily bus service to Littleton and Franconia is provided by Concord Trailways from Concord, Manchester and Boston.

Seeing and Doing

Arguably the most celebrated mountain gap in the East, Franconia Notch contains more scenic spots than any other in New Hampshire or Vermont.

Franconia Notch State Park

These 6,440 acres, the flagship of New Hampshire's state park system, are traversed by the magnificent **Franconia Notch Parkway,** a two-lane federal parkway linking four-lane portions of I-93 on either side of the notch. The parkway allows no stopping or left turns and parking only in designated areas, but it gives through visitors a brief glimpse of the treasures that lie on either side. Moose crossing signs warned of 195 collisions one year.

The Flume. When in Europe, see the cathedrals; when in Franconia, visit the Flume. Start at the $3.2 million **Flume Visitor Center** complex at the southern entrance to the park. Here you'll see a free fifteen-minute orientation movie that gives worthwhile background on the notch, which you learn was 400 million years in the making and still evolving. "Remember, when you see it today, it will never be quite the same again," the narrator intones. The visitor center contains historical displays, a cafeteria, a gift shop and, in front, a trout pond where fish leap for bread crumbs thrown by youngsters. Picnic groves are scattered around the center, as they are throughout the park. We picked some blackberries for dessert along the path from the parking lot to a picnic table not far from the car.

A bus shuttles visitors to within 1,500 feet of The Flume, a natural gorge extending nearly 800 feet along the flank of Mount Liberty. Granite walls rise 70 to 90 feet high. A boardwalk lets you look closely at the luxurious growth of flowers, mosses and ferns. A two-mile gravel nature walk displays waterfalls, glacial boulders, mountain vistas and two covered bridges. There are a few steep grades, and the walk takes about an hour.

Flume Service Road, off Route 3. (603) 745-8391. Daily 9 to 4:30, mid-May through October. Adults $6, children $3; combination with Cannon aerial tramway, $12 and $6.

The Basin, reached by a trail off Route 3 north of the Flume, is a granite pothole twenty feet across at the foot of a waterfall. Its sides have been smoothed by sand and small stones whirled around by the Pemigewasset River. Below the Basin is a rock formation called the Old Man's Foot.

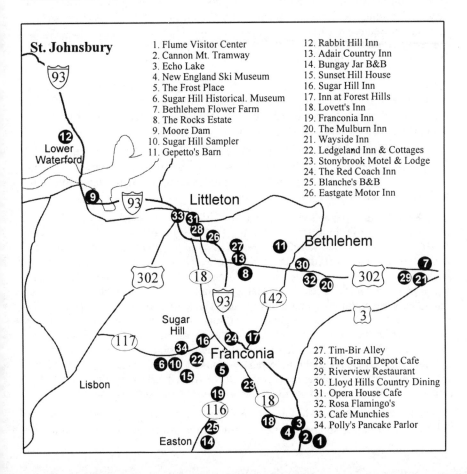

St. Johnsbury

1. Flume Visitor Center
2. Cannon Mt. Tramway
3. Echo Lake
4. New England Ski Museum
5. The Frost Place
6. Sugar Hill Historical. Museum
7. Bethlehem Flower Farm
8. The Rocks Estate
9. Moore Dam
10. Sugar Hill Sampler
11. Gepetto's Barn

12. Rabbit Hill Inn
13. Adair Country Inn
14. Bungay Jar B&B
15. Sunset Hill House
16. Sugar Hill Inn
17. Inn at Forest Hills
18. Lovett's Inn
19. Franconia Inn
20. The Mulburn Inn
21. Wayside Inn
22. Ledgeland Inn & Cottages
23. Stonybrook Motel & Lodge
24. The Red Coach Inn
25. Blanche's B&B
26. Eastgate Motor Inn

Lower Waterford

Littleton

Bethlehem

302   302

Sugar Hill

Franconia

117

Lisbon

Easton

27. Tim-Bir Alley
28. The Grand Depot Cafe
29. Riverview Restaurant
30. Lloyd Hills Country Dining
31. Opera House Cafe
32. Rosa Flamingo's
33. Cafe Munchies
34. Polly's Pancake Parlor

The Old Man of the Mountains, also called The Profile and The Great Stone Face, hovers 1,200 feet above Profile Lake. Yes, they look like an old man, these five granite ledges arranged horizontally to form a human profile and keeping vigil southward through the notch. The profile measures 40 feet from chin to forehead and is 25 feet wide. Though you can make out the profile for several seconds as you drive along the parkway, it is best viewed from parking areas on either side. Of course, no one is allowed near the Old Man but for its longtime caretaker. Directly below the Old Man and nicknamed the Old Man's Washbowl is **Profile Lake,** the headwaters of the Pemigewasset River and a favorite of fly fishermen.

Cannon Mountain Aerial Tramway. The state-of-the-art cable car replaces the nation's first, a smaller model born in 1938 and retired in 1979. It gives 80 passengers at a time a six-minute ride 2,022 feet up Cannon, a legend among skiers. The tram operator points out **Artists' Bluff** and the adjacent **Indian Head** that looks like the face on an old nickel, as well as such salient sights as **Mount Lafayette,** the highest peak (5,249 feet) in the Franconia range, which is second in height only to the Presidential Range. At the 4,160-foot summit are a cafeteria of the ski lodge variety and the well-maintained Rim Trail. The quarter-mile trail leads through spruce trees and along a ledge with a sheer drop to an observation platform yielding panoramic views in all directions. **Summit barbecues** are served on summer Saturdays from 4:30 to 7 p.m. (adults $7, children $5).
Foot of Cannon Mountain. (603) 823-5563. Daily 9 to 7 (to 7:30 Saturday) in summer, to 4:30 in late spring and through October. Adults $8, children $4.

Echo Lake, a sand and spruce-ringed beauty at the foot of Cannon Mountain, offers swimming, fishing and boating. There's a fine beach, plus grassy areas for picnicking. Canoes, kayaks, paddleboats and rowboats are rented for $10 an hour at the beach. Beach rates, $2.50; under 12 free.

Lafayette Place, just west of the parkway in the center of the park, (603) 823-9513, is the camping and hiking hub of the notch. A new lodge serves as a hiking information center, offering advice and guides to miles of hiking trails. The **Lafayette Campground** provides 97 wooded tent sites.

HIKING. Park officials recommend four hikes in particular for families and novices. A 1.5-mile loop from Cannon's Peabody Base Lodge goes to **Artists Bluff,** where artists used to set their easels to paint the notch, and on to the open summit of **Bald Mountain,** a great place to watch the sunset. Another 2.5-mile round trip rises from Lafayette Place to **Lonesome Lake,** an undeveloped alpine lake some 1,000 feet above. There, a lakeside trail leads to the Appalachian Mountain Club's hut at the lake's far end and passes an active beaver lodge. The 2,557-foot summit of **Mount Pemigewasset (Indian Head)** can be reached via a 1.4-mile trail from the Flume Visitor Center or the Indian Head Trail, which starts one mile south off Route 3. The views from the summit, both to the north and south, are awesome. The easiest and an often overlooked hike is a half-mile walk along the Basin-Cascades Trail beside Cascade Brook from the Basin to **Kinsman Falls.** The brook's basins and ledges make for a pleasant half-hour diversion.

BIKING. One of the little-known treasures of the park is a paved, eight-mile bikeway running from the Flume Visitor Center north to the Skookumchuk trailhead. The bikeway is reasonably level, which makes it popular with walkers as well. A concession at the Cannon Mountain parking lot rents mountain bikes.

Other Attractions

New England Ski Museum. Some of America's earliest skiers were introduced to the sport at nearby Peckett's-on-Sugar-Hill and at Cannon, so it is fitting that this small museum of historic ski equipment, clothing and photography occupies a lodge at Cannon's base. Founded in 1982, it recently mounted a milestone exhibit called "A Ski Museum Sampler," including "some of the more obscure aspects of collections not often exhibited." Obscure much of it was, but even non-skiers were impressed by the wall of old and rare skis built around the turn of the century and the antiquated ski boots that resemble the hiking boots of today. Of special interest were one of the chairs from the original single chairlift at Stowe and the old red car from the Mount Cranmore Skimobile, both of which we've ridden in our skiing days. Multi-projector slide shows, old ski films and push-button audio-visual kiosks trace the development of skiing in New England.

Next to the tram station at Cannon Mountain, Franconia. (603) 823-7177. Daily except Wednesday, noon to 5, late May to mid-October and late December through March. Free.

The Frost Place. The rooms where Robert Frost wrote many of his best-loved poems – and the sights that inspired him outside – are on view at the farmhouse in which he lived from 1915 to 1920 and in which he summered through 1938. The house remains essentially unchanged from the 1920s. Each summer a different visiting poet occupies most of it, writing new poems as Frost did and giving poetry readings in the old timbered barn. The front room and a rear barn are open with displays of Frost memorabilia, including his handwritten "Stopping by Woods on a Snowy Evening" and a rare, large photo of Frost at age 40 working at his desk in the room. Out back, plaques along a half-mile nature trail bear Frost's poems appropriate to the site; in two cases, the poems are on the locations where he wrote them. As if the poetry and setting weren't enough, the stand of woods happens to contain every variety of wildflower indigenous to northern New England.

Ridge Road off Route 116, Franconia. (603) 823-5510. Daily except Tuesday 1 to 5, July through Columbus Day; weekends 1 to 5, Memorial Day through June. Adults, $3; children, $1.25.

Sugar Hill Historical Museum. Established by proud descendants of Sugar Hill founders, this small place displays an excellent collection in a modern, uncluttered setting. It gives a feel for the uncommon history of a hilltop town, named for the sugar maples that still produce sap for syrup. The life of the community is chronicled in photographs and artifacts. The Cobleigh Room recreates a stage-coach tavern kitchen from nearby Lisbon. The Carriage Barn contains a working blacksmith's shop as well as mountain wagons and horse-drawn sleighs, including one from the Butternut estate that used to belong to actress Bette Davis.

Main Street (Route 117), Sugar Hill. (603) 823-8142. Thursday, Saturday and Sunday 1 to 4, July through mid-October. Adults, $1.

Bethlehem Flower Farm. Owners Joan and Bob Schafer grow more than 100 varieties of day lilies, with names like Ruffled Apricot, Luxury Lace and

Sombrero Way. They're at peak bloom during July and August; to purchase, pick those that you like and Joan will dig them straight from the fields. Also on the premises are a woodland walk that takes about twenty minutes, The Gift Barn and Abigail's Antiques, and Lily's Cafe where you may get ice cream or a light lunch.
Route 302 east, Bethlehem. (603) 869-3131. Daily, 10 to 6, mid-May to mid-October.

Golfing in Bethlehem

Picturesque but rather down-at-the-heels Bethlehem, astride a ridge at 1,500 feet above sea level, is the center of the area's golfing activity. The town is the smallest in New Hampshire to have two eighteen-hole courses, and the smallest in the country with two PGA-rated courses. The golf cart is the town's most popular summertime vehicle, locals say. The major presence is **Maplewood Casino & Country Club,** site of a grand hotel that burned (like most others around here) in 1963. The clubhouse occupies the hotel's activity building and casino, nicely restored in 1988. Basic golf-club lunches are served at the lounge, inside and out. The ball returns of what once was the bowling alley are still prominent in the long, narrow pro shop. Less of a presence than the Maplewood, but also eighteen holes, is the town-owned **Bethlehem Country Club** layout. Near the Maplewood along Route 302 is a quaint roadside haven that locals call the **Caddy Shrine,** erected by former Maplewood caddies and dedicated "to the traveler along this way."

Another summertime presence in Bethlehem are Hasidic Jews, who are much in evidence at a couple of old hotels in the center of town and in motels on the west side. Mainly from metropolitan New York and New Jersey, they come and go throughout July and August, relax on the lawns and walk along Main Street in their distinctive (and quite unsummery) attire. Otherwise Bethlehem, whose name was changed from Lloyd Hills on Christmas Day in 1779, has an interfaith Bethlehem Christian Center, a Catholic church, a Methodist church, an Episcopal chapel and a small Hebrew Congregation synagogue not used by the Hasidic visitors.

Picnicking and More

The Rocks Estate. Ice Age glaciers left rolling fields and boulders for stone walls on this 1,300-acre property west of town, donated in 1978 by the grandchildren of Chicago industrialist John Glessner, who summered here. Picnic areas, working woodlands, three miles of self-guided trails and a variety of entertainment and educational events can be enjoyed. This is one of more than 60 properties run by the Society for the Protection of New Hampshire Forests, which was organized to save Franconia Notch from runaway commercialism. Now a working Christmas tree, timber and maple syrup farm, it offers a one-mile woodland trail through fields and forests to an overlook onto Beaver Pond. A loop trail goes past Beaver Pond, and the return loop trail passes the Glessner children's playhouse and a bee house. Strollers and hikers give way to cross-country skiers in winter. The Rocks Christmas Tree Farm offers fresh-cut and cut-your-own trees and horse-drawn sleigh rides in December.
Glessner Road off Route 302, Bethlehem. (603) 444-6228 or (800) 639-1931. Daily, dawn to dusk. Free.

Moore Dam and Power Station. A power station may be an unusual site for a picnic, but New England's largest conventional hydroelectric station is situ-

Maplewood Casino & Country Club is a major presence in Bethlehem

ated beside the scenic Moore Reservoir created by a 178-foot-high dam across the Connecticut River between Littleton and Waterford, Vt. The station is the newest of New England Power's Fifteen-Mile Falls Development, a three-station project that has been producing electricity from the water created by the river's steep falls since 1926. A visitor center provides information on the generating stations and recreational facilities, including a number of nearby picnic and boat launching areas. One picnic area is on an island accessible by boat. Picnic tables out on a shady point of land near the visitor center offer considerable serenity along with water views. The largely undeveloped reservoir is frequented by osprey and bald eagles as well as the occasional powerboat, water skier and canoeist.

Off Route 18, Littleton. (603) 638-2106 or (888) 356-3663. Daily, 6 a.m. to 9:30 p.m.

Shopping

For some, the most intriguing shopping emporium hereabouts is the **Sugar Hill Sampler,** Route 117, Sugar Hill. The large dairy barn, with nooks and crannies full of New England items for souvenir shoppers, is literally a working museum of Sugar Hill history. Owner Barbara Serafini is the sixth-generation descendant of one of Sugar Hill's founders and delights in sharing her thoughts and possessions, even posting handwritten descriptions on the beams. Amid all the memorabilia is an interesting selection of quaint and unusual merchandise, from New Hampshire foods to Christmas decorations. Nearby in Sugar Hill is **Harman's Cheese and Country Store,** a tiny place selling "the world's greatest cheddar cheese" retail and through a large mail-order business. You'll also find pure maple syrup, great preserves, wildflower honey and tinned smoked salmon. Elegant and exquisite hardwood furniture is produced and on sale at **P.C. Anderson Handmade Furniture,** 253 Center District Road.

Antiquing is the main shopping attraction in Bethlehem, which calls itself **Antiques Alley North.** About a dozen shops are scattered along Main Street. Surrounding one unnamed house in the center of town was such a mishmash of junk, both inside and out, that only the intrepid would venture in. We know a couple who did and turned up some prizes amid others' trash. A better bet is **Checkered Past,** the area's only multi-dealer shop, a kaleidoscope of antiques and collectibles displayed in an 1820s barn off Old Bethlehem Road.

At **Gepetto's Barn,** retired writer and editor Winston Prescott Brebner, a.k.a. Gepetto, joyfully follows his hobby of woodworking. In his big red barn he crafts puzzles, toys, dollhouses, furniture and even a mobile of sailboats. Much of his production involves unfinished pine furniture, and all those Shaker step stools, sewing benches and spice cabinets beckon to artistic painters and stencilers. The barn is at the end of bumpy Blaney Road, off Brook Road, off Route 302, and is open daily from Memorial Day to Columbus Day. It's hard to find, but Gepetto pledges to visitors young and old that they will enjoy both the trip and the destination.

Littleton's Main Street has developed into an interesting shopping area, from the expanded **Village Bookstore** to **North Country Outfitters,** where store personnel give climbing lessons on a two-story "climbing wall" open to a rooftop skylight. The **Gale River Outlet,** relocated from Franconia, is an outlet for pretty cotton clothes (and stocks some of the things offered in the Garnet Hill catalog). **New Magoon's** is where you can find gourmet foods from Thai coconut milk to pappadams. **Duck Soup** is a good gift and kitchen shop, purveying everything from Christmas ornaments to coffee grinders. In the same Parker's Marketplace building are **The Elephant's Trunk** for clothing and **The Healthy Rhino** for everything that's good for you. You can try on funky clothing and look at antiques at **All That Jazz.** The new **Deacon's Bench Furniture** purveys beautiful home furnishings, accessories and gifts, and is known for its potpourri and scent items.

Stop at the highly touted **Bishop's Ice Cream Shoppe,** 183 Cottage St., for carrot cake ice cream (one scoop, $1.10), a banana split or a "Chill Out" T-shirt. There are those who think Bishop's homemade ice creams and frozen yogurts are the best anywhere.

Where to Stay

Accommodations range from rustic cabins to luxury lodges. Most of those detailed here fall into two categories: places preferred by couples and those that cater to families.

Sophisticated Inns and B&Bs

Rabbit Hill Inn. Just across the Connecticut River from Littleton, this very special "inn for romantics" is worth the short trip from Franconia or Bethlehem – indeed, from anywhere. Guest diaries in each of the 21 rooms are long on praise: "The inn of everyone's dreams." "Your love for this inn is reflected in every detail." "An opportunity to drink in a way of life that is relaxing, enveloping and most romantic." "I feel as if I've had 24 hours of heaven." And so on. The tributes please innkeepers John and Maureen Magee, who lavish TLC on their rooms and their guests. Consider our stay in Victoria's Chamber, where a fire was laid (this in August), Victorian magazines filled the shelves of the nightstands beside the canopied bed, and there were a settee for lounging, a bathroom full of amenities and a wicker-filled balcony just outside. Downstairs, iced tea, lemonade and cookies were available in the parlor, and drinks were served with conviviality in the Snooty Fox pub. Upon our return from dinner (see Where to Eat), a small stuffed heart had been hung on the door to use as a "do not disturb" sign and was ours to take home, the bed had been turned down, the radio was playing soft music, the lights were off and a candle was aglow, and more candles in hurricane chimneys beckoned from the balcony. And the handwritten letter of welcome from Maureen, personally tailored to every guest, thanked *us* for staying with them. Breakfast the next morning was up to the rest of the experience: a buffet of juices, breads and muffins, granola and hot strawberry oatmeal in a chafing dish, followed by a choice of wonderful banana-stuffed french toast or quiche lorraine with potatoes and mixed vegetables. Then we toddled off to see The Loft, the inn's newest "fantasy chamber" with fireplace and double jacuzzi – a companion to the Nest, the Tavern's Secret and the Turnabout in the Magees' testaments to the ultimate in luxury.

Lower Waterford, Vt. 05848. (802) 748-5168 or (800) 762-8669. Fax (802) 748-8342. Doubles, $189 to $239, MAP; fantasy chambers and suites, $269, MAP.

Adair Country Inn. A hilltop mansion on a 200-acre estate off Route 302 has been converted into a country inn and restaurant of great charm. Hardy Banfield, a former Portland (Me.) contractor, his wife Patricia and daughter Nancy offer seven large bedrooms (all with private baths and king or queensize beds) and two fireplaced suites in the house built in 1929 as a wedding gift for Dorothy Hogan Guider, who occupied it until her death in 1991. The Banfields named their rooms after nearby mountains, which is fitting considering their fabulous setting. Rooms are tastefully decorated and comfortable, particularly the Waterford in which we first stayed. The new Kinsman Suite offers a kingsize sleigh bed, a Vermont Castings stove, the biggest "double" jacuzzi we ever saw and a private rear balcony. Public areas include a spacious living room with several sitting areas, a couple of dining rooms (run as a restaurant by Tim-Bir Alley – see Where to Eat), a library on the stairway landing and a remarkable, all-granite (from walls to ceiling) basement tap room with TV/VCR, billiards table and bar with setups. The rear yard, landscaped by Frederick Law Olmsted, slopes down to a tennis court and a water garden beside a gazebo. The Banfields serve an elegant breakfast, starting with fresh berries, granola and popovers and wrapping up perhaps with eggs florentine or french toast. A personal welcoming note, iced tea and cookies, Woods & Windsor toiletries, automatic closet lights and tins of Les Citrons candies are other treats.

80 Guider Lane, Bethlehem 03574. (603) 444-2600 or (888) 444-2600. Fax (603) 444-4823. Doubles, $135 to $155; suites, $185 and $220 add $70 for MAP.

Bungay Jar Bed & Breakfast. The mountains of the Kinsman Range loom behind this exceptional B&B, hidden on eight wooded acres and named for the legendary wind that funnels from Mount Kinsman through the Easton Valley. Innkeeper Kate Kerivan and her lawyer-husband, Lee Strimbeck, built their place from a four-level, 18th-century barn that was dismantled and moved to the site in 1967. The hayloft became a two-story living room holding many sitting areas, a reading corner and a fireplace. Each of the three upper floors contains two guest rooms – the higher you go, the more remarkable the room and the more stunning the vista. The four on the top two floors have private baths, while two on the main floor share. Top of the line had been the Stargazer Suite, with a telescope aimed on the Kinsman Range. It has a kingsize bed beneath four skylights, an antique gas fireplace, a clawfoot tub under antique leaded-glass windows, a toilet behind a cloister table, and a twig loveseat and armchairs. In 1996 on the lower level, Kate added a Garden Suite with kingsize bed, gas fireplace, free-standing double jacuzzi, TV/VCR and small kitchen area, as well as a smaller room with queen bed and private bath. Both open through french doors onto private patios overlooking the rear gardens. Energetic Kate, a landscape architect, developed the showplace gardens around a lily pond, where she had a lotus flower blooming at our latest visit. She's also quite a cook, offering breakfasts with fresh fruit and edible flowers, popovers and perhaps zucchini quiche or french toast with crushed walnuts. She was planning to operate a greenhouse and run garden symposiums on the property, and was looking to add a duplex cottage with two more fireplaced guest rooms.

Easton Valley Road (Route 116), Franconia 03580. (603) 823-7775. Fax (603) 444-0100. Doubles, $60 to $100; suites, $105 and $120.

Sunset Hill House. Situated along a 1,700-foot-high ridge, this historic hotel has been transformed into an urbane country inn by Michael Coyle, a gregarious ex-Boston entrepreneur who's into good food, golf and romance. His spacious restaurant overlooking the mountain range provides the former. He took over the operation and upgraded the derelict Sunset Hill nine-hole golf course across the road. And he married a Sugar Hill woman in what by all reports was the most festive wedding among many the Sunset Hill House has seen. The restored hotel holds eighteen guest rooms, all but two small singles containing king or queen beds and private baths, plus two jacuzzi suites, with four more suites in the works. All have a simple but stylish, uncluttered look with Waverly prints and coordinated colors. We could see the sun both rise and set from the second-floor north corner bedroom with windows on three sides. The adjacent Hill House is more like a typical B&B with five bigger, quieter rooms and a family suite. Because of Sunset Hill's size and variety, "we can be a lot of things to a lot of people," says Michael, explaining how the inn can cater to both functions and the upscale couples market he seeks. There are three lovely fireplaced common rooms (one with TV), a restaurant and tavern (see Where to Eat), a pond on the golf course (for ice skating in winter) and a delightful swimming pool beside a wedding arbor framing Mount Lafayette and one of the best mountain views around. Rates include a full breakfast with juice, fresh fruit with yogurt and homemade granola, wonderful coffee cake and chocolate-chip scones and a choice of entrées, from a Cuban omelet to steak and eggs.

Sunset Hill Road, Sugar Hill 03585. (603) 823-5522 or (800) 786-4455. Fax (603) 823-5738. Doubles, $90 to $130; suites, $150. Two-night minimum on weekends.

Sugar Hill Inn. Built as a farmhouse in 1789, this old white inn has a wonderful wraparound porch sporting colorfully padded white wicker furniture and a telescope for viewing Cannon Mountain. Innkeepers Barbara and Jim Quinn have redecorated the ten inn rooms, all with private baths and full of country charm, from a hooked rug in the shape of a heart to tiny pillows shaped like ducks on most beds. Barbara did all the hand-stenciling, which even turned up on the wood rim of the bathroom mirror in the room in which we stayed. Lately, the Quinns have

updated the six cottage units in back, each with new baths and front porches, stenciling, plush carpeting and television sets. Four have gas fireplaces and king or queen beds. Guests enjoy two living rooms in the inn and a cozy pub with a small service bar. Dinner, previously served only to house guests at a single seating, has been opened to the public. Served by reservation from 5:30 to 8 in a country-pretty dining room, the four-course meal is available prix-fixe ($25) or à la carte (four choices from $14.95 for poached salmon supreme to $18.95 for roast duck or rack of lamb). The Quinns have been joined by their daughter and son-in-law, Kelly and Stephen Ritarossi, he a trained chef who teams with Jim in the kitchen. Their breakfasts are treats as well. We started with orange juice laced with strawberries, followed by blueberry muffins. Then came a choice of cinnamon french toast or swiss and cheddar cheese omelet, both excellent.
Route 117, Franconia 03580. (603) 823-5621 or (800) 548-4748. Fax (603) 823-5630. Doubles, $95 to $135, B&B; $145 to $185, MAP.

The Inn at Forest Hills. A personalized welcome letter with the history of their room greets guests at this secluded B&B, situated in an 1894 Tudor mansion that once housed the president of Franconia College. New owners Joanne and Gordon Haym undertook major refurbishing and continue to expend TLC. They offer eight guest rooms, six with private baths, and lots of comfy common areas in which to spread out: a lodge-style living room and a timbered lounge room, both with great fireplaces, a light and airy side sun room and a wide front porch upon which we observed one guest spending the afternoon with her laptop computer. The spacious Franklin Pierce room with a stunning red birch floor holds a kingsize bed and a sitting area with two sofas. The other main bedrooms have queensize beds and new or updated bathrooms. In their latest project, the Hayms created two large bedrooms out of three small rooms sharing a bath on the third floor. In their cheery dining room, they serve a five-course breakfast. The day of our visit it consisted of juice, granola, a warm spiced pear compote with vanilla ice cream, homemade date-walnut bread with cream cheese and raspberry french toast with New Hampshire maple syrup. After all that, you may be immobilized. So linger to watch the hummingbirds at all the feeders alongside the front porch.
Route 142, Box 783, Franconia 03580. (603) 823-9550 or (800) 280-9550. (Fax) 603) 823-8701. Doubles, $85 to $105.

Family Resorts and Motels

Lovett's Inn. Twenty scenic acres and Cannon Mountain are the backdrop for this venerable inn, which dates to 1794 and is listed in the National Register of Historic Places. Innkeepers Tony and Sharon Avrutine are maintaining the reputation built over 70 years by the Lovett family as they upgrade the facilities and decor and seek to attract families. The main house holds candlelit dining rooms (see Where to Eat), a lounge with mooseheads perched over a curved marble bar and a sunken sun porch with TV. Upstairs are six renovated guest rooms, four with private baths, canopy beds and antiques. Sharon thinks the nicest is a two-room suite with kingsize bed and a sitting room. We're partial to the sixteen units in seven cottages scattered beside the pool and around the lawns. Each has a wood-burning fireplace (which was especially welcome during a ski visit some years back) and a small patio with chairs for gazing upon Cannon Mountain. All come with sitting areas and small television sets. A full breakfast is served in the morning. In back, Sharon has opened the tiny Carriage House Gift Shoppe, and attracted a local following for her Lily Pulitzer fashions and upscale accessories.

Profile Road (Route 18), Franconia 03580. (603) 823-7761 or (800) 356-3802. Doubles, $115 to $156, MAP. Closed April to Memorial Day and mid-October to Christmas.

Franconia Inn. Situated amid 107 acres in the Easton valley with Cannon Mountain as a backdrop, this rambling white structure looks the way you think a country inn should look. It is the area's largest and busiest, and offers a variety of activities geared to families. Brothers Alec and Richard Morris have upgraded the 35 rooms, which vary in size and bed configuration. Some connect to become family suites, and all have private baths. Corner rooms are best in terms of size and view. The main floor has an attractive dining room where dinners are served to guests and the public (entrées, $14.95 to $19.95), a living room and oak-paneled library with fireplaces, a pool room, and a screened porch with wicker furniture overlooking a large swimming pool. Downstairs is the spacious **Rathskeller Lounge** with entertainment at night, a movie room, an arcade room with pinball machines and, beyond, a hot tub in a large redwood room. Outside are four tennis courts and a glider/biplane facility. Horses offer trail rides in season.

Easton Road, Franconia 03580. (603) 823-5542 or (800) 473-5299. Fax (603) 823-8078. Doubles, B&B, $93 to $113; suites, $133; MAP, $145 to $165; suites, $185. Closed April to mid-May.

The Mulburn Inn. Families are welcomed at this 1930 Tudor mansion, which once was part of the Woolworth family's summer retreat. It's operated by the Skeels family, who occupy the third floor and turn the rest of the very large house over to guests. The rambling second floor harbors seven large guest rooms with private baths. Rooms on either end have windows on three sides and queen or king beds; single beds and portacribs are available. The house retains its original oak staircases, stained-glass windows, rounded-corner architecture and an old elevator. The main floor contains a large, homey parlor and a gift shop. A huge glassed-in dining room, surrounded by porches, is big enough to feed an army. An enormous old stove at one end faces a stone fireplace at the other. In between are tables where guests are served a hearty breakfast. Outside are three acres of lawns and play equipment, giving plenty of space to spread out.

Main Street, Bethlehem 03574. (603) 869-3389 or (800) 457-9440. Doubles, $55 to $90.

Wayside Inn. This is a homey inn of the old school, nicely located alongside the banks of the Ammonoosuc River. Sixteen rooms in the rambling main building, nine with private bath and the rest rented as family suites, contain period furniture, twin or double beds and hardwood floors and trim. We prefer the newer motel out back, its twelve units on two floors having sliding doors onto private balconies beside the river. Decor is standard motel, although one second-floor end unit departs with a queensize bed, a sofabed and a Laura Ashley look that owner Kathe Hofmann likens to that of a city condo. The main inn also houses the **Riverview Restaurant** (see Where to Eat), a Victorian parlor, a second parlor with games and TV, plus a large lounge with TV. Outside are a swimming hole, a sandy beach, tennis court, and volleyball and basketball facilities.

Route 302 at Pierce Bridge, Box 480, Bethlehem 03574. (603) 869-3364 or (800) 448-9557. Doubles, $48 to $54.

Ledgeland Inn and Cottages. Here's the kind of place that folks return to year after year, thanks to Kay Whipple, proprietor for 50 years, who treats her guests as an extended family.. "Everybody calls me `Nana,'" says she. "I don't let young people call me Kay til they're 45." There are nine rooms with private baths in the main inn, originally a summer house that grew and grew and is open in summer and fall. Scattered across the rolling landscape with views of Cannon Mountain are several year-round cottages, most attached units with a maximum of four to a building. Eight are cottages for two, while five have two bedrooms each, a kitchen and a fireplace. A complimentary continental breakfast of homemade sticky buns, breads and such is offered buffet-style in the large dining room.
Route 117, RR 1, Box 94, Sugar Hill 03585. (603) 823-5341. Doubles, $60 to $80; cottages, $65 to $110.

Stonybrook Motel & Lodge. Nicely situated on eight landscaped acres beside Lafayette Book and beneath the Franconia Range, this is one of the area's more attractive motels. Jim and Karen Sweeney offer 23 rooms of varying sizes in the hand-timbered lodge and motel buildings. There are indoor and outdoor pools, a streamside picnic area with grills and a stocked trout pond. The lodge offers a fireplace and game room.
Route 18, Franconia 03580. (603) 823-8192 or (800) 722-3552. Fax (603) 823-8196. Doubles, $55 to $65.

The Red Coach Inn. This new motor inn, just above I-93, offers the most modern (and expensive) motel facilities in the area. The 60 rooms on two floors contain kingsize or two double beds, some with two-poster headboards and TVs hidden in armoires. Facilities include a large indoor pool, jacuzzi, sauna and exercise room. The **Coachmen Grille** serves three meals daily.
Wallace Hill Road, Box 729, Franconia 03580. (603) 823-7422 or (800) 262-2493. Fax (603) 823-5638. Doubles, $70 to $80; suites, $100.

An Arty House

Blanche's B&B. Colorful lupines are hand-painted on the front door of this simple but arty B&B, operated since 1986 by Brenda Shannon and John Vail, she an artist and he a carpenter. It was named for the family dog, who has since gone to her doggie reward. Brenda's business is Kinsman Ridge Designs, specializing in decorative paint finishes and distinctive floorcloths. Her talent is evident all through the house, from the moons and stars stenciled on the ceiling of the Sunflower Room to the pansies painted on the headboard of the bed in the Pansy Room. Lilacs are stenciled on the walls of the Lilac Room, and colorful trout float around the walls of an upstairs bathroom. Wild Rose on the first floor, the largest bedroom, has a velvet loveseat, a massive four-poster bed carved from black walnut by a grand-uncle and a tiny bathroom transformed from a closet (the other four bedrooms upstairs share two baths). Breakfast in the sunny dining room might consist of fresh fruit salad with maple yogurt, and blueberry pancakes, raised waffles or a soufflé. There are a parlor/library with a piano and lots of books, and a big lawn out back for enjoying the mountain air.
Easton Valley Road, Franconia. (603) 823-7061. Doubles, $65 to $95.

Extra Value

Eastgate Motor Inn. Up a hill not far off I-93 is this brick motel complex that started in the 1950s and grew to 55 units. Don't be deceived by the tiny room windows beside the entrances from the parking lot. The modern, well-kept rooms we saw opened to the rear with oversize windows and sliding doors onto attractive grounds. The pool and playground as well as the on-site restaurant and cocktail lounge make this a good choice for families. The large and elegant white-linened dining rooms offer an extensive menu, priced from $6.95 for fish and chips to $13.95 for shrimp dijonnaise. The prime rib dinner offered on weekends is an unbelievable $9.95. Rates include continental breakfast.

335 Cottage St. (Route 302), Littleton 03561. (603) 444-3971. Doubles, $47.70.

Where to Eat

Fine Dining

Tim-Bir Alley. For ten years, this little establishment named for its owners, Tim and Biruta Carr, was a culinary landmark in the basement of a building down an alley in downtown Littleton. In 1994, it moved to the main floor of Adair Country Inn. It's an elegant setting in which the Carrs continue to serve some of the most sophisticated and inventive food in the area. After optional BYOB cocktails with snacks served in the inn's basement Granite Tavern or outside on the flagstone terrace, patrons adjourn to the dining room for a meal to remember. Our latest began with fabulous chicken-almond wontons with coconut-curry sauce and delicate salmon pancakes on a roasted red pepper coulis. From the selection of six main courses on a menu that changes weekly, we enjoyed the breast of chicken with maple-balsamic glaze and plum-ginger puree and the pork tenderloin sauced with red wine, grilled leeks and smoked bacon. Follow this assertive fare with peach ricotta strudel with caramel sauce, chocolate-coconut bread pudding with roasted banana sauce or white-chocolate strawberry tart with mango puree. The well-chosen wine list is affordably priced.

Old Littleton Road, (in Adair Country Inn), Bethlehem. (603) 444-6142. Entrées, $13.75 to $16.95. Dinner by reservation, Wednesday-Sunday 5:30 to 9. No credit cards.

Rabbit Hill Inn. The pad of butter that accompanies the piping hot bread here is shaped like a rabbit. It's one of the trademark details that make dining at the Rabbit Hill Inn an event. Chef Russell Stannard's prix-fixe dinner menu brings five courses from soup to nuts. Consider one recent night's appetizer selections: the inn's own duck-cured prosciutto with sweet apple chips, tuna seviche and kumquats garnished with pickled papaya and baby greens, and grilled smoked chicken and fontina ravioli with pea-ginger-arugula pesto. At our autumn visit, a smooth pork and venison pâté and a zesty smoked salt cod with buckwheat polenta preceded a traditional caesar salad and an unusual layered taco salad. Kiwi sorbet with champagne cleared the palate for our main courses, marinated duck breast with raspberry sauce and grilled tenderloin on an eggplant-walnut pancake, each with exotic garnishes. Blueberry cheesecake and bread pudding with raspberry sauce capped a memorable meal. A harpist played, service was polished and the

ambiance serene. You don't really expect a lot of style in the North Country, but that's what you get here.
Lower Waterford, Vt. (802) 748-5168. Prix-fixe, $34. Dinner by reservation, nightly 6 to 8:45.

Sunset Hill House. Four elegant dining rooms seating a total of 100 are strung along the rear of this refurbished inn, their tall windows opening onto the Franconia, Kinsman and Presidential ranges. Innkeeper Michael Coyle, who managed a restaurant after graduating from college, knows the food and service business and has succeeded handsomely here. Chef Joe Peterson's contemporary fare and the staff's flawless service are the match for a mountain view unsurpassed in the area. We were delighted by starters of wild mushroom gratin and the unusual house salad tossed with a tequila-jalapeño dressing. Main courses included a superb roasted filet of beef with a lemon-spinach peanut sauce, served with shiitake mushrooms and roasted new potatoes, and a mixed grill of duck sausage, pork and lamb loin, slightly overcooked but redeemed by a cilantro pesto and served with wild rice. English trifle and bananas foster were sweet endings. An appealing tavern menu offers most of the dining-room appetizers and light fare, from nachos to baked Cuban pork sandwich and a couple of entrées in the $6 to $11 range.
Sunset Hill Road, Sugar Hill. (603) 823-5522. Dinner nightly, 5:30 to 9. Entrées, $15.50 to $21.50. Closed Monday and Tuesday in November and April.

The Grand Depot Cafe. The restored railroad depot was gutted in 1995 to become this handsome restaurant. The high-ceilinged dining room is dressed with white-clothed tables, tiny oil lamps and fine paintings, and the small lounge has an ornate gold mirror and quite a collection of hats around the bar. Without advertising, well-known local chef-owner Frederick Tilton attracted a following for his contemporary continental fare, ranging from chicken forestière to tournedos of beef crusted with five peppers and filet mignon served with braised lettuce and mushroom caps and finished with a roasted garlic and cognac demi-glace. Appetizers could be terrine of smoked Scottish and fresh Atlantic salmon or blackened carpaccio of barbary duck marinated in armagnac and fennel. Desserts include lime cheesecake and cappuccino silk pie. The blackboard menu appeals for lunch ($5 to $9): perhaps grilled lamb sandwich, seafood crêpes or grilled chicken caesar salad. Chef Rick is especially proud of the extensive wine list and the roster of single-malt scotches.
Cottage Street, Littleton. (603) 444-5303. Entrées, $14.95 to $21.95. Lunch, Monday-Saturday 11:30 to 2; dinner, Wednesday-Sunday 6 to 9.

Lovett's Inn. A little concrete fisherman sits with his pole at the end of the diving board over a pond formed by Lafayette Brook across the road. Illuminated at night, he attracts the curious to this inn's well-known restaurant, a fixture in the area since the days of Charlie Lovett. Before dinner, people usually gather around the curved marble bar (obtained from a Newport mansion) in the renovated lounge for socializing. Traditional, hearty New England fare is served in three beamed-ceilinged dining rooms. A plate of pâté with crackers, marinated herring and the chilled White Mountain wild blueberry soup make good starters. Salad, warm biscuits and assorted relishes accompany. Entrées might be panfried trout, poached salmon with dill sauce, veal marengo, sautéed chicken livers, curried lamb with Lovett's grape chutney, and broiled sirloin smothered with onions and mushrooms. The menu rarely changes, and emphasizes that the curries and sauces are "mild." Desserts are extravagant, from hot Indian pudding with ice cream to meringue glacé with strawberries. We remember fondly the chocolatey Aspen crud, a fixture on the menu, from more than two decades ago. There's a choice but select wine list, and a new children's menu.

Profile Road, Franconia. (603) 823-7761. Entrées, $13.50 to $17.50. Dinner nightly, 6 to 8.

A Budget Choice

Riverview Restaurant. The place to eat here is on the enclosed porch opening off the dining room onto lovely gardens beside the Ammonoosuc River. Tables covered with red and white checked cloths and oil lamps are the setting for chef-owner Victor Hofmann's American and Swiss fare. His extensive menu mixes shrimp and scallops California (with vermouth and green grapes), chicken oriental, lamb forestière, wiener schnitzel and pork Victor, the chef's favorite, doused with wild mushrooms. Most are under $13.

Route 302, Bethlehem. (603) 869-3364. Entrées, $8.50 to $14.95. Dinner, Tuesday-Sunday 6 to 9.

Casual Eating

Lloyd Hills Country Dining. Borrowing the original name of the town, Bill and Dianna Green have created a rustic restaurant and bar that's highly regarded locally. "We're known for our specials," says Bill, pointing to a scrapbook full of literally hundreds of variations on a theme. There are twenty kinds of eggs benedict ($4.95), for instance, and a couple of pages devoted to potato skins. "We try to keep it fun," explains Bill. That they do, from late breakfast through dinner. Skillet specials topped with two eggs are favored in the morning. At night try the shrimp New Orleans, pork chops calvados, chicken chasseur or beef brochette from the printed menu, or perhaps the seafood riviera special (shrimp, scallops and crab in garlic cream sauce over linguini). Ample portions at reasonable prices are the rule here.

Main Street, Bethlehem. (603) 869-2141. Entrées, $11.95 to $16.95. Breakfast and lunch, Monday-Friday 11 to 2, weekends 8 to 2; dinner nightly, 5 to 9.

Opera House Cafe. Down a side alley, this tiny cafe occupies the space where Tim-Bir Alley got its start. Steve Bromley, who had been chef-owner of the nearby Ammonoosuc Inn, took it over in 1996 and drew on the restored Littleton Opera House for its theme. He dressed up the interior with red brocade swags around the windows and green and pink walls that look like wallpaper but turn out to have been handpainted by artist Brenda Shannon of Blanche's B&B. Twenty-five hungry people can crowd in for lunch or dinner. The menu follows a cutesy opera motif, as in the "standing ovation" sandwich of roast beef and smoked turkey in a flour tortilla, as opposed to the "phantom of the opera" with almost the same ingredients baked open-faced on homemade bread, both served with homefries or rice salad. Fortunately, the food measures up, and we heard nothing but raves for the snacky appetizers, burgers, stir-fries and vegetarian items, pleasantly priced in the $3.95 to $5.95 range. "Star performers" at night range from baked haddock to steak topped with shrimp, scallops and béarnaise sauce. Shrimp scampi, chicken oscar and filet mignon are among the possibilities. Desserts continue to be a strong point in this sweet little space. Expect treats like sacher torte, black forest cake and a pear-port tart.

28 Main St., Littleton. (603) 444-0986. Entrées, $11.95 to $15.95. Lunch, Tuesday-Saturday 11 to 2:30; dinner, Wednesday-Sunday 5 to 9.

Rosa Flamingo's. This is not the Mexican eatery that one of us expected, but rather an Italian-American restaurant in a contemporary gray wood building with dining on the main floor, a bar below and a wraparound outdoor deck. The menu is large and varied to attract families and the younger set. We can vouch for the tortellini carbonara (a house specialty) and the chicken with garlic and artichoke hearts, both $9.95 and both of which lived up to their advance billing from a local innkeeper. The rest of the extensive dinner menu ranges from manicotti and baked ziti to steak and scampi. Pizzas, nachos and sandwiches are among the possibilities. Burgers and sandwiches in the $4 to $5 range are available at lunch.

Main Street, Bethlehem. (603) 869-3111. Entrées, $6.25 to $16.95. Lunch daily, 11:30 to 4; dinner, 5 to 10; light fare, 11:30 to 11.

A 'True' Place

Polly's Pancake Parlor. Only in a "true" place like Sugar Hill would a pancake house be a restaurant of note. Folks pour in at all hours from all over to partake of pancakes and local color at this institution founded in 1938. Bare tables sport red mats shaped like maple leaves. Red kitchen chairs and sheet music pasted to the ceiling add color to the 1820 building, once a carriage shed. Its most appealing feature is big louvered windows with a view of Mount Lafayette and the Franconia Range. Watch the pancakes being made in the open kitchen; the batter is poured from a contraption that ensures they measure exactly three inches. Pancakes are served with maple syrup, granulated maple sugar and maple spread; an order of six costs $4.60 for pancakes made with buckwheat, whole wheat cornmeal or oatmeal-buttermilk. All are available with blueberries, walnuts or coconut for $5.80. If you don't really crave pancakes in the middle of the day, try the homemade soups, quiche of the day (our ham and cheddar melted in the mouth) or a super-good BLT made with cob-smoked bacon. Eggs, muffins made with pancake batter, baked beans sweetened with syrup, salad plates and sandwiches are available. The homemade pies are outstanding. The coffee, made with spring water, is excellent and a glass of the spring water really hits the spot (no liquor is served). The shop at the entry sells pancake packs, maple syrup and sugar, jams and even the signature maple-leaf painted wooden plates.

Hildex Maple Sugar Farm, Route 117, Sugar Hill. (603) 823-5575. Open daily 7 to 3, weekends to 7, mid-May to mid-October; weekends only 7 to 2, April to mid-May and late October.

FOR MORE INFORMATION: Franconia Notch Chamber of Commerce, Box 780, Franconia 03580, (603) 823-5661 or (800) 237-9007.

5 ✸ Summer

Mystic Seaport Photo

Sailing vessels and historic structures draw visitors to Mystic Seaport.

A Whale of a Family Weekend
Southeast Connecticut: Mystic to Misquamicut

Looking for a place to keep the youngsters amused and expand your own horizons? Perhaps a place that Grandma and Grandpa or visiting Aunt Tillie from Peoria would enjoy as well?

This area is for you – the perfect summer spot for the young and young at heart, with enough diversions to keep the entire family amused all weekend or longer.

Here is New England-by-the-sea. It's a place for beaching and boating, but also a place for rediscovering and reliving our early seafaring days. From the mid-1600s to the battles of the Revolution, from the whaling and shipbuilding eras to the early submarines and nuclear Tridents, this is maritime country with all its trappings.

Nowhere else in this country are so many varieties of maritime interests evident. Many are wrapped up in one appealing package at Mystic Seaport, the nation's premier maritime museum and long one of the area's leading tourist attractions. But it's not the only attraction.

To the west is Groton, "Submarine Capital of the World." The huge U.S. Naval Submarine Base keeps alive a tradition dating from before the Revolution, when the colonies launched the first naval expeditions here. Beneath old Fort Griswold, site of the bloody Revolutionary massacre where the traitor Benedict Arnold did

Groton in, the Electric Boat Division of General Dynamics became famous as builder of the nation's nuclear subs.

Maritime history also hides behind the bustling facade of New London, the area's largest city. The U.S. Coast Guard Academy takes full advantage of its site along the Thames River – pronounced locally "Thames," not "Tems," despite the city founders' ties with old London.

Attracting those of a different persuasion are two of the nation's largest and most profitable casinos. The Mashantucket Pequot Indians' new Foxwoods Resort and Casino in rural Ledyard proved so successful that a neighboring tribe opened the Mohegan Sun Casino and entertainment complex in 1996. Meanwhile, zoning approvals were being sought for a Six Flags Theme Park in North Stonington, and a domed theme park was proposed for the Groton area.

East of Mystic along the shore, the pace is considerably quieter and the signs of tourism, if any, are different. Twentieth-century life has almost passed by the coastal "borough" of Stonington, an old fishing village with Connecticut's last commercial fleet. It's still living a history that helps put Mystic Seaport into perspective.

Across the Rhode Island line, Long Island Sound opens into the Atlantic at Watch Hill, a fabled seaside society resort of the Newport-Bar Harbor ilk. Just beyond are the beaches at Misquamicut, where surf and sand are everything. This is a mecca for sun-worshipers and kids, young and old.

The whole maritime strip from New London to Weekapaug is no more than 30 miles long, but there's plenty to appeal to every taste and age.

See the seaport, submarines and shore. Bet you didn't know there was so much to Southern New England's maritime heritage.

Getting There

The area is easily accessible. Interstate 95 from New York to Boston cuts through the region a few miles inland and coastal Route 1 hugs the shore.

Train service is excellent, with frequent Amtrak runs from New York and Boston stopping at Mystic, New London and Westerly, R.I. Greyhound buses stop at all three towns as well. US Airlines and charter airlines serve the Groton-New London Airport.

In the summer, a trolley links Mystic's tourist attractions with motels and businesses. Price per boarding is $2; all-day pass, $5.

Seeing and Doing

The focal point for most tourists is Mystic, so that's where we'll start – with the caveat that some of the area's best features are in the twin cities of Groton-New London and in the shore towns toward the Rhode Island beaches.

Mystic

Mystic's ties with the water are epitomized by its unusual bascule bridge. Where else would busy Main Street traffic stop every hour as a 70-year-old drawbridge lifts for waiting yachts and sailboats on the Mystic River?

A diorama at the seaport shows how Mystic looked in the mid-1800s when it built more ships than any other town in America. The gleaming white homes of 18th- and 19th-century sailing captains still line the river shore across from Mystic Seaport.

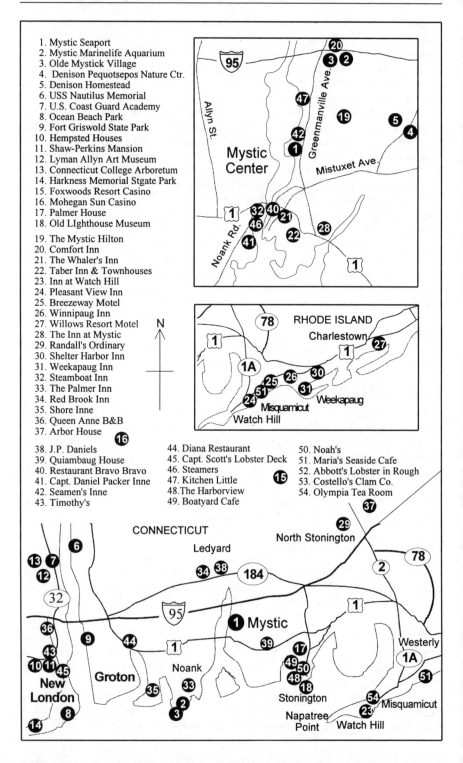

Mystic Seaport. Plan on at least half a day to visit this seventeen-acre riverfront complex of ships and sailing memorabilia in a restored 19th-century coastal village. The old Greenman family shipyard, which launched nearly 100 vessels between 1838 and 1878, became a one-building exhibit in 1929. Now more than 40 shops, homes, work buildings and the Henry B. DuPont Preservation Shipyard give an authentic taste of the lure, the lore and the life of the sea. You can visit the old bank, chapel and newspaper office, watch shipbuilders and craftsmen at work, view early gardens, clamber aboard three sailing vessels, see a planetarium show and play a role in the fun participatory show called "Fishtory." The permanent exhibit in the Stillman Building, "New England and the Sea," is the museum's largest and most comprehensive, representing a successful effort to put the seaport's 60 other exhibits into historical context. Don't miss it or the Charles W. Morgan, the last of the nation's 19th-century wooden whalers and a National Historic Landmark. This is a low-key place where craftsmen answer questions and exhibit interpreters at major sites spin their tales; in between, you wander at will.

Sailors love the seaport and can spend hours in each building. For others, all the exhibits and boats may start to overwhelm after half a day, but there's plenty more: the Seamen's Inne for food and drink, the steamboat Sabino for river excursions, a boathouse for boat rides and rentals, and the vast Mystic Seaport Museum Stores for gifts, contemporary marine art and a book shop with the best commercial collection of maritime volumes around.

50 Greenmanville Ave. (Route 27), Mystic. (860) 572-0711. Daily, 9 to 6 in July and August, 9 to 5 in spring and fall, 10 to 4 in winter. Adults $16, children $8.

Mystic Marinelife Aquarium. An institution with a mission (educational and scientific), this place is big on numbers – like the 750,000 visitors who make the expanding facility Connecticut's single most popular tourist attraction (after the new Foxwoods and Mohegan Sun casinos), or the more than 6,000 specimens in its 49 aquariums. Two sea lions greet visitors outside the gray monolith just a gull's glide from I-95. Inside, the main level contains "themed" New England, tropical and Pacific coast communities, with everything from Atlantic salmon and a rare blue lobster to sharks, a 25-pound Pacific octopus and a 175-pound jewfish. Alone worth the price of admission are the hourly demonstrations upstairs in the 1,400-seat marine theater, where Skipper, a 500-pound sea lion, joins dolphins and beluga whales in marvelously entertaining shows. On your way out, a marsh pond features a variety of waterfowl, and the indoor-outdoor Seal Island allows closeup looks at seals and sea lions in a variety of habitats. The new Penguin Pavilion is the outdoor home of adorable African black-footed penguins. Beyond is the site of the aquarium's $50 million expansion program started in 1996 and funded partly by the Mashantucket Pequot tribe. The expansion will produce a one-acre Alaskan coast habitat featuring the world's largest beluga whale exhibit, a new Aquatic Animal Study Center and a state-of-the-art home for renowned ocean explorer Robert D. Ballard's Institute for Exploration, where giant video screens will take visitors on a simulated sea-exploring adventure.

55 Coogan Blvd. off Route 27 at I-95, Mystic. (860) 572-5955. Daily, 9 to 7 in summer, to 5 rest of year. Adults $9.50, children $6.50.

Olde Mystick Village. Seldom is a shopping center a tourist attraction, but this one is. Opened in 1973, it's a collection of more than 60 shops, restaurants and

services in a well-landscaped setting like that of an old New England village. Sunday services are conducted in the Meeting House, now St. Alban's Anglican Church. Music from its carillon lends a happy air, and youngsters love to feed the ducks in a pond beside the water wheel. The old buildings and landscaped grounds are as appealing as what's inside; the kids and Dad can stroll while Mom shops.
Route 27 at I-95, Mystic. Monday-Saturday 10 to 6, to 8 in summer, Sunday noon to 5.

Denison Pequotsepos Nature Center. Here's a change of pace: 125 acres of wildlife sanctuary and peace with seven miles of self-guiding trails, including the Four Seasons trail for the blind (with handrails, guide-ropes and taped signs in English and Braille). Near the entrance, a tree grows from a huge solid rock; red-tailed hawks and owls live in large outdoor aviaries. A sign explains one of the many stone walls winding through the sanctuary (be on the lookout in this area for the thousands of miles of stone walls made by pioneer farmers near the sea as a windbreak to prevent farmland from disappearing and to keep cattle out of the crops – the sign here tells that they also were a way to dispose of all the rocks removed from the soil).
Route 27 at I-95, Mystic. (860) 536-1216. Tuesday-Saturday 9 to 5, Sunday noon to 5; closed Sunday in winter. Adults $3, children $1.

Denison Homestead. Just down the road from the nature center is this 1717 home, authentically furnished with heirlooms from eleven generations of Denisons. The wildlife sanctuary was the bulk of a land grant given to Capt. George Denison in 1654 by the King of England; the homestead was the working farm for the family, who saved their possessions in the attic and barn. Billed as the only New England home restored in the style of five eras, it has a Colonial kitchen with fireplace, a Revolutionary era bedroom with four-poster bed, a Federal parlor, a Civil War bedroom with ornate franklin stove and an early 1900 living room with fine Dutch china.
Pequotsepos Road, Mystic. (860) 536-9248. Wednesday-Monday 1 to 5, mid-May to mid-October. Adults $3, children $1.

BOAT TRIPS. The 1908 **S.S. Sabino,** (860) 572-5351, the last coal-fired steamboat in New England, takes 100 Seaport visitors from Mystic Seaport on leisurely half-hour summer cruises up and down the Mystic River every hour on the hour from 11 to 4 (adults $3,50, children $2.50). Even better are the 90-minute cruises at 5 (also Friday and Saturday at 7) out past Noank and Mason's Island toward Fishers Island; on the way you see some striking homes (adults $8.50, children $7).

Longer excursions on Long Island Sound are offered out of Mystic by **Voyager Cruises,** (860) 536-0416, and the **Mystic Whaler,** (800) 697-8420. **Project Oceanology,** Avery Point, Groton, (860) 445-9007, offers instructive oceanographic expeditions on board its EnviroLab research vessels, twice daily in summer.

You can see submarines by boat via **Thames River Cruises,** City Pier, New London. (860) 444-7827. The 49-passenger launch makes nine trips daily, hourly 9 to 5, June-September. Adults $10, children $6.

Groton-New London

Submarines and history vie for the visitor's attention in these bustling towns linked by the dual, ten-lane Gold Star suspension bridge.

USS Nautilus Memorial/Submarine Force Library and Museum. The submarine base, the Western Hemisphere's largest, is visible from much of New London on the east bank of the Thames in Groton. At the entrance to the tight-security installation is the Nautilus, the world's first nuclear-powered sub, the first ship to go to the North pole and the first submarine to journey 20,000 leagues under the sea. It was built nearby in Groton's Electric Boat Division shipyard. The submarine museum traces the history of underwater navigation, showing a sub-marine control room, three working periscopes and model subs. The highlight for most is a tour of portions of the 519-foot-long Nautilus. The visitor is guided by a free audio wand that explains the torpedo and sonar rooms, the control and navi-gation rooms, the crew's living quarters, galley and other spaces.
U.S. Naval Submarine Base, Route 12, Groton. (860) 449-3174. Daily 9 to 5, Tuesday 1 to 5, mid-May through October; 9 to 4 and closed Tuesday rest of year. Closed first full week of May and last full week of October. Free.

U.S. Coast Guard Academy. Founded in 1876, the academy trains 1,000 cadets, male and female, at its striking red brick campus on the west bank of the Thames, across the road from the gray stone buildings of Connecticut College, a private liberal-arts institution. The grounds are open to the public; a guard at the gate issues each car a visitor's permit. A visitor pavilion and museum has displays and a multi-media show on cadet life; open daily 10 to 5, May-October, free. The 295-foot training barque **Eagle** may be boarded when in port on weekends from noon to 5. The cadet corps passes in review most Fridays at 4 in spring and fall.
Mohegan Avenue (Route 32), New London. (860) 444-8270. Grounds open 9 to sunset.

Ocean Beach Park. Kids especially like this city-owned property "dedicated to summer fun." It has a good sand beach with smaller waves than the Rhode Island beaches, an Olympic-size saltwater pool that was used for the Special Olym-pics World Games in 1995, a new bathhouse and changing area, a triple water slide, a curving boardwalk flanked by an amusement arcade, concessions and a midway with kiddie rides and bumper cars. Ocean Beach has seen better days, but it's pleasant when not crowded; nights and weekends get hectic.
Ocean Avenue, New London. (860) 447-3031. Daily, 9 a.m. to 10 p.m., Memorial Day to Labor Day. Adults $2, children $1; parking $2 an hour.

Fort Griswold State Park. The 135-foot-high obelisk commemorates one of the bloodiest battles of the American Revolution, the 1781 massacre of 67 Colo-nists by British troops under turncoat Benedict Arnold. It provides a great view of the waterfront. At its base is a free DAR museum with historic displays and down-hill is the 1750 **Ebenezer Avery House,** a center-chimney Colonial with period furnishings open summer weekends from 1 to 5, free. The remains of the fort are fun to explore; kids climb the embankments and prowl through a curving tunnel and brick storeroom.
Monument Street and Park Avenue, Groton Heights. (860) 445-1729. Park daily 8 to dusk, year-round; monument and museum, daily 9 to 5 May 30 to Labor Day, weekends to Columbus Day. Free.

Hempsted Houses. The Joshua Hempsted House (1678), the oldest house in New London and one of the oldest in Connecticut, re-creates the color and atmo-sphere of the Pilgrim era. The detailed diary kept by the son of the builder helped

the Antiquarian & Landmarks Society of Connecticut furnish the house authentically. The colorful stained-glass casement windows, the fine pewter and the exceptional furnishings, including a primitive baby walker and folding bed, are treasures. In front, the rough stone Nathaniel Hempsted House built during the 1750s
has seven rooms furnished to the period.

*11 Hempstead St., New London. (860) 443-7949. Thursday-Sunday noon to 4, mid-
May to mid-October. Adults $4, children $1.*

Shaw-Perkins Mansion. Looking quite Southern with its pillars, veranda
and wrought iron, this stone house was Connecticut's Naval Office during the
Revolution – the cradle of the American Navy and headquarters for George Washington on several visits. The paneled cement fireplace walls, oil portraits and books
and documents are of interest. Visitors can see the differences a century made
between the Hempsted and Shaw houses.

*305 Bank St., New London. (860) 443-1209. Wednesday-Friday 1 to 4, Saturday 10 to
4, April-October. Adults $3, children $1.*

Lyman Allyn Art Museum. A room full of Indian artifacts and a collection
of dollhouse furniture and toys delight children here. The outstanding collection
of Lilliputian furniture and decorative arts is displayed in room-size cases on the
lower level of this beautiful museum founded in 1932. Part of the Connecticut
Impressionist Art Trail, the museum has Egyptian, Roman, Greek, Medieval and
Renaissance items, and changing exhibitions are mounted in four galleries. The
Primitive Gallery with native art from the South Pacific "scares the wits out of
kids, but they love it!" says a staff member. The gift shop is unusual in that it sells
antique silver and other collectible small antiques, not reproductions. 625 Williams St., New London, (860) 443-2545.

*625 Williams St., New London. (860) 443-2545. Tuesday-Saturday 10 to 5, Sunday 1
to 5, July to Labor Day; rest of year, Tuesday-Sunday 1 to 5, Adults $3.*

Connecticut College Arboretum. The magnificent mountain laurel display
in June is appropriate since it's the state flower. Visitors can explore the 415-acre
area via a marked trail that is about three-quarters of a mile long. The staff suggests you allow an hour or more to observe the 300 varieties of native shrubs and
trees. Children enjoy the pond area and a good portion of the trail leads along its
edge. This provides a cool, verdant interlude on a hot summer day.

Williams Street, New London. (860) 439-2140. Daily dawn to dusk. Free.

Harkness Memorial State Park. The 42-room Harkness Mansion, an Ital-
ian-style villa that has been closed for renovations, and its surrounding 231 acres
along Long Island Sound are a quiet refuge for beachcombers, picnickers and
garden enthusiasts. Beatrix Farrand, garden architect for the rich and famous, designed the extravagant plantings in the restored gardens around the mansion called
Eolia. The solitude is broken by evening concerts in the acclaimed **Summer Music at Harkness** series, headquartered in a white sail-like tent that's acoustically
excellent. Peter Sacco, founder of the festival in 1984, conducts the Connecticut
Symphony Orchestra in what has become the largest summer classical music festival in the state. Come early for a picnic supper (a catered $12 buffet is available
but you must reserve) on the grounds beside the Sound. Then settle in for one of

Gary J. Thibeault Photo

Foxwoods Resort Casino looms above forest in rural Ledyard.

the midweek or Saturday evening performances – including one year a pops concert, Ray Charles, Leon Fleisher and, our happy choice, the Empire Brass. Harkness ranks right up with the Tanglewood experience and is less crowded.

275 Great Neck Road (Route 213), Waterford. (860) 443-5725. Grounds open daily, 8 a.m. to dusk. Admission, $8 per vehicle on weekends, $5 weekdays, Memorial Day to Labor Day; free, rest of year. Festival lawn tickets generally $16, tent tickets, $21 to $28.

The Casinos

The burgeoning resort casinos have quickly become such an economic presence – not to mention tourist attraction – in this area that they rate a mention here. Both casinos have been done with style and taste, and each attracts thousands of players daily. Their locations are a bit away from the mainstream, although residents fear the spillover could affect the rest of the area.

More development is on the horizon with the first **Six Flags Theme Park** in New England, planned for a site along I-95 at Exit 92 in North Stonington, and a domed **Fun-Plex America Theme Park,** a futuristic family entertainment complex near Exit 88 off I-95 in Groton. Both hoped to be open – in their early phases, at least – by 1998.

Foxwoods Resort Casino. Built in 1992 on Indian lands by the Mashantucket Pequot Tribal Nation, this was the first casino in New England and quickly became the largest in the world. The massive casino with its skyscraper hotel rising out of the rural woods presents quite a sight for the first-time visitor – "gaming in its natural state," the casino bills it. Up to 40,000 people a day are attracted to its 5,500 slot machines, roulette wheels, bingo tables and the like. Name entertainers attract hundreds more, Las Vegas style. The casino's interior seems bigger than huge, but it's bright, airy and suavely done in contemporary pastel colors. It looks more like an urbane hotel, perhaps, than the expected casino and we, who have seen many, have never seen one as pleasant as this. There's even a smoke-free casino. The original low-rise Two Trees Inn with 280 rooms was dwarfed by a eight-story, 312-room casino hotel, and that was small potatoes next to the seventeen-story hotel and conference center opening in phases in 1997. The 900 rooms give it the largest number of hotel rooms under one roof in New England, and a rooftop lounge and observation deck offer views across Long Island Sound. A brief look at the history of the Mashantucket Pequots, many of whom have become millionaires thanks to Foxwoods, can be found in the basement exhibit space below the casino's waterfall. That is, until the Pequots' $130 million museum and research center is ready in 1998.

Route 2, Ledyard. (860) 885-3000 or (800) 369-9663. Open daily, 24 hours.

Mohegan Sun Casino. Upon opening in late 1996, this became the second-largest and most expensive casino ever built in the United States (after the MGM Grand in Las Vegas, and bigger than Foxwoods when it opened, thanks to backing by Sol Kerzner, the man behind Sun City in South Africa and ten other casinos world-wide). Compared with Foxwoods, which hides in the woods out in the middle of nowhere less than ten miles away, the Mohegan tribe's casino seems more urban. The 240-acre complex looks not unlike a shopping mall with its vast parking lots, five-story parking garage, one-way service roads and a four-lane access highway connecting directly with Route 2A and Interstate 395. The Mohegan differs from Foxwoods because its gaming is all in one large circular room and because of its obvious emphasis on Indian design, tradition and imagery. Besides upwards of 3,000 slots and related paraphernalia, the building holds a giant food court, three restaurants, several cocktail lounges, a large nightclub and even a day-care center. But no hotels – yet.

Mohegan Sun Boulevard (off Route 2A), Uncasville. (860) 646-5682 or (888) 226-7711. Open daily, 24 hours.

Shore Towns and Beaches

Very different from the bustling cities and tourist centers are the coastal villages around Mystic and the beaches in Rhode Island.

Noank is a quaint fishing village and arts colony, so untouched by the surrounding tourism that most hardly realize its presence. We like it for Abbott's Lobster Pound and the nice public beach and picnic area nearby at Esker Point (no surf, but uncrowded and one of the pitifully few public places where you can get to the water along the Connecticut shore). To the east, Stonington is our favorite coastal village in Connecticut.

The Rhode Island shore from Watch Hill to Weekapaug harbors excellent beaches and rolling surf from the open Atlantic.

STONINGTON. "Take a walk," advises the historical society's guide to this charming seaside community. And walking is the best way to see and savor this living anachronism jutting into the Atlantic. Connecticut's oldest borough has been cut off from the mainstream by a railroad track spanned by a viaduct. The two main roads through the borough are narrow; they and their cross streets are crammed with history dating back to 1649. Sea captains sailed the Seven Seas from Stonington, which became known as the "Nursery of Seamen." Around 1800, this was Connecticut's most populated town and the Wadawanuck Hotel could sleep

1,300 guests – that's long-gone and the only accommodations now are at a couple of small guest houses. The last commercial fishing fleet in Connecticut is manned by the resident Portuguese community, which stages a Blessing of the Fleet festival annually in late July.

The Stonington Historical Society, founded in 1910 and one of the first around, has marked with signs many structures from the 18th and 19th centuries. One is the 1780 Col. Amos Palmer House at Main and Wall, where artist James McNeil Whistler once lived; it was later the home of poet Stephen Vincent Benet and since was occupied by his granddaughter. On Harmony Street is the 1786 Peleg Brown House, birthplace of Capt. Nathaniel Palmer, who at age 22 discovered Antarctica. The appeal of the old houses is enhanced by all the garden courtyards and glimpses of the harbor with its fishing trawlers. On Cannon Square are two "18-pounders" that repulsed the British in the War of 1812; beside the square, the old Ocean Bank is a replica of the Athenian Treasury at Delphi, Greece. From Stonington Point you can see across Long Island Sound to Fishers Island, N.Y., and east to Watch Hill, R.I.

Palmer House. The majestic, sixteen-room Victorian mansion that Capt. Nathanial Palmer and his seafaring brother Alexander built in 1852 was saved by the historical society from demolition in 1994 and opened to the public as a fine example of a prosperous sea captain's home. Several rooms contain memorabilia from the brothers' adventures, family portraits and local artifacts. The piano in the parlor is the only original piece remaining in the house, but rooms are furnished with period pieces. The craftsmanship completed by local shipwrights is evident in the sweeping staircases and built-in cabinetry. Climb the winding staircase off the servants' quarters to the cupola for a view of the surrounding countryside and sea.
40 Palmer St., Stonington. (860) 535-8445. Daily except Tuesday, 10 to 4, May-October. Adults $4, children $2.

Old Lighthouse Museum. The first lighthouse in Connecticut is perched on a rise above Stonington Point, where the villagers turned back the British. Opened by the historical society in 1927, this museum is a tiny storehouse of Stonington memorabilia. Whaling and fishing gear, portraits of the town's founding fathers, a bench dating back to 1674, articles from the Orient trade and an exquisite dollhouse are included in the six small rooms. You can climb up circular iron stairs of the tower to obtain a view in all directions.
7 Water St., Stonington. (860) 535-1440. Daily 11 to 5; closed Monday from September-June. Adults $3, children $1.

WATCH HILL. For a staid, storied resort of the old school, things get pretty crowded on summer weekends. And costly, as you might expect from a protective place trying to retain the exclusivity it had when it was the preserve of the Carnegies, the Procters and the Harknesses. Several shops still cater to the carriage trade, although others have less lofty aspirations. Parking in downtown is limited and expensive (up to $8 weekdays, $12 on weekends). Admission to the public beach costs $6, children $1. The beach club and yacht club are off-limits and a policeman likely will discourage out-of-state cars on a Sunday afternoon. The beachside **Flying Horse Carousel** at the foot of Bay Street, a treat for children who line up for $1 rides, is said to be the oldest merry-go-round in the country.

Napatree Point extends nearly a mile from the Watch Hill parking lot along a narrow sandy spit into Block Island Sound. If you find a place to park, walk out past the Watch Hill Yacht Club to the privately owned conservation area. Signs warn that "Ospreys are nesting here – please aid their survival." The walk to the ruins of a Spanish-American fort at the point's far end opposite Stonington can take an hour or half a day. It's a refuge for waterfowl, tidal creatures and beach-combers – a fun adventure for the entire family.

MISQUAMICUT. Watch Hill and Misquamicut are as different as night and day. This beachside strip is hot and honky-tonk, the state beach is crowded and the public is obviously welcome. The beaches are sandy and wide-open and the roll-ing surf is fairly warm – our intrepid sons when young were known to body-surf in May and September and to make sand castles in April and October. The state beach, with concession stands and locker rooms, is open daily from mid-June to early September. Parking $8 weekdays, $10 weekends.

Shopping

The **Mystic Seaport Stores,** outside the south gate so you don't have to pay admission, is a collection of marvelous shops including a book and print shop specializing in nautical books (even seafood cookbooks). It has a gallery with expensive paintings and prints, mostly of the sea, plus ship's models, a Victorian Christmas shop, a bakery with gourmet coffees and specialty foods, and much more. Lamps, furniture, scrimshaw belt buckles, a bakery – you name it, it's here.

Mystic is chock full of shops, most in the Main Street block beside the draw-bridge or out at Olde Mystick Village (see above) and the new Mystic Factory Outlets, two complexes with about a dozen outlets each. In the downtown, **The Bermuda Shop** and **Sea Weeds** are two nice women's clothing stores. **Pepper-grass & Tulip** offers a selection of things for the boudoir, preserves, chocolates, wood carvings and such. **Whyevernot** has unique items from jewelry to fabrics, and **The Velvet Swan** is a good gift shop. **The Company of Craftsmen** carries choice stock; we liked a fused-glass plate with cows marching around the rim. **McMonogram** sells personalized bags, aprons, sweaters and the like. **Good Hearted Bears** has them in all guises, even in reindeer outfits at Christmas. Everything's feline at **Cat-a-Tonic.** The best ice cream in town is made at the **Mystic Drawbridge Ice Cream Shoppe,** beside the drawbridge.

The Emporium at 15 Water St. is a three-story Victorian landmark filled with things you don't really need but are fun to buy. A 1940s jukebox (with appropriate music) is at the entrance. The store is so jammed that many items for sale hang from the ceiling. Records, prints and unusual wrapping paper vie with such things as T-shirts for toilet seats.

In Stonington at 105 Water St. is the **Hungry Palette,** where fabric silkscreened and printed by hand in "an obscure town in Rhode Island," say the owners, can be purchased by the yard or already made up into long skirts, sundresses and accesso-ries like Bermuda bags. The colors are beautiful. A standout among the many antiques shops is **Grand & Water,** which stocks accessories and mahogany furniture as well. **Quimper Faience** at 141 Water St. has a large selection of firsts and seconds of the popular handpainted French china. **Anguilla Gallery** is a stunner with brass fish and flying sculptures among its handicrafts from around the world.

Watch Hill, as one would imagine, is full of expensive shops, some selling clothing and some rather intimidating. **Coppola's of Watch Hill, R.W. Richins** and **Wilson's of Wickford** specialize in clothing and resort wear. T-shirts and sweats are the forte at **Special-T** and swimware at **Ride-a-Wave.** We were struck by the Feather Bed & Breakfast birdhouse in the window at the **Country Store of Watch Hill,** full of gifty items. Unique interior accessories and gifts are featured at **Puffins,** and colorful and exotic handpainted dishes and furniture at **Comina.** The **Watch Hill Fly Fishing Co.** offers fishing gear and outdoor clothing. **A Little Something** specializes in food-related items, as does **Watch Hill Gourmet,** which also carries dishware. Pick up a sandwich or ice cream at the **Bay Street Deli** or the **St. Clair Annex.**

Where to Stay

The area is somewhat short on classic New England country inns, but it has a variety of motels – from new chains to old independents, large and small – plus B&Bs, newer inns and even a few cabins on the water. Chain motels in Mystic, a major tourist destination, charge premium prices in season: even the budget Days Inn costs $109 to $139 a night. Many establishments requires two-night minimum stays in summer.

Hotels/Motels

The Mystic Hilton. Across from the Mystic Marinelife Aquarium, this attractive hotel, lately purchased by the Mashantucket Pequot Tribal Nation, is not the typical Hilton in terms of high-rise glass and steel. Its low red-brick exterior and peaked roofs emulate the look of 19th-century mills and warehouses. All is glamorous and up-to-date inside, from the grand piano and intimate sitting areas in the fireplaced lobby to the 184 guest rooms, each containing two large prints of Mystic Seaport scenes. The meandering, angled layout puts some rooms far from the elevators but contributes to peace and quiet. There are a fitness center and an indoor pool, as well as **The Mooring** restaurant, featuring new American cuisine at reasonable prices for lunch and dinner. Dinner entrées start at $10.95 for charbroiled pesto chicken. We've had a couple of wonderful dinners here, but it's a grown-up treat; let the kids eat early at the McDonald's down the street.
20 Coogan Blvd., Mystic 06355. (860) 572-0731 or (800) 826-8699. Fax (860) 572-0328. Doubles, $205 to $240.

Comfort Inn. This brick structure with gabled windows, cupola and porte cochere is among the newest of the chain motels proliferating around the main I-95 interchange. Along with the new Marriott Residence Inn all-suites hotel next door and the Days Inn across the street, it shares a happy distinction: a relatively secluded location back from the highway. Most of the 120 rooms are on the small side, but kingsize rooms contain loveseats. Luxury suites hold jacuzzis. An indoor fitness center and an outdoor pool are assets, as is the complimentary continental breakfast.
48 Whitehall Ave., Mystic 06355. (860) 572-8531. Fax (860) 572-9358. Doubles, $69 to $139.

The Whaler's Inn. The folks from the luxury Steamboat Inn across the Mystic River have acquired this venerable inn and motel in the heart of town, which is well situated for walking expeditions but can get noisy. Their first order of business was to reduce the number of rooms from 45 to 41 by enlarging four in the main inn. They also modernized bathrooms and redecorated throughout. All rooms come with TVs and phones; motel units in the Noank House have showers; those in the Stonington House, bathtubs. The top of the line are in the adjacent 1865 House, where a common sitting room is available to guests in nine rooms with private baths. The ground floor of the main inn has been leased to a jewelry store, a sweets shop and Restaurant Bravo Bravo (see Where to Eat).

20 East Main St., Mystic 06355. (860) 536-1506 or (800) 243-2588. (Fax) (860) 572-1250. Doubles, $102.50 to $135.

Taber Inn and Townhouses. Built in 1980, this attractive looking motel in a quasi-residential area has sixteen rooms with kingsize or two double beds plus an 1829 guest house, where the six small rooms have private baths and air-conditioning and from the second-floor balconies you can see Long Island Sound. A family of four to six may choose the two-bedroom country guest house next door. Other rooms and configurations are available in the farmhouse. Eight townhouse suites out back offer one or two bedrooms, fireplaced living rooms, wet bars and jacuzzis. Altogether there are 28 units.

29 Williams Ave. (Route 1), Mystic 06355. (860) 536-4904. Fax (860) 572-9140. Doubles, $95 to $185; townhouses, $240 to $295.

The Inn at Watch Hill. Transformed from a rooming house with 32 rooms above stores along Watch Hill's Main Street, this row of motel-type accommodations has sixteen spacious rooms with contemporary furnishings and sliding doors opening onto small balconies above the street. The rooms are plain but pleasant, with bare wood floors, white walls, full baths and color TV. Most have a sink, refrigerator and microwave, but no dishes.

Bay Street, Watch Hill, R.I. 02891. (401) 596-0665. Fax (401) 348-0860. Doubles, $160 to $188. Closed November-April.

Pleasant View Inn. Many accommodations in honky-tonk Misquamicut are on the tacky side, but this establishment at the Watch Hill end is a cut above. A bright blue and white, three-story edifice of the Virginia Beach variety, it has 112 rooms, most with balconies facing the ocean (by far the most choice) or the much-used outdoor pool and spa in front. A lineup of lounge chairs on a grassy crest faces what, for all intents and purposes, is the inn's private beach. The fairly formal dining room overlooking the ocean serves three meals daily. Get the kids to bed early and dance in the Down-the-Hatch lounge.

65 Atlantic Ave., Box 1965, Misquamicut, R.I. 02891. (401) 348-8200 or (800) 782-3224. Fax (401) 348-8919. Doubles, $104 to $170, EP; $149 to $215, MAP. Closed late October to May.

Breezeway Motel. Nicely tucked back from the street in a residential section is this good-looking, two-story brick and frame motel in an L-shape around a pool. Lovingly run by the Bellone family, who now own Maria's Seaside Cafe (see Where to Eat), the 44 rooms contain the usual motel amenities, and a complimentary continental breakfast is served. Six are junior suites with a kingsize bed and living area with a sofabed and wet bar, and two more are luxury suites with a king bedroom, living room with sofabed and double jacuzzis. The block-square property also holds a couple of two-bedroom villas rented by the week. The area is quiet and shady – in contrast to Misquamicut's prevailing noise and sand – but it's a bit of a trek to the beach. To be closer, consider the Breezeway's Seaside Annex: two efficiency units and a penthouse suite above Maria's.

70 Winnapaug Road, Box 1368, Misquamicut, R.I. 02891. (401) 348-8953 or (800) 462-8872. Fax (401) 596-3207. Doubles, $104 to $119, suites to $179. Closed November-March.

Winnapaug Inn. Erected in 1988, this three-story motor inn offers 28 rooms off central corridors and pleasant motel furnishings. Most rooms open onto balconies, the nicest on the east side facing Winnapaug Golf Course with a view of Winnapaug Pond in the distance. Rooms on the west side face a parking lot. At the rear of the property is a large swimming pool. Five more lodging units are in cottages or efficiency apartments.

169 Shore Road, Westerly, R.I. 02891. (401) 348-8350 or (800) 288-9906. Fax (401) 596-8654. Doubles, $85 to $130.

Willows Resort Motel. For those who arrive by small plane, the Willows has a 1,800-foot-long grass landing strip. Its extensive grounds are at the edge of a saltwater inlet for sailing, waterskiing and fishing. There are 34 units with Mediterranean decor (each has a porch and some have kingsize beds) and thirteen efficiencies, which rent by the week. The resort's restaurant features local seafood and serves breakfast and dinner. Facilities include a pool, boats, golf driving range, a tennis court, nature trails, a game room and reading room.

5310 Post Road (Route 1), Box 1260, Charleston, R.I. 02813. (401) 364-7727 or (800) 842-2181. Fax (401) 364-0576. Doubles, $92 to $120. Closed mid-October to mid-May.

Inns

The Inn at Mystic. Although this thirteen-acre complex includes the fine Inn at Mystic in a white-pillared mansion and twelve deluxe inn-style rooms in its East Wing, it started as a motor inn and is, we think, by far the nicest in the area. It's the only one overlooking the water and at least looks like New England, with brown shingles and blue shutters. On thirteen acres atop a hill, it catches the breeze, has a tennis court, a small outdoor pool and a whirlpool, and guests can canoe out onto Pequotsepos Cove. The 67 rooms vary from good to spectacular. The newest deluxe units come with queensize canopy beds, wing chairs, antiques, bidets, fireplaces, jacuzzis and patios or balconies with water views. Complimentary tea for guests is served daily at 4 in the adjacent **Flood Tide Restaurant,** perhaps the area's most glamorous restaurant, serving three meals a day. Lighter fare is offered in the Crystal Swan Lounge. Definitely not for youngsters is the actual Inn at Mystic, the 1904 Colonial Revival mansion with a veranda and incredible gardens atop a hill behind the motor inn. It and the nearby gatehouse offer luxury accommodations in handsomely decorated rooms.

Route 1, Mystic 06355. (860) 536-9604 or (800) 237-2415. Fax (860) 572-1635. Entrées, $18.25 to $28.95. Lunch daily, 11:30 to 2:30; dinner, 5:30 to 9:30 or 10. Doubles in motor inn, $115 to $230; inn, $165 to $250.

Shelter Harbor Inn. The best choice for dining and lodging in this area is the restored 18th-century farmhouse set back from Route 1 (behind two paddle-tennis courts) and off by itself not far from Quonochontaug Pond. Owner Jim Dey has redone nine guest rooms with private baths in the main house, where he added a rooftop deck with a hot tub, from which a distant water vista must be seen to be believed. He also renovated the barn next door to include ten rooms with private baths and a spacious living room on the upper level opening onto a large deck. The inn's crowning glory is the Coach House, with four deluxe guest rooms with fireplaces, upholstered armchairs, phones and small TVs. Guests crowd around the bar in the cheery sun porch after a round of croquet or a fast game of paddle tennis and, in summer, a shuttle bus takes guests to a private beach. A full breakfast is served to overnight guests in the attractive dining areas, which are open for three meals a day (see Where to Eat).

10 Wagner Road, Westerly, R.I. 02891. (401) 322-8883 or (800) 468-8883. Fax (401) 322-7907. Doubles, $104 to $136.

An Out-of-the-Ordinary Ordinary

Randall's Ordinary. You can harken back to the old days, enjoying hearthside dinners and historic accommodations, in this new/old inn secluded in the midst of 27 acres at the end of a dirt road. We say "new" because the inn opened in 1987 and quickly added eleven rooms and a suite in a renovated English barn notable for lofts, skylights, spiral staircases, modern baths, phones and TV. We say "old" because the main house dates to 1685, has three guest rooms with queensize four-poster beds and working fireplaces (although the bathrooms are so modern as to have whirlpool jets in the tubs), and is the site of Colonial hearthside meals from yesteryear. Up to 40 diners gather at 7 in the taproom for drinks and a tour of the house; they also watch cooks in Colonial costumes preparing their meals over the open hearth. The $30 prix-fixe dinner, served at old tables in two beamed dining rooms, offers a choice of up to five entrées – perhaps roast capon with wild rice, roast pork loin, hearth-grilled salmon or Nantucket scallops. They come with soup, anadama or spider corn bread, a conserve of red cabbage and apples, squash pudding, and maybe apple crisp or pumpkin cake for dessert. Open to the public, it's a memorable experience for the entire family. With similar food but less fanfare, lunch is à la carte and considered quite a steal at $4.95 to $8.50. A continental breakfast is served to overnight guests. More substantial breakfast fare is available to guests and the public. The establishment was acquired in 1995 by the Mashantucket Pequot Tribal Nation, who maintained things as they were, but planned eventually to add more rooms and dining space, according to manager Bill Foakes.

Route 2, Box 243, North Stonington 06359. (860) 599-4540. Breakfast daily, 7 to 11; lunch, noon to 3; dinner, Sunday-Friday at 7, Saturday 5 and 7:30. Doubles, $75 to $115; suite, $195.

Weekapaug Inn. The weathered brown shingles of this large inn conceal a homey and tasteful interior where guests have been hosted by four generations of the Buffum family. This is an exclusive, expensive and non-commercial inn, almost like a private club and definitely not for the casual transient. Repeat guests are drawn by the setting (it's surrounded by ocean, coves and wonderful beaches), water sports, tennis, lawn bowling, shuffleboard and good food. No liquor is served, but guests bring their own for cocktails in the Pond Room. Entertainment at night includes movies, bingo and bridge. A buffet lunch is served every day but Sunday.

Lobster is often among the eight or so choices on the dinner menu, which is $28 prix-fixe for six courses to the public (by reservation only and jackets are required). The inn's 30 double rooms and 20 singles, all with private baths, are simple but immaculate with twin beds (some joined to form kingsize). There also are six suites with sitting area and two baths.

25 Spring Ave., Weekapaug, R.I. 02891. (401) 322-0301. Doubles, $320 to $350, AP. Three-night minimum stay. Open late June through Labor Day. No credit cards.

Guest Houses and B&Bs

Steamboat Inn. Mystic acquired deluxe waterfront lodging with the opening of this small B&B fashioned from a former restaurant along the Mystic River in the heart of town. A local decorator outfitted the first six rooms in lavish style with mounds of pillows and designer sheets on each canopied bed, loveseats and plush armchairs in front of the fireplace, and distinctive mantels and cabinet work. All have such creature comforts as jacuzzi baths and TVs hidden in armoires or cupboards. We like best the two rooms at either end of the second floor, with big windows onto the water. Newer are four deluxe ground-floor suites with double jacuzzis, wet bars with refrigerators and microwaves, extra sofabeds and lots of space (the front foyer in one appearing rather useless). They lack the upstairs fireplaces, however, as well as a sense of privacy because their windows are right beside the public wharf. A complimentary continental-plus breakfast is served in an upstairs common room.

73 Steamboat Wharf, Mystic 06355. (860) 536-8300 or (800) 364-6100. Fax (860) 572-1250. Doubles, $175 to $195; suites, $175 to $275.

The Palmer Inn. You can stay in the heart of the quaint seafaring hamlet of Noank in this imposing, sixteen-room mansion, built in 1907 in pillared Southern plantation style for Robert Palmer Jr. when the Palmer Shipyards were among New England's largest. Until 1984 a private home, it was restored with taste and energy by Patricia White into an appealing B&B. A mahogany staircase leads from an impressive main hall with thirteen-foot-high ceilings to six guest rooms on the second and third floors, all with private baths. A couple have balconies and views of the water and one has a fireplace. Furnished with family heirlooms and antiques, rooms also include such amenities as designer sheets, hair dryers and Crabtree & Evelyn toiletries. Guests play checkers in the library or gather for afternoon tea in the parlor; a continental-plus breakfast is served in the dining room. Hats and stuffed animals are among the collections displayed in the entry foyer.

25 Church St., Noank 06340. (860) 572-9000. Doubles, $115 to $215.

Red Brook Inn. Colonial dinners (for house guests only, by reservation, Saturdays in November and December) are a specialty at this historic B&B run by ex-Californian Ruth Keyes, who looked all over eastern Connecticut for a house to make into an inn. She was thrilled in 1983 to find the four-bedroom Creary Homestead, dating from about 1770, with a floor plan identical to that at the showplace 1717 Denison Homestead nearby. She was doubly thrilled three years later to find the historic 1740 Haley Tavern, which was disassembled and moved from Groton to a site behind the Creary Homestead, where it was reassembled in a fascinating inn restoration. Interestingly, Nancy Creary, who was born in the homestead, married the son of Elija Haley, "so we've brought the tavern back into the same family," Ruth says. The tavern structure has seven luxurious guest rooms, all with private baths (two with whirlpool tubs) and three with working fireplaces, two common rooms full of pewter and early American glass, and a 300-year-old stagecoach room now given over to games, TV and VCR. Otherwise, Ruth is a stickler for authenticity; "people who stay here get a feel for the way life was," says she. Her brochure statement that "young children who appreciate antiques are welcome" tells it like it is. Full breakfasts are served in the tavern's keeping room.

2800 Gold Star Highway at Welles Road, Box 237, Old Mystic 06372. (860) 572-0349 or (800) 290-5619. Doubles, $119 to $189.

Shore Inne. This "inne on the water," facing Long Island Sound in a community of fine old summer homes, is wonderfully homey in a 1950s kind of way. Innkeepers Judith and Harold Hoyland upgraded in 1996, enlarging two sets of bedrooms that used to share baths and now offering five rooms, all with private baths. One new room in back contains a queen bed and two twins placed end to end; the other along the side has a king bed and two twins placed side by side. Three original rooms across the front of the house with king/twin beds look out onto Mouse Island and, beyond, Fishers Island. "We still sleep fourteen people, but do it more comfortably," Judith says, justifying the increase in rates. Guests enjoy a living room full of wicker, a dining room and a sun room with library and TV. Judith serves a continental breakfast in the mornings, urges her guests to relax on the lovely grounds, and gives beach privileges at two private beaches that are among the nicest in Connecticut.

54 East Shore Ave., Groton Long Point 06340. (860) 536-1180. Doubles, $95 and $120. Closed November-March.

A Family Find

Arbor House. With two young daughters of their own, Allen and Michelle Kruger welcome families with children to what's locally known as the Old Maine Farm. Now reduced to a few of its original 400 acres, the property contains a four-bedroom B&B in the century-old farmhouse, chickens and sheep in the barn and the fledgling Kruger's Old Maine Farm Winery in the state-of-the-art facility once known as Crosswoods Vineyards. The Krugers liken their B&B experience to a family farm stay, where youngsters can visit the animals and fish in the pond while their parents sip chardonnay or pinot grigio on the side veranda, cooled by the breeze, in an utterly rural setting. Inside the house, guests enjoy their own living room and family room with a potbelly stove and a small upstairs sitting room from which they can see the lights of Long Island's North Fork and the flashing Montauk Light at night. The accommodations are up-to-date and stylish in pastel colors. The second floor holds a bedroom with private bath and a two-room suite with private bath. The skylit attic has two more bedrooms that open onto a common room with a sofabed and a shared bath. All the beds are queensize, the floors carpeted and the window treatments spiffy. Michelle serves a full farm breakfast: at our visit, a fruit kabob, blueberry coffee cake and belgian waffles with sausage and homefries. "Nobody leaves hungry," she says.

75 Chester Maine Road, North Stonington 06359. (860) 535-4221. Doubles, $90 to $125; suite $150 to $180.

The Queen Anne B&B. A large, wicker-filled porch fronting onto a busy street leads into this 1880 Victorian structure that was converted into a B&B in 1987. Eight air-conditioned rooms with modern baths are nicely decorated in period style. Three come with TV sets and two with fireplaces. Two other rooms share a bath. The bridal suite has a brass canopy bed, fireplace and private balcony. Afternoon tea is served in the parlor, which is full of lace and oriental rugs. Resident innkeepers offer a full breakfast, perhaps southwestern egg casserole, fresh berry crêpes or grand marnier french toast.

265 Williams St., New London 06320. (860) 447-2600 or (800) 347-8818. Doubles, $89 to $185.

Where to Eat

Mystic-New London

J.P. Daniels. A restaurant of quiet elegance in an old, high-ceilinged dairy barn, J.P. Daniels has been going strong since 1981. Tables are covered with white linens and centered with fresh flowers, and on certain evenings you may hear a harpist or a pianist in the background. Lanterns on the walls and oil lamps on the tables provide a modicum of illumination on two dining levels. Start with the house special, a fresh fruit daiquiri. Appetizers include grilled mussels, escargots and stuffed mushrooms. Among entrées are seafood casserole, chicken française, lamb tenderloins, petite filet and stuffed shrimp and twin tournedos with two sauces. We applaud their practice of offering most entrées in lighter portions at lighter prices ($8.50 to $10.95). The house specialty is boneless Long Island duck stuffed with seasonal fruits and finished with apricot brandy. The wine list is moderately priced and contains explanations of the offerings. And, rare for a fine-dining establishment, there's a children's menu priced from $2.99 to $3.99, including a soft drink and an ice-cream sundae.

Route 184, Old Mystic. (860) 572-9564. Entrées, $8.50 to $18.95. Dinner nightly, 5 to 9 or 9:30; Sunday brunch, 11 to 2.

Quiambaug House. "Deja-view at the Q" was the billing for this newcomer opened in 1996 by Jerry and Ainslie Turner, who retired early from The Harborview in Stonington. They re-emerged a few years later in a sprawling building that housed Mystic's oldest restaurant (1924), with three paneled, country-pretty dining rooms and a lounge that recreates the Harborview's tavern menu and ambiance. The Turners, known for their French cuisine, retained old favorites like a robust tomato-saffron bouillabaisse, coquilles St. Jacques parisienne and grilled swordfish niçoise. The main dinner menu ranges widely from bombay scallops over puff pastry and stuffed shrimp to roast duckling with plums, prime rib with horseradish sauce, veal saltimbocca and steak au poivre. Starters include French onion soup gratin, the famed baked oysters Ainslie, crispy fried calamari and the specialty strudel bearing country sausage and wild mushrooms. For dinner in the lounge or lunch in the **Atlantic Grille,** expect most of the dining-room appetizers as well as main courses (generally $6.95 to $10.95) ranging from Guinness beer-battered fish and chips to london broil with whiskey sauce.

29 Old Stonington Road, Mystic. (860) 572-8543. Entrees, $16.95 to $22.95. Lunch daily, 11:30 to 3; dinner, 5 to 10.

Restaurant Bravo Bravo. This newish restaurant on the main floor of the Whaler's Inn, with a sidewalk cafe spilling off to the side near the drawbridge, captures a receptive audience. Well-known area chefs Robert Sader and Carol Kanabis produce contemporary Italian fare. For dinner, sirloin carpaccio, mussels marinara and Roman-style grilled mozzarella skewered between garlicky croutons make good starters. Pasta choices are many and varied. The dozen entrées might include seafood stew, stuffed chicken breast, osso buco and braised lamb shanks. Dining is in a spare, often noisy room at tables rather close together, or outside on a canopy-covered terrace with white molded furniture. The outdoor **Cafe Bravo** menu features grilled pizzas (we like the one with pesto, sundried tomatoes and goat cheese for $7.95), pastas and more substantial fare.

20 East Main St., Mystic. (860) 536-3228. Entrées, $13.95 to $24.95; cafe, $10.95 to $14.95. Dinner, Tuesday-Sunday 5 to 9 or 10; lunch in off-season; cafe, May-October, lunch, 11:30 to 2:30; dinner, 5 to 9 or 10.

Captain Daniel Packer Inne. This 1756 inn, once a stagecoach stop on the route from New York to Boston, was owned by the Packer-Keeler family for all its years until Rhode Islander Richard Kiley bought it in 1980 and spent three years redoing it into a handsome restaurant with historic ambiance. The pub in the basement is especially cozy, with brick and stone walls and a huge fireplace; the two dining rooms on the main floor have working fireplaces as well and floors of wide-board pine and formal mats with pictures of sailing ships on the tables. Chowder, salads, sandwiches, pastas and entrées from $7.95 to $10.95 (for tenderloin tips or scallops Nantucket) are offered at lunch. The menu expands at night, and ranges from lemon peppered chicken to sautéed veal tenderloin, rack of lamb dijonnaise and steak black jack, glazed with Jack Daniels. A pub menu similar to that offered at lunch is available in the pub.

32 Water St., Mystic. (860) 536-3555. Entrées, $12.95 to $18.95. Lunch daily, 11 to 4; dinner, 5 to 10; pub daily, from 11.

Seamen's Inne. This popular old warhorse beside Mystic Seaport has been upgraded by new owners who keep the place humming in a variety of venues. There are two main dining rooms, properly historic, and the Samuel Adams Pub. We've found the last a fetching place for lunch or supper with its pressed-tin ceiling, bare wood floors and tables, and a greenhouse window filled with plants. We liked a lunch of clam chowder (thick and delicious for $3.75 a bowl), the steamed mussels in a wine garlic sauce and shrimp and oyster pasta with a spicy cajun sauce (both $7.95). The dinner menu blends yankee with cajun and Southern. Yankee pot roast, barbecued ribs, carpetbagger steak and prime rib vie with such seafood specialties as shrimp creole, fried catfish, Maryland crab cake, broiled seafood platter and seafood pot pie. Enormous numbers of people eat inside or out, on the canopy-covered riverside terrace out back. The dixieland jazz breakfast buffet ($9.95) is a festive Southern feast (from cheddar cheese grits to biscuits and honey) enjoyed by upwards of 500 patrons every Sunday.

Route 27, Mystic. (860) 536-9649. Entrées, $14.95 to $22.95. Lunch daily, 11:30 to 3; dinner, 4:30 to 9 or 10; Sunday jazz breakfast, 11 to 2.

Timothy's. The Groton-New London area has spawned some good restaurants lately. The best is this, which debuted in 1996 in the storefront space long

occupied by James' Gourmet Deli and still retaining store shelves displaying antiques and wine bins. Chef-owner Timothy Grills offers updated continental/American fare. For lunch ($4.50 to $10.95), he touts the lobster and crab bisque, the shrimp and scallops over angel-hair pasta, the grilled chicken sandwich and the "focaccia vegwich." Pastas may be ordered as appetizers or entrées for dinner. Main courses vary from grilled chicken to grilled loin of veal to grilled tournedos served on a bed of escarole. The signature dessert is a white chocolate-raspberry ganache tart.
181 Bank St., New London. (860) 437-0526. Entrées, $12.95 to $19.95. Lunch, Monday-Saturday 11:30 to 2:30; dinner, 5:30 to 9 or 10. Closed Sunday.

Diana Restaurant. Oriental rugs cover the walls and floors of this shopping-center storefront, a family operation that offers the most authentic Lebanese cooking in Connecticut. The three Saad family chefs (two of them culinary graduates of Johnson & Wales University in Providence) attract throngs from miles around for stuffed leg of lamb, beef kabob, broiled kafta, shrimp curry, half pepper and garlic chicken, and lamb and eggplant stew. Mighty popular is the lamb feast, $38 for two. Lebanese wines are featured at this place that's true as true can be.
970 Fashion Plaza, Poquonnock Road (Route 1), Groton. (860) 449-8468. Entrées, $9.95 to $15.95. Lunch and dinner, daily 11:30 to 9 or 9:30, Sunday 4 to 8:30.

Budget Choices

Captain Scott's Lobster Dock. The local newspaper reviewer gave a rare "near perfect" rating to this hard-to-find lobster shack amidst the marinas of Shaw Cove. Head down a gravel road along the railroad track across from Crocker's Boat Yard to the jaunty new adjunct to T.A. Scott Fisheries. Find a takeout counter and fifteen umbrella-covered picnic tables on a deck beside the water. Owner Susan Eshenfelder, sister of the fisheries owner, offered a lobster dinner with corn and fries for $11.99 when we were there; a lobster roll was $7.99, and fish and chips, $4.95. Hers is more than the usual clam shack, however. Specials might be deep-fried shrimp in a basket and cold lobster knuckles with drawn butter (both $4.95), and the reviewer raved about the mako shark cooked Jamaican style. The only thing she didn't like was the long waits, but the low prices were drawing crowds.
80 Hamilton St., New London. (860) 437-1890. Open daily, 11 to 9, May-October. BYOB.

Steamers. This little hole in the wall with a neon lobster lit in an upstairs window opens on nice days onto an unexpectedly appealing dining terrace up against a rocky backdrop. It's a quirky kind of place that appeals to guests of the luxury Steamboat Inn nearby. They and others go for the lobster dinner, served with chowder, fries, corn and coleslaw, plus a glass of beer or wine, for a bargain $12.99. There's a raw bar for fresh oysters and clams, but the rest is mostly basic fare of the fish-fry variety, except for the baked stuffed shrimp with potato and broccoli or the bouillabaisse with garlic bread. Italian ices ($1) are the dessert of choice. You can BYOB, but why not accept the complimentary beer and wine served with each entrée (limit of two per)? Launched in 1996, the place hoped to remain open year-round. But with only a handful of tables inside and free drinks, who knows?
13 Water St., Mystic. (860) 536-1168. Entrées, $5.99 to $11.99. Open daily, 11:30 to 10, Wednesday from 5.

Breakfast Plus

Kitchen Little. This really is a tiny kitchen (indeed, the whole establishment is only nineteen feet square), but it serves up some of the greatest breakfasts anywhere. Chef-owner Florence Klewin's repertoire is extraordinary. Consider the three specials one time we stopped: meatloaf and cheese omelet; baked stuffed potato topped with scrambled eggs, cream cheese, scallions, sour cream and bacon, and a chicken-filled french toast sandwich with cranberry sauce and cheese. Prices are gentle ($3.25 to $6.95), the coffee flows into bright red mugs, and the people at nine tables and five stools at the counter are necessarily convivial. In summer, the overflow spills outside onto mini-picnic tables on a shady gravel patio right beside the Mystic River.
Route 27, Mystic. (860) 536-2122. Breakfast and lunch, Monday-Friday 6:30 to 2; breakfast only, 6:30 to 1, Saturday and Sunday; dinner to 9, Thursday-Saturday in summer.

Shore Towns and Beaches

The Harborview. New owners have upgraded this destination restaurant, long considered the spot for a splurge. Viktor Baker, restaurant concept designer who had headed New York's Rainbow Room, came out of semi-retirement in 1996 to stop the landmark's recent downhill slide. He gutted the kitchen, lightened up the dining room and revamped the menus. The new fare is haute-continental and locally considered very expensive, which is a bad rap. Dinner dishes run the gamut from chicken caprice to bouillabaisse containing a whole lobster. Indeed, lobster is offered about twenty ways, from fricassee to crêpe to savannah to thermidor. Duck and veal are other specialties,. The flourless chocolate torte is so acclaimed it's served in the Harborview's two other dining venues as well. The popular **Bistro at the Bar** in front offers an interesting all-day menu with good values, from a seafood club sandwich to Portuguese fisherman's stew to specials like soft-shell crabs for $9.95. Behind the Harborview at water's edge is the recently upscaled **Skipper's Dock,** where you can order a burger with the works for $6.75 or a complete shore dinner for $32.50. The latter and all the fancy lobster and seafood dishes give it the reputation as pricey, but it's all to match the great water setting.
60 Water St., Stonington. (860) 535-2720. Entrées, $17.50 to $25.50. Lunch and dinner daily except Monday, 11:30 to 10; Skipper's Dock, closed November-April.

Boatyard Cafe. This tiny cafe in the Dodson Boatyard comes with a great outdoor deck beside the harbor. Co-owner Deborah Jensen, a former New York restaurateur and cooking school instructor, offers kicky "combination scrambles" like the Soho – eggs with sundried tomatoes and goat cheese – for breakfasts that lure the locals. The lunch menu adds an oyster po'boy, a signature grilled chicken sandwich and some trendy salads. Fresh Stonington flounder and Stonington scallops take top billing at dinner, each prepared four ways. There are pastas, lobster sauté, veal scaloppine and New York sirloin. Start with smoked salmon and capers; finish with lemon charlotte cake or plum pie. Everything's made here from scratch and oh-so-good. And there's no better place for eating it than on the deck.
194 Water St., Stonington. (860) 535-1381. Entrées, $10.95 to $19.95. Breakfast, 8 to 11:30; lunch, 11:30 to 2:30; dinner, Wednesday-Sunday 6 to 9. Closed Tuesday.

Noah's. This small restaurant seating 65 people in two rooms is well liked locally because of the refreshingly moderate prices and good, unpretentious food. Noah's opens at 7 to serve breakfast, with thick wedges of french toast made from challah bread going for $4.35. Chowder with half a BLT sandwich and the house pâté with a bacon-gouda quiche and green salad made a fine lunch for two recently. Regional or ethnic specialties are listed nightly to supplement the dinner menu of broiled flounder, cod Portuguese, grilled breast of chicken and such, with everything except the filet mignon under $12.25. Be sure to save room for the apple brown betty, bourbon bread pudding, tangerine mousse or what a local gentleman told us was the best dessert he'd ever tasted: fresh strawberries with Italian cream made from cream cheese, eggs and kirsch. Noah's is fully licensed and most wines are priced in the teens.

113 Water St., Stonington. (860). 535-3925. Entrées, $10 to $15. Breakfast, 7 to 11, Sunday to noon; lunch, 11:15 to 2:30; dinner, 6 to 9 or 9:30. Closed Monday.

Shelter Harbor Inn. Pretty as a picture are this inn's two-level dining rooms dressed in white. The creative American food is consistently good and equal to the setting, and the wine list has been honored by Wine Spectator. Dinner entrées are as diverse as seafood fettuccine, pecan-crusted salmon, finnan haddie, hazelnut chicken, sautéed calves liver and grilled black angus sirloin. Be sure to try the Rhode Island jonnycakes with maple butter, a fixture among appetizers for $2.95. Finish with the award-winning sour cream apple pie, Indian pudding or chocolate mousse cake. Equally interesting fare at breakfast and lunch make this a dining destination. Eggs benedict for $5.95 is the priciest morning item. At midday, try the toasted lobster sandwich or the crab and salmon cakes with red pepper sauce, both $9.95.

10 Wagner Road, Westerly, R.I. (401) 322-8883. Entrées, $12.95 to $21.95. Breakfast daily, 7:30 to 10; lunch, 11:30 to 3; dinner, 5 to 10.

A Trip Down Memory Lane

Olympia Tea Room. With a melange of booths and tables and bubblegum-pink walls, this local icon remains much as it was when it opened in 1916. The menu offers something for everyone, and everyone always seems to be partaking, inside the atmospheric room with a soda fountain at one end and out front at tables on the sidewalk. You can snack on smoked bluefish pâté, nachos with homemade guacamole, hummus, steamed mussels or pizza, or order a fried fish sandwich or a turkey waldorf plate. More substantial offerings range from fish and chips to mixed seafood over fettuccine alfredo, seafood casserole and filet mignon. Finish with Hartford cream pie or "our world-famous Avondale swan," a puff-pastry swan filled with ice cream, topped with whipped cream and piled on a pool of hot fudge. Between meals, stop in for Darjeeling teas, cappuccino, a glass of beer or wine, a frappe or an ice-cream sundae.

Bay Street, Watch Hill, R.I. (401) 348-8211. Entrées, $8.95 to $17.95. Daily, 8 a.m. to 10 p.m., May-October.

Maria's Seaside Cafe. The umbrella-covered roadside deck across from the beach holds the tables of choice in summer at this Misquamicut eatery opened by the owners of the Breezeway Motel. They lured as executive chef Modesto Moran, who triples as owner of the much-acclaimed Modesto's in Norwich, Conn., and of Modesto's Pizza and Pasta in Westerly. Here he features fresh seafood, pasta and grilled Mediterranean specialties. For dinner, the extensive menu ranges from broiled scrod, lemon sole and grilled swordfish to veal or chicken parm, broiled New Zealand lamb loins and tournedos Moran. Rigatoni vodka and lobster fra diavolo are among the signature pasta dishes. The wine list is affordable. Dining inside is at a mix of tables and booths and a simple gray and red decor.

132 Atlantic Ave., Misquamicut, R.I. (401) 596-6886. Entrées, $9.95 to $18.95. Lunch daily, noon to 3; dinner, 4 to 10. Closed late October to late April.

Seafood in the Rough

Abbott's Lobster in the Rough. For years we've been taking visitors from all over (one of the latest a Russian who had never seen a lobster) to Abbott's, partly because of the delectable lobsters and partly because of the view of Fishers Island and Long Island Sound, with a constant parade of interesting craft in and out of Mystic Harbor. We like to sit outside at the gaily colored picnic tables placed on ground strewn with mashed-up clam shells. Kids can look at the lobster tanks or scamper around on the rocks, finding jellyfish and snails. You order at a counter and get a number – since the wait is often half an hour or more and the portions to come are apt to be small, we bring along drinks and appetizers to keep us going. Lobster, last we knew, was $14.95 for a one-and-one-quarter pounder. It comes with a bag of potato chips, a small container of coleslaw, melted butter and a paper bib. Also available are steamers, clam chowder, mussels, and shrimp, lobster or crab rolls. Adjacent shacks dispense desserts and shellfish from a raw bar. The wholesale side sells lobsters to go, as well as cans of Abbott's own lobster or clam bisque and chowder.

117 Pearl St., Noank. (860) 536-7719. Daily noon to 9, May to Labor Day; weekends only to Columbus Day.

Costello's Clam Co. This fried-seafood place in the Noank Shipyard was taken over by the folks from Abbott's next door in 1996 and voila! They're Abbott's and Costello's, and competing with themselves. Here you'll find an enclosed kitchen and open-air tables under a blue and white canopy on a wharf right over the water, where gulls await the diner's slightest crumb. The lobster dinner was going for $9.95; ditto for the lobster roll. But most folks come here to avoid Abbott's waits and crowds, to get up close to the water, and for the fried clams and fried scallops, served with fries and coleslaw. Burgers, hot dogs and chicken sandwiches also are available.

End of Pearl Street, Noank. (860) 572-2779. Daily noon to 9, Memorial Day to Labor Day. BYOB.

FOR MORE INFORMATION: Southeastern Connecticut Tourism District, 470 Bank St., Box 89, New London, Conn. 06320, (860) 444-2206 or (800) 863-6569. Its large visitor center in Olde Mystick Village has materials for Mystic and environs as well as for much of Southern New England. The Greater Westerly-Pawtucket Area Chamber of Commerce, 74 Post Road, Westerly, RI 02891, (401) 596-7761 or (800) 732-7636, operates a new visitor center off Route 1 just east of Westerly.

6 ✦ Summer

Marshall C. Webb Photo

Dairy cows graze in field above Inn at Shelburne Farms, against backdrop of Adirondacks.

The Queen City and Isles
Burlington and the Champlain Islands, Vt.

"The most beautiful place in the world," William Dean Howells is said to have called it. The 19th-century novelist was referring to the lake country around Burlington, the Queen City by the lake, situated against a stunning backdrop of Adirondack Mountains rising across Lake Champlain.

The accolades continue for the state's largest city (population, 39,100), which has blossomed into Vermont's downtown – "as downtown as Vermont gets," in the laconic words of Vermont Life magazine. The nation's mayors recently voted it America's most livable city. The University of Vermont adds vitality. Beauty unfolds all along Lake Champlain, the 120-mile-long waterway that reaches into Quebec province and, after the Great Lakes, is America's next largest freshwater lake.

Just south of Burlington lies Shelburne, with its famed Shelburne Museum, Shelburne Farms and a rolling, pastoral landscape that gives new definition to suburbia, Vermont style. To the north are the Champlain Islands, a remote cluster of isles and byways lightly touched by civilization.

Nowhere this side of Washington's Puget Sound are the vistas of lake and mountains quite so stunning, thanks to the Green Mountains on the east and the Adirondacks to the west. Little wonder they call the area "the West Coast of New England."

The Champlain Islands remain in a time warp. In fact, time and transportation had pretty much passed by the entire region – old Indian country discovered by the French explorer Samuel de Champlain in 1609, eleven years before the Pilgrims landed at Plymouth Rock. The once-busy waterfront had fallen into disrepair, the Rutland Railroad was abandoned and, until the 1960s, Burlington was little more than a staid university town that happened to be Vermont's largest city. And that wasn't saying much.

The arrival of International Business Machines Corp. and General Electric Co. plus the completion of Interstate 89 changed all that. The city started renewing its lakefront, which most visitors and passers-through barely realized was there, clearing rundown areas, restoring buildings and partially opening up the expanse from downtown to lake into what the mayor called "a people place." A Montreal developer built Burlington Square, including a shopping mall, a 650-car parking garage, five office buildings and a hotel. Vendors and sidewalk cafes open onto the

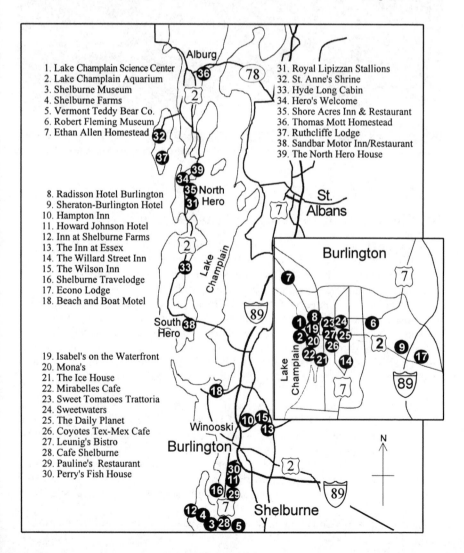

1. Lake Champlain Science Center
2. Lake Champlain Aquarium
3. Shelburne Museum
4. Shelburne Farms
5. Vermont Teddy Bear Co.
6. Robert Fleming Museum
7. Ethan Allen Homestead

8. Radisson Hotel Burlington
9. Sheraton-Burlington Hotel
10. Hampton Inn
11. Howard Johnson Hotel
12. Inn at Shelburne Farms
13. The Inn at Essex
14. The Willard Street Inn
15. The Wilson Inn
16. Shelburne Travelodge
17. Econo Lodge
18. Beach and Boat Motel

19. Isabel's on the Waterfront
20. Mona's
21. The Ice House
22. Mirabelles Cafe
23. Sweet Tomatoes Trattoria
24. Sweetwaters
25. The Daily Planet
26. Coyotes Tex-Mex Cafe
27. Leunig's Bistro
28. Cafe Shelburne
29. Pauline's Restaurant
30. Perry's Fish House

31. Royal Lipizzan Stallions
32. St. Anne's Shrine
33. Hyde Long Cabin
34. Hero's Welcome
35. Shore Acres Inn & Restaurant
36. Thomas Mott Homestead
37. Ruthcliffe Lodge
38. Sandbar Motor Inn/Restaurant
39. The North Hero House

Church Street Marketplace, a downtown pedestrian mall. The result is a user-friendly downtown that works. And, after decades of neglect, the diamond-in-the-rough waterfront is beginning to shine.

The area's cultural heritage has been enhanced in the summer by the outstanding Vermont Mozart Festival, outdoor Vermont Symphony pops concerts and chamber music at Shelburne Farms.

Don't think Burlington is all culture and gleam, however. Vermont author Ralph Nading Hill summed up well his native city: "Add to Burlington's natural endowments – Lake Champlain at its doorstep and the Green Mountains in its backyard – its Vermont birthright as a sensibly small but vital metropolis that has never overgrown its cultural and architectural heritage, and you have a northcountry mecca with one of New England's, and the country's, choicest futures."

Getting There

The area is reached by Interstate 89 from the southeast and north, U.S. Route 7 from the south and north, and U.S. Route 2 from the east and west.

Excellent bus service into and through the state is provided by Vermont Transit Co., headquartered at 135 Paul St., Burlington, (802) 864-6811 or (800) 451-3292.

Amtrak's Vermonter offers daily service to and from New York, Philadelphia and Washington, D.C.

Burlington International Airport is served by Continental, US Airlines, United and smaller airlines.

Seeing and Doing

After years of neglect, Burlington has opened its lakefront to public access and, on pleasant days, the public responds in droves. Appealing people places are the nine-acre Waterfront Park with its flower gardens and swinging park benches, and a new floating Community Boathouse. The Lake Champlain Basin Science Center and Aquarium are in their infancy. The free College Street shuttle bus, running every fifteen minutes, connects the waterfront to downtown shopping and the university on the hill.

Explore the Waterfront

A floating freighter known as the **Burlington Community Boathouse** has anchored the downtown waterfront since 1988. It is operated under auspices of the city recreation department as a center for water sports, renting sailboats and kayaks and offering scuba classes. There are picnic tables along the entry path, and **Whitecaps** serves casual food and drink seasonally beside the water. Stretching north along the lakeshore is a boardwalk promenade, where you can rest on solid wooden glider swings and look at Lake Champlain.

The futuristic-looking **Wing Building** at Main Street Landing was the first of several planned incubator spaces for small businesses, artist studios, shops and restaurants along the waterfront. More were about to open at our 1996 visit in the restored **Union Station.** The upscale **Cornerstone Building** contains shops, the new Mona's restaurant and condominiums. More condos and commercial enterprises were planned for two large buildings rising across Battery Street.

TOURING. An 8.2-mile-long **bicycle path** stretching from Oakledge Park on the south along the downtown waterfront to the Flynn Estate at the mouth of the Winooski River gets closer to the lake than any other shore route. Plans are eventually to continue the bikeway across the Winooski River through Colchester to South Hero and the Champlain Islands. Access to the path is via Oakledge and Leddy parks, North Beach, Perkins Pier and the Waterfront Park. The ribbon of tarmac winds around historic sites and through verdant corridors as it offers scenic water views. It's used by walkers, joggers and roller bladers as well as cyclists.

Motorists as well as cyclists can travel Pine Street south from downtown and North Avenue toward Colchester for interesting diversions. Pine Street ends near **Red Rocks Park,** a heavily wooded picnic grove with a small beach for swimming. At the foot of Flynn Avenue, **Oakledge Park** offers picnicking, four tennis courts near the water and a rocky shoreline with good views back toward the city skyline. **Battery Park,** downtown on a crest near the lake, harbors guns that repulsed British ships in the War of 1812 and telescopes for viewing 75 peaks in the Adirondacks. Out North Avenue is the **Municipal Beach,** locally known as North Beach, with the city's best swimming, campsites, picnic tables and grills, playground and a view of the ferry (admission $1). Nearby **Leddy Park** also offers nicely wooded picnic sites near the shore. Up a winding road off Ethan Allen Parkway through **Ethan Allen Park** is a hilltop with the city's best all-around view: the Adirondacks to the west and the Green Mountains to the east. Continue out North Avenue and follow Route 127 to Colchester. Marble Island Road and Barney Point from Colchester Point Road give vistas of what the natives call "the Broad Lake," and Lakeshore Drive hugs the shore along Malletts Bay.

Vermont Rail Excursions. The lakeside views between Shelburne and Burlington are memorable from the **Sugarbush Express** as it wends through picturesque communities and along Shelburne Bay between Middlebury and Burlington. The diesel-powered train with two air-conditioned passenger cars, a dining car and bar car stops at Vergennes and Shelburne before unloading and loading passengers at a covered platform beside the Burlington Waterfront Park. Narration outlines the history, folklore and attractions along the way. The round trip takes three hours (at speeds up to 55 miles an hour).

Marble Works Complex, Middlebury. (802) 388-0193 or (800) 707-3530. Train leaves Middlebury Wednesday-Sunday at 9, 12:40 and 4:20 and departs Burlington at 10:50, 2:30 and 6:10, June 26 to Labor Day; weekends in June and early September; daily half an hour earlier, Sept. 21 through Oct. 20. Adults, $10, children $5.

Lake Champlain Basin Science Center. "Come in to see live turtles, frogs, snakes and much more," urges the sign outside the fledgling science center, the first stage of a planned world-class research and education center. An old Naval Reserve Building was retrofitted with wave-shaped awnings forming pavilions that housed initial exhibits. The hands-on focus of "Secrets of the Lake" and "Song of the Wetlands" exhibits had children looking eye-to-eye at live fish, touching fossils, viewing shipwrecks and learning about zebra mussels at our visit. "Geology of the Basin" was the special demonstration of the day.

Foot of College Street, Burlington, (802) 864-1848. Daily, 11 to 5, mid-June to Labor Day; weekends only after Labor Day. Adults $2, children under 12 free.

Lake Champlain Aquarium. At least 83 species of fish have been caught in the "Sixth Great Lake," and three dozen of them are on display in thirteen tanks here. Many originate in June's annual Lake Champlain International Fishing Derby, which encourages live release of its catches. There are young specimens of endangered lake sturgeon as well as a twenty-pound channel catfish named Felix, plus prehistoric long-nosed gar, slippery American eel, crayfish and a tankful of emerald shiners.

King Street Ferry Dock, Burlington. (802) 862-7777. Open daily 11 to 5, mid-June to mid-October. Adults $2, children $1.

Take a Boat Ride

Spirit of Ethan Allen II. The new, triple-deck Spirit of Ethan Allen II is the 500-passenger successor to the quaint paddlewheeler. The largest excursion boat on Lake Champlain leaves from the Community Boathouse at the foot of College Street for 90-minute narrated cruises four times a day. Be on the lookout for Champ, the legendary lake serpent; 70 passengers aboard the original paddlewheeler tour boat in 1984 became believers in the largest mass sighting ever. We took the 2 p.m. cruise and found it quite interesting, if slow. The boat went north to Apple Tree Bay, then south to Shelburne Point and back, and much of the narration was about the height of the various Green Mountains. The only choices for seating were on the enclosed first deck, all set up for dining with chairs at long tables, or on the (too) sunny top deck. We would have liked to be able to sit outside in some shade. The captain's buffet dinner cruises on weekends (adults $24.95, children $15.95) are popular with families, while the sunset and comedy cabaret cruises appeal to romantics.

Burlington Community Boathouse, Burlington. (802) 862-8300. Trips daily at 10, noon, 2 and 4, May 25 to Oct. 20. Adults $7.95, children $3.95.

Lake Champlain Ferries. The working Burlington Ferry leaves for a scenic one-hour ride across the lake to Port Kent, N.Y., roughly every hour during the summer. You get to see more of the lake than on the Spirit, although without the benefit of narration, and walk-on passengers and bicyclists are welcomed. The Lake Champlain Transportation Co. is the oldest steamship operator in the country and one of its boats, the Adirondack (1913), is the oldest double-ended ferry still in operation. Cheaper and more frequent ferry rides are offered from Grand Isle in the Champlain Islands to Plattsburgh (crossing time twelve minutes) and from Charlotte to Essex (twenty minutes).

King Street Dock, Burlington. (802) 864-9804. Car and driver, $21 round trip, adult passengers $5.50, children $1.50; maximum car fare, $28.

Lake Champlain Cruise and Charter. The ferry company has outfitted two of its boats for scenic lake cruises. Three cruises focusing on the history of the Champlain Valley are offered daily at 11:30, 2 and 4 from early summer through Columbus Day (adults $7, children $3.50). Evening music, dinner and Sunday brunch "cruise-ine" trips ($25 to $35) feature wine tastings, beers from local microbreweries and food from area restaurants.

King Street Dock, Burlington. (802) 864-9804.

Enjoy Downtown

Burlington's downtown is one that's truly enjoyable. It's a prospering, people place by day and night as well as on weekends.

Stroll along the boardwalk in the nine-acre Waterfront Park, go up to Battery Park and through Burlington Square's lawns and enclosed shopping arcades to the Church Street Marketplace, an exceptionally nice, landscaped pedestrian mall transformed from the city's main street, headed by the historic brick Unitarian Church. The pedestrian mall is alive with shopping carts, sidewalk cafes, restaurants and good stores (see Shopping), both local and of the variety normally associated with upscale shopping malls.

Not for nothing is Church Street so named. Close by are the spectacular Episcopal Cathedral Church of St. Paul, rebuilt after a 1971 fire and well worth a visit; the striking Catholic Cathedral of the Immaculate Conception, and the Congregational and Baptist churches with their soaring spires. A number of buildings around City Hall Park, College Street and the Battery Street waterfront are of architectural merit.

Special Attractions

Shelburne Museum. A worthy destination in itself, this "collection of collections" depicting three centuries of Americana is truly mind-boggling. If you're a collector, you could spend day after day here. If you are a typical tourist, you may find that after six hours or so you don't want to look at another tool, quilt, painting, decoy, carriage or what have you.

Founder Electra Havemeyer Webb presided until her death in 1960 over the family collections, which are housed in 37 buildings spread over 45 acres, all beautifully landscaped with wild roses twining over rustic fences, fruit trees and flowering shrubs. A free shuttle tram takes visitors from the visitor center near the entrance to the far ends of the grounds every fifteen minutes.

The sidewheeler Ticonderoga excursion boat that cruised Lake Champlain for 47 years is what many visitors tour first. It is especially interesting to view the staterooms – some elegant and some holes in the wall – with their corner washstands; the dining-room tables are set with Syracuse china. A movie that runs occasionally explains how the ship was brought overland two miles from the lake. It has just undergone a $2 million refurbishing, we hear.

Among the historic structures worth visiting are a one-room schoolhouse from Vergennes, an 1871 lighthouse from the lake, a 1733 saltbox from Massachusetts, a Shaker barn filled with a fantastic collection of carriages and the last remaining two-lane covered bridge with footpath in the United States. Don't miss the Weed House, which has remarkable collections of dolls, toys, pewter and glass, and the Stencil House, with its original and very handsome stenciled walls from 1790. Our favorite is the Electra Havemeyer Webb Memorial Building, a Greek Revival mansion housing a six-room apartment taken from the Park Avenue residence of the museum founders; it is totally charming and filled with priceless paintings. The Shelburne Depot from 1890 and the private railroad car parked beside it are worth a look. The collection of wildfowl decoys here is considered the most important in the world. Altogether there are more than 80,000 pieces of Americana in this national treasure described by the New York Times as "Vermont's Smithsonian."

The Dog Team Tavern Cafe and a snack bar serve predictable fare. The good museum store is open year-round.

Route 7, Shelburne. (802) 985-3346. Daily 10 to 5, late May to late October; rest of year, guided tours of selected buildings by reservation daily at 1. Adults $17.50, children $6; second consecutive day free.

Shelburne Farms. Guided tours of the 1,400-acre agricultural estate of Dr. William Seward Webb and his wife, the former Lila Vanderbilt, leave every 90 minutes from the visitor center. Following a free multi-media slide presentation, visitors board an open-air wagon to view the huge Farm Barn, the Dairy Barn, the Coach Barn Education Center, the beautiful gardens and the exterior of the Shelburne House, now an inn and restaurant and the delightful, Camelot-like site for concerts and special events in the summer. Shelburne Farms combines an active dairy and cheese-making operation, furniture-making, a market garden and other leased enterprises in a working farm setting flanked by lake and mountains. The cheddar cheese (we always buy some of the delectable extra-sharp) from a herd of cows descended from Swiss stock raised for cheese-making is sold in the fine visitor center shop, which also sells other Vermont farm products and crafts and is open daily year-round. A walking trail from the visitor center winds through woods and fields for about a mile to the top of Lone Tree Hill, which yields a superb view of Lake Champlain and the mountains. Youngsters can mix with the farm animals in the **Children's Farmyard** in the Farm Barn.

102 Harbor Road, Shelburne. (802) 985-8686. Tours daily at 9:30, 11, 12:30, 2 and 3:30, late May to mid-October. Adults $6.50, children $3.50. Farmyard, $4 and $3.

Vermont Teddy Bear Co. Several hundred thousand bears are produced annually in this rapidly expanding company's playful, crayon-colored barn of a factory south of the Shelburne Museum. Who would guess that the now-national phenomenon started from a pushcart on the Church Street Marketplace? Its latest 62,000-square-foot facility attracts more than 125,000 visitors a year, making it one of Vermont's top tourist attractions. Guided tours (adults $1, children free) offer a glimpse of the innards of the workshops where the bears are created. Tours leave every fifteen minutes from the entry atrium centered by a bear-shaped topiary. Costumed "bear ambassadors" lead visitors through the production line, interspersing campy comedy routines with doses of company history and a play-by-play on how teddy bears are made. The bears in the retail showroom were more expensive than we would have thought, with tiny pooh-bears going for $20, and rising well above $100. They take on varying human roles simply by a change of costume, of which there are more than a hundred. The mobs of visitors, young and old, obviously love them.

2236 Shelburne Road, Shelburne. (802) 985-3001. Open daily, 9 to 6, Sunday 10 to 5.

Other Attractions

Robert Hull Fleming Museum. This expanded museum is a high point of the large and fairly nondescript University of Vermont campus. More than 17,000 works of fine, decorative and ethnographic arts are shown in several galleries in the museum, designed by McKim, Mead and White in 1931. The Egyptian mummy is usually the star of the show, as far as youngsters are concerned. A selection of Burlington artist Fleming's finest paintings and sculptures is on display in the permanent galleries. Other highlights are Northern Plains Indian Art, early 20th-century American drawings and unusual examples of Rookwood pottery. Interesting pictures and displays depict Burlington during the Victorian era and before. The gift shop has a good collection of cards and books.

61 Colchester Ave., Burlington. (802) 656-0750. Open Tuesday-Friday 9 to 4, Saturday and Sunday 1 to 5. Donation, $2.

Ethan Allen Homestead. Guided tours show the restored 1787 farmhouse of Ethan Allen, Vermont founder and Revolutionary War hero. Exhibits trace his life and times in the orientation center, which has a multi-media show and a gift shop. The homestead consists of the timber frame house, working gardens and several acres with hiking trails and access to the Winooski River.
    Off Route 127 in north Burlington. (802) 865-4556. Daily, 10 to 5, Sunday 1 to 5, mid-May to mid-October. Adults $3.50, children $2.

Summer Entertainment

Vermont Mozart Festival. A summer-in-Vermont tradition since 1973, the festival fills the air with music for three weeks starting in mid-July at some of the area's most picturesque settings. The festival orchestra and guest soloists give twenty concerts annually at sites as diverse as the Lake Champlain Ferry, the Shelburne Farms Coachyard, the Robert Frost cabin in Ripton, the Trapp Family Meadow in Stowe, and local colleges and churches. Innovative programming draws thousands of concertgoers annually. The grand opening and closing concerts at the palatial lakeshore Shelburne Farms spread are highlights.
    Box 512, Burlington. (802) 862-7352 or (800) 639-9097.

The **Vermont Symphony Orchestra,** (800) 876-9293, presents its annual summer festival in observance of Independence Day at scenic locations around the state from roughly June 27 to July 7. Most of the family concerts include fireworks, and the concert at Shelburne Farms is not to be missed.

Vermont's oldest resident equity theater company presents four recent Broadway and off-Broadway shows for two weeks each, Tuesday-Saturday at 8, from mid-June into August at **St. Michael's Summer Playhouse,** St. Michael's College, in Colchester, (802) 654-2535.

The **Craftsbury Chamber Players** alternate Thursday concerts in Hardwick with Wednesday evening performances in Burlington at the University of Vermont Recital Hall from mid-July to mid-August.

A pre-summer highlight is the **Discover Jazz Festival** in which some 200 state and national musicians are heard in parks, beaches, restaurants, concert halls, clubs and on the streets for six days around the second week of June.

Shopping

Burlington's **Church Street Marketplace,** four landscaped blocks of the main street that are closed to traffic and enlivened by sidewalk cafes, is lined with more than 100 stores and eateries as well as assorted pushcarts, from **The Cow Cart** to **Street Smart Accessories.** Off it is **Burlington Square,** an indoor shopping mall with the usual mall stores – an interesting adjunct for a lively downtown.

Thriving Church Street has lost two old-line stores, Abernethy's and Magrams. But trendy galleries and boutiques compensate, at least for the visitor. Here you'll find the **Peace & Justice Store** side by side with **Laura Ashley.** Local merchants compete head-to-head against such national retailers as **The Nature Company, Pier One Imports, Banana Republic** and **Pompanoosuc Mills.** Among the treats for shoppers are **Chico's** for Southwest apparel, **Apple Mountain** for Vermont souvenirs and specialty foods, the high-ceilinged **Chassman & Bem** bookstore with its European-style cafe and a rack of foreign newspapers, the **Vermont**

Trading Co. for all-natural fiber clothing, and a wine shop with a great name, **Romancing the Vine. Ap Ro Pos** has with-it clothes for the young. We love **Frog Hollow at the Marketplace,** a branch of the Vermont State Craft Center at Frog Hollow in Middlebury; an exhibit of prints by our favorite Vermont artist, Sabra Field, was an attraction at our latest visit.

Stop at **Bennington Potters North,** 127 College St., as much to see how an old brick warehouse can be restored with taste as to view the myriad items for sale: everything from aprons to egg cups to clay bird feeders to rugs and furnishings (and, of course, that good-looking pottery).

Handsome Vermont-crafted cherry furniture and Italian pottery are featured at **The Courtyard Collection,** 171 St. Paul St.

The Shelburne area has many interesting shops. The first **Talbots** store in Vermont anchors Shelburne Square, an upscale strip plaza. The **Shelburne Country Store** has been in continuous operation since 1859, but never with more flair than lately. There are still penny candy and homemade fudge, as well as room after room full of fine crafts, toys, candles, folk art notes, lamp shades, kitchenware, specialty foods and more. Sample a taste of smoked ham and you'll probably buy some at **Harrington's,** which specializes in cob-smoked meats, pheasants, turkeys and hams, and offers "the world's best ham sandwich."

More interesting shopping is found in Winooski at the **Champlain Mill,** three floors of shops and restaurants fashioned from a 1909 textile mill beside the river. We love the **Book Rack** store here.

Where to Stay

The Burlington area is full of chain hotels and motels, plus a handful of inns and fifteen or so small B&Bs, many of which seem to operate only on weekends or whim.

Larger Hotels

Radisson Hotel Burlington. Built in the late 1970s as part of the Burlington Square retail/office complex at the edge of downtown, with a sweeping view of Lake Champlain across the street, the 255-room Radisson is for those who want a central location and all the amenities of a downtown hotel. We found the lobby austere, but our room was spacious and nicely decorated. The rooms on the lake side and particularly those on the corners are most requested. There also are twelve suites and fourteen cabanas beside the indoor pool. The pool has a great jacuzzi on one side, which proved a boon for aching muscles after a day's sightseeing, and an adjacent bar and sidewalk cafe. There's also a health facility. **The Oak Street Cafe** in the lobby is for breakfast, lunch and dinner at moderate prices. The large lakeside restaurant, **Seasons on the Lake,** opens for weekend dinners for those who want something fancier.

60 Battery St., Burlington 05401. (802) 658-6500. Fax (802) 658-4659. Doubles, $143 to $164.

Sheraton-Burlington Hotel & Conference Center. What started out looking like a picturesque barn on a rise near an I-89 exit is the Sheraton, which actually was built around a 150-year-old barn. It expanded like topsy in the late 1980s – to the point where you need a map to find your room and to get around the campus-like complex. Enclosed pedestrian bridges and directional signs help. Some of the 309 rooms ring an interior courtyard open to the sky. Others face the indoor atrium, some of those with sliding doors onto a garden-style restaurant with an L-shaped indoor pool and fitness center beyond. Those would be fine in winter, we suppose. But, hey, this is summer in Vermont and we want a breath of fresh air; those who agree should ask for an outside room. The rooms we saw were stylish, with comfortable armchairs, work desks and TVs tucked away in cabinets. Meals are served in the four-story-high "summerhouse" atrium at **G's,** the aforementioned garden restaurant where diners could feel on public display. Drinks and light meals are available nearby in **Tuckaway's,** a lounge with a sun deck on the roof for swimmers who want some sun along with a splash in the indoor pool.

870 Williston Road, South Burlington 05403. (802) 862-6576 or (800) 677-6576. Fax (802) 865-6670. Doubles, $93 to $149.

Hampton Inn Hotel & Conference Center. Recently erected at a rural location just north of the Winooski exit off I-89, this is one classy Hampton Inn that calls itself a hotel and conference center. The budget chain goes upscale here with a spacious lobby, full of comfortable seating and tables with window views onto Mount Mansfield and the Worcester Range. The 188 rooms on three floors are outfitted in rich greens and burgundies; those ensconced on the third floor with dormer windows present interesting angles. Rooms facing east enjoy views of the distant mountains beyond a garden patio complete with gazebo. Even the complimentary continental breakfast here is a cut above, with bagels and jars of cereals to supplement the usual. With a replica of the Colchester Reef lighthouse atop its roof, the **Lighthouse Restaurant** displays old lake photographs and serves a steak and seafood menu from $9.95 to $15.95.

8 Mountain View Drive, Colchester 05446. (802) 655-6177. Fax (802) 655-4962. Doubles, $85 to $95.

Howard Johnson Hotel & Suites. The newest and biggest motor inn along a strip of many is this five-story hotel, which is tiered back into the woods off Route 7. It really is a hotel, with the obligatory lobby, an indoor pool, two saunas, exercise room and an adjacent restaurant called **What's Your Beef,** fashioned from an old house that was home to a number of short-lived restaurants and is now run by the Dog Team Tavern Group out of Middlebury. The original 121 rooms are well furnished in contemporary hotel style with two doubles or a kingsize bed. The kingsize rooms are particularly nice, each equipped with a sofa as well as a plush chair for viewing the TV hidden in the armoire. The hotel was expanded lately with the addition of 84 kitchen/living room/bedroom suites in back.

1720 Shelburne Road, South Burlington 05403. (802) 860-6000 or (800) 874-1554. Fax (802) 864-9919. Doubles, $70 to $85; suites, $70 to $170.

Inns and Motels

The Inn at Shelburne Farms. On their 1,400-acre agricultural estate beside Lake Champlain, the 100-room summer home of Dr. William Seward Webb and Lila Vanderbilt Webb has been refurbished into a grand inn of the old school The rambling Queen Anne-style mansion offers 24 bedrooms and suites in interesting configurations. Most have twin beds and their original furnishings from the turn of the century, and seventeen have private baths. Rooms vary widely from deluxe to tiny, from corner rooms with armoires and chaise lounges and lake views to a third-floor hideaway in the front of the house (no view) where the bedroom is dwarfed in size by the bathroom. The main-floor public rooms are a living museum: several sitting rooms (one for afternoon tea), a library with 6,000 volumes, porches full of wicker, a game room, and a formal dining room in which breakfast and dinner are served to house guests and the public (see Where to Eat). Between meals, guests walk the grounds designed by Frederick Law Olmsted, swim at a small beach, enjoy the gardens, play croquet, shoot billiards in a game room to end all game rooms, and thoroughly savor a choice piece of property with an aura of yesteryear.

Shelburne Farms, Shelburne 05482. (802) 985-8498 or 985-8686 (mid-October to May). Doubles, $90 to $250, EP. Open mid-May to mid-October.

The Inn at Essex. It's a surprise to find a small country hotel of this elegance in the midst of a large field, seemingly in the middle of nowhere. But this is near an interchange of a new highway skirting Burlington. And it's where the next accidental city may rise, what with a designer outlet center just opened, expansion plans for nearby IBM and a new town center in the works for Essex. The three-story inn, two restaurants and adjacent Governor's Mansion are built around what innkeeper Jim Lamberti likens to a New England village green. Decor in the 97 guest rooms varies from Shaker to Queen Anne, from canopy to pencil-post to brass beds. All come with up-to-date conveniences, and 30 have working fireplaces. An attractive new outdoor swimming pool is located off the rear courtyard, which is often used for weddings and functions (we swam as wedding guests danced beneath the canopy, and no one seemed to mind). Faculty and students of the New England Culinary Institute operate the inn's two restaurants, which seem to be of most interest to people staying there. The formal, 50-seat **Butler's** serves dinner only, while the more casual **Birch Tree Cafe** with a Vermont country setting offers three meals daily. We've enjoyed superior meals in both venues, from a $4.75 Vermont cheddar omelet with whole wheat toast for breakfast in the cafe to exotic appetizers and an entrée of crispy salmon with wilted greens ($17) in the urbane Butler's.

70 Essex Way, Essex Junction 05452. (802) 878-1100 or (800) 727-4295. Fax (802) 878-0063. Doubles, $109 to $190.

The Willard Street Inn. The Burlington area got a badly needed city B&B in 1996. Beverly Watson, the restaurateur who runs Isabel's on the Waterfront, bought an 1881 brick mansion that had been a retirement home and readied it in three weeks for the first guests during fall foliage. The fifteen guest rooms on the second and third floors are furnished in traditional style with period antiques and reproductions, plus TVs and phones. Seven have private baths, two share an adjoining bath and the rest share one bath on each floor. Rooms vary from large master bedrooms with ornamental fireplaces to a few small rooms with in-room sinks. Those on the west side yield views of Lake Champlain in the distance. Guests enjoy the high-ceilinged living room and dining room and a plant-filled solarium looking onto beautiful gardens below. Breakfast is continental on weekdays, full on weekends, when the main course might be french toast or vegetable frittata. A striking marble staircase descends to the back lawn, where bocci ball and croquet may be enjoyed.

349 South Willard St., Burlington 05401. (802) 651-8710 or (800) 577-8712. Fax (802) 651-8714. Doubles, $75 to $150.

The Wilson Inn. This contemporary building reflects what manager Margaret Wilson, for whom the inn is named, says was her idea for what was one of the first all-suites hotels. Geared to families and business travelers (the inn is not far from the airport), each of the 32 suites has a full kitchen, dining area, living room with sofabed and a separate bedroom with bath; several have a second loft bedroom up a circular stairway. A snack of Vermont crackers and cheese welcomes guests upon arrival. A hearty complimentary continental breakfast is served in the morning at **Maggie's,** a pub that also offers appetizers in the evening.

10 Kellogg Road, Essex Junction 05452. (802) 879-1515 or (800) 521-2334. Fax (802) 878-7950. Doubles, $81 to $121.

Shelburne Travelodge. The advantage here is that some of the 73 rooms facing away from the road offer views of Lake Champlain – a rare commodity along the busy Route 7 strip south of Burlington. Rooms on three floors in the franchised chain motel vary in style and size. Facilities include an indoor pool, sauna and fitness room. A continental breakfast is complimentary.

1907 Shelburne Road, Shelburne 05482. (802) 985-8037. Fax (802) 985-8037. Doubles, $54 to $120.

Extra Value

Beach and Boat Motel. This nine-unit motel a few miles north of Burlington is one of the few we found right on Lake Champlain; it has a small pool as well as a private beach. Rooms share a common concrete balcony overlooking Malletts Bay. One unit has a fullsize bed; the others contain two beds. This is a great location for those who want to be beside the water, but nearby sections are somewhat honky-tonk. You can sleep four people in a room for a mere $57.

218 Lake Shore Dr., Colchester 05446. (802) 863-6577. Doubles, $49. Open mid-May through October.

A Family Choice

Econo Lodge. In this area (Exit 14 off I-89) are many of the big chain motels, most quite near the road. But the 176-unit Econo Lodge is tucked back from the highway in a grove of trees and offers a quiet night and an attractive outdoor pool at good value. Amenities include a free continental breakfast, a fitness center with jacuzzi and a nature trail meandering through part of the 52-acre property. Twice in four years, the motel won the chain's national gold award as the No. 1 Econo Lodge in the nation and after our stay here, we understood why, since this is far from a bare-bones budget facility. Next door is the **Windjammer Restaurant,** featuring beef and seafood dishes ($8.95 to $16.95) and a 40-item salad bar built into a replica of a windjammer. Families appreciate the McDonald's across the road.

1076 Williston Road, South Burlington 05403. (802) 863-1125 or (800) 371-1125. Fax (802) 658-1296. Doubles, $72 to $82.

Where to Eat

In summer, Burlington appears to be one big sidewalk cafe, especially along the downtown Church Street Marketplace. And restaurants are proliferating, with three opening within six weeks in a short block along lower Church Street at a recent visit. Outlying South Burlington and Shelburne claim good restaurants as well.

On the Waterfront

Isabel's on the Waterfront. Growing from a catering service into a thriving lunch-brunch spot, Isabel's now serves dinner as well. The dinners are a great addition, served inside in a couple of high-ceilinged rooms partitioned off from the self-service lunch counter and open kitchen, and outside on a canopied terrace not far from the lake. The short menu changes frequently. Entrées, including soup or salad, run from chicken primavera to sautéed beef tenderloin with a house-smoked portobello mushroom demi-glace. Sweet and sour shrimp with Vietnamese vegetable wonton cups and Maine crab cakes with sweet tomato salsa are typical appetizers. Regulars remain partial to Isabel's for lunch, when you pick your selection from the samples displayed on show plates at the counter. We enjoyed a platter of shrimp and snow peas oriental with fettuccine and a build-your-own salad. You might try sautéed scallops with salad, mushroom ravioli alfredo or soup and chicken caesar salad, generally in the $5.95 to $8.50 range. A light grill menu is offered between meals from 2 to 5:30. Arriving a few minutes too late for lunch at our latest visit, we sat on the lakeview terrace and enjoyed a zesty sausage quiche and a grilled chicken sandwich with mango chutney (both $5.95). For a closer view of the water, head out to the nearby Community Boathouse, where Isabel's runs **Whitecaps,** a casual cafe for light food and drink, daily from 7:30 to sunset in summer and weekends in late spring and early fall. The blackboard menu there ranges from hot dogs to caesar salad with crab cakes.

112 Lake St., Burlington. (802) 865-2522. Entrées, $12.95 to $19.95. Lunch, Monday-Friday 11 to 2; light grill menu, 2 to 5:30; dinner, Tuesday-Sunday 5:30 to 9; Saturday and Sunday brunch, 10:30 to 2.

Mona's. The best thing about this elegant newcomer in the restored Cornerstone Building at the foot of Main Street is the view – if you know about it. We apparently entered through the wrong door of the showy, copper-ceilinged bar beside the semi-open kitchen, asked for an outdoor table and were seated by ourselves on a side patio, with only a hint of a lake view across the rusting roof of an industrial shed. It was not until after lunch that we found where the views and the action were – upstairs in three Mediterranean-style dining rooms and a jaunty outdoor balcony stretching across the rear of the building, yielding a wide-angle view of Lake Champlain. That setting would have been enough to compensate for what we found to be unexpectedly mediocre food. The signature Vermont cheddar and ale soup was rather tasteless, and the spinach salad had the strangest dressing we ever tasted (the waitress noticed our uneaten plate, and took the salad off the bill). The specialty flatbread pizza topped with calamari and roasted garlic ($6.95) was good, however. At dinner, entrées range widely, reportedly to mixed success. The grilled fillet of tuna on a bed of gingered fettuccine, the roast duck and the tournedos are great, according to Manon O'Connor, wife of the chef and owner. She and Art O'Connor earned their spurs uptown at the **Bourbon Street Grill,** 211 College St., and their fans were hoping their much larger offspring would measure up. It certainly has the decor and the setting, and the menu reads well.

3 Main St., Burlington. (802) 658-6662. Entrées, $10.95 to $21.95. Lunch daily, 11:30 to 3; dinner, 5 to 10 or 11; Sunday, brunch 10 to 3, dinner 5 to 9.

The Ice House. Even if you don't eat here, drive by to see the charming Brueghel-like sign in front depicting ice skaters on the lake. The inside of this massive, restored stone waterfront building (it was an ice house early in the century) is charming as well, with a few sofas to sink into in the large upstairs lounge with its huge and rough original beams. Our relatives from Montreal sometimes come here for lunch and think the sandwiches and snack fare are great. For dinner downstairs in the main restaurant, you might try as an appetizer the baked artichoke hearts stuffed with crab salad or the sautéed crab cakes served with a black bean sauce and chile crème fraîche. Entrées run the gamut from chicken alfredo or roast pork loin in a spiced cider sauce to roasted rack of lamb with a curried eggplant coulis. Since our early meals here, the fare seems to have lost some of its luster, but there's no denying the setting. In nice weather, eat outside both upstairs and down on covered decks with glimpses of the lake beyond the sheds of a boat yard.

171 Battery St., Burlington. (802) 864-1800. Entrées, $14.95 to $20.95. Daily, 11:30 to 10, Sunday from 10:30.

Mirabelles Cafe. Situated near the water in the new Wing Building, this popular offshoot of the equally popular Mirabelles bakery and deli at 198 Main St. packs folks in all day long. You order from an immense blackboard menu at the rear counter, then find a table inside or outside on a courtyard terrace. Sandwiches in the $3.95 to $4.95 range run the gamut from artichoke pesto with vegetables to peppered turkey with cheddar cheese and apple chutney. If the myriad choices don't suffice, you can create your own. You also might opt for soup and salad or the signature ploughman's lunch ($5.95). Come here early for wake-up cappuccino and croissants. Return for afternoon tea and one of the fantastic desserts, served Monday-Saturday 2:30 to 5.

1 Steele St., Burlington. (802) 658-1466. Daily in season, 7:30 to 7.

Be advised that assorted mobile and stationary snack bars and food wagons also peddle their wares along the waterfront area. And, shades of the real West Coast, the quirky **Skinny's Juice Bar** in the Wing Building slakes the thirsts of vegetarians and others.

Downtown Dining

Sweet Tomatoes Trattoria. Capitalizing on their smash-success restaurant of the same name in Lebanon, N.H., Robert Meyers and James Reiman run a carbon copy here and recently opened another in Rutland. From Burlington's first wood-fired brick oven come zesty pizzas like the namesake sweet tomato pie, a combination of tomato, basil, mozzarella and olive oil ($7.75). From the rest of the open kitchen that runs along the side of the long, narrow and surprisingly large downstairs space come earthy pastas, grills and entrées at wallet-pleasing prices. The top tab is $10.95, for the mixed grill or skewers of lamb. For a quick dinner, we were impressed with the cavateppi with spit-roasted chicken ($8.95). The special of linguini infused with olive oil and mushrooms proved rather bland. A huge salad topped with romano, a basket of bread for dipping in the house olive oil and a $14 bottle of Orvieto accompanied. The stark decor in white and black is offset by brick arches and stone walls. It's a convivial, noisy setting for what Robert

Eating at outdoor cafes is a pleasant summer pastime in downtown Burlington.

calls "strictly ethnic Italian cooking, as prepared in a home kitchen." The sidewalk cafe out front is one of Burlington's busiest.

83 Church St., Burlington. (802) 660-9533. Entrées, $10.95 and under. Lunch, Monday-Saturday 11:30 to 2; late lunch to 4; dinner 5 to 9:30 or 10, Sunday to 9.

Sweetwaters. An old brick bank, built in 1925, houses one of Burlington's more popular restaurants. Dining is on several levels around an atrium bearing an enormous mural depicting life on Church Street in the 1980s (including faces of local residents as well as dignitaries), and outside on a canopy-covered sidewalk cafe that's always crowded in summer. A all-day cafe menu offers snacks like potato skins, Buffalo wings, cheese nachos, chicken fingers and flatbread pizzas ($3.95 to $6.95). Interesting salads and Perry Farm bison burgers, from a herd raised on the Perry restaurant chain's farm in Charlotte, are featured at lunch ($4.95 to $7.95). Pastas and fajitas are available all day. At night, more substantial entrées include wood-grilled chicken with shiitake mushrooms and sundried tomatoes, grilled shrimp with gazpacho sauce and couscous, teriyaki steak and grilled sirloin topped with sundried tomato butter.

120 Church St., Burlington. (802) 864-9800. Entrées, $10.95 to $14.95. Daily from 11:30 to 2 a.m., Sunday from 10:30 to midnight.

The Daily Planet. The name of this funky place reflects its global fare, which is consistent and creative. The chefs shine with things like Vietnamese shrimp patties, Korean vegetable pancakes, Brazilian seafood stew, roast duck with rhubarb sauce, Moroccan vegetable sauté, chicken with goat cheese, and grilled lamb loin with a salad of fennel, red onion and orange with feta flatbread, pleasantly priced in the $5.95 to $6.50 range at lunch and under $18.50 at dinner. For lunch if they offer it, try the pan bagnat, a baguette stuffed with cheese, grilled provençal vegetables and arugula. The smoked salmon flatbread pizza is a hit any time. Desserts range widely from pear-blueberry pie to fresh plum ice cream and Southern nut cake with bourbon crème anglaise. Besides a large bar popular with university types, there are several dining rooms in which the oilcloth table coverings at noon give way to white linens at night.

15 Center St., Burlington. (802) 862-9647. Entrées, $9.95 to $18.50. Lunch, Monday-Friday 11:30 to 3; dinner nightly, 5 to 10:30 or 11; Saturday and Sunday brunch, 11 to 3.

Coyotes Tex-Mex Cafe. Brothers Eric and Jeff Lipkin from Kennebunkport, Me., teamed with Jim Glatz of Philadelphia to produce as authentic a Tex-Mex menu as possible (considering the far northern location) in a rather authentic setting. The interior is striking for its inlaid tile tables imported from Mexico, walls sponged burnt orange and shelves of pottery from the famed Goose Rocks Pottery owned by the brothers' parents. Rattlesnake beer and "ultimate" margaritas are served at a long bar converted from a bowling lane. Texas Hellfire sauce is on each table to add heat to the already hot fare: things like three-bean chipotle chili, potato burritos, a basket of corn fritters and lamb fajitas. Main-courses range from Mexican mussels to Texas baby back ribs. The tortilla chips, crisp and light, come with a zesty salsa that's addictive. We also liked the black bean soup, again with its own kick, served in a heavy custom-made bowl. The Amarillo appetizer sampler (five changing choices, $5.95) was less successful, and the taco chicken salad ($4.95) proved far too much to eat for lunch. Next time we'd try the tequila chicken ($8.95), served with rice and sautéed vegetables. Sopapillas and flan are the desserts of choice.

161 Church St., Burlington. (802) 865-3632. Entrées, $6.95 to $11.95. Lunch daily, 11:30 to 4; dinner, 4 to 10; late-night menu to 12:30.

Leunig's Bistro. For years, this has been everyone's idea of a European old-world cafe and bar. Under new owners Kathryn and Attila Keller, it's a full restaurant as well. The interior is attractive in peach with black trim, but we prefer Leunig's in summer when the old garage doors rise and open the place onto the sidewalk. Attila, former manager of the Four Seasons restaurant in New York, has expanded the menu. Grilled pizzas and pastas are featured at lunch ($4.95 to $7.95), along with such interesting sandwiches as prime rib lavasch and grilled yellowfin tuna with wasabi mayo. The Mediterranean-inspired dinner menu adds more pastas and entrées like pan-roasted salmon with mussels, tomato, leeks, garlic and couscous salad; poached chicken with rosemary goat cheese, sundried tomato pesto and mesclun salad, and grilled black angus steak with roquefort peppercorn butter and warm potato salad. Start with grilled crab cakes with citrus-mustard vinaigrette. Finish with espresso chocolate nougat or fresh apple crisp.

115 Church St., Burlington. (802) 863-3759. Entrées, $10.95 to $19.95. Breakfast daily, 7:30 to 11; lunch, 11:30 to 4; dinner, 5 to 10.

On the Outskirts of Town

Cafe Shelburne. This prize of a small provincial French restaurant is better than ever following its acquisition by Patrick Grangien, a Frenchman who trained with Paul Bocuse. The copper bar, several dining areas that look as if they're straight from the European countryside and an idyllic screened and latticed rear patio all appeal. So does Patrick's updated-French menu, skillfully executed and nicely priced for entrées like chicken à l'orange and roasted veal tenderloin with a corn galette. Among the not-often-seen dishes are steak tartare and sautéed rabbit with a wine and sage sauce and fettuccine. To start, the creamy mussel soup is perfumed with saffron, the chilled cucumber-dill soup is garnished with curried shrimp and water chestnuts, and the house-smoked salmon is sliced over grilled polenta. End a memorable meal with the specialty crème brûlée.

Route 7, Shelburne. (802) 985-3939. Entrées, $17 to $19.50. Dinner, Tuesday-Saturday 6 to 9:30, also Sunday from Labor Day to mid-October.

The Inn at Shelburne Farms. This landmark inn beside Lake Champlain harbors one of the area's more acclaimed restaurants. Dining is an event in the serene Marble Room, quite stunning with formally set tables, red fabric-covered walls and tiled floors in black and white, or outside at white-clothed tables on a veranda overlooking the lake with the Adirondacks rising beyond. Chef Tom Bivins, who has been with the inn since its beginning, changes the menu frequently to feature the freshest of local ingredients. You might start with salmon tartare, confit of duck with wilted greens or a spicy Louisiana caesar salad with tasso-wrapped shrimp and cornbread croutons ($5.75 to $9). For a main course how about pan-roasted yellowfin tuna with a toasted sunflower crust, roasted chicken stuffed with spinach and crabmeat or a grilled eggplant and blank angus tenderloin napoleon with an oriental ginger sauce? Dessert could be maple crème brûlée with cookies or a chocolate mousse torte with four sauces.

Shelburne. (802) 985-8498. Entrées, $22 to $28. Dinner nightly by reservation, 6 to 9. Closed mid-October to mid-May.

Pauline's Cafe & Restaurant. Once known as Pauline's Kitchen, this has been expanded under the ownership of chef Robert Fuller. The main floor is a clubby cafe paneled in cherry and oak, with a new side addition yielding big windows for a lighter look. Upstairs is a ramble of small, elegant dining rooms, the main room serene in sponged yellow and green beneath a striking green ceiling. A hidden brick patio outside is enclosed in evergreens and a trellis decked out with small international flags and tiny white lights. The cafe menu delivers a good meal of appetizers and light entrées ($7.50 to $11.95) such as pastas, crab cakes, grilled pork tenderloin, chicken with Shelburne Farms cheddar-cream sauce and seafood mixed grill. The more formal upstairs dinner menu changes nightly and is offered in the cafe and on the patio as well. Entrées might include baked bluefish provençal, salmon Siciliana and Mediterranean veal. We fondly remember a spring dinner that began with morels and local fiddleheads in a rich madeira sauce and a sprightly dish of shrimp and scallops in ginger. The entrées of thick filet mignon and three strips of lamb wrapped around goat cheese were superior. A honey-chocolate mousse from Pauline's acclaimed assortment of desserts and a special coffee with cointreau and apricot brandy ended a fine meal.

1834 Shelburne Road, South Burlington. (802) 862-1081. Entrées, $14.95 to $22.95 Lunch daily, 11:30 to 2:30; cafe menu, 2:30 to closing; dinner, 5 to 10; Sunday brunch, 10:30 to 2.

Perry's Fish House & Market. The locals love this vast seafood emporium, as they do the local chain's Dakota steakhouses and Sirloin Saloons. One reason is the nautical decor (the outside, from driftwood to landscaping, looks like something you'd find in Florida; inside, maritime memorabilia hangs on walls and ceilings in four dining areas). Another is the "daily delivery report" on the blackboard, which details species, origin and price. The large menu has all the standards, including a signature seafood stew and broiled seafood platter. But the centerpiece is the nightly specials, unadulterated preparations of, say, broiled sea scallops, wood-grilled mako shark and tuna, grilled swordfish, Maryland crab cakes and king crab. There's a minnow's menu for youngsters, who really eat this place up. Homemade key lime pie is the dessert of choice.

1080 Shelburne Road, South Burlington. (802) 862-1300. Entrées, $10.95 to $19.95. Dinner nightly, 5 to 10 or 11, Sunday 4 to 10.

The Lake Champlain Islands

Starting a dozen or so miles north of Burlington, these four pencil-shaped, inter-connected islands stretch 30 miles to the Canadian border. Here is where you really can get away from it all and revert to the past.

Tourist trappings have bypassed this lovely island setting (we'll never forget the Fourth of July parade in South Hero some years ago – a couple of makeshift floats and bands, plus our children's flag-waving cousins from Montreal, whose photo made the front page of the next day's Burlington Free Press; this was small-town America at its smallest).

The southern entrance to the islands via Route 2 passes the area's best lake swimming at Sand Bar State Park, where Burlington residents go to swim and picnic in a scenic grove. Beside it is the Sand Bar Wildlife Area for birdwatchers. Another recreation spot farther along is Knight Point State Park, with swimming, boating and campsites.

Things to See and Do

Water activities, birding and biking are the chief activities on the islands, where a Roman Catholic shrine is the leading tourist destination.

Royal Lipizzan Stallions. Since 1992, the islands have been the summer home for the stallions, which winter in Myakka City, Fla. The fourteen purebred descendants of a line established in 1580 are known for their acrobatic leaps and other precisely executed maneuvers. They entertain on a field above the lake in North Hero, where spectators occupy folding chairs beneath a striped canopy or a couple of sections of open-air bleachers. The Lipizzans are owned and directed by Col. Ottomar Herrmann, who with his father and the help of General Patton smuggled them out of Austria during World War II. You can meet the royal horses and their riders before or after their performances. The stallions can be viewed in their off-hours in their tent stable or working out on the field off Route 2, just south of North Hero.

Route 2, North Hero. (802) 372-5683. Performances late July to Labor Day, Thursday and Friday at 6 and Saturday and Sunday at 2:30. Adults $15, children $8.

St. Anne's Shrine. Thousands of pilgrims visit the peaceful shrine, site of Vermont's first white settlement, where the first Mass was celebrated in 1666. An open-sided chapel in a lakeside pine grove marks the spot where Samuel de Champlain landed in 1609. Conducted by the Edmundite Fathers and Brothers, the shrine is primitive, in keeping with island tradition. Visitors may swim from the beach, picnic or have an inexpensive meal in the cafeteria in a new, architec-turally striking multi-purpose building.

Isle La Motte. (802) 928-3362 or 928-3385. Daily, May 15 to Oct. 15. Free.

Hyde Log Cabin. This is considered the oldest log cabin standing in the United States and an official state historic site. Built in 1783 of hand-hewn logs, it is maintained by the Grand Isle Historical Society and displays tools, furnishings and documents.

Route 2, Grand Isle. Thursday-Monday 11 to 5, July 4 through Labor Day. Admission $1.

Ed Weed Fish Culture Station. Next to the ferry terminal in Grand Isle, this is the newest of five fish hatcheries maintained by the state to provide fish for public waters throughout Vermont. The multi-million-dollar facility is state of the art. A visitor center includes aquaria, displays on the lake's ecology and self-guided tours. *14 Bell Hill Road, Grand Isle. (802) 372-3171. Daily, 8 to 4.*

Places to Eat or Stay

Shore Acres Inn and Restaurant. Here is a secluded complex set nicely back from the highway on 50 acres of rolling grounds above the lake. Nineteen lakeview rooms with waterfront decks are situated in two motel-type wings on either side of the pleasant dining room. Four queensize rooms are in a garden house annex that operates as a B&B in the off-season. Each room has private bath, cable TV, pine paneling and maple furniture. The lakeview restaurant serves breakfast, lunch and dinner daily in summer. At dinner, begin with coconut beer-battered shrimp or grilled crostini of the day. Entrées ($12.95 to $17.95) range from grilled tuna with fruit salsa to an oversize New York strip steak. *Route 2, North Hero 05474. (802) 372-8722. Doubles, $77.50 to $99.50. Open May to mid-October; B&B open all year.*

Thomas Mott Homestead. Ex-Californian Pat Schallert transformed an 1838 farmhouse into a homey B&B, one of our favorites anywhere. It offers five spacious guest rooms with private baths and a secluded lakeside location with panoramic water and mountain views that won't quit. The fireplaced living room is stocked with books and magazines, three porches invite lounging, and Pat cooks up a hearty breakfast in a spacious dining room open to the kitchen. Raspberry or blackberry pancakes, crab or shrimp omelets, and french toast spread with cream cheese and five kinds of nuts are in his repertoire. Other special touches that make this place a winner: a stash of Ben & Jerry's ice cream and chilled ice cream dishes in the refrigerator, a lakeside gazebo, a 75-foot boating dock, a patch of "stealing" raspberries and a pen beside the barn where Pat raises quail. *Blue Rock Road, Alburg 05440. (802) 796-3736 or (800) 348-0843. Doubles, $69 to $89.*

Ruthcliffe Lodge. Excellent dining and comfortable lodging right beside the lake are the attractions here. Chef-owner Mark Infante has gained quite a following for his Italian-American fare, ranging from $10.95 for baked manicotti to $17.95 for New York strip steak with peppercorn sauce. We liked a special of crab cakes with pasta and the signature shrimp marco, served over linguini with sundried tomatoes and shiitake mushrooms, all the better because it was eaten on the lakeside deck with a citronella candle and a full moon for light. Kathy Infante is responsible for most of the homemade desserts, and also oversees the lodging. Besides the restaurant, the lodge holds two guest rooms with half baths and shared shower. The lodgings of choice are six nicely decorated units and a family suite in the adjacent lakefront motel, which come with a full breakfast of the guests' choice, from eggs benedict to belgian waffles. *Old Quarry Road, Isle La Motte 05463. (802) 928-3200. Doubles, $58 to $70; suite, $91.50. Lunch in summer, noon to 2; dinner nightly, 5 to 9. Open mid-May to Columbus Day.*

The Sandbar Motor Inn & Restaurant. Just across the Sand Bar causeway from the mainland, this is a simple motel with a million-dollar Hilton view.

Its 37 generally smallish rooms bear such caring touches as homemade wreaths above the beds and bouquets of fresh flowers gathered from prolific gardens out front. There are housekeeping units as well. Sit by the fire in the locally popular restaurant (open for breakfast and dinner) and sample the "Green Mountain Surprise," a homemade spicy preserve served with cream cheese and crackers. The dinner fare ($9.95 to $16.95) ranges from roast turkey and seafood newburg to chicken cordon bleu. Our New York strip steak and filet mignon dinners were so filling we had no room for dessert. The Sandbar has a private stony beach, rental boats and sailboards, a playground and games area on the lawn, and views of the lake and mountains from both front and back.

Route 2, South Hero 05486. (802) 372-6911. Doubles, $57 to $60; efficiencies, $65 to $70. Open May to mid-December.

The North Hero House. Right beside Lake Champlain and good for all kinds of boating activities, this complex emits a homey, old-fashioned summer resort feeling. It offers six simple rooms in the main inn and seventeen more in three lakeside houses, all with private baths. Those on the lakefront come with porches, and the Cobbler's Suite is a prime choice. Lately, the housekeeping has left something to be desired, according to disappointed guests, who also report the meals have not been up to snuff. Breakfast has been scaled down to continental and lunch no longer is served. The continental/Italian dinner menu ($11.95 to $16.95) is the islands' most prodigious.

Route 2, North Hero 05474. (802) 372-8237. Doubles, $69 to $89; suite, $119. Open May to mid-October.

A Welcome Respite

Hero's Welcome General Store. Let's conclude with a hero's welcome for this sophisticated new general store, bakery and cafe. Here is a good stop for oversize muffins and a morning espresso, as well as afternoon ice cream and cookies. If you can get beyond all the wines and foodstuffs in front, you'll find display area after display area chock full of everything from Tide and aspirin to expensive china handpainted with iris by a Vermont artist. The shed in back stocks everything a boater could need. Browsers could happily spend hours in this complex, and those who wait for them can enjoy the lake view from picnic tables and benches across the street.

Route 2, North Hero. (802) 372-4161.

FOR MORE INFORMATION: Lake Champlain Regional Chamber of Commerce, 60 Main St., Burlington 05402, (802) 863-3489. Also, Lake Champlain Islands Chamber of Commerce, Route 2, Box 213, North Hero 05474, (802) 372-5683.

7  Summer

More than 100 steps lead to ocean beach at Mohegan Bluffs on Block Island.

An Island Idyll

Block Island, R.I.

Block Island is a seascape in bright green, soft blue and touches of gray. The greens are the rolling hills; the blues, the sky and sea; the grays, the weathered houses and the old stone walls.

We first visited the island in 1970. At that time, The Block (as it's affectionately known) was barely awakening from its postwar lethargy. Big old Victorian hotels that had drawn crowds via steamer from New York City at the turn of the century were boarded-up hulks. A guest house or two – notably the 1661 Inn – were just beginning to get into the business again.

Only seven miles long by three miles wide and lying thirteen miles off the Rhode Island mainland, Block Island was, for years, bypassed by those who made Martha's Vineyard and Nantucket *the* places to go. Its tiny town of Old Harbor (officially

New Shoreham) didn't have much to offer: no hospital, few stores, a couple of independent groceries. The weather was occasionally so blustery that neither ferry nor airport could function. Only 500 people hung around in the winter.

Yet, among those who spent part or all of their summers on Block Island, fierce loyalties developed. They returned year after year, and still do. And Block Island, in recent years, has experienced an incredible resurgence. Hotels are back in business, guest houses are sprouting up everywhere, and the activity on summer weekends can be fairly intense.

Fortunately, two and three-acre zoning outside town has limited the number of houses that can be built on the island. It also has preserved the vistas of rolling green hills with distant views of the water. The island has been likened to Ireland. Artists love it for its light and the charm of its old buildings and beautiful vistas.

In the 1990s, The Nature Conservancy, an international organization serious about protecting biodiversity, gave Block Island its blessing. It proclaimed Block Island one of America's "Last Great Places" – and Chris Littlefield, whose family goes back to 1670 on the island, is doing his best to keep it that way. As bioreserve manager for the conservancy on the island, he works full time to acquire land and protect open space, to acquaint people with the island's history and habitats, to get them on his side: the side of the environmentally concerned.

The effort is working.

Block Island is for the carefree traveler, the kind who can be happy with a book on the beach or a bike ride to the far end of the island. He's the type who has learned to entertain himself and who doesn't expect a song and dance band to greet him wherever he goes. He might be found in cutoff jeans and a T-shirt or, at most, a pair of casual pants. He doesn't expect, nor does he want, a TV or a telephone in his room (although a few of the newer places have them). If you're that kind of traveler, then Block Island is the place for you.

Getting There

The main port of embarkation for ferry service to Block Island is Point Judith, R.I., from which year-round service is offered by Interstate Navigation Co., Galilee State Pier, (401) 783-4613. There are eight to ten trips a day each way from mid-June to September; ferries run less often at other times. The trip takes an hour. Approximate one-way fares: adults $6.60, children $3.15, cars $20, motorcycles $12, bicycles $2. One-day round trips are available at a reduced rate. Reserve well in advance to take a car during the summer.

Daily ferries also are provided in summer from New London, Conn., by Nelseco Navigation Co., 2 Ferry St., (860) 442-7891. The Anna C takes two hours to reach the island. One-way costs: car $25, adults $14, children $9.

More and more people are reaching the island by air. New England Airlines offers nearly twenty flights a day from Westerly, R.I. Call (401) 596-2460 in Westerly or (401) 466-5881 on Block Island or (800) 243-2460 (outside Rhode Island).

Flights from Groton/New London, Conn., and New York/LaGuardia are offered by Action Airlines, (800) 243-8623. One-way fare to the island from New London is about $30; from New York City, about $150.

Seeing and Doing

You don't need a car, particularly for a stay of two or three days.

Bicycles, leisurely and quiet, are the preferred mode of travel. They can be rented for $10 to $16 a day. Mopeds are noisy and often the drivers are inexperienced, making for some hairy adventures. Should you feel confident, expect to pay $40 to $50 a day for a single-passenger vehicle, $60 for a two-seater.

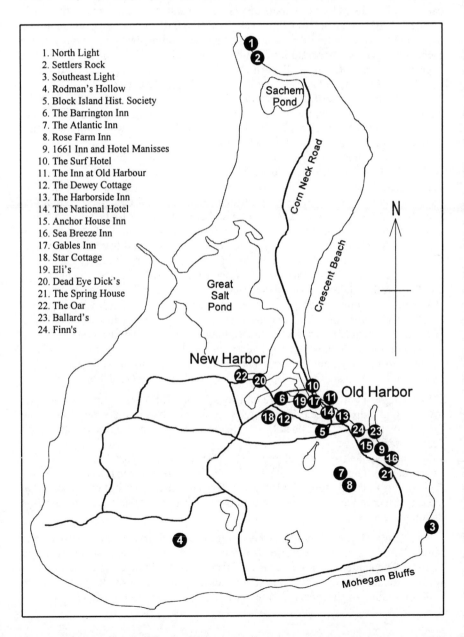

1. North Light
2. Settlers Rock
3. Southeast Light
4. Rodman's Hollow
5. Block Island Hist. Society
6. The Barrington Inn
7. The Atlantic Inn
8. Rose Farm Inn
9. 1661 Inn and Hotel Manisses
10. The Surf Hotel
11. The Inn at Old Harbour
12. The Dewey Cottage
13. The Harborside Inn
14. The National Hotel
15. Anchor House Inn
16. Sea Breeze Inn
17. Gables Inn
18. Star Cottage
19. Eli's
20. Dead Eye Dick's
21. The Spring House
22. The Oar
23. Ballard's
24. Finn's

Sachem Pond

Corn Neck Road

Crescent Beach

N

Great Salt Pond

New Harbor

Old Harbor

Mohegan Bluffs

Walking is also recommended. If you stay in Old Harbor you can walk to just about everything, including the beach.

A handy map of the island is available in the Block Island Times, the indispensable weekly newspaper.

Exploring the Island

Bicycling has long been a favorite pursuit on the island, so much so that we can't imagine the place without its bikers – some call it the Bermuda of the north.

North Light at the end of Corn Neck Road (the Indians used to grow their corn there) at the northern tip of the island is a favorite cycling destination and you can picnic once you get there. Built of Connecticut granite in 1867, the lighthouse has been restored recently. A small maritime museum inside is open from 10 to 4 daily in July and August, and on weekends in late spring and early fall. Admission, $2. The trip by bike to North Light is about five miles each way and is slightly hilly, but reasonably easy. Out by the freshwater **Sachem Pond** at this end of the island, you'll find **Settlers Rock** with the names of the sixteen stalwart souls who first settled on the island, coming ashore in 1661.

Hardy sorts (you don't have to be *too* hardy) like to make a bicycle circuit of the island. Begin in Old Harbor and travel north along the shore to the intersection with Beach Avenue, then west past New Harbor with its marinas (you can find restrooms here), the Block Island Historical Cemetery and onto West Side Road. From West Side Road you can take any number of dirt roads to the water; we like Cooneymus Road to reach a wild, wonderful stretch of beach, often deserted. Retrace this dirt stretch to the paved portion of Cooneymus and follow Cooneymus east to Lakeside Drive, then south to Mohegan Trail with its fabulous high views over Mohegan Bluffs (toward Montauk, Long Island) and down to **Southeast Light**, an 1874 brick lighthouse whose lantern can be seen 35 miles at sea. A small but interesting new museum at the lighthouse is operated by the Block Island Historical Society. Rooms detail the history of the island in appropriately low-key style, stressing its early families, resort status and development over the years. You can watch a couple of videos, too. Open daily in summer, 10 to 4. Admission, $3.

This end of the island has been likened to Ireland. Follow Mohegan Trail to Southeast Light Road, then to Spring Street, and back into Old Harbor

Walking is a particular pleasure on Block Island, for it's a compact place. The town of Old Harbor is fine for moseying. You can poke in the shops, watch the ferry come in, or visit the Block Island Historical Society exhibitions or the Island Free Library.

Out on the island are several good places for walking. Delightfully meandering paths cut through eleven acres of natural growth at **The Maze** in the island's northeast corner. Located atop Clay Head, it offers fantastic views out over the ocean, the surprise of hidden ponds and many birds since it's one of the Audubon Society's banding stations.

Rodman's Hollow, a wild and beautiful cleft in the rolling southwestern terrain, adjoins a 200-acre parcel of land managed by the Rhode Island Audubon Society. The cemetery on Center Road is an interesting place for exploring, and some of the tombstones bear unusual legends. Be watchful for ticks when you are walking around in shrubbery; Lyme disease is a problem on the island.

Outdoor Activities

Beaching is best along the island's east coast. There are several names for what is essentially the same strand, from Surfer's Beach to Fred Benson State Beach to Scotch Beach and ultimately to Mansion Beach. The whole stretch is sometimes referred to as Crescent Beach. The state beach has the gentlest section, plus a pavilion, snack bar and lifeguards; it's great for kids. You can rent umbrellas and beach chairs here ($5 each). The water is crystal-clear and inclined to be brisk, especially before mid-July. Locals love Mansion Beach, reached via dirt road from Corn Neck Road. Charleston Beach on the west side of the island, just southwest of the Coast Guard Station, is more rugged, less populated and better for exploring and walking than swimming. We've found good driftwood here. Reach it via dirt roads from West Side Road.

Horseback riding is available. Guided trail rides are offered on beaches and through meadow lands by Rustic Rides Farm , (401) 466-5060.

Kite flying. Don't miss a chance to use the great island breezes and have some fun. You'll find a good selection at the Block Island Kite Company on Corn Neck Road.

Boating can be approached two ways: do-it-yourself or watch others. You can rent rowboats at the Twin Maples on Beach Avenue, New Harbor. The marinas where you can watch graceful sailboats and huge power boats are Champlin's and the Block Island Boat Basin. Payne's Dock at New Harbor is another good place for a view of the boating action.

Kayaking is coming on strong. You can rent a kayak at Oceans and Ponds to explore Trims Pond, the Great Salt Pond, Sachem Pond, and the waters around Mansion and Scotch beaches. You can also rent kayaks at Fred Benson State Beach. Oceans and Ponds, an official outlet of Orvis of Manchester, Vt., offers fly-casting lessons and fishing gear.

Parasailing is relatively new on The Block and very popular.

Sportfishing is big. Stripers, blues and swordfish are caught in abundance in the waters off Block Island. You can easily find a charter boat by walking along the dock near Ballard's restaurant, not far from the ferry dock slip where several tie up. **Oceans and Ponds** on Ocean Avenue, an official outlet of Orvis of Manchester, Vt., offers fly-casting lessons and fishing gear.

Birding is a big attraction, especially in spring and fall when the island is directly on the migratory paths of many species. The Rhode Island Audubon Society, based in Smithfield, R.I., (401) 949-5454, leads interesting walks. The Nature Conservancy, (401) 466-2129, sponsors various migration field trips in September and October.

Indoors

The **Block Island Historical Society** at Old Town Road and Ocean Avenue is open daily in summer from 10 to 4. In addition to permanent historical exhibits portraying the island's farming and maritime past, it mounts changing exhibitions from time to time. The **Island Free Library** on Dodge Street is surprising for its contemporary design and is a beehive of activity, especially on a rainy day. Leave a deposit and borrow a book. Flyers advertising island events are usually posted here.

You can see a movie or attend live theater on the island. The **Oceanwest Theater,**

(401) 466-2971, near Champlin's Marina presents first-run movies (including matinees on rainy days) and productions by a professional summer stock theater in July and August. The **Empire Theater** in Old Harbor changes flicks every three or four days and is a great old-time place to watch a movie.

Shopping

We used to dismiss the shopping on Block Island as unexciting. No more. Old Harbor has most of the stores and can occupy you the better part of a rainy day, if you really get into it.

Our favorite shops include **The Scarlet Begonia** on Dodge Street and **The Red Herring** upstairs above **The Shoreline,** a clothing shop, on Water Street. The former has wonderful Irish pottery, rag rugs, tablecloths and button covers. In the latter you'll find fabulous "monotints" by island artist Jessie Edwards, throw pillows, dried flowers, bowls and – for our patio at home – squat glass hurricane lamps in pale green.

Joan Mallick's **Block Island Blue** pottery, displayed in its own Cape Cod house on Dodge Street, is exceptionally attractive and quite affordable. **The Glass Onion** on Water Street is one of the most tasteful and unusual gift shops on the island and has some good reading material, as well. **Watercolors** on Dodge Street is another favorite with nice pottery, mobiles, artwork, and such.

The Shoreline! on Water Street turned up the best of all Block Island T-shirts for a college-age son. In **Eté,** you can buy T-shirts and other summer clothes and jewelry.

The women's clothing store, **Rags,** carries Esprit and other good lines in casual summer wear. At the venerable **Star Department Store** you can find T-shirts, shorts and sundresses; also ceramic lobsters, kids' games and beach toys, greeting cards and wild bumper stickers.

Bruce Johnson's **Oceans and Ponds** is the place to get Block Island baseball caps made of "Nantucket red" heavy sailcloth with the island logo hand-embroidered in black. Or you can have the name of your boat embroidered here on a sweatshirt. A bargee (boat flag) can be made for you overnight, and you'll find T-shirts with a map of the island on them. This is a fine place for water lovers, boaters and fishermen.

Among the art galleries, check out **The Spring Street Gallery, Sea Breeze Gallery, The Ragged Sailor** and **Square One.**

You can buy wine, beer and harder stuff at the **Red Bird Liquor Store** on Dodge Street. We found the wine selection to be quite adequate. **Block Island Grocery** on Ocean Avenue has a fairly extensive selection of foods.

Where to Stay

Accommodations on Block Island are found in simple summer hotels with rocking chairs on the porches, in refurbished Victorian hostelries full of pressed-oak furniture and floral wallpapers, in small cottages and rental houses, and in increasingly sophisticated bed and breakfasts. Camping on the island is prohibited. In summer, it is imperative to have a reservation before you go. You may feel as if you've undergone a reverse time warp and are back at the turn of the century; in

Boating scene at New Harbor.

some ways you will be right. Three-night minimum stays are common on weekends in season.

To write for accommodations, simply address the establishment as listed in care of Block Island, R.I. 02807. Rates listed below are basically those for high season. Lower rates prevail during spring and fall.

The Barrington Inn. Joan and Howard Ballard are consummate hosts at this six-room B&B, located high on a knoll with a view of Great Salt Pond and its inner harbors. They also rent a couple of two-bedroom housekeeping apartments for $700 a week in summer, sometimes for shorter periods off-season. Location is excellent: just a short walk into Old Harbor, and down the street from a great beach. Around the corner is Payne's Dock at New Harbor. The Ballards put out fluffy striped beach towels in the parlor for guests to use. We like Room 4 with its own deck overlooking the pond. A grassy terrace with lawn furniture is good for lounging. A continental-plus breakfast is served in a large, bright room where most guests share one big table. The muffins are always freshly baked, fresh fruit is served in addition to juice, and you can scoop up the inn's own granola and yogurt. The Ballards rent kayaks and eighteen-speed bikes to guests.
Beach and Ocean Avenues, New Harbor. (401) 466-5510. Doubles, $105 to $149.

The Atlantic Inn.. Situated on a grassy hilltop where it gets the best of the island's breezes and distant views of the sea, this large Victorian hotel was totally redone in 1986. It is most welcoming, from the blue deck chairs and white tables scattered on the front lawn and across the large front porch to the Victorian furniture with needlepoint-look upholstery in the lobby. Check out the antique wooden phone booth with a working pay phone. The bar is one of our favorites, outfitted with bentwood bar stools, Victorian settees and sofas; it's a nifty place to sip sherry on a rainy evening, listening to classical music on tape. On a nice afternoon the porch is crowded for happy hour. The 21 rooms, all with private baths, feature off-white Victorian-style bedspreads with pillow shams, antique oak armoires and dressers, floral carpeting and baskets of amenities on the bureau.
High Street, Box 188, Old Harbor. (401) 466-5883. Fax: (401) 466-5678 Doubles, $110 to $195; suites, $210. Open April-October.

Rose Farm Inn. Robert and Judith Rose operate this comfortable B&B located off a road behind the Atlantic Inn and with the same wonderful breezes and views. Once the original farmhouse for the area, it has a marvelous stone porch that has been enclosed and turned into a multi-windowed breakfast room. Eight rooms have private tiled baths, and two share. Rooms on the inn's east side enjoy views of the water. A second building with porches all around, the Captain Rose House across the way, adds nine quite large rooms with private baths. Constructed recently, it lacks the charm of the original, but is comfortable and one room has handicapped access. All second-floor rooms have distant ocean views. Cereal, fruit and homemade breads are the fare for continental breakfast. Guests are provided beach towels for a day at the beach; they also may use an attractive sun deck. Daughter Janie operates Beach Rose Bicycles next door.

Box E, off High Street, Old Harbor. (401) 466-2034. Fax: (401) 466-2053. Doubles, $90 to $175. Open March-November.

1661 Inn, Guest House, Dodge Cottage and Hotel Manisses. The Abrams family of Providence opened the 1661 Inn, a refurbished and pleasant B&B, in 1969. Since then, they have added and upgraded, and taken over the large Victorian hotel down the street. The properties are just a short walk from the center of town. In 1996, they opened the nearby Dodge Cottage with nine rooms, six of which are queen-bedded with private baths; two are small efficiencies and one has a king bed and a kitchen. Guests at the inn and hotel have a good choice of accommodations, and all are fairly elegant. The nine plush rooms in the 1661 Inn are furnished in antiques and come with private baths and refrigerators. Five have jacuzzis and eight have private sun decks. Breakfast is served daily in its oceanview dining rooms, either inside or on a covered deck. All guests – including those at the Dodge Cottage – enjoy the same huge buffet breakfast. The Guest House offers a range of rooms; a few shared baths and a wicker-filled living room, some have private baths and ocean views, and three new rooms in the Nicholas Ball Cottage possess loft areas and fireplaces. In the Victorian hotel, the Manisses, seventeen rooms with private baths and telephones are attractively decorated with turn-of-the-century furniture. Some have jacuzzis. Beds are double, queen or kingsize. The large lobby with dramatic wallpaper (pink flowers on a blue background) is a terrific place to relax. In the evening, flaming coffees and desserts are served here. Outside are an exquisite flower garden and even a petting zoo. The main dining room downstairs is highly regarded (see Where to Eat).

Spring Street, Old Harbor. (401) 466-2421 or 2063 or (800) MANISSE. Fax: (401) 466-2836. Doubles, $85 to $275 depending on location and amenities. Some rooms are available year-round.

The Surf Hotel. This grand old Victorian hotel, built in 1876, is perfectly situated between the activity of Old Harbor and the glorious beach that runs for miles along the island's east coast. You can walk to everything. To some visitors the Surf is synonymous with the island itself, and the Ulric Cyr family, which has run the hotel for more than 40 years, keeps things pretty much the same from year to year. You will still find the popcorn wagon on the rocking-chair-lined front porch, where people-watchers have their fill; just about everyone on the island passes here sooner or later. The oversize chess set and a color TV in the lobby are often in use. Out back is a small porch for those who like to read and to contemplate the sea. All 35 rooms in the hotel share baths, but each has its own sink. Wallpapering and woodwork have been redone recently. In the Surfside Annex around the corner are three rooms with private baths and several that share. In the Back Cottage to the rear are five singles with shared bathrooms. Views from oceanside rooms are labeled "powerful" by a friend. A light breakfast is included in the rates. The Surf requires a six-night minimum stay in July and August, and seems to fill up.

Dodge and Water Streets, Old Harbor. (401) 466-2241 or 466-5990. Doubles, $90 to $130. Open late May to early October.

The Inn at Old Harbour. Located not far from the ferry dock, this inn on the second and third floors above shops in Old Harbor is beautifully decorated. We love the romance of Room 1 with lilac-sprigged wallpaper, an iron Nantucket basket bed and white organdy curtains – perfect for honeymooners or second honeymooners. Many of the ten rooms yield ocean views, most rooms have private baths and all are furnished in period pieces. Some have outside decks from which you can watch the ferry come and go. Continental breakfast is served in a light pine lobby, bright and sunny, which overlooks the street. You can enjoy a drink and the ocean view from the porch.

Water Street, Box 994, Old Harbor. (401) 466-2212. Doubles, $95 to $150. Open mid-May through September.

The Dewey Cottage. Norris and Nancy Pike (a real estate salesman and an interior decorator) gutted this six-bedroom cottage before turning it into one of the more smashing accommodations on the island. Room 3 with a king bed and whirlpool tub on the second floor has a great view from a charming bay-windowed sitting area. Rooms on the third floor offer distant views of the water. But this is really an in-town cottage, close to everything. Two rooms have twin beds and two have kings. A large wraparound porch off the main floor and a common room with chairs upholstered in blue and white stripes are enticing places to relax. A continental breakfast of fresh fruit, croissants and muffins is offered buffet-style in the common room. This is the room where you can watch TV or take a book from a shelf to read.

Ocean Avenue, Old Harbor. (401) 466-3155 or (800) 330-3155. Doubles, $100 to $140.

The Harborside Inn. Situated across the street from the ferry landing, the Harborside's perky red and white striped umbrellas and colorful window boxes offer a cheery welcome. Its location makes it a good choice for those who want to be in on the action; the large, nautically accented bar is a gathering spot, and the street out front is bustling with activity. All 42 rooms in the main inn have private baths, and some are on the small side. Rattan beds and furniture, wall-to-wall carpeting, and good views of the harbor activity make several rooms in the front of the building especially appealing. Room fans are provided. A full breakfast is included in the room rate. The dining room also serves lunch and dinner – at those umbrellaed tables in good weather.

Water Street, Old Harbor. (401) 466-5504 or (800) 892-2022. Fax: (401) 466-5460. Doubles, $99 to $199. Open mid-May to mid-October.

The National Hotel. This gigantic white hotel dominates your view of town as you arrive by the ferry. Refurbished and restored (from several years as a decrepit, non-functioning eyesore), it attracts crowds to its porch bar and restaurant. This is a real meeting place, in fact, and by 4 o'clock of a summer's afternoon it's sometimes all you can do to find a place to sit. The porch is rather high up off the street and yields a view of all the downtown action and of everyone going by. If you want a quiet, off-the-beaten-track place, this probably isn't it. All 45 rooms have private baths, TVs and telephones and are appropriately decorated in the Victorian style. The "corner queens" are a bit larger and have good cross ventilation. Floral blue and pink carpeting runs all through the hotel. A continental breakfast is served hotel guests in the bar.

Water Street, Old Harbor. (401) 466-2901 or (800) 225-2449. Fax: (401) 466-5948. Doubles, $99 to $229.

Anchor House Inn. Across the street from the Manisses Hotel and easily spotted with its huge old anchor on the lawn, this B&B was new in 1996. Four guest rooms with private baths, all on the second floor, are spare and simple, but offer televisions on shelves easily visible from bed, wall-to-wall carpeting, overhead fans and bed quilts. Guests can sit out on a front porch, or enjoy use of a first-floor common room with piano. A buffet continental breakfast in an attractive dining room offers items like bagels, cereal, muffins and juice.

Spring Street, Old Harbor. (401) 466-5021 or (800) 730-0181. Fax: (401) 466-8887. Doubles, $120 to $130. Open May-October.

Sea Breeze Inn. This weathered inn comprises several buildings with various accommodations, from rather luxurious and pricey to more simple. Several rooms yield views or glimpses of the ocean. Five of the ten rooms come with private entrances and private baths. Breakfast is delivered in a basket to most rooms, although there's a common area for breakfast in one building.

Spring Street, Old Harbor. (401) 466-2275 or (800) 786-2276. Doubles, $80 to $170.

Gables Inn and Gables II. These two guest houses with apartments are across the street from the beach and not far from the shopping area. Accommodations are done simply; traditional wallpaper and antique furnishings are the rule. Tea and coffee are available all day and there's a refrigerator in each building for guests' use. A continental breakfast is provided in the morning; most guests carry theirs onto the front porch or lawn and watch the world of Block Island go by. Inexpensive rentals of things like beach chairs and coolers for the beach are a real plus. Barbecue grills and picnic tables in the back yard can be used for cookouts.

Dodge Street, Old Harbor. (401) 466-2213. Doubles, $75 to $135. Open May-November.

A Budget Choice

Star Cottage. An old-fashioned and simple B&B located at the edge of town, Star Cottage offers four guest rooms sharing one large bathroom. All are decorated in country style and have double beds. Guests relax on a large front porch and take continental breakfast in the parlor.

Ocean Avenue, Old Harbor. (401) 466-2842. Doubles, $75 to $85. Open mid-April to mid-October.

Where to Eat

Visitors to Block Island are most often looking for breakfast or dinner places. Lunch spots are plentiful, and many people simply buy a hot dog at the beach. Our listings are according to the meal.

For Breakfast

The 1661 Inn. The inn serves a buffet breakfast to its own guests and those of The Manisses Hotel, and the public is welcome during the summer season. You'll feast on such specialties as corned beef hash, scrambled eggs, quiche, oven-roasted potatoes and possibly a vegetable casserole or chicken tetrazzini. A whole fish on a platter is often a centerpiece.

Spring Street. (401) 466-2421. Breakfast, 8 to 11 midweek; 8 to noon, weekends. Price: $11.50.

Ernie's Old Harbor Restaurant. At the ferry dock, upstairs from Finn's, this is popular, especially with the locals. You can order anything from pancakes to eggs, many styles, and the service is quick. Slip onto a stool at the counter or find a formica-topped table. Three-egg omelets are the rule and homemade muffins and coffee cake round out the meal. "The Sunny Side" is a six-ounce steak, two eggs, homefries and an English muffin. The Egg McSprague is an egg and Canadian bacon on an English muffin with cheese sauce. Prices are in the $3 to $7 range.

Water Street, Old Harbor. Breakfast, Monday-Friday 6:30 to noon, weekends to 1.

For Dinner

Hotel Manisses. The restaurant at the Manisses is well regarded. There are three locations to choose from: an inner room, with circular flowered placemats on the tables and rattan chairs; an outer room with lots of glass, and the gazebo, new in 1995, which overlooks the back yard. The menu changes nightly in summer and has some really creative touches. Fresh vegetables and herbs from the hotel garden show up in the soups (often turnip or broccoli) and in many of the main dishes. Appetizers might be clams casino or a black bean and feta tortilla with cilantro cream. Among recent entrées were flounder française, grilled tuna with pineapple salsa, lobster cantonese and roasted half chicken with rosemary and lemon. A salad of mixed greens with a tarragon-mustard vinaigrette and a starch plus vegetable come with. Lunch options might be a cold lobster plate, or salad or sandwich specials.

Spring Street, Old Harbor. (401) 466-2836. Entrees, $17 to $23. Lunch daily in summer; dinner nightly, 6 to 10, weekends rest of year.

Eli's. Eli's motto is "Life's short – Eat large." Chef-owner David Silvernberg serves large portions at his immensely popular storefront restaurant just off the main drag. Light wood tables and chairs and bright napkins and placemats give this a beachy, casual feeling. Opened in 1995, Eli's moved next door and doubled its space in 1996. No reservations are taken, and the place, which seats about 40, plus a few at a bar in the rear, fills up by 7 when the waiting list is started. Prices also went up with the move but the food is still "large" and quite creative. We have yet to have less than a terrific meal here. Pastas are offered in several guises. Choices might be penne baked with prosciutto, mushrooms, broccoli, pine nuts and parmesan, or a pesto baked ziti. The chicken royale is stuffed with scallops, tomatoes and green beans.

Chapel Street, Old Harbor. (401) 466-5230. Entrees, $14 to $20. Dinner nightly, 5 to 10, in season, weekends in off-season. Open year-round.

Dead Eye Dick's. This low white clapboard building with window boxes is favored by boaters because of its location near the Great Salt Pond. We blew in one rainy, blustery Friday evening and had a great time. It's simple and straightforward, with bare wooden floors, paneled walls and each table with placemats, fresh flowers and a candle flickering. Entrées might include blackened swordfish with jalapeño jelly, shrimp and broccoli pasta, chicken breast in a dijon-chive sauce, and scallops over linguini with a hoisin-plum-ginger sauce. Our broiled sea scallops and a swordfish special were excellent. Appetizers are old favorites like shrimp cocktail, clams or oysters on the half shell, steamed littlenecks and – something different for the island – Maryland crab cakes with homemade salsa. Gourmet pizza is always a possibility; the ingredients change daily. Service is prompt and professional.

Payne's Dock, New Harbor. (401) 466-2654. Entrees, $14 to $21. Lunch daily, 11 to 5; dinner, 5 to 11. Open Memorial Day to mid-September.

Harborside Inn. Eat outdoors when the weather is nice or inside when it's not. Located across from the ferry dock, the Harborside is always crowded and one reason is the salad bar, which is advertised as the island's best. Nautical touches (fish nets and such) are found above the captains' tables and chairs; red placemats and napkins add warmth. But it's outdoors under those red and white striped umbrellas where everybody wants to sit – to see and be seen. Nightly specials might be grilled tuna or swordfish. Regular specialties include scallops sautéed in a light garlic and herb butter, a grilled seafood sampler and a sirloin club steak. A good pasta menu in the $14 range is an option. A New England lobster bake was being offered for $16.95 last we knew.

Water Street, Old Harbor. (401) 466-5504. Entrees, $17 to $24. Breakfast, lunch and dinner daily, May to October.

The Spring House. High marks are accorded the dining room at the Spring House, a venerable Block Island hotel that has been refurbished in recent years. Pink tablecloths and light wood chairs make an attractive dining environment at one end of the huge open lobby. Among entrées, try fresh grilled tuna or salmon sirloin, roasted chicken with garlic and rosemary, steak au poivre or double-cut lamb chops with mint pesto. A one-pound baked potato with sour cream will add another $3.25 to the tab. Light dining is available in the large Victoria's Parlor off the main lobby, which has a huge bar and is popular after hours.

Spring Street, Old Harbor. (401) 466-5844. Entrees, $17 to $27. Dinner nightly in season, 6 to 10.

The Oar. This small restaurant with a big deck overlooking the Great Salt Pond used to be a beery hangout for sailors at the nearby marinas, but little more. With its takeover by the Abrams family (of the 1661 Inn and Manisses Hotel), it's act has been cleaned up and the food is quite good. The best thing is watching all the maneuvering of yachts and sailboats as you eat outdoors at one of the umbrellaed tables on the deck, where there's an L-shaped bar in the corner. The all-day menu is nicely balanced with appetizers and sides such as vegetarian chili, beer-batter french fries, rice and beans, and clam chowder, plus club sandwiches ($6) with grilled chicken, roast beef and, for $11.75, lobster. Our BLT was perfect: luscious tomatoes, crisp bacon and a hearty, grainy wheat bread. Fried chicken is available in many sizes and is probably carried back to many a boat. Grilled shrimp kabobs and fried clams are other entrée possibilities .

New Harbor. (401) 466-8820. Entrees, $8 to $14. Open daily in season, 11:30 to 11 or midnight.

Ballard's. "You haven't been to Block Island if you haven't been to Ballard's," goes the saying. Ballard's attracts boaters and daytrippers, fishermen and year-round residents and, one day when we were there, the Travelers Insurance Cos. women's club from Hartford. It's enormous, with long tables and bentwood chairs. Flags of supposedly every nation on earth fly overhead; there are a slew of them, and we wonder how all are kept straight with the sudden changes in alliances. The famed bar is appropriately large for the cavernous dining hall. It's not exactly atmosphere that customers here are seeking, but rather the seafood and the bustle (at night, various bands hold forth). Ballard's "best buy" is lobster family style, where each diner gets two lobsters, a choice of potato and vegetable for $21.95. Variations are offered, including lazy lobster. The baby shore dinner brings a steamed lobster, a bowl of clam chowder, steamed mussels and clams, fish of the day, an ear of corn and watermelon for $19.75. Fried clams, fish and chips, a seafood sampler and a complete tuna dinner are other possibilities. You can understand why all the boaters and fishermen hang out here.

Old Harbor. (401) 466-4231. Entrees, $15 to $23. Open daily in season, 11 to 10.

The National Hotel. The National's big and popular front porch overlooking the harbor is where people prefer to dine, if they can find a seat. The menu stresses beef – a bit of a departure for seafood-oriented Block Island – and many visitors are grateful for all the options. Grilled pork chops, filet mignon, ribeye and porterhouse steaks, and a New York strip topped with a saga blue dressing are among the possibilities. There are also pasta dishes (chicken-artichoke and mussels over angel hair, for example) and sandwiches such as grilled eggplant with melted brie on the all-day menu. This place seems always to be crowded. Because of the porch overhang, it is also shady, and that can sometimes be a blessing. There's a bar right on the porch to make specialty drinks like a frozen mudslide, piña colada or a "Pain Killer" with rum, crème de coconut, pineapple and orange juices, and a sprinkling of nutmeg on top.

Water Street, Old Harbor. (401) 466-2901. Entrees, $12 to $19. Open daily, 11:30 to 11, mid-May to Columbus Day.

Finn's Seafood Restaurant. You can't beat the freshness of the fish (from its seafood market next door) nor the prices at Finn's, which is especially popular with locals. The restaurant on the lower level is reached directly from the ferry parking lot. Upstairs is a raw bar where you can feast on clams, oysters or shrimp, sip a drink and enjoy the view of ferry comings and goings. There is an outdoor terrace as well as simple tables indoors. This is uncomplicated fare. Lobster comes in many sizes up to three-pounders. Other possibilities are shrimp scampi, broiled swordfish, linguini with white clam sauce, and broiled yellow or bluefin tuna. Entrées can be had with coleslaw and french fries or with corn on the cob, salad and/or baked potato. Fruit pies and something called a chocolate suicide cake are on the dessert menu.

Water Street, Old Harbor. (401) 466-2473. Entrees, $9 to $17. Open daily in season, 11:30 to 9:30 or 10.

The Water Street Cafe – with umbrellaed tables on a grassy knoll above the ferry dock and a takeout window from which they blare numbers – is a good place to wait for your ferry and the food is good, too, in case you want to get lunch or an early supper. Sandwiches, salads and light entrées are the rule. The chicken caesar salad looked scrumptious when we were there. Next door is **Sweet Inspiration,** an ice-cream shop serving Ben & Jerry's. Eat in the small but cheery interior, with tiled floors and ice-cream tables and chairs, or outside on that grassy knoll..

Sunset sipping. The best view of the sunset may be from **Trader Vic's,** at the end of the dock at Champlin's Marina. Here you sip tropical drinks and watch the sun sink into the ocean. It's a fun way to start an evening.

Picnicking

We like best to picnic at the beach. You can enter the sandy strand from many points along Corn Neck Road leading north from town, beginning just after the bend in the road where there are suddenly small dunes and beach grass. Or you can enter at the main entrance of Fred Benson State Beach with its pavilion and racks for bicycles, especially if you need to get a drink or something to eat (they grill hamburgers and hot dogs over charcoal here).

Another popular spot is at the North Light, a five-mile bicycle or car ride from town.

We also enjoy sitting on Payne's Dock in New Harbor, eating a sandwich and watching all the boating action.

FOR MORE INFORMATION: Block Island Chamber of Commerce, Drawer D, Block Island, R.I. 02807, (401) 466-2982 or (800) 383-2474.

8 ✹ Summer

Summer farmers' market draws throngs to downtown Portland.

Maine(ly) City

Portland, Maine

Few people think of a city as a focal point for a summer weekend, but then, few cities make the prospect attractive. One that does is Portland, which combines urban amenities with rural and coastal opportunities. The natives desert their city on weekends, naturally, to make the most of the leisure possibilities virtually in their back yards. Basing yourself in or near the city, you can do as they do and enjoy the best of both worlds – what native son Henry Wadsworth Longfellow described as "the beautiful town that is seated by the sea."

The sea is everything – or almost everything – to Portland. Although actually beside Casco Bay, the city is a peninsula ringed on all flanks by water, and the proximity of the water on every side is the first thing a visitor notices. The second may be the city's height. The downtown is on a crest that gives it something of the look of an old European town – where else in this country does one find a downtown located higher than its suburbs?

The height is fortuitous. On a clear day, the view of the shimmering waters of Casco Bay from the Eastern Promenade is breathtaking. From no other Eastern city do the blues of the water, the greens of the islands and the whites of the sailboats seem quite so pristine.

Other good views are the ones at sunset toward the city's skyline across the Back Cove from Baxter Boulevard, and toward New Hampshire's White Mountains from the Western Promenade. Between the mountains and the city is the Sebago Lakes region, an inland area that vies with the sea for the attentions of Portlanders.

When they're not taking advantage of their surroundings, Portlanders are likely helping to revive – and enjoy – their revitalized city. Variously described as a big town or a little city (population, 65,000), Portland is the center of the largest urban complex in the largest state in northern New England. Its manageable size combined with a potent civic pride make it "a unique experiment in urban revival," according to one Portland newspaper writer.

Portland slumbered longer than many New England cities, so it is perhaps a surprise that it has come farther and faster than most. Ravaged by Indians and the British twice in the 1700s and destroyed by fire started by a July Fourth firecracker following the Civil War, Portland was a dying port in the 1950s. But business interests gave the city a new downtown with mini-skyscrapers and plazas, landscaping and monuments, kiosks and elan. They also gave it a thriving cultural and entertainment life, including the Portland Performing Arts Center, the Portland Symphony Orchestra and the expanded Museum of Art with its collection of paintings by Winslow Homer, the pride of Portland. The city's professional teams consistently set attendance records for minor-league baseball and hockey.

A lively group known as Greater Portland Landmarks Inc. is responsible for 35 years of restoration efforts that are turning Portland into what some call, on a lesser scale, "the Savannah of the North."

The crowning restoration achievement is the Old Port Exchange, a near-downtown historic district fashioned from a decaying waterfront where restaurants, boutiques and galleries flourish side by side with sailmakers and ship's chandlers.

Some of the city's best restaurants and most interesting shops are located here. The nearby waterfront is headquarters for the Casco Bay Lines, which offers a variety of cruises from morning to moonlight. They show some of the Calendar Islands (so named because they number approximately 365), four of them occupied by year-round residents.

Savor this rejuvenated city, which is compact enough to get around and see in a day (make it a Saturday, for like most cities much of Portland closes down on summer Sundays). But also get out of the city. Head north along Route 88 through suburban Falmouth Foreside and old Yarmouth. Head south through Cape Elizabeth to Two Lights, Scarborough and the coastal beaches. Head west to the Sebago Lakes region for a look at Maine's interior. And head east, out onto the Casco Bay islands.

Portland, for the summer weekender, offers a little of everything.

Getting There

The Interstate 295 loop serves Portland from the Maine Turnpike (I-95) toll road, which is the fastest route into Portland. U.S. Route 1 goes through the center of the city on its coastal meandering from Canada to Florida.

Greyhound and Trailways provide bus service to the city. Delta, United, Continental and US Airline serve Portland International Jetport. Portland is also linked by ferry to Yarmouth, N.S., daily in the summer by Prince of Fundy Cruises.

Seeing and Doing

Sightseeing

Old Port Exchange. The restored port district southeast of downtown between Monument Square and the waterfront is at once the city's oldest and newest neighborhood. Settled in the 1600s, the area was ravaged by the British during the

Revolution and by the Great Fire of 1866. It was rebuilt, but was going downhill until Greater Portland Landmarks started revitalizing the area in the 1960s.

An old-town restoration like those out West, Portland's is particularly successful and well done, although the accouterments of a sophisticated city tend to overshadow what boosters describe as "a working harbor full of the sights, sounds and smells of the sea."

Exquisite architecture, landscaping, colorful signs, benches, mini-parks and a lifelike trompe- l'oeil mural on a building at Middle and Exchange streets make this a fine place in which to stroll and browse as well as partake of scores of shops and restaurants. Exchange, Fore and Middle streets are the core, but don't overlook the side streets in this approximately five-block-square area stretching between Congress and Commercial streets.

WALKING TOURS. Congress Street, the city's main thoroughfare from historic Stroudwater to the Eastern Promenade, is also the main business street and is

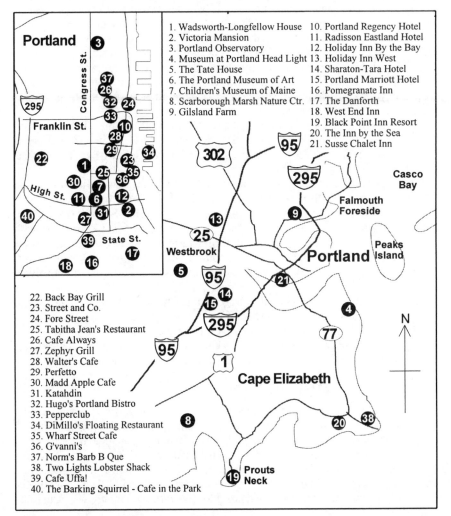

Portland

1. Wadsworth-Longfellow House
2. Victoria Mansion
3. Portland Observatory
4. Museum at Portland Head Light
5. The Tate House
6. The Portland Museum of Art
7. Children's Museum of Maine
8. Scarborough Marsh Nature Ctr.
9. Gilsland Farm
10. Portland Regency Hotel
11. Radisson Eastland Hotel
12. Holiday Inn By the Bay
13. Holiday Inn West
14. Sharaton-Tara Hotel
15. Portland Marriott Hotel
16. Pomegranate Inn
17. The Danforth
18. West End Inn
19. Black Point Inn Resort
20. The Inn by the Sea
21. Susse Chalet Inn

22. Back Bay Grill
23. Street and Co.
24. Fore Street
25. Tabitha Jean's Restaurant
26. Cafe Always
27. Zephyr Grill
28. Walter's Cafe
29. Perfetto
30. Madd Apple Cafe
31. Katahdin
32. Hugo's Portland Bistro
33. Pepperclub
34. DiMillo's Floating Restaurant
35. Wharf Street Cafe
36. G'vanni's
37. Norm's Barb B Que
38. Two Lights Lobster Shack
39. Cafe Uffa!
40. The Barking Squirrel - Cafe in the Park

noteworthy for its landmark buildings, from the old Romanesque public library at 619 to the French Renaissance City Hall at 389. A Greater Portland Landmarks brochure ($1) guides the way, as do others to the Old Port Exchange, Western Promenade and the State and High street area, which was added in 1971 to the National Register of Historic Places in recognition of its architectural examples. These were the grand homes of old Portland, many of them Federal and Greek Revival; they give sections of the city a red-brick look unusual for New England. On the other side of Congress Square is Deering Street, an enclave of notable Victorian residences only a block removed from the city's business heart.

DRIVING TOURS. Although downtown and the Old Port are for walking, cars are a necessity for most Portland visitors, and the city and surroundings are extraordinarily easy to traverse by car (with a good map). Drive out Congress Street past the landmark Portland Observatory to the **Eastern Promenade,** an aptly named residential street along the crest overlooking Casco Bay. It's bordered by parkland with a municipal pool, benches where you can enjoy a panoramic view and the occasional picnic table. You can even pick up a lobster roll or a hot dog from a lunch truck parked here. Fort Allen Park boasts a cannon from the USS Maine and overlooks old Fort Gorges in the harbor. Continue your tour to Route 1 and Baxter Boulevard around the Back Cove, past more water and parks. Eventually get to the **Western Promenade** and its Reed Monument. From here on a clear day you see Mount Washington and tour another area of imposing, architectural-landmark residences.

Head north on Route 88 through Falmouth Foreside, home of the Portland Country Club, Portland Yacht Club and waterfront estates. Beyond, Yarmouth has some of the area's earliest buildings, plus the **Cousins Island Beach,** which is excellent for swimming and picnicking.

Head south on Route 77 through suburban Cape Elizabeth, with fine residential sections beside Casco Bay. A favorite stop is **Fort Williams Park** and the Portland Head Light and museum. Farther on are **Two Lights State Park** and the Lobster Shack at Two Lights, where you can feast on lobster at picnic tables with a spectacular view of the open Atlantic. Still farther are **Crescent Beach State Park, Higgins Beach** and the exclusive community of **Prouts Neck,** whose rugged cliffs inspired artist Winslow Homer and where his studio is now a private residence.

Head west for fifteen miles on Route 302 to touristy North Windham and Sebago Lake, which you seldom get to see from the main highways. **Sebago Lake State Park** is a well maintained, spectacularly situated beach and picnic grove with a setting reminiscent of the north end of Lake Tahoe. The old Songo Lock separating Sebago Lake and Brandy Pond attracts sightseers and fishermen.

Cultural and Historic Sites

Portland Museum of Art. This is considered northern New England's most important museum, all the more so since the opening of the $11.6-million Charles Shipman Payson Building. The local philanthropist not only sparked the museum's major expansion with his gift of seventeen Winslow Homer paintings, but provided the funding for the showcase addition. The magnificent I.M. Pei-designed structure joins the original McLellan-Sweat House (1800) and L.D.M. Sweat Memorial (1911) museum buildings and provides five times as much space. The four-story structure with its enormous elevator, a staircase that makes you feel as if you're floating upstairs and portholes through which you look outside is intriguing. So are Payson's Homer collection, the works of Wyeth and Sargent, the American Galleries, the decorative arts galleries, the Pepperrell Silver Collection and changing exhibitions. The Joan Whitney Payson Collection, a remarkable group of Impressionist and Post-Impressionist works by Picasso, Monet, Degas, Renoir, Van Gogh and others, was given to the museum in 1991. A special exhibition, "Picasso, Braque, Legar and the Cubist Spirit, 1919-1939", was causing a stir in regional art circles at our latest visit.

7 Congress Square. (207) 775-6148. Monday-Saturday 10 to 5, Thursday and Friday to 9, Sunday noon to 5; closed Monday, mid-October to July. Adults $6, children $1. Free, Friday 5 to 9.

The Children's Museum of Maine. A youthful counterpoint to the sophisticated treasures of the nearby art museum, this new state-of-the-art facility in an old brick building is of interest to families with young children. Youngsters can work their own lobster boat, pilot a space shuttle, operate a grocery store or learn what it's like to milk a cow. Interactive, hands-on exhibits are entertaining as well as instructive. The "Camera Obscura" yields a 360-degree view of the city.

142 Free St. (207) 828-1234. Open in summer, Monday-Saturday 10 to 5, Friday to 8, Sunday noon to 5; closed Monday and Tuesday rest of year. Admission, $4. Free, Friday 5 to 8.

Wadsworth-Longfellow House. Henry Wadsworth Longfellow wrote much of his early poetry in Portland's first brick building (1785), the oldest surviving residence on the Portland peninsula. A beauty it is, with original furnishings and possessions of the Wadsworth and Longfellow families. The Maine Historical Society headquarters and library are located behind the house and its lovely garden.

485 Congress St. (207) 879-0427. Tuesday-Sunday 10 to 4, June-October. Adults $4, children $2.

Victoria Mansion. One of the nation's most opulent Italian villas, this 1860 structure has been described as "an encyclopedia of mid-19th-century decoration, domestic life and determined elegance." It is notable for richly carved woodwork, colorful frescoes, trompe-l'oeil walls and ceilings, carved marble fireplaces, French porcelains and much stained and etched glass.

109 Danforth St. (207) 772-4841. Tuesday-Saturday 10 to 4 and Sunday 1 to 5,May-October. Adults $4, children $2.

Portland Observatory. Although closed for repairs at our latest visit, usually you can climb the 102 steps of this 1807 signal tower for a panoramic view of the city, Casco Bay and the White Mountains.

138 Congress St. (207) 772-4841. Wednesday-Sunday 1 to 5 (Saturday from 10), July-August; Saturday-Sunday 1 to 5 in June, September and October. Adults $1.50, children 50 cents.

The Museum at Portland Head Light. The East's oldest operating lighthouse, commissioned in 1791 by George Washington, is said to be the Atlantic coast's most photographed. Following $600,000 worth of renovations, the Town of Cape Elizabeth operates the new museum on the first floor of the lighthouse keepers' quarters. Exhibits chronicle the history of Portland Head Light and Fort Williams, a military outpost that developed for coastal defense next to the lighthouse and now is an appealing town park with trails, picnic tables and great views of the harbor. A small museum shop is housed in an adjacent garage.

1000 Shore Road, Cape Elizabeth. (207) 799-2661. Daily 10-4, June-October; weekends, April-May and November-December. Adults $2, children $1.

Tate House. Built in 1755 by George Tate, mast agent for the Royal Navy, this house in historic Stroudwater is maintained by the National Society of Colonial Dames of America in Maine. With gambrel roof, eight fireplaces and the parlor table set for tea, it reflects an 18th-century London townhouse. Out back, a raised-bed herb garden of 18th-century plants overlooks the Stroudwater River. Saturday afternoon architectural tours show the cellar, servants' quarters and attic.

1270 Westbrook St., Stroudwater. (207) 774-9781. Tuesday-Saturday 10 to 4 and Sunday 1 to 4, mid-June to mid-September, Friday-Sunday through October. Adults $4, children $1.

Shopping

With the distinctive sound of seagulls all around, the shops in the Old Port Exchange draw their share of browsers and buyers. For traditionalists, the huge Maine Mall at Turnpike Exit 7 in South Portland is anchored by Filene's and Macy's and has the usual complement of stores.

In the Old Port Exchange we love to hang around **Whip and Spoon,** 161 Commercial St., a place for the serious cook. From fifteen-cent lobster picks to supplies for making beer, they've got it all. There's a section for "made in Maine" foods that are fun to buy and try. **The Stein Gallery** at 30 Milk St. showcases perfectly stunning glass pieces by artists from across the country. A Los Angeles couple staying at our B&B were about to buy a spectacular large vase for $650 and considered it a bargain. The **Paper Patch** at 17 Exchange St. carries cards for all occasions and we stock up every year.

The Ecology House offers good tote bags, T-shirts and books about animals, and part of the purchase price goes to environmental causes. Of course, many of their items are made of recycled material. The poster on the door says "You should be ashamed to wear fur." At **Portmanteau** you can watch colorful handbags and totes of canvas and tapestry being made. One of us has bought a couple of tapestry handbags here over the years – the nice thing about them is that they are sold nowhere else. **Serendipity** offers lovely sweaters, mohair throws and Geiger clothes, while **Abacus** stocks unusual and very contemporary jewelry, pottery and other craft items. For years, **Amaryllis** has been the place to go for unique and trendy clothing. Windsocks shaped like lobsters, cows, parrots and carrots hang outside **Ye Old Port Kite Shoppe,** which also has an extensive collection of banners and kites. **The Foreside Company** has interesting accessories for the home, many from Indonesia, and everything at factory prices. A complex called Two Portland Square at Fore and Union Streets holds some of the suavest shops, including **Bertini, Carla Bella** and **Kristen Scarcelli** for clothing. **Covent Garden** has especially nice soaps and Caswell-Massey items, as well as MacKenzie-Childs pottery. The selection of pottery at **Maxwell's Pottery Outlet** at 384 Fore St. is outstanding. The **Maine Potters Market,** a co-op just across the street, is also a worthwhile stop.

If all this shopping (and we haven't told you the half of it) gets to be too much, stop at **Portland Wine & Cheese,** a store and deli at 188 Middle St., for a bowl of soup or a sandwich. Or at **Mister Bagel** for a lobster roll, $6.25 with two sides. Or at **Beals** for ice cream; a cone of, say, red raspberry-apple, strawberry-colada or cotton candy is $1.50. Eight almost fat-free yogurts are offered.

Outside town, **White Pepper,** billing itself as "a summer shop by the sea," is at the end of Prouts Neck and is suavely run by summer residents Josie Scully and Patsy Timpson. Besides selling all kinds of sophisticated gifts, they continue their predecessors' tradition of selling penny candy to local youngsters.

And to the north await the huge L.L. Bean Co. and the outlet stores of Freeport.

On or Near the Water

Swimming is offered at Crescent Beach State Park, where sand dunes lead to a gentle beach with locker rooms, concession stand and picnic grills. Higgins Beach in Scarborough is fine, but parking is limited; beyond is Scarborough State Beach with good surf. Far less crowded and free, to boot, is the delightful Cousins Island Beach across the causeway from Yarmouth. There's no surf and it's a bit of a climb down (stairs provided), but the bay waters are warmer (65 degrees, compared with the ocean's 58) and the beach far less populated.

Gilsland Farm. The Maine Audubon Society's headquarters has several miles of free nature trails through woods, meadows and marshes in the Presumpscot River estuary. The society's chief claim to fame here is its striking two-and-a-half-story shingled headquarters built in 1976 as the nation's first large building heated only by the sun and firewood. Designed in the old New England saltbox style, it has attracted energy experts who want to see how solar heating works (a brochure illustrates a self-guided tour of the heating apparatus around the building's perimeter). The society's gift shop stocks all sorts of nature-related items, posters, prints, nature books and cards.

118 Route 1, Falmouth. (207) 781-2330. Monday-Saturday 9 to 5, Sunday noon to 5.

Scarborough Marsh Nature Center. The Maine Audubon Society center offers a variety of naturalist-led tours of the shore and marshes as well as bird walks (most cost $3). You can rent canoes ($8 an hour) to explore the wilds of the marsh on your own. The center has rotating exhibits, aquariums and a nature store as well as 3,000 acres of salt marsh rich in plant and animal life.

Pine Point Road, Scarborough. (207) 883-5100. Daily, 9:30 to 5:30, mid-June to Labor Day.

BOAT TOURS. Several daily cruises are offered by **Casco Bay Lines** from the ferry terminal at Commercial and Franklin streets, (207) 774-7871. These are the sidelines to a working ferry service, said to be America's oldest. They're the lifeline to the Calendar Islands, transporting residents, school children, mail and necessities along with visitors. The mailboat stops twice daily at Cliff, Chebeague, Long, and Little and Great Diamond islands, giving visitors dockside views of island life (see below). The premier cruise (adults $13.75, children $6.25) is a six-hour trip to Bailey Island, where you can get off for lunch or stay on board for a nature cruise. Other cruises go to Diamond Pass or involve sunset and moonlight excursions and Sunday music on the bay.

The smaller **Bay View Cruises**, 184 Commercial St. on Fisherman's Wharf,

(207) 761-0496, offers seal watch, island, harbor, cocktail, brunch, lobster bake and sunset cruises, daily in summer; adults $8, children $5. **Eagle Tours,** 1 Long Wharf, (207) 774-6498, has good island and seal-watching cruises every after-noon and evening, Memorial Day to Columbus Day; adults $8, children $5. A four-hour narrated tour at 10 a.m. daily goes to Eagle Island and Admiral Robert E. Peary's summer home (adults $15, children $9). **Olde Port Mariner Fleet,** 170 Commercial St., (207) 775-0727, offers whale watches, island and seal cruises, lunch and dinner cruises and even a lobster bake on Long Island. The 58-foot ocean racer **Palawan,** (207) 773-2163, gives half-day, all-day and sunset sails from Custom House Wharf through the Calendar Islands for $20 to $75 per person.

Touring the Casco Bay Islands

One of the joys of being in Portland is its proximity to the 365 Calendar Islands just offshore in Casco Bay. Several thousand people live on five main islands, many commuting to jobs and school in Portland. The islands are rustic, even primi-tive. Although partly within view of the city, Portlanders say, "it's a different world out there."

Visitors can get onto the islands via the Casco Bay Lines mailboats and working ferries, which in summer run as frequently as hourly. The oldest chartered ferry line in the nation, the fleet of five diesel-propelled vessels is operated by a quasi-municipal transit district owned by the islanders.

Peaks Island, the closest major island to the city, has a year-round population of 1,500 and up to 6,000 in summer. Mainly residential and accessible by car ferry, it offers three small restaurants, stores, the Island Bike Rental, a sea kayaking outfit and Keller's B&B. It is a good destination for those with limited time or budget (the passenger ferry runs every hour or so, and you can walk around the entire island in an hour or two).

Long Island recently separated from the city to run its own affairs. It offers a fine public state beach on the ocean side, a fifteen-minute walk across the island from the ferry landing. The year-round population of 300 swells to 1,500 in the summer.

Great Chebeague, the largest island in the bay, is six miles long and has 400 permanent residents. It's the destination of choice for those who can take a day (and a bicycle) to explore. You can play nine holes of golf, eat at the Nellie G Cafe and stay overnight at the Chebeague Inn or a couple of B&Bs. Cliff Island is the smallest of the major inhabited islands (273 acres).

Great Diamond Island offers a "cocktail cove" favored by boaters and a residen-tial community called Diamond Cove with condo rentals and a good restaurant.

The twice-daily mailboat run is the best way to see all the major islands. With a couple of blasts on the ferry horn ("cover your ears," the loudspeaker warns), the ferry starts on its leisurely, three-hour journey from the Casco Bay Lines ferry terminal at Commercial and Franklin streets. The visitor's first impression is that these islands are surprisingly densely populated, especially along the shore and especially Peaks Island, the first major island you see (but the mailboat doesn't visit). Also you soon realize this differs from the usual ferry, in that it's used primarily by islanders rather than tourists. Which explains why there's no narra-tion. You have to guess what you're looking at or overhear the regulars pointing out favorite sights. At the dock at Long Island, we watched as an older couple

Casco Bay Lines mailboat arrives from Portland at Chebeague Island.

arrived with a wagon to pick up a delivery of groceries. The crew gingerly lowered a pallet of soft drinks, perhaps destined for the Spa Marina and Restaurant alongside. At Chebeague, a mother directed a bevy of youngsters unloading a pallet of roofing materials into a pickup truck. That and a Dodge van that got stuck as it tried to get up a makeshift ramp off the ferry provided twenty minutes of entertainment. Cliff Island proved the busiest stop on our tour as passengers debarked and boarded and what little there was of the day's outgoing mail was picked up. The return trip was enlivened by a couple of performing seals, a passing Russian freighter, and a frenzied flock of gulls chasing a fishing boat back to Portland. Mailboat leaves Portland daily at 10 and 2:45. Adults $9.50, children $4.25.

Where to Stay

Portland has its share of chain motels, large downtown motor inns, hotels and B&Bs. Most raise the rates considerably for the summer season. Two excellent inns are located on the water at the fringes of suburban Portland, but if you stay at either, you may never want to leave their grounds.

Hotels and Motels

Portland Regency Hotel. New in 1987, this downtown hotel is superbly located in the heart of the Old Port Exchange, which might justify the extra charge for valet parking. The fact that it's in the restored 1895 armory, providing some unusual architectural treatments, is a bonus. Most of the 95 guest and suites go off a three-story atrium above the dining room. Rooms are plush, many with kingsize four-poster beds and minibars. Complimentary coffee and newspapers are placed at your door with your wakeup call. The health club is up-to-date, and Salutes lounge offers complimentary hors d'oeuvres with cocktails and nightly entertainment in a warren of downstairs rooms. The **Market Street Grille** has a with-it menu for breakfast, lunch and dinner. Dinner entrées are in the $12 to $20 range for the likes of grilled halibut with a lobster-basil-tomato puree and sea scallops with pernod, pinenuts and bell peppers. *Dinner entrées are in the $12 to $20 range*

20 Milk St., Portland 04101. (207) 774-4200 or (800) 727-3436. Fax (207) 775-2150. Doubles, $149 to $199.

Radisson Eastland Hotel. A decade or so ago, the Sonesta chain renovated the old Eastland downtown hotel, redoing 100 large guest rooms in the old structure and adding a thirteen-story tower with 85 more. New owners took over in 1992 and launched more needed interior redecorating and refurbishing, the public areas having looked a bit shabby at our visit. Now the Radisson chain has continued the upgrading, offering a fitness center and 202 rooms and suites. The **Rib Room** restaurant still features the traditional prime rib with rosemary popovers and whipped horseradish cream, but adds more contemporary offerings like pan-seared salmon with arugula and tomatoes, grilled pork tenderloin with leeks and capers, and pepper-crusted medallions of beef with herbed cabernet sauce ($12.95 to $18.50). Portland's only rooftop lounge, The Top of the East, offers a panoramic view of the city during nightly cocktails and Sunday brunch.

157 High St., Portland 04101. (207) 775-5411. Fax (207) 775-2872. Doubles, $90 to $150.

Holiday Inn By the Bay. A good location, just across the street from the Civic Center and within walking distance of the Old Port Exchange, is one reason to stay in this eleven-story, 240-room motor hotel that used to be called simply the Holiday Inn-Downtown. Another is the view from the higher floors. We especially enjoyed watching the Scotia Prince ferry, lit up like a Christmas tree, dock at her berth around 8 one night from our room overlooking the Fore River. If you pay a bit extra, you might get an end room with two big windows instead of one. The indoor pool room is windowless, which is fine for a rainy day, but if it's a sunny weekend you might prefer the attractive **Holiday Inn-West** out Brighton Avenue with its well-landscaped outdoor pool. The downtown inn's lobby and dining room are large and ornate, and a plus for a city hotel is free in-and-out covered parking.

88 Spring St., Portland 04101. (207) 775-2311. Fax (207) 761-8224. Doubles, $128 to $134.

Sheraton Tara Hotel. Two striking glass circular towers contain 220 guest rooms at this suburban hotel located in a busy commercial area between the Maine Mall and the Maine Turnpike. The eight-story inn hotel has a glass-domed pool area, and there's a well-equipped fitness center. The **Silver Shell** restaurant offers dinner entrées from $12 to $21. You can walk to the Maine Mall and several cinemas, which could prove a boon for families with restless children.

363 Maine Mall Road, South Portland 04106. (207) 775-6161. Fax (207) 775-0196. Doubles, $145 to $165.

Portland Marriott Hotel. Another suburban high-rise, this fancy new six-story hostelry across the Maine Turnpike from the Maine Mall offers 227 guest rooms and suites with the usual amenities. Besides a skylit indoor pool, there's a

health club with sauna, whirlpool and exercise room. The eighteen-hole Sable Oaks Golf Course is adjacent. Creative dishes share the spotlight with updated New England standbys in **Allie's American Grill**; snacks are served in the lounge.
200 Sable Oaks Drive, South Portland 04106. (207) 871-8000. Fax (207) 871-7971. Doubles, $144.

Bed and Breakfasts

Pomegranate Inn. Two exotic plant sculptures (holding live plants, no less) might welcome summer guests at the entrance to this exceptional in-town B&B run with T.L.C. by Connecticut transplant Isabel Smiles. The art theme continues inside the handsome 19th-century house, which Isabel's antiques collections and contemporary artworks make a cross between a museum and a gallery. Walls in the guest rooms were handpainted by a local artist and are themselves works of art, bearing no resemblance to the typical inn's folksy stenciling or sprigged wallpaper. The eight rooms, all with modern tiled baths, come with telephone, television and a mix of antique and contemporary furnishings as well as prized art. We splurged for a new room in the side carriage house with two plush chairs and a puffy duvet on the queen bed, a marble bathroom and walls painted with riotous flowers. It opened onto a secret courtyard, so quiet and secluded it was hard to imagine we were in a city. A full breakfast is served at a long communal table or a couple of smaller ones in one of the eclectic parlors. The fare might be creamy quiches, pancakes with sautéed pears or, in our case, tasty waffles with bananas and raspberries.
49 Neal St., Portland 04102. (207) 772-1006 or (800) 356-0408. Doubles, $125 to $155.

The Danforth. The landmark 1821 mansion that had been the rectory for the Archdiocese of Portland has been converted into an urbane, full-service inn by Barbara Hathaway from Connecticut. She offers nine deluxe guest rooms, a number of intriguing common areas (from a basement billiards room to a main-floor library to a third-floor solarium and a rooftop widow's walk, which yields one of the best wraparound views in town). Each guest room (including a two-bedroom suite) comes with private bath, queensize bed, wood-burning fireplace, remote-control television, telephones, loveseats or wing chairs and antique armoires. Breakfast is served in the formal dining room or in an adjacent sun porch. The menu posted the day of our visit called for baked apple, bacon and scrambled eggs in puff pastry. Optional prix-fixe dinner service is available nightly for house guests. A typical menu offers appetizer, salad, a choice of braided salmon and flounder fillet with portobello cream sauce over pasta or black pepper-crusted pork tenderloin with roasted peppers, plus dessert, in the $25 range.
163 Danforth St., Portland 04102. (207) 879-8755 or (800) 991-6557. Doubles, $95 to $140; suite, $160.

West End Inn. Another of the B&Bs that keep popping up in Portland's residential West End, this 1871 townhouse offers six rooms with private baths and television. Three rooms with extra beds accommodate up to four persons, making them good for families. Rooms take their names from islands in Casco Bay. The newest, Cliff Island, off the dining room, has a queensize four-poster bed and its own private side deck. Three more rooms on the second and third floors have queen beds and two have kingsize. The third-floor Great Chebeague Room comes with a kingsize canopy and a day bed, plus a jacuzzi; the floral fabrics of the decor are repeated on the shower curtain in the bathroom. Guests enjoy a formal living room with an Oriental flair, plush leather seating and an intricate, hand-carved étagère. A sideboard at the side of the dining room is stocked with complimentary liqueurs. For breakfast, manager Teri Dizon is likely to prepare stuffed french toast, belgian waffles, steak and eggs or, her specialty, roast beef hash.

146 Pine St., Portland 04102. (207) 772-1377 or (800) 338-1377. Doubles, $89 to $169.

Inns and Resorts

Black Point Inn Resort. The gray shingled inn built in 1925 is not all that imposing – although very attractive and impeccably kept up – but you can tell from all the expensive cars in the parking lot that this is one elegant resort. The location not far south of the city on Prouts Neck is smashing, with Sand Dollar Beach on one side and Scarborough Beach on the other. The delightful public rooms contain overstuffed chairs, fireplaces, game tables and books to read. Breakfast and dinner are served in a pleasant pine-paneled dining room; on good days a buffet lunch is set out outside beside the large heated saltwater pool overlooking the ocean (there's also an indoor freshwater pool). Staying in one of the 81 rooms in the inn or cottages is also one way to get to see the exclusive summer community of Prouts Neck. The famous Cliff Walk passes Winslow Homer's studio, and the pine woods between inn and ocean are a national bird sanctuary. Guests enjoy an adjacent eighteen-hole golf course and fourteen tennis courts hidden away in the woods.

510 Black Point Road, Prouts Neck 04074. (207) 883-4126 or (800) 258-0003. Fax (207) 883-9976. Doubles, $280 to $370, MAP; three-night minimum stay in summer. Closed November-April.

The Inn by the Sea. If the Black Point Inn is the grand old resort, this is one for contemporary luxury. Nearly $7 million went into the place that opened in 1987 on the site of the former Crescent Beach Inn and it looks it. Handsomely designed in the Maine shingle style to blend with the oceanside setting, the angled complex has 25 one-bedroom suites in the main building and eighteen condo-style units of one or two bedrooms in four attached cottages. All have living rooms with reproduction Chippendale furniture, TVs hidden in armoires, kitchenettes, and balconies or patios looking onto manicured lawns, a pleasant pool and the ocean in the distance. We liked being able to walk right outside onto a patio from the living room of our first-floor garden suite, but found the water view better from the balcony of a loft suite at our next visit. We swam in a pleasant pool and ambled down a boardwalk to Crescent Beach. Public rooms include a delightful rooftop library and the serene Audubon dining room, which under new owner Maureen McQuade has been opened to the public and serves three meals a day. Rack of lamb is the specialty on a diverse menu priced from $13.95 for seared chicken with artichokes and yellow sundried tomatoes to $21.95 for filet mignon with potatoes galette. An ample section of the dinner menu is devoted to light fare and pastas in two sizes.

Route 77, Cape Elizabeth 04107. (207) 799-3134 or (800) 888-4287. Fax (207) 799-4779. Breakfast, 7 to 11; lunch, noon to 2; dinner, 5:30 to 9:30. Doubles, $180 to $250; cottage suites, $330 to $410.

Extra Value

Susse Chalet Inn. One of the budget chain, we found this 105-room, four-story motor inn off the tourist path to be a relative bargain – a summer special of $65 for a spacious room with two double beds, comfortable chairs, good reading lights, a bathroom with separate vanity (but no amenities other than soap), and away from highway noise. There's a pint-size outdoor pool. Complimentary juice, coffee and pastries are doled out in the lobby in the morning. Another, more bare-bones **Susse Chalet-Saver** (doubles, $60 to $70) is at 1200 Brighton Ave. near the Maine Turnpike.

340 Park Ave., Portland 04102. (207) 871-0611. Fax (207) 871-0611. Doubles, $70 to $77.

Where to Eat

Portland's dining scene has improved markedly in the past fifteen years. Many of the more popular restaurants, however, do not take reservations and the weekend traveler may find it annoying to have to eat at 6 p.m. or wait in a bar or outside on the street for up to an hour to get a table. On the plus side, the prices are generally considerably less than in Boston or New York.

Fine Dining

Back Bay Grill. In its relatively short existence, this stylish establishment with two dining rooms and a fanciful, twenty-foot-long mural along one wall has become the city's most urbane restaurant – among the few we've seen lately that makes one think one should dress up for dinner on a summer night in Portland. The place attracted such a following that in 1995, owner Joel Freund opened a similar but more casual establishment, Ida Reds, next to the Ogunquit Playhouse in Ogunquit, but he's still very much in evidence here. The menu changes monthly. To begin, you might try peeky-toe crab cakes, the house-smoked arctic char with rémoulade sauce or one of the pastas, perhaps lobster ravioli with scallions and ginger-orange beurre blanc. Move on to entrées like pecan-crusted salmon on sweet potato sauce, swordfish with tapenade croutons and sundried tomato-basil vinaigrette, grilled chicken with scallion-chèvre cream sauce or veal chop with pancetta. A dessert like pecan puff pastry napoleon with cannoli cream and toasted almond anglaise is a fitting finale. The inspired wine list is fairly priced.

65 Portland St. (207) 772-8833. Entrées, $16.95 to $21.95. Dinner, Monday-Saturday 5:30 to 9:30 or 10, also Sunday 5 to 9 in July and August.

Street and Co. Seafood, pure and simple, is the staple of this Old Port Exchange restaurant that's wildly popular with locals and visitors alike. Owner Dana Street stresses the freshest of fish on his blackboard menu. An open grill and kitchen are beside the door; beyond are 60 seats in an old room with bare pegged floors and strands of herbs and garlic hanging on brick walls and in a smaller room adjacent.. Outside are twenty more seats along Wharf Street during good weather, and the tables might turn four times on a busy night. Half a dozen varieties of seafood can be grilled, blackened or broiled. Or you can order mussels marinara, clams or shrimp with garlic, all served over linguini. The only other entrées at our latest visit were scallops in pernod and cream, sole française and lobster fra diavolo ($34.95 for two). The wine list is affordable, and there are great homemade desserts. *33 Wharf St. (207) 775-0887. Entrées, $14.95 to $17.95. Dinner nightly, 5:30 to 10 or 11.*

Fore Street. "Refined peasant food" is how Sam Hayward describes the fare at this wildly popular new restaurant. Sam, one of Maine's best-known restaurateurs, left the Harraseeket Inn in Freeport to join forces with Portland restaurateur Dana Street in 1996. They transformed a former tank-storage warehouse at the edge of the Old Port Exchange into a soaring space of brick and windows, all overlooking a large and busy open kitchen with an applewood-fired grill, rotisserie and oven. The menu, printed nightly, offers about a dozen main courses. They're categorized as roasted, grilled or braised and the descriptions are straightforward and understated. Expect treats like wood-oven roasted Maine lobster, spit-roasted pork loin, seafood misto, grilled duckling breast with pancetta and roasted shallots, grilled hanger steak and grilled venison steak. Start with a grilled garlic and mushroom sandwich or a pizzetta with roasted garlic, shiitakes and taleggio. Finish with roasted banana mousse or a trio of mango, blackberry and peach sorbets. The wine list is short but select and affordable. *288 Fore St. (207) 775-2717. Entrées, $13.95 to $19.95. Dinner nightly, from 5:30.*

Tabitha Jean's Restaurant. The daughter of Maine author Stephen King opened this stylish restaurant featuring contemporary American and vegetarian cuisine. Naomi King named it for her mother, Tabitha, and the mother of her former partner. Both the food and service impressed at a summer lunch, chosen from a diverse menu upon which every item appealed. The crab cakes with jalapeño peach relish ($6.95) were assertive, and the chicken quesadilla ($6.95) with a chunky tomato, avocado and watercress salsa was more than one could finish. At night, when white tablecloths cover the speckled black tables, expect entrée choices like grilled vegetable paella, hot Thai basil leaves with baby bok choy, a spicy sauté of shrimp and tomatillos with black beans and yellow tomatoes, lobster and capellini, saffron-roasted chicken breast over Tuscan crostini and grilled filet mignon with a sour cream horseradish sauce. Save room for dessert, perhaps chocolate mousse cake, cappuccino cheesecake or an innovative blueberry tirami su. *94 Free St.. (207) 780-8966. Entrées, $10.95 to $19.95. Lunch, Monday-Friday 11:30 to 3; dinner nightly, from 5.*

Cafe Always. A new-wave-style cafe with white tablecloths, different-colored utensils, black chairs and multi-colored walls has been winning accolades and packing in appreciative diners since it opened in 1985. Maureen Terry, a one-time cook here, took over in 1996 when the founders left to start a catering business. She was aiming to continue the tradition, but lightened up some of the traditionally assertive fare we remember fondly. Expect entrées like grilled swordfish with a tomato-olive-caper salsa, Maine mussels with spicy marinara over linguini, pork chop with cajun orange-pecan barbecue sauce, grilled sirloin with a roasted shallot demi-glace and steamed tofu spring rolls served with Asian slaw and Thai dipping sauce. Starters could be lobster risotto cakes, asparagus strudel with gruyère and Thai beef salad with lemon grass, onions and a lime dressing. Among desserts are chocolate-espresso terrine with chocolate-mint anglaise, blueberry-plum upside-down cake and homemade strawberry-wine sorbet. *47 Middle St. (207) 774-9399. Entrées, $18 to $20. Dinner, Tuesday-Sunday from 5.*

Casual Choices

Zephyr Grill. Like its owner's former Alberta's Cafe, this new grill is short on decor and long on inspiration and value. The downtown storefront has sponged tangerine walls above green wainscoting, custom-designed mod tables randomly painted by a local artist, and crazy orange shaded lamps hanging from the ceiling. The menu is made for grazing. We loved the chilled tomato and lemongrass soup garnished with cilantro and laden with shrimp, a huge salad of mesclun greens and assorted vegetables with roasted garlic, and the succulent grilled salmon with watercress garnish. The wonderful-sounding, crisp-fried Cuban-style sandwich of lobster, smoky bacon, marinated tomato and blended cheeses with shaved lettuce and banana-chipotle catsup ($6.95) was fried so crisply that it was difficult to cut or chew. Other main courses ranged from vegetarian dishes to grilled lamb loin and Korean-style barbecued sirloin with kimchi stir-fried vegetables and roasted potatoes. Desserts seemed fairly standard: among them, chocolate cheesecake and lemon mousse with berries. The wine list, all available by the bottle or the glass, was quite exotic and downright cheap.
653 Congress St. (207) 828-4033. Entrées, $9.95 to $15.95. Dinner, Wednesday-Sunday 5 to 10.

Walter's Cafe. Noisy and intimate, this place has been packed to the rafters since it was opened by Walter Loeman and Mark Loring in 1990. So much so that it opened an Italian bistro called Perfetto (see below) across the street to accommodate its overflow and, most recently, the casual Joe's Boathouse at Spring Point Marina in South Portland. At Walter's, we faced a twenty-minute wait for a weekday lunch in July, but thoroughly enjoyed a BOLT ($6.75) – bacon, lettuce, tomato and red onion sandwich with sweet cajun mayonnaise, served in a pita with a pickle and gnarly fries. The "chilling pasta salad" ($7.75) yielded a zesty plateful tossed with chicken, avocado and red peppers. From our table alongside a brick wall in the long and narrow high-ceilinged room we could see the cooks splashing liberal amounts of wines into the dishes they were preparing in the open kitchen. At night, dinner entrées include Thai spice-rubbed shrimp with lobster nori rolls, grilled mustard-crusted salmon over watercress and cucumber salad, Southwestern grilled breast of chicken over avocado and roasted chili polenta. Dessert might be Irish cream cheesecake or orange mousse with wild blueberries.
15 Exchange St. (207) 871-9258. Entrées, $12.95 to $17.95. Lunch, Monday-Saturday 11 to 3; dinner nightly, 5 to 10.

Perfetto. Some fans of Walter's Cafe think its appealing northern Italian eatery across the street is even better. The convivial setting here is similar: brick walls, exposed piping, high-back cane chairs at butcher-block tables and an open kitchen at the rear. The fare is similar to Walter's with an Italian accent. For dinner expect things like seared Atlantic salmon stuffed with crabmeat and artichokes, sautéed shrimp and lobster tossed with capellini, grilled lamb loin and smoked duck sausage, chicken stuffed with goat cheese and roasted peppers, and grilled veal chop with a rosemary-balsamic caramel sauce. You might start with pickled garden vegetables on baby greens or the pizzetti misto ("a skyscraper of mini flatbreads" that changes daily). Or how about a special of spicy seared sea bass salad?
28 Exchange St. (207) 828-0001. Entrées, $13.95 to $17.95. Lunch, Monday-Friday 11 to 3; dinner nightly, from 5:30; closed Sunday in winter.

Madd Apple Cafe. 23 Forest Ave. (207) 774-9698. Southern cooking with a Louisiana flair is the forte of Martha and James Williamson, who run this charming cafe beside the Portland Performing Arts Center. Jim grew up in the South, which explains the barbecue items from secret family recipes and the fresh catfish, crayfish, vegetable boudin, cornbread, bananas foster and sweet-potato pie on the menu. Typical dinner entrées range from grilled lamb patties with minted demiglace to steak New Orleans. Carolina pulled pork barbecue sandwich is usually available under light fare, along with smoked salmon and seafood club sandwiches and a creole salad full of shrimp, scallions, peppers and cornbread croutons.
28 Exchange St. (207) 828-0001. Entrées, $13.95 to $18.95. Dinner, Tuesday-Saturday from 5:30.

Wharf Street Cafe. Former Minneapolis caterer Steve Massing has expanded his restaurant operation on the "in" street in the Old Port Exchange, where a single block harbors eight restaurants (with more on the way) and live music and a strolling crowd make for festive weekend evenings. He added a funky upstairs wine and espresso bar, full of couches and stuffed chairs and a piano, where you can get appetizers, desserts and fourteen wines by the glass. For dinner, the main-floor cafe sheds its earthy daytime image in favor of tablecloths and dimmed lamps. The contemporary American menu offers interesting pastas and "specialties." Expect dishes like pistachio-crusted salmon with citron soy sauce and soba noodles, grilled salmon with lobster mashed potatoes, grilled swordfish with garlic potato turnovers, chicken saltimbocca and mustard grilled beef tenderloin. Seafood sausage and cafe pizzas are tempting starters. Warm chocolate truffle torte with caramel sauce is a sweet ending.
38 Wharf St. (207) 773-6667. Entrées, $10.95 to $16.95. Lunch, 11:30 to 2; dinner, 5:30 to 9 or 10.

G'vanni's. This new branch of a Boston and Fort Lauderdale outfit gets high marks from those into Italian food. It occupies the former Cybele's space with a bistro and bar open to the street on one side and a sunken, cozy, black and white dining room on the other. The food is predictable; some say inspired. Look for pastas and main courses ranging from lasagna and ravioli to salmon piccata, chicken parmesan, veal marsala and tenderloin with porcini mushroom sauce. Tirami su is the dessert of choice. The pricey wine list is mainly Italian.
37 Wharf St. (207) 775-9061. Entrées, $9.95 to $19.95. Lunch daily, 11:30 to 4:30; dinner, 4:30 to 10:30 or midnight.

Extra Value

Cafe Uffa! This new storefront eatery facing Longfellow Square is known for creative, healthful fare and good value. It's pretty much vegetarian, with some fish dishes, as in hickory-smoked trout with grilled potato, red onion, avocado and lemon-dijon vinaigrette, and applewood-grilled salmon with salsa romesco, saffron rice and asparagus, at $10.95 the most expensive dish on the menu. You could start with tomato-leek soup and end with bourbon pecan tart or chocolate-raspberry truffle cake. Prices are most gentle.
190 State St. (207) 775-3380. Entrées, $7.95 to $10.95. Dinner, Wednesday-Saturday 5:30 to 10; Sunday brunch, 9 to 2.

Someplace(s) Different

DiMillo's Floating Restaurant. The old DiMillo's Lobster House now occupies the 206-foot-long ship Newport, converted for $2 million into one of the largest floating restaurants in the nation and probably "the busiest restaurant in Maine," according to a member of the DiMillo family. Nearly 900 people can be accommodated at once in two outdoor cafe lounges fore and aft, a new side deck, the Quarterdeck Dining Room and three private rooms, plus a very long bar, which helps those with endurance tolerate the one-hour (or more) waits on weekends. The sign at the gangplank saying "browsers welcome" and the gift shop at the entry set the theme. From the rare albino and orange lobsters in the tank at the reception desk to the blue and red linens, the place is incredibly nautical. The emphasis is on seafood, from four versions of haddock to twin lobsters, "served to one person only," the menu advises. A complete shore dinner costs $27.95.

Long Wharf, Commercial Street. (207) 772-2216. Entrées, $11.95 to $21.95. Lunch daily, 11 to 4; dinner, 5 to 11.

Hugo's Portland Bistro. Named for the young son of the owner from Dublin, this is a pleasant room with beaucoup bric-a-brac and a short, appealing menu. The fare is a mix of American and ethnic but the specialty is Maine crab cakes with carrot and raisin slaw. You might start with Thai spring rolls with chicken and basil or spicy black bean cakes with roasted corn salsa before digging into sole veronique, quinoa pasta with watercress pesto, roasted duck breast with mango or filet of beef with green peppercorn sauce. Dinners come with homemade Irish sodabread and salad. Crème brûlée, fresh raspberry trifle, and bittersweet and white chocolate mousse are some of the desserts, available with Irish coffee.

88 Middle St. (207) 774-8538. Entrées, $10.95 to $16.95. Dinner, Tuesday-Saturday 5:15 to 9.

Pepperclub. Among the players on Portland's Restaurant Row is this organic-vegetarian-seafood establishment, billed as a smoke-free environment and colorful as can be. It's the inspiration of artist Jaap Helder, Danish-born chef-artist who owned the late, great Vinyard restaurant nearby. He re-emerged with his paintings and a new partner, former art editor Eddie Fitzpatrick, to produce a triumph of culinary design. The blackboard menu lists starters like Armenian stuffed flatbread, Moroccan vegetable stew and hummus salad. Main dishes include Maine shrimp with pasta and pesto, Greek lamb with minted green beans, Mongolian cashew chicken, Tunisian couscous and pinto bean burrito with salsa. Dessert could be orange-chiffon cake, strawberry-raspberry pie or bourbon-pecan pie. Fresh flowers on the table, a crazy paint job on the walls and a bar made of old Jamaican steel drums, painted and cut in half, make for a vivid setting.

78 Middle St. (207) 772-0531. Entrées, $6.95 to $10.95. Dinner nightly, 5 to 9 or 10.

Norm's Barb B Que. Some of the best barbecue in town is served here. Consider the pulled pork sandwich ($6.95) with homemade fries and coleslaw. The extensive menu also features duck salad, clam cakes from Norm's own recipe, baked beans, ribs and barbecued catfish ($8.95 with cucumber salad, cilantro and beans and rice).

43 Middle St. (207) 774-6711. Open Tuesday-Saturday noon to 10, Sunday 3 to 9.

Two Lights Lobster Shack. Here is a no-frills place within the shadow of two lighthouses. Picnic tables on the bluff beside the ocean are where we like to dig into a boiled lobster dinner ($10.95) or a fisherman's platter ($11.95). There are hot dogs, hamburgers and fried chicken for the non-fish eaters.

Two Lights Road, Cape Elizabeth. (207) 799-1677. Open daily, 11 to 8, early April to mid-October.

A Budget Choice

Katahdin. There's a lot to look at in this with-it, offbeat eatery, where a creative hand is at work with the decor as well as in the kitchen. Mismatched chairs (some of them upholstered armchairs) are at tables whose tops are painted with different vegetable and fruit designs. A large 1950s mural adorns one wall; others bear quilts and changing artworks. There's a collection of mortars and pestles in one window. A variety of oldies but goodies on tape plays rather loudly. Such is the vibrant backdrop for the cooking of chef-owner Gretchen Bates, who named the restaurant for Maine's highest mountain to reflect Maine home cooking and, explained the bartender, "mountains of food" and "the summit of fine dining." The ambitious menu always includes a blue plate special (smothered beef and onions the night we were there) with soup and salad for $9.95. Lamb stew with tomatoes, white beans and rosemary is $7.95, and nothing on the regular menu is over $14.95 (for sirloin steak with garlic onion rings). Meals come with buttermilk biscuits, Aunt Nina's pickles and a salad, starch and vegetable. You may not have room left for dessert, especially the chocolate mountain – a brownie shell filled with chocolate mousse fudge sauce, whipped cream and nuts. Refresh instead with mint-orange sherbet or blueberry-cinnamon frozen yogurt. A good, short wine list is priced from $11 to $21.

Spring and High Streets. (207) 774-1740. Entrées, $7.95 to $14.95. Dinner, Monday-Saturday 5 to 10 or 11.

Picnic Spots

The Barking Squirrel - Cafe in the Park, set in the middle of Deering Oaks Park off State Street near I-295, is a great place to have a summer lunch under Poland Spring umbrellas on the terrace while watching the paddle boats navigate the nearby pond. You order at the counter and are served at a table or for takeout. We had the most delicious Mediterranean rollup sandwiches, with herbed white bean spread, feta cheese, mixed greens, oil-cured olives and red onions on lavash bread ($3.75). A lobster roll with handcut french fries was a mere $6.95, and those fries sure did look good, as did the burgers and the Thai salad.

Another favorite picnic spot, this one with a great view of Casco Bay and its islands, is from **Fort Allen Park** alongside the Eastern Promenade. Bring your own picnic and spread out on one of the picnic tables along the hillside. Or pick up a snack from the Flash Lobster truck (clam burger $1.75, lobster roll $6.95) parked near the entrance.

FOR MORE INFORMATION: The Visitor Information Center of the Convention and Visitors Bureau of Greater Portland, 305 Commercial St., Portland 04101, (207) 772-5800. The Maine Tourist Bureau at the rest area on the Maine Turnpike at Kittery has information on Portland.

9 🍁 Fall

Roadside stand is decked out for fall along Route 7 between Bennington and Williamstown.

Mountains and Museums

Bennington, Vt., and Williamstown, Mass.

Two towns on the western edge of New England – one in Massachusetts and the other in Vermont – are paired for the weekender. Although situated in different states, Bennington in Vermont and Williamstown in Massachusetts are just a scenic twenty-minute drive apart by car. Together they have three outstanding museums and fine cultural offerings, appealing natural areas for hiking and biking, mountain vistas and rushing streams, and such quintessential New England locales as picturesque covered bridges and maple sugarhouses. Two well-known colleges add their influence. And there is history galore.

It is the towns' location amid the Green Mountains of Vermont and the Berkshire hills in Massachusetts that most influenced their development. Mount Greylock, just southeast of Williamstown, is the highest peak in Massachusetts and a dominating presence. The mountains proved isolating, forcing the towns to develop hardy, do-it-yourself-type people. At the same time, the beauty and ruggedness of these hills eventually lured visitors – hikers and sightseers who were charmed by the views they offered.

All those mountain streams meant ample water power and Bennington developed as a mill town and ceramic center of note. Today, Bennington Potters still turns out attractive and sought-after table items.

Bennington is the proud site of the Battle of Bennington, an important Revolutionary War skirmish in 1777 when the Green Mountain Boys helped to rout the British under Gen. John Burgoyne. He finally surrendered a couple of months later in Stillwater, N.Y. The event is commemorated by the famous Bennington

Battle Monument, a granite obelisk rising 306 feet and visible for miles around; you can ascend by elevator for a 360-degree view of the area. Bennington College is located nearby.

Williamstown dates to 1753, when the plantation, West Hoosuck, was founded as the Massachusetts Bay Colony's front line during the French and Indian Wars. After Col. Ephraim Williams was killed in battle, his will provided for a free school in West Hoosuck – if it was named for him. Williams College opened in Williamstown to fifteen students in 1793; today, the fine liberal arts institution has about 2,000.

Tony Williamstown is a true college town, the mostly red brick buildings of the college dominating the center on velvety green lawns, and the purple and gold college colors showing up everywhere. Students constitute one-fourth of the town's population. As an art center, Williamstown is famed both for the collections at the Williams College Museum of Art and those at the Sterling and Francine Clark Art Institute, the latter particularly rich in the works of French Impressionists.

Bennington is twice as big as Williamstown and parts are a trifle seedy, as you might expect in an old mill town. But check out the fine old mansions in Old Bennington, the Old Burying Ground where poet Robert Frost and five Vermont governors have been laid to rest, the Bennington Museum with its stunning collection of Grandma Moses paintings, the crafts and antiques shops, and the diverse restaurants. The Main Street (Route 9) has undergone something of a renaissance of late, with new restaurants and shops.

In the fall, the hillsides flame with the colors of foliage. Roadside stands along Route 7 offer apples, maple syrup, pumpkins and cider. Cheers emanate from the football stadium at Williams on Saturday afternoons (particularly vigorously if archrival Amherst is the opponent) and the soccer or frisbee teams might be practicing on the fields along North Street. The aroma of wood fires from inns and restaurants fills the crisp air.

The area's eclectic mix of offerings is enough to make your weekend interesting and plenty busy.

Getting There

Williamstown, in the northwest corner of Massachusetts, and Bennington, in the southwest of Vermont, lie along Route 7. The nearest major airport is in Albany, N.Y. The Massachusetts Turnpike, Route 90, south of Williamstown, is a major access road.

Peter Pan Bus Lines, headquartered in Springfield, has regular service to Williamstown.

Seeing and Doing

A wide range of activities awaits you in this area. Of particular interest are fine museums, cultural opportunities, the outdoors (especially in leaf-peeping season) and shopping. People who stay in Bennington often spend a day in Williamstown, and vice-versa. Each destination has its champions.

The Great Outdoors

Getting out into the crisp fall air is a must. Many visitors like just to drive around, enjoying mountain vistas, Colonial houses and roadside stands. One trip we love is Route 43 south from Williamstown toward Hancock, Mass. Another is a bypass

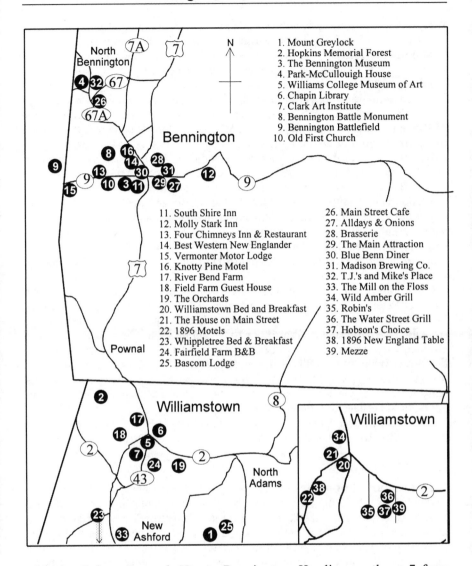

1. Mount Greylock
2. Hopkins Memorial Forest
3. The Bennington Museum
4. Park-McCullough House
5. Williams College Museum of Art
6. Chapin Library
7. Clark Art Institute
8. Bennington Battle Monument
9. Bennington Battlefield
10. Old First Church

11. South Shire Inn
12. Molly Stark Inn
13. Four Chimneys Inn & Restaurant
14. Best Western New Englander
15. Vermonter Motor Lodge
16. Knotty Pine Motel
17. River Bend Farm
18. Field Farm Guest House
19. The Orchards
20. Williamstown Bed and Breakfast
21. The House on Main Street
22. 1896 Motels
23. Whippletree Bed & Breakfast
24. Fairfield Farm B&B
25. Bascom Lodge

26. Main Street Cafe
27. Alldays & Onions
28. Brasserie
29. The Main Attraction
30. Blue Benn Diner
31. Madison Brewing Co.
32. T.J.'s and Mike's Place
33. The Mill on the Floss
34. Wild Amber Grill
35. Robin's
36. The Water Street Grill
37. Hobson's Choice
38. 1896 New England Table
39. Mezze

of Route 7 from Pownal, Vt., to Bennington. Heading north on 7 from Williamstown, take a right onto Barber Pond Road, following it to South Stream Road and thence to South Branch Street and Route 9 (East Main Street) in Bennington.

There are special places for those who like to hike or walk. The famed **Appalachian Trail** cuts right across Mount Greylock in Massachusetts as it marches north toward its terminus on Mount Katahdin in Maine. There are still more than 500 miles of hiking ahead of those who are going from south to north, but many hikers simply do sections of the trail. The Mount Greylock area is one of the more popular.

The **Long Trail** is a section of the Appalachian Trail that basically runs across the ridge of the Green Mountains and the Berkshire Hills. It is accessible from a number of points off main roads, many of which provide parking areas for vehicles.

A central access point is from East Main Street in Bennington. There are 71 shelters along the trail, which is marked by white paint, with side trails designated in blue.

Mount Greylock, at 3,491 feet, is the highest peak in Massachusetts. Much of the mountain is protected as a state reservation. Roads climb to the summit from Lanesborough, New Ashford and North Adams and it's a pleasant and free ride. The bare summit offers views in all directions from the 92-foot War Memorial Tower. It also has Bascom Lodge, built by the Civilian Conservation Corps in the 1930s and operated by the Appalachian Mountain Club. The lodge is the starting point for 40 miles of hiking trails and nature walks. It's a pleasant place to get a snack, have your picnic or enjoy a hearty, hot dinner. Dinner costs $12 per person and reservations, (413) 743-1591, must be made by noon the day you plan to attend. Bascom Lodge also has overnight accommodations (see Where to Stay).

Walkers enjoy ambling around the Williams College campus in Williamstown or around **Field Farm** in South Williamstown (site of Field Farm Guest House), which has about three miles of interesting walks and trails, most of them not particularly strenuous. The Bennington Chamber of Commerce puts out an attractive brochure, "Two Walking Tours of Bennington." One guides you to Old Bennington, the other to downtown Bennington.

Hopkins Memorial Forest in the northwestern corner of Williamstown and adjacent Petersburg, N.Y., covers more than 2,200 acres. It is managed by the Williams College Center for Environmental Studies for research, education and recreation. Ten miles of trails are open to the public for hiking, snowshoeing and cross-country skiing. The Rosenberg Center is located at the eastern entrance to the forest off Northwest Hill Road. A museum area offers interpretive displays on the natural world; a display of mushrooms was on when we were there. Diagonally across from the center is the Hopkins Forest Farm Museum, dedicated to the agricultural heritage of the Berkshires.

Covered bridges. There are three in Bennington, one off Silk Street and two near Murphy Road. All cross the Walloomsac River, which runs through town.

The Museums

The Bennington Museum. One of the finest regional art and history museums in New England, this has the largest public collection of paintings by Grandma Moses, America's beloved folk artist. Anna Mary Robertson Moses lived just across the state line in New York, but she spent three years in Bennington, making her something of a native daughter. She painted scenes that would have been familiar to townspeople and some, in fact, are of Bennington. Twenty-eight of her paintings are on display here, as is the tilt-top table that she used as her easel and whose base she painted with scenes. In addition, the schoolhouse that she attended as a child was moved here from Eagle Bridge, N.Y., and contains many of her personal belongings. The military gallery in the museum features a red coat from a Redcoat along with artifacts from not only the Revolutionary War, but from every war in which Bennington men fought. An unsurpassed collection of Bennington pottery fills two galleries in the museum. Other attractions are a fine collection of American glass, a grouping of American furniture and relics of Bennington's proud past. The gift shop features Vermont-made items and museum reproductions.

West Main Street (Route 9), Bennington. (802) 447-1571. Daily 9 to 6, June-October, rest of year to 5. Adults, $5.

Park-McCullough House. For one hundred years, from the time the house was built in 1865 until Bess McCullough Johnson died, this imposing house was lived in by members of one family. Two of them, Hiland Hall and John G. McCullough, were Vermont governors. Today, the grand old place with its fourteen-foot ceilings, dark mahogany woodwork, pocket doors, parquet floors and original furnishings is a rich collection of Victoriana. In fact, it provides an unusually complete record of an important New England family. One-hour guided tours are offered. Of particular interest are the extravagant indoor plumbing, beautiful fireplace mantels and many of the clothes worn by the inhabitants.

Corner Park and West streets, North Bennington. (802) 442-5441. Daily 10 to 4, late May through October; tours on the hour, 10 to 3. Adults $5, students $3.

Williams College Museum of Art. This is one of the best college art museums in the country. It houses 11,000 works spanning the history of art, but the emphasis is on contemporary and modern art collections, American art from the late 18th century to the present and non-Western art. The neoclassical rotunda of the original structure is augmented by extensive additions designed in 1983 and 1986 by architect Charles Moore. His dramatic three-story entrance atrium connects the original building with the four-story addition. The college has extensive holdings of works by Maurice and Charles Prendergast. Perhaps because much of the museum is devoted to modern works, the Edwin Howland Blashfield Memorial Room, installed in 1983 and centered by an old French baptismal font from the 12th century, seems such a gem. The entire collection is staggering, though, from a 3,000-year-old Assyrian stone relief to the last self-portrait by Andy Warhol.

Main Street, Williamstown. (413) 597-2429. Tuesday-Saturday 10 to 5, Sunday 1 to 5. Free.

Chapin Library. Nowhere else are the founding documents of the country – original printings of the Declaration of Independence, the Articles of Confederation, the Bill of Rights and drafts of the Constitution – displayed together in a simple glass case on the second floor of a college hall. This fine library contains more than 30,000 rare books, first editions and manuscripts. The lowest level of Stetson Hall contains the archives of band leader Paul Whiteman, including 3,500 original scores and a complete library of music of the 1920s.

Stetson Hall, Williams College. (413) 597-2462. Monday-Friday, 9 to noon and 1 to 5. Free.

Sterling and Francine Clark Art Institute. An heir to the Singer Sewing Machine fortune, Sterling Clark collected art avidly and, it is said, without assistance from dealers or advisers. He simply had a good eye. While living in Paris from 1911 to 1921, he laid the foundation of his own collection, buying many paintings of the old masters and the first of his favorites – Degas, Renoir, Sargent and Homer – who are well-represented here. There are also extensive collections of silver, prints, drawings and sculpture. It is said the Clarks chose Williamstown because they wanted their collection safeguarded in a place where nuclear attack would be unlikely. The original 1955 building of white marble was designed by Daniel Perry of Long Island; it is like a little Parthenon and is quite lovely. A large red granite structure, designed by Pietro Belluschi and The Artists Collaborative, was added in 1973. A neat little cafe serves from late morning to mid-afternoon.

225 South St., Williamstown. (413) 458-9545. Tuesday-Sunday (also Monday holidays, including Columbus Day), 10 to 5. Free.

Williams College, Williamstown. Just a stroll around the campus is of interest and the houses and buildings along Main Street (Route 2) are beautifully sited. The old **Hopkins Observatory** is the oldest observatory in the country; on Friday nights during the school year there are programs in Milham Planetarium here.

Cultural Offerings

Williamstown and Bennington form a cultural center. In the summer, the **Williamstown Theatre Festival,** (413) 597-3399, mounts productions in the Adams Memorial Theatre at Williams College. Considered one of the best professional regional theaters in the country, it attracts major actors and actresses to its stage.

In Bennington, the **Oldcastle Theatre Company,** (802) 447-0564, stages performances from April through October on the campus of Southern Vermont College.

Images Cinema, 50 Spring St., Williamstown, (413) 458-5612. This "art" cinema shows films for a few days at a time, often those that have attained a cult status but haven't been huge box-office draws. Many are foreign films. The collegians appreciate them and you may, too.

The **Williams College Department of Music** maintains an ambitious schedule during the school year with appearances by the Berkshire Symphony, Williams Choral Society, Williams Jazz Ensemble, Williams Symphonic Winds, recitals with guest artists and so forth. Performances are usually given on weekends.

History

Bennington Battle Monument. The tallest structure in Vermont, this 306-foot granite monument on a hill overlooking Bennington marks the site of a Continental Army storehouse that was the objective of the British Army in August 1777. That force was met and defeated by local militiamen, including the legendary Green Mountain Boys, just across the border in New York State on Aug. 16. Many historians consider this battle the turning point in the War for Independence. Each year on the weekend closest to the date a parade is held in Bennington. The monument was dedicated in 1891 by President Benjamin Harrison on the occasion of the 100th anniversary of Vermont's becoming a state. It contains a diorama of the battle and the large army field kettle that supposedly belonged to British General John Burgoyne, surely a sweet spoil of war. You can ride the elevator to an observation area about two-thirds of the way up the monument. Glass windows allow good views in all directions. A gift shop stocks made-in-Vermont items.

15 Monument Circle, Old Bennington. (802) 447-0550. Daily 9 to 5, April-October. Adults $1, children 50 cents.

Bennington Battlefield, (518) 686-7109, is on Route 67 in Hoosick Falls, N.Y., about two miles across the Vermont-New York border. It contains markers and bronze raised maps of the Aug. 16 battle. The natural beauty and tranquillity of the well-kept grounds belie the violent struggle that took place here more than 200 years ago. There are picnic benches and restrooms. Free.

Old First Church, Monument Avenue, Old Bennington. This edifice, erected in 1805 to replace the First Congregational Meeting House built in 1763-65, is one of the most beautiful examples of early Colonial architecture in the country. It was

White marble building of Sterling and Francine Clark Art Institute resembles little Parthenon.

designed in the Wren-influenced style by Lavius Fillmore. In the historic grave-yard next to the church are buried Revolutionary War soldiers, Vermont governors and the poet Robert Frost, whose gravestone reads "I had a lover's quarrel with the world."

Shopping

In **Bennington**, you will want to visit Potter's Yard at 324 County St. **Bennington Potters** is the contemporary manifestation of the historic "Bennington" pottery, which was actually made by several different firms. On-site manufacturing of the new Bennington ware, plus a retail shop, are here. There are seconds and sale items available. Also in Potter's Yard are **Cinnamons,** a kitchen store; **John McLeod,** a wood products store; **Terra,** handcrafts from around the world, and the **Brasserie** restaurant (see Where to Eat).

On East Main Street, one of the nicest women's clothing stores and gift shops is **Panache,** and the good **Bennington Bookshop** is nearby. There is a **Dexter Shoe Factory** outlet on Route 7A heading north.

Hawkins House Craft Market at 262 North St. (Route 7) offers quite an array of handcrafted items. **Camelot Village** on Route 9 West is a barn-like building with works by some 200 artisans on display and for sale. Also on Route 9 West is a sales and tasting room of the **Joseph Cerniglia Winery.**

The **Apple Barn** on Route 7 South, Bennington, is a good stop for cider, apples, baked goods, cheddar cheese and maple products. Other roadside stands also are located along this stretch of highway toward Williamstown. The **Village Gift Barn** on Route 7 is chock-full – everything from penny candy to Halloween items.

In **Williamstown,** browse along Spring Street, site of college shops like the **Williams Co-op** and gift and clothing stores. Don't miss **The Library,** an exceptional antiques and gift shop that takes up three storefronts. On Water Street we like **Water Street Books,** where the college students buy their texts, and **The Cottage,** which has funky as well as traditional clothing and gifts. There are antiques galore in a warehouse atmosphere at **Collectors Warehouse,** off Route 7 North.

The **Store at Five Corners** along Route 7 in South Williamstown, taken over in 1992 by Andy and Stuart Shatken and renovated to their specifications, is now an updated country store with gourmet items, wines, hand-scooped ice cream, a deli, baked goods, groceries and gifts. Lunch is served on a patio to one side. This is a good place to pick up unusual souvenir items.

You can tag a tree for Christmas at **Mt. Anthony Farms,** Pleasant Valley Road, off Route 9 just west of Bennington. Tagging begins around Oct. 1, but you'll have to come back for the tree.

Where to Stay

Bennington

South Shire Inn. This large cream-colored Victorian house with olive trim in one of Bennington's nicer residential areas has been turned into a posh B&B. The main house was designed by architect William C. Bull, who did many stately Bennington homes. Ten-foot ceilings, a mahogany-paneled library where guests can read and relax, and fine plaster moldings are marvelous touches. All nine spacious guest rooms have private baths and seven have fireplaces. Five are in the main house and four in the Carriage House. Chippendale chairs are set at individual tables in the handsome peach dining room, where a full breakfast includes fresh fruit, muffins and a hot entrée. Resident innkeeper Kristina Mast says "I'm the muffin queen!"

124 Elm St., Bennington 05201. (802) 447-3839. Fax (802) 442-3547. Doubles, $95 to $165.

Molly Stark Inn. Cammie and Reed Fendler are innkeepers at this welcoming old house that they turned into a B&B with charm. Painted a deep Colonial blue with white trim, the house has a porch with wicker furniture, rockers and hanging plants. There are two front parlors for guests, one with a wood stove that Reed keeps stoked all season. Six guest rooms are furnished eclectically, the common theme being antique quilts on the beds. Reed calls the top-floor room with private bath "really cozy," although all rooms seem warm and welcoming. Some baths are private; some shared. A full breakfast is served (apple puff pancakes at our visit). For a private getaway, consider the guest cottage close to Barney Brook out back with a kingsize brass bed in the loft, jacuzzi, woodstove and wet bar.

1067 East Main St. (Route 9), Bennington 05201. (802) 442-9631 or (800) 356-3076. Doubles, $65 to $90; cottage, $130.

The Four Chimneys Inn and Restaurant. This old-timer under new ownership is known for its food, but there are lodgings as well. Nine guest rooms, rather large and elegantly furnished, are located on the ground floor and on the second and third floors of the building. All rooms come with private baths and king or queensize beds. Many have fireplaces and some have jacuzzis. Shades of pink and cranberry dominate in many guest rooms as they do in the downstairs restaurant. Two new deluxe rooms with sitting areas and whirlpool tubs are found in out-buildings in back. Owners Ron and Judy Schefkind serve a continental breakfast by tray in the bedrooms or in the restaurant.

21 West Road, Old Bennington 05201. (802) 447-3500 or (800) 649-3503. Fax (802) 447-3692. Doubles, $100 to $175.

Best Western-New Englander. This member of the national chain is well situated and comfortable. The 58 large units are located on two levels of two long gray buildings with white trim. Many rooms have king or queensize beds and 35 have refrigerators. There's a small swimming pool for summer use. In the morning, juice, pastries, donuts and coffee are complimentary in the main lobby. The Heritage House restaurant on the premises is well rated.

220 Northside Drive, Route 7A, Bennington 05201. (802) 442-6311. Fax (802) 442-6311. Doubles, $80 to $92.

Vermonter Motor Lodge. There is a Vermont feeling all over this place, which may be its greatest appeal. Set back from the road, the 32 units include typical individual cottages as well as simple motel rooms. A tranquil bass pond on the property and a quite good restaurant, the Sugar Maple Inne, under the same management, are pluses. Decor is simple and some of the stall showers in the cabins looked in need of updating, but the place is neat and clean. Three meals a day are served in the restaurant. Prices at night are in the $8 to $14 range, with prime rib on the menu at $12.95 the night we stayed. Pastas and seafood are also featured.

West Road, Route 9, Bennington 05201. (802) 442-2529 or (800) 382-3175. Fax (802) 442-4782. Doubles, $60 to $85.

A Good Value

Knotty Pine Motel. Tom and Barbara Bluto have been running this small, impeccable and friendly motel for more than twenty years and show no signs of slowing down. The eighteen units come with either a queen or two double beds, knotty pine walls, color cable TV and in-room perked coffee. There is a small pool for use in good weather.

130 Northside Drive, Route 7A, Bennington 05201. (802) 442-5487. Fax (802) 442-2231. Doubles, $58 to $66.

Williamstown

River Bend Farm. Dave and Judy Loomis have opened this Georgian Colonial farmhouse, built in 1770, to guests for twenty years. The house, which is on the National Register of Historic Places, is kept as an authentic 18th-century experience (the Loomises' own more modern digs are attached at the rear). Guests sleep in four antiques-furnished bedrooms that share two baths; the bathroom on the first floor was created out of the old pantry off the keeping room and still has shelves of crockery along one wall. For breakfast, Judy serves her own granola, along with fruit, juices and homebaked breads – possibly spread with the couple's own honey – in the keeping room in front of the huge hearth. River Bend Farm offers one of the most historical experiences we know of; this really *is* back in time. The severe portrait of the founder of Williamstown, Benjamin Simonds, copied from that in the Williams College collection, enjoys a prime location on a front parlor wall. Should you be sailors, the Loomises may share with you tales of their own transoceanic sailing experiences.

643 Simonds Road (Route 7 North), Williamstown 01267. (413) 458-3121. Doubles, $80. Closed late October to April.

Field Farm Guest House. This 1948 country estate was owned by an art collector, Lawrence H. Bloedel, and became available following his widow's death in 1984, when it was given to the Trustees of Reservations. The 296-acre site is stunning, with a beaver pond, views of Mount Greylock, and hiking and walking trails. And the house was perfect for conversion into a B&B, especially since all five bedrooms already had private baths. The house was in great shape and the furnishings – right out of the 1940s and 1950s, with lots of built-ins – were interesting. There are also second-floor balconies with ship's railings, a main-floor terrace with tables, contemporary sculpture on the grounds, and views all around from picture windows. Guests enjoy a spacious living room with tiled fireplace, furnished mostly with pieces made by Mr. Bloedel, who was a 1923 Williams graduate and onetime college librarian. The huge first-floor Gallery Room, which the owner used as a studio, has a double bed, two twins and a separate entrance. Upstairs are four more rooms, one with tiles of butterflies around the working fireplace. A full breakfast is made by Jean and Sean Cowhig, resident innkeepers. Dutch apple french toast, which Sean describes as "a mix between bread pudding and upside-down cake," is a specialty. A tennis court, pool and three miles of trails are more assets.

554 Sloan Road, Williamstown 01267. (413) 458-3135. Doubles, $100.

The Orchards. Opened in 1985, this small hotel in the English country tradition was meant to fill a gap in terms of accommodations in Williamstown. The exterior of salmon-colored stucco is a bit confusing, but plantings are gorgeous, especially those in an interior courtyard with fountain and pool. Inside, graciousness reigns. The 49 guest rooms in different wings have TVs in armoires, bathroom phones and refrigerators. Some have four-poster beds and working fireplaces. Pink and green predominate in the decorating scheme, both in guest and public rooms. Guests enjoy afternoon tea, including several breads, sandwiches and tea cakes, in the elegant drawing room. There are an English-style pub with fireplace and dart board, and a handsome dining room where we've enjoyed a couple of fancy lunches. Typical dinner entrées run from $17.95 for grilled salmon in leek-champagne sauce to $22.95 for tournedos of beef madagascar.

222 Adams Road, Route 2, Williamstown 01267. (413) 458-9611 or (800) 225-1517. Fax (413) 458-3273. Doubles, $155 to $225.

Williamstown Bed and Breakfast. Conveniently located at the crossroads of Williamstown, this comfortable and squeaky-clean B&B in a big white house is run by Lucinda Edmonds and Kim Rozell, who met when both were working in Boston. Kim is the cook, Lu handles the cleaning, and both are experts at what they do. All four guest rooms come with private baths. Beds are topped with cream-colored comforters, which are puffy and warm. Bottled water awaits guests in each room, where braided rugs and comfortable chairs add homey touches. Kim makes the full breakfasts, which are served in a simple dining room furnished in pressed oak. "I bake bread and muffins and I always have a hot entrée, sometimes cheese blintzes or blueberry pancakes," says she.

30 Cold Spring Road, Williamstown 01267. (413) 458-9202. Doubles, $85.

The House on Main Street. Located next to the Williams Inn, this white house offers six comfortable guest rooms, three with private baths and three sharing one and a half baths. There are a comfortable living room with TV, a wicker-filled side porch, and a tranquil, flower-filled yard in which to sit. Phyllis and Bud Riley are the innkeepers and Bud handles the breakfast duties. Guests can pick up cereals and fruit at a buffet counter, then sit at one of two large tables in the kitchen and adjoining dining area, where a hot entrée is served. The largest room, and the only one with a TV, is the ground-floor Posie's Room, which was a 1986 addition to the 18th and 19th-century structure. The Blue Room, with a twin and full bed, and floral wallpaper, is also on the first floor. The other four rooms are upstairs. *1120 Main St., Williamstown 01267. (413) 458-3031. Doubles, $75.*

1896 Motels. Among motels along Routes 7 and 2, these two motels – one on each side of the road – stand out. Sue Morelle and Denise Richer joined forces seven years ago to take over the 1896 Motel Brookside – set back from the road on shady grounds reached by a tiny bridge across Hemlock Brook. Guests like to sit near the brook, which runs in front of the motel, while taking their continental breakfast in the morning. The sixteen units have knotty pine walls and wonderful old rock maple furniture including the most comfortable chairs imaginable. "Guests are always wanting to buy them," says Sue. Two airedales, Dacey May and Chelsea (mother and daughter), are also "on staff." Now part of the complex across the road is the 1896 Motel Pondside, a thirteen-unit motel with Cape Cod decor and a spring-fed duck pond in back. It also has a heated pool that all guests may use. *910 Cold Spring Road, Williamstown 01267. (413) 458-8125. Doubles, $70 to $98.*

Whippletree Bed & Breakfast. A pretty restored Federal Colonial farm-house twelve miles south of Williamstown is perched high on a knoll overlooking the highway. Innkeeper Chuck Lynch operates it as a friendly, accommodating B&B. He offers five rooms, three in the main house with shared baths, the Loft and the Suite, an efficiency apartment. We stayed in the second-floor Loft in the red barn addition to the back of the house, with our own outdoor staircase and a real sense of privacy. The large room has a queen bed, a twin bed, a full bathroom and a great view, through sliding doors, of the hills out back. A nicely landscaped pool and plenty of yard chairs are welcoming. Just a few yards south is the road to the summit of Mount Greylock, so this is a good location for hikers. A continental-plus breakfast of cereals and muffins is served at a large table in the dining room. *10 Bailey Road at Route 7, Lanesborough 01237. (413) 442-7498. Doubles, $65 to $95.*

Good Values

Fairfield Farm B&B. If you'd like to be on a 600-acre working farm away from the town activity, book one of two simple guest rooms rented out in their old white farmhouse by Dan and Mary Lou Galusha. The second-floor rooms, one with double bed and one with twins, are paneled in wood and share a hall bath. A continental breakfast with homemade granola is served on the front porch, weather permitting. Guests also have use of a parlor. *Route 43, Green River Road, Williamstown 01267. (413) 458-3321. Doubles, $50.*

Bascom Lodge. This rustic fieldstone and dark wood lodge offers over-night accommodations – mostly in clean and orderly bunkrooms at $13 for Appalachian Mountain Club members; $20 for non-members. There are also a couple of private rooms, doubles $52 ($62 for non-members). Bathrooms are shared, at the end of the hall. Most of those who stay are hikers who are climb-ing in the area. Three meals a day are available in the dining room. Entertain-ment is often scheduled on weekends, especially in summer. *Top of Mount Greylock. (413) 743-1591. Open from mid-May through late October.*

Where to Eat

The choices for dining are quite good. In addition to solid New England fare, there is a surprising number of new, sophisticated restaurants.

Bennington

Main Street Cafe. Jeffrey Bendavid and his wife Peggy oversee this intimate restaurant in a storefront location. Jeff, who hails from New Brunswick, N.J., was a musician before he turned his creativity to food and he makes beautiful music here. The sponged peach walls of the front room, under a deep burgundy pressed-tin ceiling, display the works of local artists and photographers. A second, smaller room with sponged yellow walls to the rear has a view of a millpond. Each table sports bottles of red and white wine as centerpieces. Chefs work in a small kitchen open to the dining room, and waiters clad in tuxedoes give attentive service. Typical entrées are charcoal-grilled sea scallops served on spinach linguini, chicken and spicy Italian sausage with braised onions and mushrooms, and chicken in a wine sauce with green peppercorns and portobello mushrooms. Starters might be sautéed mussels, charcoal-grilled eggplant over spinach, and vegetable cannelloni. Desserts like tirami su made with Tia Maria and Meyers's dark rum, lemon sponge cake and chocolate-mocha cake are hard to pass up.

1 Prospect St., North Bennington. (802) 442-3210. Entrées, $15 to $18. Dinner nightly from 6.

Alldays & Onions. Chef-owners Maureen and Matthew Forlenza are both in the kitchen – and their young daughter sometimes is, too – at this popular restaurant, one of the best in town. Regional American food with many interesting choices is served inside at well-spaced tables and a couple of booths, or on a screened porch to the side. There are even a few tables outdoors on the grass. For lunch, you can build your own sandwich of traditional deli meats, cheeses and condiments, or have something like cream of golden squash soup, quiche or cheese tortellini. Dinner menus change frequently but might include appetizers of smoked salmon cakes, caesar salad with smoked trout or grilled spicy shrimp. Veal sweetbreads with wild mushrooms are one of the signature entrées. Others might be a Southwest cowboy steak, roast chicken with lingonberries or stir-fried vegetables. Meals come with a house salad and the restaurant's own herb bread. Fresh peach pie was a dessert choice at our last visit.

519 Main St., Bennington. (802) 447-0043. Entrées, $11 to $15. Daily except Sunday, 8 to 5; dinner, Wednesday-Saturday 6 to 9.

Brasserie. David Gill has owned this charming little European-style cafe for more than 30 years, but his real genius has been in attracting fine chefs. Originally, it was the late, great Dionne Lucas; since the early 1970s, Sheela Harden has overseen the kitchen. "People rave about the consistency," said the manager when we stopped by. They also love to sit outside on the broad and shady terrace in good weather. The all-day menu offers lighter lunch-type foods ($5 to $8) as well as dinner entrées up to $12. One of the more famous items, one rarely seen hereabouts, is pissaladière, a snack from Provence that involves a thick slice of Rock Hill bread, smothered with sweet onions cooked in olive oil almost to a jam consistency, then baked with anchovies and calamata olives on top. It is served with a tomato salad vinaigrette. The pastas are especially good, and you also can get quiches, omelets, a Greek salad, a Scandinavian sampler (smoked bluefish, parslied potato salad, pickled beets and dilled cucumbers), a mozzarella loaf as luscious as the name implies, and even a chunk of chèvre marinated in olive oil and served with a loaf of whole wheat-sunflower seed bread and tomatoes. Heartier dishes may include oyster stew, herb-crusted ribeye steak and pasta tossed with bacon, onion, zucchini and pinenuts. Crème caramel is a signature dessert.

324 County St. (Potter's Yard), Bennington. (802) 447-7922. Entrées, $9 to $12. Daily, 11:30 to 8, May-October; rest of year, Sunday-Thursday 11:30 to 3:30, Friday and Saturday to 8.

Four Chimneys Inn and Restaurant. The gorgeous old white mansion in Old Bennington has a main dining room, a lounge and a dining porch overlooking restored gardens, and is the sort of place you might choose for a special occasion. The inn attracts weddings and functions, moreover, and when we last tried to stop in for lunch, it was closed for a wedding. The dining rooms are decorated in romantic shades of pale mauve, pink and rose. Flickering oil lamps in hurricane chimneys and classical music in the background add to an elegant, formal setting. Chef Scott Hunt, who had worked with former chef-owner Alex Koks, is continuing the tradition of classic French fare with a touch of nouvelle. At lunch, entrées ($8 to $13) might include shrimp and pasta, smoked salmon croissant and petite filet mignon in cabernet sauce. At night, the meal is prix-fixe for three courses, with the possibility of Burgundy-style snails in garlic butter or a house specialty, mustard soup, to start, and entrées such as a fish medley in herb sauce, chicken breast with wild mushroom cream sauce or rack of lamb.

21 West Road, Old Bennington. (802) 447-3500. Prix-fixe, $32.50. Lunch, Tuesday-Saturday 11:30 to 2, July-October; dinner, Tuesday-Sunday 5:30 to 9; Sunday brunch, 10:30 to 3.

The Main Attraction. This bright, contemporary spot on the main drag has tables on two different levels, lots of TVs (a happy circumstance for a husband wanting to catch a football game one Saturday afternoon) and a good following. Large contemporary poster-style art fills the walls painted peach with aqua trim. The all-day menu is supplemented by specials. You can get sandwiches like grilled chicken teriyaki melt, the French dip or a Monte Cristo ($6 average); salads such as grilled chicken caesar and Greek salad, and entrees like grilled swordfish, baked scrod and fish and chips. A special was apple and rosemary stuffed pork. Service is friendly and prompt.

421 Main St., Bennington. (802) 442-8579. Entrées, $8 to $12. Daily, 11:30 to 10 or 11.

Blue Benn Diner. The vintage diner with blue stools and booths, blue and white ruffled curtains, and individual booth-operated jukeboxes is a Bennington institution. Breakfast is served here all day, but you also can get lunch and light supper. We managed to snag one of the coveted booths for a Saturday breakfast, and feasted on whole wheat harvest pancakes filled with blueberries, blackberries, raspberries and strawberries ($3.50). The meal held us until a mid-afternoon lunch. There is something of an emphasis on healthful foods and you are asked not to smoke.

Route 7, Bennington. (802) 442-8977. Open daily at 6 for breakfast and lunch, Sunday at 7; dinner Wednesday-Friday.

Madison Brewing Company. Here's a new brew pub, opened in 1996 by the Madisons, a local family consisting of parents and three adult sons. Seven beers and ales are on tap. Local brews include Crowtown Pale Ale (for Bennington's nickname), Old '76 Strong Ale and Battlefield Stout. There's also a selection of micro-brew bottled beer. During the day, you can get sandwiches and specialties like a nacho platter. After 5, the dinner menu includes blackened tuna, vegetable stir-fry, chicken teriyaki and surf and turf.
428 Main St., Bennington. (802) 442-7397. Entrées, $11 to $16. Daily, 11:30 to 10.

T.J.'s and Mike's Place. Locals tout the food in this casual dining room next to a small sports bar. Half-pound burgers, sandwiches like roast beef and smoked ham and cheese and entrées that include chicken parmigiana and fried flounder are available.
27 Main St., North Bennington. (802) 442-0122. Entrées, $7 to $11.

Williamstown

The Mill on the Floss. Chef Maurice Champagne, a native of Montreal, his American wife Jane and their daughter Suzanne run what many consider the area's best restaurant. Located just south of Williamstown, it is incongruously announced by a neon sign that also advertises the motel up the hill in back. But inside the dark brown wood building is a cozy main dining room with white linens, windsor chairs and a fireplace, onto which the kitchen opens with its gleaming copper pots and pans. A second wraparound garden room, looking onto the lawns out front, has been attractively redecorated. Sweetbreads in black butter is the signature dish on the classic French menu. Chicken amandine, veal piccata, sliced tenderloin with garlic sauce and veal kidneys in mustard sauce are among other entrées. Start with prosciutto and melon, escargots or fettuccine alfredo, among appetizers for $3 to $8. Jane's impressive homemade desserts include chocolate truffle with raspberry sauce, deep-dish pies, and crème caramel. What's really remarkable is the long tenure of most of the staff at the 25-year-old restaurant. And the bartender makes a mean cocktail.
Route 7, New Ashford. (413) 458-9123. Entrées, $17 to $26. Dinner, Tuesday-Sunday from 5.

Wild Amber Grill. Identical twin brothers and local chefs, Ned and Sandy Smith, opened this hot spot in 1996 on the site of the old Le Country restaurant, a sprawling brown building just north of the center of town. The place sprawls even farther now that they've reopened the attached screened porch and are cooking and serving there. Indoors are a fireplaced dining room and a new bar where cigars may be smoked. Ned says they aim for a "comfortable, sophisticated" atmosphere. The pair, who also own the popular **Cobble Cafe** on Spring Street, have brought over their popular sesame-seared tuna on basmati rice because of customer demand. Osso buco and rack of lamb are other favorites. All the cooking for outdoor dining is done on a grill on the porch. We had a beef kabob with Moroccan spices and a shrimp salad niçoise when we lunched there (lunches, $6 to $10). Porch dinners ($12 to $17) might include grilled salmon, shrimp kabobs and mixed grill – chicken, sausage and shrimp served with roasted potato.
101 North St. (Route 7), Williamstown. (413) 458-5000. Entrées, $13 to $16. Lunch, noon to 2; dinner, 5:30 to 9 or 10. Closed Tuesday.

Robin's. Robin MacDonald, a talented young chef from California, is the inspiration behind this restaurant in a house at the foot of Spring Street. The decor is simple yet effective: salmon walls, white curtains draped interestingly across the front and side windows, black contemporary chairs and white tablecloths. Each table in the front room holds a small bouquet of flowers. Out back is another room for dining. An outdoor deck is popular in good weather. From a small but efficient kitchen, Robin turns out creative meals. Lunches include pâté platters like Tuscan walnut or white bean and roasted garlic pâté ($6 to $8), salads (mandarin steak, for example) and hot specials such as quiche or wild mushroom ravioli. For dinner, we chose the grilled tuna with thyme butter and the penne pasta roasted with smoked salmon and shrimp, both scrumptious. A house salad of mixed greens with a light vinaigrette was served with an edible flower on top. Other entrées could be roasted boneless trout, garlic-rosemary chicken and country-style spare ribs roasted in a black bean sesame garlic sauce. Sunday brunch includes such enticements as blueberry bread pudding served hot with maple syrup.

Latham and Spring Streets, Williamstown. (413) 458-4489. Entrées, $14 to $22. Daily, 11 to 11; Sunday, 9 to 9.

The Water Street Grill. The former Savories became a new restaurant, open for dinner only, in 1996. Folks like the option of the more formal Grill Room with its huge fireplace to the rear of the building and the informal tavern room, with lighter options and paper placemats, up front. Starters in the Grill Room include mussels scampi, fried calamari rings and Boston clam chowder. Entrées could be grilled swordfish with herb and white wine sauce, Absolut chicken over linguini, a sirloin steak; and a soft taco platter. Barbecued ribs with a smoky barbecue sauce is a specialty. Fudge swirl cheese cake, apple pie and "Chocolate is my Life Sundae" are among the dessert offerings. You can get sandwiches in the tavern, as well as some items from the main dinner menu.

123 Water St., Williamstown. (413) 458-2175. Entrées, $10 to $15. Dinner nightly, 5 to 9 or 10.

Hobson's Choice. Sited in an old house, this eatery is furnished with old tools on the walls and Tiffany-style lamps. There are several blue-green booths with high backs, windsor chairs at wood-topped tables and aqua carpeting. Red, green or blue napkins add brightness. Chef-owner Dan Campbell offers blackened prime rib, many fish dishes, Southwestern favorites like chicken Santa Fe and a couple of vegetarian pastas. The salad bar is popular. At lunchtime, consider the chicken Santa Fe sandwich, salmon sandwich, crab salad, seafood pasta or a cheeseburger. Mud pie and a grand fudge parfait are signature desserts.

159 Water St., Williamstown. (413) 458-9101. Entrées, $11 to $17. Lunch, Tuesday-Saturday 11:30 to 2; dinner, Tuesday-Sunday 5 to 9:30.

The 1896 House New England Table. Sue Morelle and Denise Richer, who own the 1896 Motel next door, re-opened this classic Williamstown eatery in a huge red barn just south of town in 1996. Prospects are good, although they were still in the shakedown period when we had dinner one Friday evening. The main dining room is attractively furnished with reproduction wing chairs, settles and windsor-style chairs and area rugs on wide floorboards for a Colonial atmosphere. Sofas and chairs surround a huge stone fireplace in one corner. A second dining room is more formal, and there is a large Cabaret room out back for evening shows connected with the Williamstown Theatre Festival. Upon arrival, diners are treated to delicious hot corn fritters with syrup and to hot breads later. The large menu offers starters like ale-battered chicken rasher, cornmeal fried oysters and Maine crab cakes. Entrées are offered under headings like Grazing Board (salads); Sandwich Board; Yankee Comfort Fare (country meatloaf, lamb stew, baked stuffed peppers); Savory pies (meat, seafood or vegetable pie of the day) and Groaning Board (roasts, steaks, seafood, vegetarian specialties). Our dinners – liver and onions for one, and stuffed peppers for the other – were fine. The most expensive dish is porterhouse steak.

Route 7, Williamstown. (413) 458-1896. Entrées, $8.96 to $22.96. Dinner nightly except Monday, from 6; Sunday buffet brunch, 10 to 2.

Mezze. Owner Nancy Thomas took a low brown building, once used as a craft gallery, and turned it into a popular eatery in 1996. Theater people from the Williamstown Theatre Festival were drawn to it, and Nancy said "star gazing" was an attraction. The food got high marks, too. It ranged from light fare like a Turkish white bean salad or smoked trout plate for $5 to $7, to entrées such as grilled flank steak or Mezze chicken (a changing presentation). The interior is contemporary with banquette seating and a few tables in the center of the floor. No reservations are taken, but you can wait with a drink on the tiny deck out back overlooking the rushing Green River.

84 Water St., Williamstown. (413) 458-0123. Entrées. $8 to $11. Dinner nightly from 5:30.

Picnicking

Great picnic spots abound. We think there's no more pleasing idea than to settle in at one of the scenic overlooks of **Mount Greylock** (reached from Lanesborough or North Adams, Mass.), spread your blanket and enjoy your picnic with the world seemingly at your feet. In South Williamstown, the property called **Field Farm,** owned by the Trustees of Reservations, harbors picnic spots. **Mount Hope Park** off Green River Road, Williamstown, has picnic tables. **The Deer Park** is located on Route 7 in Bennington. Picnic there under the trees near a herd of white-tailed deer in their own preserve. A state park in **Woodford** on Route 9 east of Bennington also offers picnicking..

A good place to get provisions is the **Store at Five Corners** in South Williamstown.

FOR MORE INFORMATION: Bennington Area Chamber of Commerce, Route 7, Bennington, VT 05201, (802) 447-3311. The Williamstown Board of Trade, Box 357, Williamstown, MA 01267, (413) 458-9077.

10  Fall

Outstanding early structures line The Street in Deerfield.

Arts and Antiques

The Pioneer Valley, Mass.

The Connecticut River cuts a swath through hilly west-central Massachusetts, creating rich agricultural lands that drew early settlers and turned them into well-to-do farmers. Hence the name, the Pioneer Valley.

The valley is rich not only in agriculture (Connecticut River shade-grown tobacco among other products) but in education and industry as well. In the 19th century, the bucolic setting was thought appropriate to the pursuit of higher learning. Noah Webster, the lexicographer, was one of the founders of Amherst College in 1821. In 1837, just down the road, the nation's first permanent women's college, Mount Holyoke, was founded in South Hadley.

Sophia Smith started the college that bears her name across the river in Northampton in 1875. With the huge University of Massachusetts (almost a city unto itself) and much newer Hampshire College, both in Amherst, the institutions form a five-college consortium and students benefit from their proximity.

The tourist can be a student, too, of a different sort. The valley's rich heritage is reflected in its early architecture and antiques, and the colleges are the focus for art museums and cultural events. In addition, more craftspeople per capita are found in the Pioneer Valley than any other section of New England except Vermont.

There's something quite 1960s about Amherst and Northampton. It's as if they got stuck in the era of the flower children. Along with young women in standard-issue jeans, you may see pigtailed lasses in batik and tie-dyed dresses and sandals, walking arm-in-arm with their long-haired escorts, eating granola and sunflower

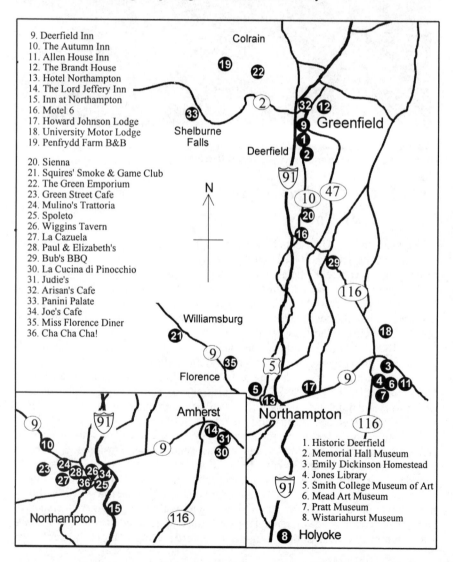

seeds. In fact, one of the great natural foods stores of all time, Bread and Circus, flourishes in the area.

The bucolic setting is still evident once you get off I-91, the major north-south highway. The rich alluvial soil that first attracted settlers now nourishes their descendants, and a patchwork of green fields stretches across the land.

A prime tourist attraction is Historic Deerfield, a walk-through museum village with an unparalleled collection of furniture, textiles and porcelain stunningly displayed in renovated houses from the 18th and 19th centuries. As much as we dislike the phrase, you really do "step back in time" when you visit the village of Deerfield, which doesn't have so much as a traffic light or a supermarket to detract from the setting. There's education here, too; tiny Deerfield is home to three private schools, including the prestigious Deerfield Academy.

9. Deerfield Inn
10. The Autumn Inn
11. Allen House Inn
12. The Brandt House
13. Hotel Northampton
14. The Lord Jeffery Inn
15. Inn at Northampton
16. Motel 6
17. Howard Johnson Lodge
18. University Motor Lodge
19. Penfrydd Farm B&B

20. Sienna
21. Squires' Smoke & Game Club
22. The Green Emporium
23. Green Street Cafe
24. Mulino's Trattoria
25. Spoleto
26. Wiggins Tavern
27. La Cazuela
28. Paul & Elizabeth's
29. Bub's BBQ
30. La Cucina di Pinocchio
31. Judie's
32. Arisan's Cafe
33. Panini Palate
34. Joe's Cafe
35. Miss Florence Diner
36. Cha Cha Cha!

Colrain
Shelburne Falls
Deerfield
Greenfield
N
Williamsburg
Florence
Amherst
Northampton
Holyoke

1. Historic Deerfield
2. Memorial Hall Museum
3. Emily Dickinson Homestead
4. Jones Library
5. Smith College Museum of Art
6. Mead Art Museum
7. Pratt Museum
8. Wistariahurst Museum

Possibly the proximity of Deerfield, and perhaps the ease with which customers can get to them (via I-91 and the Massachusetts Turnpike), have encouraged antiques dealers and auctioneers to settle. This is an area for serious searching as well as light-hearted browsing. Auctions, flea markets and special antiques shows are frequent.

Autumn and antiques have always had an affinity, and the valley is at its best in the golden days of Indian summer when the foliage burns brightly along the river banks and into the foothills of the Berkshires to the west, and students scuff through the leaves across tree-studded campuses. The college art museums are open, with the special enthusiasm that greets the first show of the semester.

All told, the valley has 72 towns, of which we concentrate on only a handful: Deerfield, with its history and heritage; Amherst and Northampton, with their colleges, art museums, antiques shops and galleries; Colrain, with its orchards and neat small shops and restaurants; eclectic Shelburne Falls, and Greenfield, which is finally getting a much-needed infusion of new shops and restaurants. And if you become tired of antiquing and museum-going, remember one very special Saturday afternoon diversion – college football, played with all the fun and sportsmanship that must have been there when the sport began.

Getting There

The Pioneer Valley stretches the length of Massachusetts along the Connecticut River, from the Vermont border on the north to Connecticut on the south. Interstate 91 runs north and south through the valley and the Massachusetts Turnpike (I-90) goes east and west near Springfield.

Several bus lines serve the area, including Greyhound, Bonanza Bus Lines and Peter Pan, the largest, based in Springfield, the major city on the southern approach.

Amtrak trains serve Springfield. Major airlines fly into Bradley International Airport between Springfield and Hartford, Conn. From there, buses travel north to Springfield, Holyoke and Northampton.

Seeing and Doing

Deerfield

Historic Deerfield. This village has a mile-long Main Street (called simply "The Street"), which is unique. It is lined with huge trees and outstanding examples of 18th- and 19th-century homes, thirteen of which are beautifully restored and open to the public year-round. A Connecticut couple, the Henry Flynts, whose son attended Deerfield Academy, were the benefactors. Their vision was to create a walk-through museum that would allow current generations to view and revere the architecture and furnishings of the past, while at the same time preserving that treasure. They succeeded admirably.

The houses, for the most part, are on their original sites and, as much as possible, original pieces of furniture have been obtained. The collection is priceless and contains furniture, ceramics and textiles of outstanding quality. You can't see it all in an afternoon or a day, but you can in a long weekend. If you choose carefully, you can get a taste of Deerfield in a one-day visit. Even if you don't enter any of the homes, a drive or a walk through the village is highly recommended.

A first-time visitor might want to see the Wells-Thorn House, the oldest, which has been recently revamped to show seven time periods in a series of different rooms, a quite remarkable history lesson. The Jonathan Ashley House, with its matching shell-corner cupboards in the parlor, is gorgeous. The Allen House, which was the home of the Flynts from 1946 to 1974, contains their collection of needlework and period furniture, representing some of the museum's finest pieces.

Admission, good for two consecutive days, includes an orientation program and a walking tour of the houses, although not all may be open on the day you visit. *The Street (off Routes 5 and 10). (413) 774-5581. Daily, 9:30 to 4:30. Adults $10, children $5. Combination ticket with Memorial Hall Museum (below), $12.*

Memorial Hall Museum. Deerfield's oldest museum occupies the original Deerfield Academy school building dating to 1798. This is the museum of the Pocumtuck Valley Memorial Association, and was one of the first museums in the country to emphasize historic preservation. The first period room in America, a kitchen, was opened here in 1880 and is still on view among the nineteen rooms open to the public on three floors. The Indian House Door, the oldest external door in America, dating from 1698, is a particularly unusual item in a most interesting museum collection. The quilt collection on the top floor is incredible. Taped oral histories, done by actors who tell about the Deerfield Massacre of 1704 from the viewpoint of several of those involved, are fascinating.

Memorial Street, Deerfield. (413) 774-7476. Weekdays 10 to 4:30, weekends 12:30 to 4:30, May-October. Adults $5, children $1; combination ticket with Historic Deerfield, $12.

Other Museums

Emily Dickinson Homestead. Arguably America's best woman poet, Emily Dickinson was born in this house in 1830 and, except for ten years when the family occupied another Amherst home, lived here until her death in 1886. The house is owned by Amherst College, which uses it as a faculty residence; open to the public are the parlor, the music room and, most important, the poet's second-floor bedroom. It was in this room that the increasingly reclusive Emily penned her poetry on scraps of paper, envelopes, whatever was handy, and stuffed them into drawers for safekeeping. In the room are a small table about the size of her writing desk (the original is at Harvard University), a franklin stove, a family cradle and, on a mannequin, a white dress she wore during the last decade of her life (you will note her small stature). On the window sill is a basket; a lover of children, the poet was known to lower gingerbread to her nieces and nephews and their friends when they played below. You must call ahead to reserve a tour, although we luckily were squeezed in on the day of our visit. Nearby is the West Cemetery, where Emily is buried in the family plot with her parents and her sister. Her tombstone has the simple phrase "Called Back" on it.

280 Main St., Amherst. (413) 542-8161. Tours by reservation, Wednesday-Saturday at 1:30, 2:15, 3 and 3:45, May-October; Wednesday and Saturday only in March, April, November and early December. Adults $3, children $1.

Jones Library. This small public library, arranged to resemble a luxurious private home, is notable for its fine Emily Dickinson memorabilia. The collections include some of her personal possessions, manuscripts and a model of her bedroom. Several rooms, paneled in walnut and Philippine white mahogany, are adorned with paintings and oriental rugs.

43 Amity St., Amherst. (413) 256-4090. Monday-Saturday 9 to 5:30, Tuesday and Thursday to 9:30, Sunday 1 to 5. Free.

Smith College Museum of Art. One of the most important college art collections in the country is housed in this contemporary gallery. Spanning almost all art periods and genres, the museum shows the works of world-famous painters such as Degas, Monet, Renoir, Picasso, Cezanne and Gauguin. There are also paperweights, Greek vases, pieces of Medieval and Renaissance sculpture, and a representative collection of contemporary artists. Rodin's bronze works, including "Walking Man," are also here. Just off Green Street is the prized **Lyman Plant House** and its adjoining botanical gardens containing perennials from around the world. The chrysanthemums are spectacular in fall. Plant House is open daily 8 to 4.

Elm Street, Northampton. (413) 584-2770. Wednesday-Thursday and Saturday-Sunday, noon to 4, also Thursday, 4 to 8. Hours vary in summer; closed school vacations. Free.

Mead Art Museum. A smaller art gallery than Smith's, this features the works of several outstanding artists. And it has one gem: the 1611 Rotherwas Room, moved to the college from the home of an alumnus who had brought it to America from a British castle. Carved walnut paneling, an exceptionally ornate mantelpiece and fireplace, and stained-glass windows give the Jacobean banquet hall a baronial feel.

Amherst College campus, Amherst. (413) 542-2335. Monday-Friday 10 to 4:30, weekends 1 to 5. Closed school vacations and August. Free.

Pratt Museum of Natural History. This museum focuses on the geological nature of the Pioneer Valley. Home of the world's largest mastodon skeleton, the museum also exhibits meteorites, dinosaur tracks, rare minerals, crystals and fossils.

Amherst College campus, Amherst. (413) 542-2165. Monday-Friday 9 to 3:30, Saturday 10 to 4, Sunday noon to 5; weekends only in summer. Closed school vacations. Free.

Hadley Farm Museum. Antique farm implements and tools are arranged here in a renovated 1782 barn. Exhibits include plows, hay tenders, bean shellers, spinning wheels and hand-held carpenter tools.

Junction of Routes 9 and 47, Hadley. (413) 584-8279. Tuesday-Saturday 10 to 4:30, Sunday 1:30 to 4:30, May to Columbus Day. Donation.

Wistariahurst Museum. This huge Victorian house was the family home of the Skinners, owners of the famed Skinner Silk Mills in Holyoke. The name is for the wistaria vines that still drape the mansion. Built in the mid-1800s, the house stood originally in Skinnerville (part of nearby Williamsburg), but was brought to Holyoke in sections and rebuilt on its present site in 1874. Tiffany windows in the conservatory, an English wrought-iron balustrade on the main staircase and a checkerboard parquet floor are among the fine architectural details. Unfortunately, none of the original furniture is in the house, although there are interesting historical exhibits. One room is filled with Shaker furniture; another has Chinese furniture.

238 Cabot St., Holyoke. (413) 534-2216. Wednesday, Saturday and Sunday 1 to 5, April-October; rest of year, noon to 4. Adults, $2.

The Art of Nature

Don't overlook the artistry of nature during beautiful autumn days in the valley. For the foliage freak, the place near Amherst to view the most trees from one point is **Mount Sugarloaf,** off Route 116 in nearby Sunderland. This state park has an observation tower at the summit, from which you can see the whole sweep of the river valley and the treed hillsides flanking it.

How about a hike? The **Holyoke Range State Park** off Route 116 just south of Amherst offers great hiking trails, all leading from a modern visitor center. The Mount Norwottuck Loop, four miles long, is moderately strenuous and takes two and a half hours. There are also shorter and easier trails.

The **Mohawk Trail** (Route 2) west of Interstate 91 is a favorite foliage route. From Route 2, head north into **Colrain** and drive among its hilly orchard country, or detour south into **Shelburne Falls,** a funky little town with craft shops, restaurants and book dealers. We also like Route 9 west of Northampton to **Cummington** for foliage.

If you want to get out onto the Connecticut River, you can. The **Northfield Mountain Recreation and Environmental Center,** (413) 659-3714, operates special fall foliage cruises aboard the **Quinnetukut II,** a riverboat, from the Riverview Picnic Area off Route 63, Northfield April through October. Reservations are required. Northfield Mountain has fine hiking trails and picnic areas, too.

For a different perspective on nature, visit the historic **Montague Mill** in Montague Center, east of Deerfield across the Connecticut River. Here you can pick out a volume from the Book Mill, a multi-story labyrinth of new and used books, and get a cup of coffee, a pastry, or lunch at the adjoining cafe with great views of the Saw Mill River just outside. Sit on one of the outdoor decks – or in a window seat inside as the sun pours in – and take in the view of the waterfall.

The Art of Football

Football in a low-key, understated way is practiced by the small but top-notch New England colleges known as the Little Ivy League, and Amherst is among them. The Lord Jeffs take to Pratt Field several Saturday afternoons in autumn. Students and faithful alumni sit on low wooden bleachers, wave the purple and white, and sing the familiar college song, "Lord Jeffery Amherst." With archrivals Williams and Wesleyan, these teams form the Little Three and the competition is spirited. Except for Homecoming, tickets usually can be purchased the day of the game.

Across town at the larger Alumni Stadium of the University of Massachusetts on University Drive, you can see the state universities of New England battle with the Minutemen. These games have a bit more big-league flavor.

Shopping

The area's best shopping is in Northampton, where the downtown appears thriving with serious adult shoppers (as opposed to the young people who flock to Amherst). On Saturdays, there are also teenagers – many of them into counter-culture with dyed hair and very original outfits. Green Street, adjoining the Smith College campus, is home to a number of smart boutiques, art galleries and antiques shops.

In the center of Northampton, stop at **Thornes Marketplace** at 150 Main St. to see how an old department store can be recycled. The four floors here are fun to stroll through, with craft shops, art galleries, a large home furnishing and kitchen store, boutiques, a health foods store, all sorts of gift and clothing shops, and usually someone selling fresh flowers by the entryway. It has a European carnival atmosphere with awnings, bright signs and music.

Two of the better galleries along Main Street are **Pinch Pottery,** where we admired cats on bowls made by Ohio craftsmen, and the outstanding (and expensive) **Don Muller Gallery.** Colorful sweaters, sportswear and "exciting clothes" for women are stocked at a store named for its owner, **Cathy Cross.** Too exciting? Satisfy your sweet tooth at **Ben & Bill's Chocolate Emporium,** two side-by-side storefronts dispensing ice cream, baked goods and truffles. If you're really hungry, stop at one of our favorite bakeries anywhere, **Konditorei Normand** at 192 Main, which has an authentic European flavor and more fancy pastries than you'll find this side of Paris. We bought freshly baked raisin bread and a delectable linzertorte. Often there's a special for on-the-street munching.

Go under the railroad viaduct to 11 Bridge St., where you'll find **Collector Galleries,** a large and rambling collection of antiques, memorabilia, coins and just plain junk. Other antiques shops near the same corner make it worthwhile to park the car and browse.

Look for used and vintage clothing on Market Street. Some nice women's lingerie can be found at **Gazebo** on Center Street.

In the **Old Deerfield Country Store** on Route 5 just south of the village, you'll find dried flowers, candy, puzzles, stoneware, hand-dipped candles, gourds, pumpkins, Indian corn and more. Speaking of candles, the **Yankee Candle Company** in South Deerfield, also on Route 5, is a well-advertised stop and just keeps growing and growing. We have never seen so much square footage devoted to Christmastime anywhere and the candle company has a Bavarian Christmas Village with fourteen themed shops, where Santa is "in" from September on. For a nice selection of history-oriented items, visit the **Museum Store** run by Historic Deerfield on The Street in Old Deerfield. You'll find many books and good little gift items, along with stoneware pottery and hooked wall hangings. The **Antique Center of Old Deerfield** includes fifteen shops in a barn just north of town. Quite a few antiques shops also are strung along Routes 5-10 south of Deerfield.

The **Lunt Design Center & Marketplace** on Federal Street in Greenfield, new in 1996, offers an opportunity to watch silversmiths and glass blowers at work at this, the home of Lunt silverware. In the bright new marketplace area are many related products to purchase, from placemats and napkins to kitchenware and seasonal decorations. You can stop for lunch at the Artisan's Cafe (see Where to Eat).

Premium traditional hard ciders and fruit wines are available from **West County Winery** at Pine Hill Orchards on the Colrain-Shelburne Road in Colrain. These are among the best fruit wines we've tasted.

The **Hadley Village Barn Country Store** and surrounding shops on Route 9 in Hadley are a destination for many.

Amherst has stores of appeal to the campus set, including an uncommon number of small and specialized bookstores. **The House of Walsh** offers men's clothing and **Zanna** is a boutique for women. **Global Trader** stocks gifts and clothes from across the world. **Silverscape,** headquartered in a huge turreted yellow house, sells fine gold and silver jewelry. There are plenty of funky boutiques in the **Amherst Carriage Shops** out North Pleasant Street.

One of the best book stores of the many in the area is the **Odyssey Bookshop** in the center of South Hadley. The venerable bookstore had been forced to move because of a couple of fires, but its new home is a smashing two-story building in **The Village Commons**, a stylish complex with other good shops. The **Shelburne Falls Old Bookshop** on Bridge Street in Shelburne Falls specializes in used books, as does **Bookends** in Florence. **Salmon Falls Gallery** in the **Salmon Falls Marketplace** in Shelburne Falls offers fine arts and crafts.

The **Whistling Crow** in Shelburne Falls has wonderful environmental stuff. You can watch glass blowers at work and purchase unusual handmade glass pieces at **North River Glass.**

Where to Stay

Accommodations in the valley range from a few old Colonial inns to modern motels and hotels with indoor pools, saunas, entertainment, the works. While you can easily find a chain hotel/motel in the cities, we've concentrated on places and towns where the real ambiance of the valley can be sensed.

Inns and B&Bs

Deerfield Inn. The Deerfield Inn is owned by Historic Deerfield and situated smack dab in the middle of the historic village. An obvious choice for the serious history and antiques hound, the inn has softened its somewhat formal image to take on the feeling of a comfortable country inn. Under the management of inn-keepers Jane and Karl Sabo, the public rooms of the inn have been refurbished. The mahogany tables in the lovely dining room are often left bare, the better to show off their pewter service plates and white napkins. The front parlors are done in soft tones of gold and blue, and gourds and corn husks decorate the fireplace in one. There's a small tavern-type bar for a pre-dinner drink. The inn offers 23 guest rooms, several in the main building and others in the newer south wing, which has barn siding and which blends nicely with its surroundings. All are quite spacious and have Colonial appointments. Each is named, with a card describing who the namesake is. Typical is the Samson Frary (named for Deerfield's first settler), with twin beds covered with Bates spreads, cable TV and a large bathroom. Guests may take lunch or dinner in the main dining room, or have lighter snacks in the **Stenciled Horse Coffee Shop** downstairs. A full breakfast is included. Tea and cookies are set out in the afternoon.

The Street, Deerfield 01342. (413) 774-5587 or (800) 926-3865. Fax: (413) 773-8712. Doubles, $146 to $236.

The Autumn Inn. This red brick inn/motel is one of our favorites. Veteran innkeeper Vince Berger refers frequently to the establishment as "the house" (which it resembles from the front), as when he points out that "the walls are insulated, so this is a quiet house to stay in." Located near the Smith College campus and set back from the main route (Route 9) leading to the quaint towns of Williamsburg, Goshen and Cummington, the Autumn Inn is one of those places to which travelers return time and again. The thirty rooms and two suites are decorated in a simple, homey style, but there are percale sheets and fluffy towels, original artworks on the walls (we liked the framed Saturday Evening Post covers in one), color TVs, many Hitchcock chairs and rockers, Stieffel lamps and the occasional poster bed.

Rooms have queensize, twins or two double beds, and all have private baths. Breakfast daily and lunch Monday through Friday are available in the **Harvest Room** off the lobby, a comforting space with a huge old-fashioned fireplace in which the embers glow on chilly days. The menu is comforting as well, featuring grilled cheese and other old-fashioned sandwiches for $3.15 to $5.75 and including juice or soup of the day. Downstairs is an attractive cocktail lounge.

259 Elm St., Northampton 01060. (413) 584-7660. Fax (413) 586-4808. Doubles, $96; suites, $115.

Allen House Inn. Elegant Victoriana reigns in this prized B&B, located at the edge of Amherst in a Queen Anne stick-style house built in 1886. Alan and Ann Zieminski, he a biochemist in research at UMass and she a dental hygienist, opened it as a B&B after fifteen years in residence and promptly won the 1991 Amherst Historical Commission preservation award. Sticklers for authenticity, they offer seven guest rooms with private baths and a couple of uncommonly elaborate common rooms. The Victorian dining room, for instance, is finished in anglo-Japanese style; it harbors an ornate cherry fireplace mantel recorded in the Metropolitan Museum of Art, a stunning stained-glass window in the corner and no fewer than nine patterns of English wallpapers. The William Morris living room is papered in terra cotta, and holds a dining table in the middle for those who wish to breakfast in semi-privacy. Bedrooms feature Eastlake-style furnishings, ornate bedsteads, goose down comforters and pillows, armoires, antique AM-FM radios that work, Gilbert & Soames toiletries and more fancy wallpapers by period designers Christopher Dresser, William Morris, Walter Crane and the like. The Eastlake Room is dark and masculine, while the Peach Room is light and airy with white wicker and a queensize bed. The rear Scullery, done in Laura Ashley for a seaside look, adjoins an enormous bathroom with a clawfoot tub; a puce-colored marble desk top covers the scullery sink. Guests relax on wicker rockers on the small front veranda upstairs. Afternoon tea with oatmeal shortbread, cookies and cheesecake may run into the evening. For breakfast, the Zieminskis go all-out with such treats as Swedish pancakes with peach-raspberry sauce, stuffed french toast, eggs benedict and soufflés. The pumpkin pancakes with maple syrup are popular in autumn.

599 Main St., Amherst 01002. (413) 253-5000. Doubles, $85 to $135.

The Brandt House. Set atop a hill on more than three acres in the high-rent district just east of downtown Greenfield, this is one magnificent, sixteen-room Colonial Revival house. Phoebe Brandt Compton has turned it into an elegant and welcoming B&B, conveniently located just north of Deerfield. She offers seven guest rooms, five with private baths. The exceptional public areas include a fireplaced parlor, a game room with billiards and chess tables, a dining room with french doors opening onto the rear terrace, a wraparound porch and, the crowning touch, a cheery sun porch with three sofas and a TV (plus phones and fax machine) off the stairway landing. From the sun porch or terrace you can gaze across the back yard and tennis court onto woods and hills, part of vast municipal parklands called Highland Park, containing hiking and cross-country trails and an ice-skating pond. Phoebe has furnished her attractive guest rooms with antiques, taking in the auctions every week in Deerfield. Most rooms come with king or queensize featherbeds, loveseats, armoires, and good artworks and rugs. Two have working fireplaces. Family photos line the stairway to the third floor, where two bedrooms with twin beds share a bath and form a family suite. Energetic Phoebe used to run a B&B in Brookline before the family moved to Greenfield in 1986. Breakfast – served at an expandable table for ten in the dining room, at a table for two in the bay window of the living room or outside on the terrace or veranda – is a treat. It includes fresh fruit, two homemade pastries (perhaps Danish cheese bread and streusel coffee cake) and, on the weekends, a main course of quiche, marinated french toast or oven-baked pancakes topped with fruit.

29 Highland Ave., Greenfield 01301. (413) 774-3329 or (800) 235-3329. Fax: (413) 772-2908. Doubles, $100 to $165.

A Rural Experience

Penfrydd Farm B&B. If you'd like to be truly out in the country at a working farm with llamas and horses, consider this B&B in the hills of Colrain. The approach is magnificent, especially in autumn, although you need good directions. Innkeeper Ceacy Griffin offers a large double room with private bath and whirlpool tub plus four rooms sharing one bath. All are furnished in country fashion. Guests enjoy a full breakfast – yogurt, fruit salad, pancakes or french toast and sometimes eggs. "I really like to stress that this is a farm," Ceacy says, where guests will see ducks, dogs, cats and larger farm animals.

105 Hillman Road, Colrain 01340. (413) 624-5516. Doubles, $55 and $65.

Hotels and Motels

Hotel Northampton. In the center of downtown, this columned, four-story brick classic has been refurbished and a new wing added to make it a more desirable place to stay. The fireplaced lobby with wing chairs and Chippendale sofa is welcoming, and all the 72 rooms have been decorated nicely, many featuring feather duvets and Laura Ashley linens and draperies. We liked one room with a kingsize canopy bed and access through french doors to a large balcony in the front of the hotel. Wicker chairs add a light touch to many rooms and to the glassed-in outer lobby, which also has ice-cream-parlor tables and chairs – it's a nice spot for a drink. The **Coolidge Park Cafe** (named for Calvin, who was once mayor of Northampton) offers drinks, light fare and weekend entertainment. **Wiggins Tavern** is a quintessential Colonial dining spot (see Where to Eat). A continental buffet breakfast is included in the rates.

36 King St., Northampton 01060. (413) 584-3100. Fax: (413) 584-9455. Doubles, $79 to $195; three suites, $195 to $325.

A Family Budget Choice

Motel 6. An unusual member of the nationwide budget chain, this was originally built as a Ramada Inn and its amenities are a notch above what you'd expect for the price. It attracts some trade from nearby Deerfield and guests have the use of an Olympic-size indoor pool. There are 123 rooms, each with two double beds. Even though the office is tucked away clear around the parking lot in back, they do, as the commercial says, leave the light on for you. With prices the way they are, this motel is particularly popular with families.

Routes 5 and 10, South Deerfield 01373. (413) 665-7161 or (800) 466-8356. Fax: (413) 665-7437. Doubles, $45.95; each additional $10, children under 17 free.

The Lord Jeffery Inn. The "Lord Jeff" is a white brick Georgian Revival landmark in town, favored by Amherst alumni and parents of students. Owned by the college, it has been run by a succession of management groups in recent years. Of the 50 rooms, favorites are those in the Garden Wing with french doors that open onto the garden. All rooms have private baths, many quite small, and half have working fireplaces. Room 47 on the third floor is especially nice with a neat angled ceiling and a fireplace, which, unfortunately, can only be looked at. But the huge fireplace in a parlor off the lobby will probably suffice; it seems there's always a fire burning in it. Lunch and dinner are served daily in the dining room, attractive with salmon walls and napkins and a matching rosebud on each table; four lovely chandeliers light the room. Entrées are $14 to $23, and tableside preparation is featured in fettuccine alfredo, châteaubriand and bananas flambé. A light menu is available in Boltwood's Tavern.

On the Common, Amherst 01002. (413) 253-2576 or (800) 742-0358. Fax (413) 256-6152. Doubles, $80 to $120; suites, $110 to $165.

Inn at Northampton. Until 1992 the Northampton Hilton, this hotel has had a quick series of owners, with a local investment group taking over in 1996 and renovating most of the entire property. When we visited, much was under plastic. The hotel is arranged in three sections, each with its own courtyard. A real draw in the past was the glass-domed center courtyard with an indoor pool, saunas and whirlpools, and officials assured that it would be continued. Among the 124 rooms are eight mini-suites.

1 Atwood Drive, Northampton 01060, (413) 586-1211 or (800) 582-2929. Fax (413) 586-0630. Doubles, $109.

Howard Johnson Lodge. This two-story, 62-room motel is standard for the chain, but is conveniently located between Northampton and Amherst. Each room has two double beds, and comes with private terrace or balcony. There's an outdoor pool for use in summer. A continental breakfast is complimentary.

401 Russell St. (Route 9), Hadley 01035. (413) 586-0114. Fax (413) 584-7163. Doubles, $69 to $109.

University Motor Lodge. This Colonial-style, two-story motel is located about half-way between the high-rise campus of the University of Massachusetts and the center of town and you can walk to either. Most of the twenty rooms are furnished with two double beds. It's a fairly low-key place with cable TV and in-room phones.

345 North Pleasant St., Amherst 01002. (413) 256-8111. Doubles, $52 to $89.

Where to Eat

Northampton has long prided itself on being the dining capital of the region, but interesting restaurants can be found all around the area.

Top Choices

Sienna. Transplanted New Yorker Jonathan Marohn and his wife, Kim Rosner, opened this gem of a restaurant in 1990 in a small pillared storefront that could pass for a hotel or general store on the nondescript main street of South Deerfield.

They restored the high-ceilinged main floor into a subdued dining room with washed burnt sienna walls, white linens and floral tapestry banquettes they made themselves from cut-up church pews (with clay pots fastened ingeniously on the sides to use as wine buckets), and moved into residential quarters upstairs. The local produce of the Deerfield Valley was part of the attraction for this talented team, and Jonathan takes full advantage. The short dinner menu might include seared salmon with a sweet chile marinade, roasted sweetbreads with mushrooms, carrots and peas in a sherry vinegar sauce, and duck grilled over applewood with a cider barbecue sauce, served with apple-cranberry relish and sweet potato fritters. Among recent starters ($5 to $9) were a Puerto Rican-inspired sweet chile-grilled jumbo shrimp dish and seafood ravioli made from sea scallops, shrimp and crab. This is serious, complicated fare, beautifully presented, and for some the side vegetable accompaniments are the stars. Stellar desserts include pumpkin crème caramel, thin apple tart and a refreshing cranberry "soup" made with cranberries and oranges and served with a scoop of spice ice cream. A fine wine list is available.

28 Elm St., South Deerfield. (413) 665-0215. Entrées, $17 to $20. Dinner, Wednesday-Saturday, 5:30 to 9 or 10; Sunday, 5 to 8.

Squires' Smoke and Game Club. Catherine Blinder of Hartford and Eric Lerner of Northampton joined forces in 1994 to create this hot dining spot overlooking the Mill River six miles west of Northampton. The brick building in which the restaurant is located was the welding shop for the brass factory that dominates Route 9 as you approach. Decor is simple: mustard-colored walls and spare Arts and Crafts-style furnishings, including eye-popping overhead lighting fixtures. It's a perfect backdrop for the excellent smoked and grilled fare provided by inventive chef Victor McNulty, who was previously at the Ram's Head Inn on Shelter Island, N.Y. Starters ($4 to $9) include a country game pâté with a warm slaw and caraway scones, sliced tomato and brie bruschetta with roasted fennel coulis, and smoked lobster and porcini minestrone. From the "smoked" side of the menu come osso buco with a split pea risotto, green tea duck with smoked shiitake lo mein, and pheasant pot pie with puff pastry, yams, squash and truffle. "Grilled" items include swordfish steak with a fricassee of new potatoes, beets, onions and lemongrass, pork tenderloin with carrot puree, grilled leeks and cranberry ketchup, and filet mignon with scalloped potatoes and a green peppercorn sauce. The chef also makes all the dessert pastries served here. The five tables overlooking the waterfall and the stream, which are lighted at night, are the most requested. On the wall is a quote from the Talmud: "When a man or a woman meets their maker, they will have to account for those pleasures of life they failed to experience." Catherine Blinder hopes a visit to her restaurant is not one of them.

132 Main St. (Route 9), Williamsburg. (413) 268-7222. Entrées, $16 to $25. Dinner, Wednesday-Sunday 5 to 10.

The Green Emporium. Chef Michael Collins and neon artist Tony Palumbo, who for years operated an art gallery in Manhattan's Greenwich Village, have moved to the country and are providing the folks of Colrain with some interesting food and entertainment on weekends. The location is a 150-year-old former Methodist Church right on the green in the center of what barely passes for a town. A single rose in a bud vase on each table on two levels adds a touch of class, but otherwise this is a comfortable, eclectic place where enjoyment is paramount. Mike

Deerfield Inn exemplifies the restoration of historic structures aeound the Pioneer Valley.

shops the local farms for produce, which makes him feel as if he were living in Europe. Sometimes aided by a local woman, he turns out what he calls "country fusion" food. You might begin with native butternut squash soup with pickled ginger or an appetizer of avocado with grilled shiitake mushrooms topped with lemon sauce. Entrées could be shrimp, mussels and clams marinara over linguini, sautéed pork chops with apples and prunes, or vegetarian bolognese on spinach and egg fettuccine. Ethnic festivals (Italian, Japanese, Finnish) occasionally substitute for the regular menus. All the wines are $15 a bottle, and beers from New England microbreweries are offered. Omelets in many guises are featured for brunch. A grand piano has its purpose: live jazz is offered frequently.

4 Main Road (Route 112), Colrain. (413) 624-5122. Entrées, $14 to $17. Dinner, Friday-Sunday 5 to 8 or 9, also Thursday in summer; Sunday brunch, 10 to 2.

Green Street Cafe. "American country French" is the way chef-owner John Sielski describes the food at this popular eatery, which has evolved over the past few years from a place where Smith students used to hang out for breakfast, lunch and tea into a serious, dinner-only restaurant. Enter a street-level room with murals on the walls done by an Amherst student. Head up a few stairs to the right to an aubergine dining room with minimal decor and a counter at the back. There are a couple more dining rooms beyond, mostly furnished with mismatched tables and chairs and with wonderful local artworks on the walls. Two rooms have wood-burning fireplaces where, John says, a special duck dish is grilled some evenings. Flickering mantel candles add to the atmosphere. Dinner might begin with a potato and leek tart, Maine crab cakes with endive and pear, or mussels in red wine with garlic ($5 to $7). Fall entrées include sea bass in parchment, filet mignon with roasted shallots and garlic mashed potatoes, and roast leg of lamb. A pastry chef prepares extraordinary desserts, the most well-known of which is chocolate pots au crème. Banana caramel pie, crème caramel and a delectable cranberry crisp were also on tap the evening we stopped. Fado is sung on Thursday evenings. *64 Green St., Northampton. (413) 586-5650. Entrées, $15 to 22. Dinner nightly, 5:30 to 10.*

Colonial Experiences

Deerfield Inn. The dining room at the Deerfield Inn is so beautiful and classically Colonial that it's *the* place to eat when you take a Sunday drive through Old Deerfield. The fare changes monthly, but is highly regarded at all times. A recent November dinner menu featured fillet of salmon sautéed with sea scallops and raspberries, roasted breast and confit of duck with spiced wild plums and cranberries, and venison medallions served over a julienne potato pancake. Other game dishes are likely to appear in autumn, including wild boar which "sounds awful, but really is quite good," according to innkeeper Jane Sabo. For lunch in the downstairs coffee shop, you might choose a quiche or ragoût of the day, a sandwich or a main dish ($8.95 to $11.95) like ratatouille pizza or flank steak with basmati rice. Indian pudding is a favorite dessert. *The Street, Deerfield. (413) 774-5587. Entrées, $18 to $23. Lunch in coffee shop, daily noon to 2; dinner nightly, 6 to 9.*

Wiggins Tavern. Serving guests since 1786, this landmark in the Hotel Northampton is the quintessential Colonial dining spot for someone who wants to eat by the fireplace in an old tavern atmosphere. The lighting is low and one of the fireplaces, at least, is big enough to walk into. Chef Michael McCarthy was getting good marks for updated versions of local classics such as butternut-apple-cheddar bisque and Indian pudding with ginger and apples. Starters might be New England clam chowder, smoked scallops with penne pasta and pan-seared crab cakes. Main courses include the classic chicken pot pie and roast turkey dinners, along with pan-seared salmon, herb-grilled chicken with penne and eggplant parmesan. Gigantic fresh popovers come with the prime rib, available in two sizes. *36 King St., Northampton. (413) 584-9455. Entrées, $14 to $20. Dinner, Tuesday-Saturday 5:30 to 10, Sunday 4:30 to 9.*

Italian, Etc. . . .

Spoleto. Ask anyone in town where to eat and the first place that comes to mind is an Italian high-flyer that moved to the high-visibility former location of Sze's Chinese restaurant in 1991 from smaller digs on Crafts Avenue. Chelsea Clinton and the First Lady dined here while on a college-hunting trip in 1996. Spoleto Festival posters and colorful mobiles lend color to a spacious, pale yellow and green room on two levels with a tiled bar at the center and an open kitchen to the rear. Chef-owner Claudio Guerra's contemporary Italian cuisine is colorful as well. At night, you can choose from a dozen or more pastas or from seafood, chicken, veal and beef dishes. One is a great chicken rollatini with spinach and fennel sausage. There's a fine, mainly Italian wine list, priced from $11 to $75. *50 Main St., Northampton. (413) 586-6313. Entrées, $9 to $16. Dinner nightly, 5 to 10.*

La Cazuela. There is Mexican and then there is La Cazuela. Owners Barry Steeves and Rosemary Schmidt, originally from Kansas City, say they grew up on Mexican food and like to see that it's served right. Their venture is located high off the street in what was once the old Rahar's inn and tavern – a historic plaque near the entry designates it as "long a popular gathering spot for students." Inside, everything is starkly contemporary and tables are nicely spaced. You can get enchiladas, fajitas, flautas, tacos, burritos – the full range and then some. Try the chicken in pipian sauce (pumpkin and sesame seeds, chiles, cloves, cinnamon and garlic), a bargain with rice, vegetable and salad for $10.25. Among other entrées, piñon shrimp comes with green chile pesto and toasted pinenuts. An autumn favorite is chiles en nogada, two poblano chiles roasted and stuffed with a picadillo of pork, apples, raisins and spices and covered with a creamy walnut sauce. The five versions of margaritas include the La Caz super deluxe, "as good as margarita gets," says the menu. Huevos rancheros ($6.95) is a brunch fixture.

7 Old South St., Northampton. (413) 586-0400. Entrées, $7 to $11. Dinner nightly from 5, weekends from 3; weekend brunch, 11 to 3.

Mulino's Trattoria. "Homestyle Italian cooking" is served up at this attractive restaurant in an old brick building, where most of the seats are vintage golden-hued pews from a nearby church and where the kitchen is open to view. Owners Felix and Corinne Tranghese feature pastas ($9 to $12), with variations such as penne alla vodka (with pancetta, tomatoes, vodka and cream), ziti with chicken, broccoli and grated cheeses, and spaghetti with capers, black olives, tomato, garlic and tuna sauce. You can get pizza from a wood-fired oven (ten-inch pizzas cost about $7) or a few meat choices including pork marsala and veal milanese. There's a piano lounge downstairs..

Center Street, Northampton. (413) 486-8900. Entrées, $10 to $13. Dinner, Tuesday-Friday 5 to 11, Saturday and Sunday, 4 to 10 or 11

La Cucina di Pinocchio. Mauro Aniello relocated his successful North Amherst venture of ten years into a large vacant restaurant space hidden away in the heart of Amherst. But his tradition of innovative recipes combined with the freshest ingredients continues. The front section is primarily for calzones and pizzas, priced from $3.95 to $8.25. Beyond the bar-lounge is a dimly lit larger dining room, pretty in white and pink. Interesting nightly specials supplement an already enormous selection of pastas and entrées (nine chicken and ten veal dishes), the highest priced being the grilled lamb loin at $18.95. Among the more popular dishes are the risotto alla veneziana (grilled chicken, porcini and portobello mushrooms, asparagus, fennel and smoked mozzarella) and filet mignon wrapped in prosciutto and served with black truffle and port wine sauce. La Cucina is big and bustling and strikes some as a bit overwhelming, but most locals love it.

30 Boltwood Walk, Amherst. (413) 256-4110. Entrées, $12 to $19. Lunch, Monday-Saturday 11:30 to 3; dinner, 5 to 10 or 11.

Special Interests

Paul & Elizabeth's. Paul and Elizabeth Sustick operate this large and obviously successful natural-foods restaurant in Thornes Marketplace. Regulars, many of them vegetarian, love the great fish chowder, hummus or cheese and sprouts sandwiches, fried tofu and omelets served with whole wheat bread and house tea.

At dinner, there's a curry dip and vegetables or stuffed mushroom caps as appetizers, tabouli, spinach, watercress and hummus salads, vegetable, shrimp, scallop or scrod tempura, pastas (maybe tomato-basil pasta with cauliflower and green olives), noodles with fish tempura and specials like tofu kabobs.

150 Main St., Northampton. (413) 584-4832. Entrées, $7.50 to $12.50. Daily, 11:30 to 9:30.

Judie's. Judie Teraspulsky, a former baker at the Lord Jeff, opened her own special restaurant quite a few years ago and it remains one of the more popular in this college town. You can eat under the glass front portion and watch the passing parade of Amherst, or you can sit at one of the bare wood tables in back, above which are mounted colorful parrot and elephant sculptures. The all-day menu is eclectic , with an emphasis on soups, munchies, burgers, sandwiches and salads. We liked the sound of the pesto popover caesar salwich, ($6.99), which turns out to be a caesar salad served as a sandwich. One menu section lists a dozen sautés, among them curried shrimp and scallops over fettuccine. Dinner entrées, served with a popover and tossed salad, include feta shrimp, Southwestern chicken and scampi, and steak and potato. Everyone says that no matter what you order, you can't leave until you try Judie's butter-dipped popover with apple butter ($1.99). The salad dressings and apple butter are so popular they're bottled for sale at the entry.

51 North Pleasant St., Amherst. (413) 253-3491. Entrées, $14 to $16. Daily, 11:30 to 10 or 11.

Artisan's Cafe. The high-ceilinged, multi-windowed cafe at one end of the new Lunt Design Center is the place to get lunch when you're shopping here, and that's what almost everyone else on a Friday in October seemed to be doing. The food is innovative and the ingredients fresh. Our choices were a curried turkey and wild rice salad and the Artisan's salad, made with mixed greens, mandarin oranges, crumbled blue cheese and walnuts – both wonderful. Grilled individual pizzas, sandwiches like the Vermonter (with roasted turkey, cranberry chutney, sliced granny smith apples and cheddar cheese), and entrées such as a roasted vegetable lasagna are among the choices in the $5 to $7 range. At night, you'll find entrées like salmon with a red onion marmalade, sautéed chicken breast with pears and tangerine-glazed pork tenderloin with apples. Brunch, available in the late morning, includes apple-fritter french toast and buttermilk pancakes. You can pick up a loaf of bread or desserts to go from the good bakery here.

Lunt Design Center, Federal Street, Greenfield. (413) 774-4680. Entrées, $15 to $19. Daily from 8:30 or 9:30 to 9 or 10, Monday to 4.

Panini Palate. Opened in 1996 by Nancie Rich, this small restaurant on the main street quickly gained a following. The namesake Italian grilled sandwiches on focaccia are featured on the all-day menu ($4 to $5.50), with several different fillings such as gorgonzola, mixed greens and tomato. The day's soup was pumpkin when we were here. Hot entrées include pot pies (fillings change daily), green lasagna (three cheeses and herbs) and catch of the day. Desserts are to die for: milky way tarts, nut basket tarts, incredible shortbread, and so on. Wines and local beers are available.

24 Bridge St., Shelburne Falls. (413) 625-6221. Entrées, $5 to $8. Tuesday-Sunday, 11 to 9 or 10.

Bub's BBQ. This unassuming roadside restaurant made of logs is home to the best Southern barbecue in New England, according to several experts on the topic. Former pro golfer Howard "Bub" Tiley, who hails from nearby Williamsburg, has been going strong here for twenty years. In nice weather, you can take your food out to a couple of red picnic tables perched off to the side of the parking lot, with an awning to shield you from the sun. But inside is more atmospheric, with tables in an enclosed porch or in a room where tables are covered in red and white checked cloths. Rolls of paper towels serve as napkins. "Pig Out in Style!" is Bub's motto. Barbecued spare ribs are the most popular item, although you also can order barbecued chicken, shredded beef, kielbasa, or even charbroiled or blackened catfish, red snapper, salmon or shrimp. Diners belly up to the counter to place their orders; when the food is ready, they serve themselves the "sides" of vegetable soup, bread and butter, barbecued baked beans, spicy rice, collard greens, hickory-smoked potatoes, sweet potatoes, dill potato salad, cucumber salad, coleslaw and fries. Don't blame Bub if you can't get enough food. The secret to the success here, we're told, is the barbecue sauce recipe, which Bub supposedly got from a convict when he was working at a prison in Florida. You can buy a bottle of the sauce for $5. Beer and wine are available.

Route 116, Old Amherst Road, Sunderland. (413) 548-9630. Entrées, $7 to $8. Daily, 11:30 to 9 or 10.

Joe's Cafe. If ever there were a classic, atmospheric pizzeria, this is it. College and professional sports pennants hang over the bar and all over the place, the rooms are dark and tablecloths are red and white checked. For 50 years it has been known for its thin-crust pizzas, and even chefs like Jonathan Marohn of Sienna come here on a night off. Pizzas are available in small, medium and large sizes, with the highest price $10 for Joe's house special (hamburg, onions, peppers, pepperoni, tomato and cheese). Others include pesto primavera, eggplant and Mexican. You can order bar appetizers like fried mozzarella, Buffalo wings and fried calamari ($4 to $7). Oven baked lasagna, veal marsala, chicken several ways, and spaghetti or cheese ravioli with several toppings are all possibilities. The featured wine is, appropriately, a Villa Banfi chianti, $14 a bottle.

33 Market Street, Northampton. (413) 584-3168. Entrées, $5 to $9. Daily, noon to 11 or 11:30.

Eat Cheap

Miss Florence Diner. Opened in the 1940s, Miss Flo's is a classic diner, serving an incredible variety of foods at prices that haven't caught up with the 1990s, thank goodness. When did you last see a hamburger on a restaurant menu for $1.50? Homemade soup (minestrone the day we ate here) also is $1.50. Baked stuffed lobster in a casserole was $11.95 that day, but most entrées like fried scallops, turkey croquettes, broiled chicken livers, and breaded veal cutlets with spaghetti were $6 to $10. Baked meatloaf with gravy was another classic on the menu. Entrées come with a choice of vegetable or potato. For breakfast, a big deal here, you can get juice, pancakes or french toast, bacon, ham or sausage and coffee for $4.05, an order of french toast for $1.95, or two eggs with toast and homefries for $2.15. The booths are plain and have jukebox selections in them.

99 Main St., Route 9, Florence. (413) 584-3137. Entrées, $6 to $11. Daily from 4:30 a.m. to 10 or 11 p.m.

Cha Cha Cha! Calling itself "a Mexican grill," this is one of the liveliest spots in town. You order from the counter and take your food to one of the few tables around the perimeter of the storefront space or, preferably, out front where a couple of tables allow you to watch Northampton's passing parade. The all-day menu includes the East-West burrito (stir-fried shrimp, tofu or chicken, vegetables, basmati rice and a tangy plum sauce), cajun catfish tacos (soft tortillas filled with catfish marinated in cajun spices and served with chipotle sour cream), fajitas Chela (grilled steak, chicken or vegetables served with hot flour tortillas) and the cha cha cha vegetarian platter with spicy black beans, grilled vegetables, spanish rice and salad greens tossed in lime vinaigrette. All orders come with chips and a salsa bar with many different kinds of fresh salsas. You can get ginger beer, root beer or natural sodas, but no booze.

134 Main St., Northampton. (413) 586-7311. Entrées, $4 to $7. Daily, 11:30 to 10.

Picnicking

Suppose it's Indian summer and you'd rather picnic than eat indoors? Find your supplies at **Bread and Circus,** a superior health foods superstore on Route 9 between Hadley and Amherst. This is one of a pioneering Boston-area venture, which has merged with the famed Texas-based Whole Foods Market chain. It has a fantastic selection of teas, coffees, cereals, meats and seafood, grains by the barrel, produce, even cat food. You can get salads and sandwich fixings, too. The **Black Sheep Bakery** in Amherst is an excellent place to pick up deli sandwiches and breads.

Another food emporium we like is the **Atkins Fruit Bowl** on Route 116 south of Amherst. Set in the middle of an orchard, it displays exceptionally nice produce, cheeses and ready-to-go entrées, and has a bakery where you can get a cup of coffee and a treat and sit down for a while to rest your bones. You can pick out your Halloween pumpkin here, too.

The Connecticut River Greenway State Park off Damon Road, Northampton, has picnic sites as does Mohawk Trail State Forest in Charlemont. There's also good picnicking at Mount Sugarloaf State Reservation, Route 116, South Deerfield, and at Northfield Mountain in Northfield. Historic Deerfield thoughtfully puts out a few picnic tables behind its main information area. You may find other spots to spread a blanket and enjoy your repast; for example, on one of the college campuses in the area or overlooking the Salmon Falls area of the Deerfield River in Shelburne Falls.

FOR MORE INFORMATION: Greater Springfield and Pioneer Valley Convention and Visitors Bureau, 56 Dwight St., Springfield 01103, (413) 787-1548; Amherst Chamber of Commerce, (413) 253-0700; Northampton Chamber of Commerce, (413) 584-1900.

11  Fall

Mount Monadnock is backdrop for Altar of the Nations at Cathedral of the Pines.

A Quiet Corner
The Monadnock Region, N.H.

New Hampshire's "Quiet Corner" comprises a region of small New England villages, most of them set out on winding back roads in the southwestern corner of the state. Many are picture-perfect New England, the kind often selected by landscape artists as representative.

They have the requisite white-steepled churches and village greens, the great old homes and farms with red barns, and sometimes townsfolk with the broad accents we associate with Yankees. Because the region is bypassed by expressways and the towns are few and far between and rather sparse in population, there's an unspoiled feeling.

Yet the Monadnock region has been a mecca for outdoors enthusiasts, writers and artists for more than a hundred years. Mount Monadnock, the gentle peak in its midst, is reputed to be the most climbed mountain in the world, in 1996 topping Japan's Mount Fuji for the first time. More than a quarter of a million people hike any one of a dozen routes to its summit annually. They follow in the footsteps of Ralph Waldo Emerson, who called it "The Great Inspirer," and Nathaniel Hawthorne, who described it as "a sapphire against the sky." Henry David Thoreau used to come here from Concord, Mass., for the weekend. He's known to have climbed the 3,165-foot-high mountain at least four times.

Lakes and rivers abound in the area. Several are flanked by colonies of summer homes. Dublin Lake is particularly sought after, for its shimmering waters often reflect Mount Monadnock itself.

In addition to its natural gifts, the Monadnock region has long enjoyed an active cultural life. The MacDowell Colony in Peterborough, the nation's oldest and largest artist retreat, serves as a temporary refuge for writers, artists and musicians who spend quiet, creative time here. One who did was writer Willa Cather; she so loved the region that she visited several times and is buried in the picturesque old cemetery in Jaffrey.

Peterborough, the area's focal point and largest community (population 5,200), was the inspiration for Thornton Wilder's play, "Our Town." Today it is home to a fine professional summer theater, The Peterborough Players, as well as a new, exciting marionette theater, the New England Marionette Opera. The Monadnock Summer Lyceum is a series of Sunday morning cultural events at Peterborough's Unitarian Church; often, the speakers are world-famous.

Tiny Dublin is the headquarters of Yankee magazine and the *Old Farmer's Almanac*. In Sharon, the top-quality Sharon Arts Center is a draw for fine artists and craftsmen and the site of classes in a variety of disciplines. Antiques and gift shops make the area fun for shoppers.

The real secret to the Monadnock region's richness, however, is its low-key approach. No chain motels or restaurants are located in villages east of Keene; the small city on its western border is a gateway to the Monadnock area, but to the east are the tiny towns we concentrate on. Visitors find rooms there in small bed and breakfasts and traditional, old-fashioned inns.

The Monadnock region is lovely in any season, but fall is special. The foliage is aflame, prompting one innkeeper to advise guests, "Turn off on

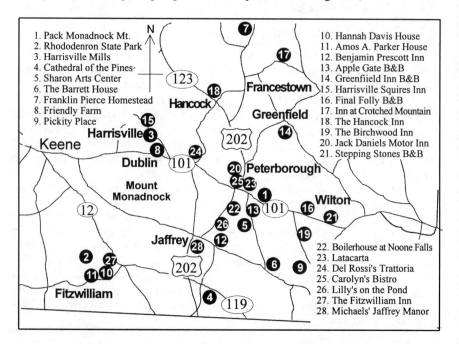

1. Pack Monadnock Mt.
2. Rhododenron State Park
3. Harrisville Mills
4. Cathedral of the Pines
5. Sharon Arts Center
6. The Barrett House
7. Franklin Pierce Homestead
8. Friendly Farm
9. Pickity Place
10. Hannah Davis House
11. Amos A. Parker House
12. Benjamin Prescott Inn
13. Apple Gate B&B
14. Greenfiield Inn B&B
15. Harrisville Squires Inn
16. Final Folly B&B
17. Inn at Crotched Mountain
18. The Hancock Inn
19. The Birchwood Inn
20. Jack Daniels Motor Inn
21. Stepping Stones B&B
22. Boilerhouse at Noone Falls
23. Latacarta
24. Del Rossi's Trattoria
25. Carolyn's Bistro
26. Lilly's on the Pond
27. The Fitzwilliam Inn
28. Michaels' Jaffrey Manor

any side road and it's like driving through a tunnel of color. You'll come out somewhere; you're not going to get lost."

Autumn is the time for the smell of smoke from inn fireplaces, for the taste of maple syrup on morning pancakes or waffles, and for the sense of well-being instilled by a walk or a hike in the crisp mountain air.

The Monadnock region is a choice for those who wish to slow down for a few days and get away from the pressures of modern life. Don't be surprised if you fall in love with the area.

Getting There

Interstate 91 is the major north-south access from the west and south. I-93 provides access from the east, and I-89 from the north. State Route 101 is the main east-west state highway through the area.

The nearest major airports are located in Hartford, Conn., and Boston, Mass., both about two hours' drive. Smaller airfields are found in Keene and Manchester, N.H. Vermont Transit buses travel from Keene to Logan Airport in Boston; there's one stop a day in Rindge.

Seeing and Doing

The Monadnock region is refreshingly uncommercial. Perhaps the most crowded it gets is on the trails leading up Mount Monadnock itself. Visitors spend much of their time outdoors, enjoying the mountain views, the lakes, the trails in parks and natural areas. Antiques and gift shops offer one-of-a-kind items, perfect for the unhurried browser but hardly alluring to the avid consumer. We've visited at the height of the tourist season and have never been in a traffic jam or had trouble getting a table for dinner. The area is particularly attractive to adults. There are not many obvious diversions to entertain children.

Outdoors

Mount Monadnock. Officially the mountain is known as Grand Monadnock to differentiate it from lesser relatives. At 3,165 feet, its summit doesn't begin to compete with the Presidential Range in the White Mountains to the northeast, but it stands well above its neighbors in the 2,000-foot-high range. Mount Monadnock has some 30 miles of trails. Ralph Waldo Emerson climbed Monadnock in 1866 at the age of 63 with his children and their friends. Five main trails lead to the summit. That used by most visitors, the White Dot trail, leaves from the entrance to Monadnock State Park off Route 124 in Jaffrey, (603) 532-8862, where park rangers hand out maps and literature. The average climber, we're told, takes three hours to get up and back. Park admission, $2.50.

Pack Monadnock Mountain. We have to admit driving to the 2,288-foot summit of Pack Monadnock and not climbing Grand Monadnock, because of the heat of one weekend we visited and the busyness of another. Pack Monadnock offers a great view of the giant. There are picnic tables from which to enjoy both the view and lunch. **The Wapack Trail** leads 21 miles from Pack Monadnock Mountain to Mount Watatic in Ashburnham, Mass. It passes through sections of Greenfield, Peterborough, Sharon, Temple and New Ipswich. For the most part, the trail follows a skyline route along the summits of the mountains. It lends itself well to day hikes, for it crosses several roads in the area.

In Miller State Park, off Route 101, Peterborough. (603) 924-3672. Park admission, $2.50.

The **Monadnock-Sunapee Greenway Trail** is a 49-mile footpath between Mount Monadnock and Mount Sunapee in South Central New Hampshire. The original trail dates to the 1920s when the path was laid along a series of abandoned roads. The new trail follows higher country. Many people obviously hike portions of the trail; a popular section extends 13.4 miles from Mount Monadnock State Park to Nelson Village

Crotched Mountain, Francestown/Greenfield. Three hiking trails lead to the summit of the 2,055-foot mountain. The Francestown Trail starts at the base of the former Crotched Mountain ski area and follows the easiest ski trail. The Greenfield Trail starts beyond the entrance to Crotched Mountain Rehabilitation Center buildings, off Verney Drive. The Bennington Trail starts three miles north of Greenfield at a sign along Route 31.

Temple Mountain, off Route 101, Peterborough, (603) 924-6949. From November to March, this year-round recreational facility operates as a family-style downhill and cross-country ski area, offering skiing at night as well as during the day. From mid-April to October, mountain bikers take over and have races.

Shieling State Forest, Old Street Road, Peterborough. This 45-acre area of tree-covered ridges and valleys offers walking trails and a wildflower preserve. The Forestry Learning Center is open to stimulate public interest and knowledge in properly managing small private woodlands.

Peterborough Walking Tour. A simple white pamphlet leads you along Grove Street in the center of town, pointing out architectural highlights and historical facts. It's an easy walk and a fun way to get to know the town.

Rhododendron State Park. This National Nature Landmark of 500 acres includes a pleasant foot trail of about one mile leading to views of Mount Monadnock and other peaks in the region. There's a one-mile walking path around the glen and picnic grounds in shaded pine groves. The park is at its best when fifteen acres of wild rhododendrons are in peak blossom annually around mid-July. Bushes up to twenty feet high are part of the largest and most vigorous grove north of the Alleghenys and east of the Mississippi.

Off Route 119, Fitzwilliam. (603) 271-3556. Adults $2.50, children free.

A Foliage Tour. Here's a colorful drive suggested by the Keene Chamber of Commerce. From Peterborough, take Route 101 west for five miles to Route 137. Turn south on Route 137 to Jaffrey, where you might want to poke around the old graveyard and restored Red Schoolhouse nearby. Head west on Route 124. This road, more than twelve miles of scenic splendor, takes you along the southern edge of Mount Monadnock to Marlborough. Turn right in Marlborough on Route 101, heading east. The road skirts Dublin Lake and bisects the town of Dublin. Turn left two miles east of Dublin on Route 137 and drive north to picturesque Hancock. Continue through Hancock on 137 and turn right on Route 202 south to Peterborough.

Harrisville. Don't miss quaint Harrisville, a few miles northwest of Dublin and the only intact 19th-century textile community surviving into the 20th century with its original plan and most of its buildings. The red brick mill buildings are stunningly situated around three ponds that drain into a rocky ravine, falling 100 feet in a quarter of a mile and eventually ending in the Merrimack River. The mill and village center are listed as a National Historic Landmark. A pamphlet outlines a walking tour, and in the autumn the reflections of foliage in the water are breathtaking.

Cathedral of the Pines. A living memorial to those who gave their lives for our country, this tranquil and inspiring spot was created by Dr. and Mrs. Douglas Sloane in memory of their son, Lt. Sanderson Sloane, who was shot down over Germany in World War II. Tall pines lead to the Altar of the Nation, behind which is a beautiful view toward Mount Monadnock. Simple wood benches offer rest for up to 2,000 persons. Services by congregations of all faiths are held regularly during the summer and into the fall. The Memorial Bell Tower, visible soon after you enter, is the only monument in the United States to women who died for their country. Also on the property are the attractive Mother's Chapel and the St. Francis of Assisi Chapel, as well as a public burial area. We enjoyed peeking at a simple summer wedding one Saturday noon.
Off Route 119, Rindge. (603) 899-3300. Daily 9 to 5, May-October. Free.

Culture

The **MacDowell Colony** in Peterborough, (603) 924-3886, celebrated its 100th anniversary in 1996. The nation's oldest and largest artist retreat attracts more than 200 writers, composers, filmmakers, visual artists and architects annually. Because the colony protects the privacy of its resident artists, only Colony Hall, the library and founder Edward MacDowell's gravesite are accessible to the public.

A cultural center of note, Peterborough is home to the **Monadnock Summer Lyceum,** a lecture series featuring nationally known speakers, and the **Peterborough Players,** a summer stock theatrical group. The **New England Marionette Opera Theatre** debuted in 1992 at the Marionette Theatre on Main Street in Peterborough, (603) 924-3333. Here, 32-inch puppets are manipulated masterfully to the recorded music of operas. Performances weekends, May-December.

Sharon Arts Center. The center shows exhibits in the Killian and Laws House galleries, offers lectures in arts and crafts, and has a terrific shop that includes the work of local craftsmen.
Route 123, Sharon, (603) 924-7256. Monday-Saturday 10 to 5, Sunday noon to 5. Free.

Points of Interest

The Barrett House. This interesting Federal mansion was built in 1800 by Charles Barrett for his son, Charles Jr., and daughter-in-law, Martha Minott of Concord, Mass. Tradition holds that the bride's father said he would furnish as large and fine a house as Mr. Barrett could build. The house contains twelve rooms and enjoyed one-family ownership into the early 20th century. It's now operated by the Society for the Preservation of New England Antiquities.
Main Street, New Ipswich. (603) 878-3283. Thursday-Sunday noon to 5, June to mid-October. Adults $4, children $2.

Peterborough Historical Society. Hour-long guided tours include a series of galleries on three floors and visits to two restored mill houses at the rear of the property. Artifacts from the town's industries are shown in the Peterborough Room.
19 Grove St., Peterborough. (603) 924-3235. Monday-Friday 10 to 4, also Saturday 1 to 4 in summer. Admission, $1.

Franklin Pierce Homestead. The boyhood home of the 14th president of the United States, this restored 1804 mansion reflects the lifestyle of the wealthy of the early 19th century.
Hillsboro. (603) 464-4260. Monday-Saturday 10 to 4, Sunday 1 to 4, July-Labor Day; weekends and holidays, 1 to 4, late spring and early fall. Adults, $2.

Friendly Farm. For more than 25 years this seven-acre farm has enchanted children and their families, who get to see farm animals up close – and to pet and feed them. Baby goats, pigs, turkeys, lambs and dairy cattle are part of the menagerie. There is also a farm-oriented gift shop.
Route 101, Dublin. (603) 563-8444. Daily 10 to 5, late April to Labor Day, and weekends through mid-October. Adults $4.75; children $3.75.

Jaffrey Cemetery, with the grave of novelist Willa Cather, is of interest in Jaffrey. Also near the Cather grave in the southwest corner of the graveyard is the gravestone of Sarah Averill, who died at age 89 after, according to the epitaph, "She done all she could."

Shopping

Quality crafts items and antiques shops are of particular interest in the Monadnock region.

The Black Swan gift shop on Route 101 in Peterborough offers dried and silk floral designs, handcrafted items and gifts. The **North Gallery at Tewksbury's** at the junction of Routes 101 and 123 in Peterborough has a great variety of fine art and crafts.

Frye's Measure Mill in Wilton has been the site of wooden-product manufacture for more than a hundred years. Today, Shaker boxes are the prize products; they are made in all different sizes and sold in the shop along with tasteful country items such as quilts, salt-glaze pottery, country folk-art pieces and Christmas ornaments. Tours of the mill, where some machinery is still water-powered, are given Saturdays at 2. Shop open daily, April to Dec. 20.

The Weaving Center at Harrisville Designs in the charming mill hamlet of Harrisville sells outstanding weaving and knitting yarns, floor looms, beginners' looms, weaving accessories and finished woven garments. The attractive center is located in one of the old brick mill buildings.

Bacon's Sugar House in Jaffrey Center is one place to stop for maple sugar, which seems to be available at every turn. The going rate in 1996 was about $8 for a pint, $12 for a quart.

Discounts can be found in special markdown rooms at **Eastern Mountain Sports,** whose headquarters buildings are located off Route 202 a few miles north of Peterborough.

Smart women's fashions are sold at **The Winged Pig** on Grove Street, Peterborough. **The Toadstool Bookshop** in town is fun to browse through; at the side is **Aesop's Tables,** a small cafe where you can get a bite. In addition to office supplies and paper goods, **Steele's Stationers** carries a surprisingly large array of cigars. **Twelve Pine** in Depot Square is an exceptional deli and gourmet store where you can buy the best fixings for a picnic or something more formal. You can get a light lunch or snack and eat here, too. **Van Campen's** offers museum-quality furniture and lighting for sale in the Marketplace at Noone Falls south of town.

Antiques are found in many shops around the area, but there's a particularly large group of along Route 101 between Marlborough and Bedford.

Pickity Place. This special spot is located at the end of a series of horrendous dirt roads (watch carefully for the small signs). A 1786 house and barn are the setting for a restaurant, an herb shop, museum and garden shop. The shop smells incredible, with herbal teas, potpourris, pomanders, soups, dried apple wreaths and even a dill pillow. A catalog with unusual items is available. Pickity Place also offers five-course herbal luncheons. The fare is appropriate to the season; an October menu included pumpkin curry soup, broccoli strudel and Swedish apple pie.
Nutting Hill Road, Mason. (603) 878-1151. Seatings daily at 11:30, 12:45 and 2.

Where to Stay

The Monadnock region is quite decentralized, with about fifteen small towns spread among its hills and gently winding roads. Old, center-of-town inns are found in Fitzwilliam, Jaffrey, Hancock and Antrim. Bed and breakfasts seem to be the prevailing accommodations; they range from small and homey to sophisticated. Prices are lower here than in many areas.

Bed and Breakfasts

Hannah Davis House. This beautiful 1820 Federal house, owned by Kaye and Mike Terpstra, has six guest rooms, all with private baths. The newest, the spacious Popover, has a queensize cannonball bed, a private deck and elevated outdoor walkway to the breakfast area, a sitting area and a wood-burning fireplace. The suite called Loft is a two-story hideaway with bedroom overlooking the sitting area. Rustic timbers original to the house form a cathedral ceiling and the bathroom contains a footed tub plus a large glass shower. Four guest rooms in the main house are compelling as well. The Canopy features a queensize pencil-post bed of cherry with an antique crocheted canopy hood; Chauncey's Room has bold red floral wallpaper and a fireplace. A first-floor suite contains a fireplaced bedroom and adjoining sitting room. Breakfast is usually served in the large kitchen, which is clearly the heart of this home; in warm weather guests can take it on the rear deck overlooking colorful gardens. Stuffed french toast with ham and cheese and a dijon sauce is one of the hot entrées in Kaye's repertoire.

186 Depot Road (Route 119), Fitzwilliam 03447. (603) 585-3344. Doubles, $60 to $95.

Amos A. Parker House. Just down the street from the Hannah Davis House is another fabulous B&B opened by Freda B. Houpt in the mid-1980s. Freda's a virtual dynamo who was a travel agent in Chicago before she came east to visit a son in Boston and fell in love with New England. She sold her Chicago digs and bought this big old 18th-century house, which is beautifully restored and graciously appointed. Upstairs are two front rooms with private baths and fireplaces. One has a double canopy bed and the other is twin-bedded. To the rear is a suite with sitting room, bedroom and bath; marvelous trompe-l'oeil murals on the walls were painted by two local women. On the main floor is a suite with private entrance containing a large bedroom, sitting area with fireplace, and bath. The dining room – with scrumptious cookies set out for expected arrivals when we stopped by – is a deep orange color; it's here that guests take a breakfast that Freda describes as "elaborate – meat and eggs and something else." Her spinach-soufflé crêpes with mushroom cream sauce and vegetable garnishes are a favorite. Guests enjoy Freda's "great room," a special place with wood stove, barnwood walls, bookcases and dried flowers hanging from overhead beams. A porch out back looks down over her extensive and colorful gardens and lily pond. Freda was planning in 1997 to go into the nursery business, selling perennials and unusual annuals on the property behind her home.

Route 119, Fitzwilliam 03447. (603) 585-6540. Doubles, $80; suites, $90.

Apple Gate Bed and Breakfast. Dianne and Ken Legenhausen left Long Island, where she was a music teacher and he a police officer, to open this B&B after having spent weekends in the area for several years. The 1832 white clapboard house with full-length front porch welcomes guests with tiny white lights in each window year-round. Inside, Dianne has decorated with an apple theme, but she doesn't overdo it. Two parlors, one with fireplace and the other with piano, TV/VCR and floor-to-ceiling books, are inviting. Full breakfasts are served by candlelight in the dining room where guests sit around one table and where a fire burns on chilly mornings. Among the specialties lately have been oven-baked apple pancakes and various types of omelets. The four guest rooms, all with private baths, are named for apples, naturally. Cortland, a front bedroom with queen bed, is much requested. Across the way, Granny Smith is done in soft peaches and greens; its full bath is downstairs, so robes are provided. Tiny McIntosh has a three-quarter bed and a bath with footed tub; Crispin, tucked down the hall, has twin beds. In the fall, you can pick apples in the orchard across the way; the Legenhausens give you a bag and take the money for the farmer. *199 Upland Farm Road (Route 123), Peterborough 03458. (603) 924-6543. Doubles, $65 to $75.*

The Benjamin Prescott Inn. This large gold-colored clapboard house set just off the road adjoins a dairy farm to the rear. Innkeeper Barry Miller was in the hotel business before he and wife Jan decided in 1988 to do their own thing. All nine guest rooms and suites have private baths. We stayed in Elder Eldad's front corner bedroom with kingsize bed, wall stenciling and private bath with stall shower. We came downstairs to Jan's exceptional breakfasts each morning; eggs benedict the first day and puffed apple pancakes with New Hampshire maple syrup the next, served at one end of a homey parlor where several small antique tables are set up. Barry renovated the attic and made a private suite on the third floor with a canopied kingsize bed in the bedroom, a living room with great views out over farmland, and a full bath in three sections. Under the eaves on both sides of the bedroom and off the living room, are sleeping alcoves with double mattresses – so you can sleep the whole gang up here. Barry says it is often occupied by brides-to-be and their attendants the night before a wedding, or by family groups. Another suite on the first floor has two bedrooms and a sitting room. *Route 124 East, Jaffrey 03452. (603) 532-6637. Doubles, $75 to $130.*

The Greenfield Inn B&B. Ebullient host Vic Mangini and his wife Barbara preside over this Victorian-style B&B in tiny Greenfield. Originally a farmhouse from the early 1800s, it has been decked it out with teddy bears and dolls, tiny dresses hanging in the front hall, lavish curtains tied with satin ribbons and the like. Before you're barely inside you'll learn that the Manginis are friends of Bob Hope and his wife Dolores, who have visited not once, but twice. The main house holds eight guest rooms, while a two-level apartment fashioned from a hayloft in the rear can sleep six — in a king bed and four day beds. Five rooms in the house have private baths and three share. Two also have jacuzzi tubs. The two front bedrooms, Delilah & Sampson and Juliet & Romeo, are the most sought-after. They are decorated with lace, fringe and floral wallpapers and, like most of the rest, have TVs, phones and complimentary sherry. A carriage house accommodates up to six but is perfect also for honeymooners, says Vic. Two bedrooms upstairs each have a private bath; downstairs are a living room and kitchen plus a studio bedroom with bath. Often Barbara makes an egg strata as the main dish in a full buffet breakfast. *Route 31, Greenfield 03047. (603) 547-6327 or (800) 678-4144. Doubles, $49 to $79; hayloft suite, $119; carriage house, $139, up to six $159.*

Harrisville Squires Inn. Close to the picturesque center of the 19th-century milltown is this comfortable B&B. Pat and Doug McCarthy – he's a school teacher and she used to be in the hotel business – offer sumptuous breakfasts and five guest rooms, all with private baths. One room also has a jacuzzi tub in the bathroom where old beams have been exposed and wallpaper with bold lilacs and roses covers the walls. "It's a very relaxing bathroom," says Pat. An off-white and green living room is a great place to gather; next to it is a den with more sofas and chairs for guests. The dining room opens onto a pleasant grass patio; in warm weather guests often eat outdoors. Pat, who is a justice of the peace, sometimes conducts weddings here. There is a quiet meditation garden out by the barn with a brick walk, fish pond, granite benches and wind chimes. Pat prides herself on her five-course breakfasts that always include juice, muffins, cold and hot cereals, an entrée and a hot fruit dessert like apple crisp or peach cobbler. The inn serves as headquarters for Monadnock Bicycle Touring and Doug will plan itineraries for guests, even getting the rental bikes. Pat makes stained-glass windows for sale. She also sells the "official" Harrisville T-shirts (her design).

Keene Road, Harrisville. (603) 827-3925. Doubles, $70 or $80.

Final Folly Bed & Breakfast. Joan and George Andersen have lived all over the United States and Joan opened their Philadelphia-area home as a B&B for five years before the couple relocated to tiny Wilton. Their big yellow house with black shutters was built in 1791 for the second minister of the town church. Joan has a sure hand in decorating; the black and white diamond painted hallway is particularly stunning. Guests use a large living room and enjoy a full breakfast in a formal dining room with a beautiful mahogany table. Three guest rooms are on the second floor. The front bedroom with long twin beds that can be put together as a king has a private bath. Two smaller bedrooms share a bath. One has a three-quarter-size canopy bed and is a cozy space; the rear bedroom has a double bed. Joan has a sense of people's needs; robes and bedside reading lamps are provided, and she delivers trays with tea or coffee before breakfast. Matilda, a friendly Irish wolfhound, is the official greeter and Joan says, "We take children; we take dogs."

203 Wilson Road, Wilton 03086. (603) 654-2725. Fax (603) 654-2734. Doubles, $55 to $65.

Inns

The Inn at Crotched Mountain. This red brick inn, with white clapboard wings attached and a red and white barn, is located about 1,300 feet above sea level with a fantastic view 40 miles across the Piscataquog Valley. The air is clear, the mood is mellow, and this is a place for getting away from it all. That is especially true since the Crotched Mountain ski area, which was practically at its front door, went out of business. Rose Perry, owner with her husband John, is an accomplished chef who offers dinners on Friday and Saturday nights (see Where to Eat). The 19th-century inn has thirteen simple guest rooms, three with fireplaces or wood stoves. Eight rooms have private baths, and beds vary from queen to double to twin. Maple furniture, tiny Colonial print wallpapers and Priscilla-style curtains at the windows are typical bedroom furnishings. One particularly private room with a fireplace in the east wing is reached by its own entrance. There are an attractive living room with oriental rugs, a fireplaced pub and a game room. In good weather, guests enjoy an outdoor swimming pool and clay tennis courts. Walkers in fall enjoy the more than five miles of cross-country trails on the prop-

Landmark hostelries like The Hancock Inn are scattered across the region.

erty and hikers can climb the trails of Crotched Mountain.. Full breakfasts are offered to house guests. Weekend guests are on the MAP plan; at other times, the rates are B&B.

Mountain Road off Route 47, Francestown 03043. (603) 588-6840. Doubles, $60 to $100 B&B; $140 to $180 MAP. Closed April and November.

The Hancock Inn. Linda and Joe Johnston admit to having been miserable after departing from the New England Inn in Intervale, N.H., which they owned for eight years. Back in the inn business, they're thrilled to be at the helm of a well-known hostelry in an especially attractive town. Proclaiming itself "the oldest inn in New Hampshire," the Hancock dates from 1789. The Johnstons' presence is being felt in the decor at the inn and in the menu in the dining room (see Where to Eat). Linda, a bundle of energy, and Joe have decorated with a sure hand. The results are most noticeable in the atmospheric pub, which sports red and white checked Colonial swags at the windows, a mural of Mount Monadnock over the fireplace, and tavern tables, cozy wing chairs and sofas. Across from the pub on the main floor is a smaller, more formal lobby and registration desk, and upstairs on the second and third floors are ten pleasant guest rooms with private baths. Linda has redecorated them in Colonial fashion with comfort in mind. The Rufus Porter room, with queensize bed and smallish private bath, features one of the itinerant artist's famed murals. Quilts cover many of the beds and crisp white curtains are at the windows. Most rooms contain a radio and simple tape player with Gershwin and other tapes. TVs are hidden in handmade quilted TV cozies. A wicker-filled lounge on the third floor is also used by guests.

Main Street, Hancock 03449. (603) 525-3318 or (800) 525-1789. Fax (603) 525-9301. Breakfast is included in the rates. Doubles, $98 to $138.

The Birchwood Inn. This big red brick house with white clapboard addition sits just off the town green in a picture-perfect New Hampshire town. Bill and Judy Wolfe have run it as an old-fashioned, true country inn for nearly twenty years, Their approach is low-key and rings with authenticity; don't expect the latest in Laura Ashley fabrics or jacuzzi tubs here. On the main floor are a dining room with restored Rufus Porter murals from the early 19th century, a friendly game room where you can bring your own drink or enjoy chess, checkers or toy trains (Bill is a train buff and has collections of train paraphernalia), and a red and green sitting room with square Steinway grand piano, sofas and chairs. Another dining room is off this room. Upstairs are six of the seven guest rooms, each decorated with a motif (The Music Room, The Seashore Room, The Editorial Room — with framed newspaper front pages — for example). There is also a larger main-floor guest bedroom. All have small private baths and black and white TVs. A full breakfast is served and is also available to the public for $3.95. One entrée is offered, such as waffles, or bacon and eggs. Fresh baked items accompany. For dinner, expect three main entrées; seafood, red meat, and veal or fowl. The price, $16.95 to $19.95 on average, includes all courses. The dining room is popular with locals both for breakfast and dinner.

Route 45, Temple 03084. (603) 878-3285. Doubles, $60 to $70. Dinner, Tuesday-Saturday 5 to 8:30. BYOB.

Motels

Jack Daniels Motor Inn. Located next to the Contoocook River, this small, family-owned-and-operated motel with seventeen units has porches and flower gardens. Its location is central for exploring the area. Most rooms have two double beds; three have one queensize bed. Coffee and juice are set out for guests in the morning..

Route 202N, Peterborough 03458. (603) 924-7548. Doubles, $84 to $98.

Larger chain motels are located to the west in Keene.

A Budget Choice

Stepping Stones Bed & Breakfast. It's not hard to believe that Ann Carlsmith is a landscape designer; her lovely gardens are the draw at this 19th-century B&B, tucked off a back road in tiny Wilton. Follow the path and find charming sitting areas amid the flora, where you'll be quite off by yourself. The interior of the large white house is light and cheery with skylights and white paint. Guests enjoy a common living room, and breakfast is served in an airy new kitchen. Creative Ann also is a weaver, and her looms have a room to themselves. Three guest rooms are on the second floor. A double and a twin-bedded room share a bath, while one with a queensize bed has its own. All are carpeted and nicely decorated with handwoven throws, pillows and rugs in natural fibers and gentle colors – all created on the looms in the weaving room. A reservoir across the street is a good place for walks. Ann loves to cook and her breakfast could include cheese strata or eggs benedict..

Bennington Battle Trail, Wilton Center 03086. (603) 654-9048. Doubles, $50 to $55.

Where to Eat

The Monadnock region has a few fine restaurants, but most tend to serve simpler fare in comfortable, unpretentious surroundings.

The Boilerhouse at Noone Falls. This expansive second-level dining area has white-linened tables and black lacquered chairs facing huge windows overlooking a waterfall. It's part of an old mill complex that also houses a few retail shops. Votive candles flicker on the tables and a romantic, relaxing atmosphere prevails. A bit higher priced than other restaurants in the area, the Boilerhouse is nonetheless praised for its food, and since David McCarty became head chef in 1996, followers have been flocking in more than ever. Dinner might begin with three-onion soup or an appetizer like salmon stuffed with lobster, New Orleans-style crab cakes or escargots. A caesar salad or smoked duck salad also are offered à la carte. Entrées might be poached salmon in sherry with wild rice, veal medallions with lobster and leeks in a dry vermouth cream sauce, roast pork tenderloin with mushrooms in a madeira glace, and rack of lamb with mustard crust served on a cassoulet of white beans and tomatoes. Interesting desserts include the chef's homemade ice cream and a couple of chocolate specialties.
Route 202 South, Peterborough. (603) 924-9486. Entrées, $14 to $20. Dinner, Tuesday-Saturday 5:30 to 9; Sunday brunch, noon to 3.

Latacarta. The old Gem Theater in the center of town is the restaurant of Japanese master chef Hiroshi Hayashi, who moved to Peterborough from Newbury Street in Boston. He offers what he calls "Epicurean Collage." His restaurant is pleasantly decorated with bentwood chairs, mulberry walls, track lighting, lacy cafe curtains and a multitude of plants. The oft-changing menu arrives on a huge piece of heavy paper; green for lunch and gold for dinner. No beef is served. At lunchtime, appetizers might be marinated tuna in balsamic vinegar dressing, shrimp sautéed with sliced olives and pickles, or seafood chowder. Entrées could be a rosemary chicken, smoked salmon linguini or the "square meal," organic brown rice, miso baked beans, steamed greens and vegetables of the day, served with a salad ($10 to $12). At night, you might start with grilled tomatoes and fresh mozzarella in a light herb dressing or a soup of vegetables and herbs. Main dishes could be grilled fresh tuna in a soy and sherry sauce; tofu oden with potatoes, carrots, turnips, mushrooms and leeks simmered in a ginger and soy sauce, or the Latacarta Dinner, something that changes often but that might be stuffed cabbage leaves with vegetables and tofu, served with vegetables, rice, salad and the soup of the day.
6 School St., Peterborough. (603) 924-6878. Entrées, $15 to $18. Lunch, Tuesday-Friday noon to 2; dinner, Tuesday-Saturday 5 to 9 or 9:30, Sunday, 5 to 8.

Del Rossi's Trattoria. Jaffrey natives David and Elaina Del Rossi opened this popular place in a Colonial house out in the countryside just off Route 101. The original building dates from 1786, but there have been add-ons. The bar, a bandstand and several tables are in a newer room to the rear and there's entertainment on weekends and some weeknights. The Del Rossis planned to move their music store, Fiddler's Choice, from Jaffrey to the second floor of the restaurant in 1997. And while the restaurant has been open only for dinner, David said that

1997. And while the restaurant has been open only for dinner, David said that depending on how busy the spot became during the day from the music business, lunch might be served. All areas of Italy provide inspiration for the large menu. Appetizers include shrimp scampi, mussels florentine and polenta gorgonzola. "And people would kill me if I took the cream of garlic soup off the menu," David says. Among salads are the vintner (grapes, swiss cheese and walnuts with a red wine dressing) and tortellini with spinach and other vegetables. Besides a number of pasta selections, entrées might be calamari mediterranean, veal parmesan, steak cacciatore served with mushroom-filled raviolini, and pork medallions topped with prosciutto, mozzarella and parmesan cheese. Recent tempters for dessert were cannnoli, chocolate fudge cake, spumoni with claret sauce and coffee caramel custard. The wine choices are quite extensive.

Route 137 at Route 101, Dublin. (603) 563-7195. Entrées, $11.95 to $16.95. Dinner nightly, 5 to 9, Sunday 4 to 8.

Carolyn's Bistro. Carolyn Bonner is "a renaissance woman," says her husband, Ted, who greets diners. In addition to being chef at this newish restaurant, she painted the fine watercolors on the walls and made the cafe curtains at the windows. The Bonners took over an old furniture warehouse overlooking a rushing stream to make their two-level dining spot with an open kitchen, black and white tiled floor, and simple tables with maple captain's chairs. At lunchtime ($4 to $7), soups are served with Carolyn's homemade bread. You can get a grilled chicken breast salad, pasta or seafood of the day. "Carolyn's Famous Sandwiches" include roast turkey, the Mediterranean (grilled lemon chicken with feta, tomatoes and fresh basil) and Carolyn's Favorite (fresh mozzarella or swiss grilled with marinated sundried tomatoes). In the evening, coquilles St. Jacques and grilled eggplant with feta and tomatoes are offered as appetizers. Entrées include veal parmesan, grilled pork tenderloins in barbecue sauce served with plum chutney, bistro chicken (a boneless breast sautéed with artichoke hearts, sundried tomatoes, garlic butter and black olives), and New York sirloin. Pastas (fettuccine alfredo and shrimp and scallops fra diavlo, for example) and vegetarian or chicken stir-fries are also available. Carolyn makes the desserts, too.

5 Depot Square, Peterborough. (603) 924-2002. Entrées, $13 to $18. Lunch, Monday-Saturday, 11:30 to 2; dinner, Monday-Saturday 5 to 9.

Lilly's on the Pond. Helen Kendall and Suanne P. Yglesias, who had known each other from previous restaurant jobs, joined forces and took over this appealing dark wood restaurant building overlooking a mill pond in 1994. Views of the water are offered from the cozy lounge and main dining room, both with wood-burning stoves, and the so-called "glass room," a rear projection yielding a particularly good view of the water. In the summer, it converts to a cool, screened porch. The rustic furnishings and surroundings seem perfectly New England: bare wood tables, captain's chairs, wide floorboards, and wagon wheel chandeliers overhead. At lunchtime you can get sandwiches, burgers in eight varieties, and quiche of the day served with green salad. The dinner menu, available all day, has an eclectic range of entrées. Possibilities are baked scrod with melted havarti dill cheese, Jamaican jerk pork ribs, pork tenderloins in mustard cream, apple-brandy-walnut chicken, pasta with Italian sausage marinara or a twelve-ounce broiled sirloin. In addition, there's a lengthy list of specials. Helen favorite. Lilly, by the way, is a mermaid who supposedly returns to the mill pond each spring.

*Route 202, Rindge. (603) 899-3322. Entrées, $9 to $14. **Lunch, Tuesday-Saturday 11:30 to 5; dinner 5 to 9 or 10; Sunday, brunch 10 to 3, dinner noon to 8.***

Michaels' Jaffrey Manor. Michael Barlick grew up in the Monadnock area and worked in different restaurants before striking out on his own. The blue house with white trim is located right in the center of town and has two smallish fireplaced dining rooms plus an enclosed porch in front. Prime rib is the specialty, says Michael, whose father, also named Michael, is a silent partner. At lunchtime, he offers a three-priced menu, the "express" lunch for $4.99 (cup of soup and half sandwich); the $5.99 lunch (sandwich or burger with salad); and the $6.99 entrée such as fried or broiled haddock, prime rib, or linguini with soup or salad. The dinner menu lists appetizers like the "Monadnock mum" (a batter-dipped and fried whole spanish onion).. Entrées might be scallops, chicken breast stuffed with ham and swiss, roast duck with an orange sauce and charbroiled filet mignon. Prime rib comes in three sizes, the largest at $16.99. A champagne brunch is offered Sundays for $9.99.

East Main Street, Jaffrey. (603) 532-8555. Entrées, $10 to $17. Lunch, Thursday-Sunday, 11 to 2; dinner, Wednesday-Monday from 5:30.

Inn Dining Rooms

The Hancock Inn. Now that Linda and Joe Johnston are here, the Shaker cranberry pot roast – one of the signature items at their previous inn in Intervale – is on the dinner menu. Entrées also include Maine crab cakes with tarragon butter sauce, pan-seared salmon with roasted pepper vinaigrette, maple-mustard chicken and black angus ribeye steak. Appetizers might be lobster ragoût, house-cured salmon gravlax, wild rice and corn cakes with apple chutney and Nantucket seafood chowder. One dining room has a fireplace and a grand piano; the other is less formal with cloth mats on the wood tables.

Main Street, Hancock. (603) 525-3318. Entrées, $15 to $25. Dinner nightly, 5 to 9 or 10.

The Inn at Crotched Mountain. Owner Rose Perry is in the kitchen at this inn and the tantalizing smell of roasting meats greeted us as we peeked in one afternoon. The two dining rooms are cheerful with white linen tablecloths, green water glasses and bouquets of flowers. Fireplaces make them cozy on chilly nights. Start with herring in wine sauce, smoked Maine mussels or shrimp cocktail. For entrées, you might have roast loin of pork, cranberry-port pot roast, liver and onions, chicken teriyaki or cheesy tofu and vegetables in phyllo. Indian pudding is always an autumn dessert; others might be chocolate mousse or pecan pie.

Mountain Road off Route 47, Francestown. (603) 588-6840. Entrées, $14 to $19. Dinner, Friday and Saturday 6 to 8:30. Closed April and November.

The Fitzwilliam Inn. New owner Mark McMahon is a CIA-trained chef who worked at the Ritz-Carlton and Fenway Park in Boston and managed country clubs before taking over in 1996 with his sister, Lois McMahon. Things looked much the same as in the past, although some needed upgrading was being done and the rather tired second and third-floor guest rooms were being given new bedspreads and some fresh decorating. We enjoyed lunch here one late-summer Saturday – we and a lot of others who seemed to be out for a ride on a glorious bright day. The main dining room, with bare wood tables and chairs, has a brick fireplace which everybody wants to be near on a chilly afternoon or evening. At lunch, you can find sandwiches like ham, turkey or roast beef. The Earl of Fitzwilliam is ham, turkey and roast beef with swiss cheese and thousand island dressing. Luncheon entrées, offered à la carte or complete with appetizer and dessert ($7.95 to $11.95), include broiled scallops, southern fried chicken and sliced sirloin with garlic butter. The dinner menu is also offered à la carte or full (add $4 to the à la carte entrées). Start with marinated mushrooms, herring, fruit cup or soup of the day. Expect entrées like lobster or seafood newburg, baked stuffed chicken, several versions of steaks, roast duck with scalloped apples and veal oscar.

Fitzwilliam. (603) 585-9000. Entrées, $9 to $17. Breakfast daily, 8 to 9:30, from 7 on weekends; lunch, noon to 2; dinner, 5:30 to 9.

FOR MORE INFORMATION: The Greater Peterborough Chamber of Commerce, Junction of Routes 101 & 202, Box 401, Peterborough, N.H. 03458. (603) 924-7234.

12  Fall

Hikers scale dunes at Cape Cod National Seashore.

Autumn along Route 6A

Cape Cod, Mass.

Visitors usually feel a bit smug about being on Cape Cod after Labor Day. It's hard not to. It is a kind of "one-upmanship," we suppose, to wait until the hordes have come and gone, having jammed the sandy, surfy, sun-blessed strand for its entire length and breadth, bringing traffic to a halt and tempers to a height.

Off-season, the Cape is a different place. The clam shacks and the soft ice-cream stands are boarded up, half the motels are closed, and you can actually drive along the Mid-Cape Highway (Route 6) or the beautiful Route 6A along the north shore without encountering a traffic jam. The only one we confronted one October evening turned out to be a line of cars pulling into an elementary school for a Parents' Night.

The Cape settles down in the fall to what most people find appealing in the first place: deserted beaches, slow-paced harbors, antiques shops and boutiques where the owners take the time to talk. It is an atmosphere that retirees love; the Cape rivals the South as a retirement locale for New Englanders.

The inns and restaurants that stay open are those with year-round cheer and a local following. Many have sturdy fireplaces and serve hearty meals. Not least of their attractions can be the prices. Bargain rates prevail after mid-September.

What do you do on the Cape in the fall? Beach walking is a pleasure any time of year, but off-season you don't have to get up before the sun to have the sand to yourself. You might climb the dunes at the National Seashore and feel as if you're the first to do it. You can sit up there, seemingly on top of the world, and watch the sun rise over the Atlantic or set over Cape Cod Bay.

Autumn on Cape Cod is, for us, the best season, mellow and moody. It is a time for moseying along the Route 6A through the Cape's oldest and prettiest towns.

Here you'll see the distinctive architecture of Cape Cod cottages, weathered gray or sparkling white, hung with bittersweet in the doorways. And, because of the salubrious effect of the ocean and the bay that surround it, Cape Cod experiences autumn later than most of New England.

Others, of course, have appreciated this season on the Cape. Henry Beston, author of the classic, *The Outermost House*, came for a fortnight in September and stayed for a year. Henry David Thoreau's first walking tour was in October 1849. And the Pilgrims made landfall in Provincetown Harbor in November 1620.

Historically, the Pilgrims weren't the first to touch the Cape. Before them came Samuel de Champlain, who called it "Cap Blanc," and Capt. John Smith, who named it "Cape James" after England's ruler. Verrazzano and Henry Hudson sailed past.

And then there was Bartholomew Gosnold. He stepped ashore in 1602 and found the fishing was great. There were so many codfish, in fact, that no other name would do. He named it "Cape Cod."

Sandwich was the first town to be incorporated on the Cape, in 1637, and it is the first town of our chapter as well. If Cape Cod is shaped like a flexed left arm, the area we concentrate on extends from the shoulder, along the biceps and forearm. Stretching along charming Route 6A after Sandwich come Barnstable, Yarmouth Port, Dennis and Brewster.

Here we find a group of bed-and-breakfasts in historic buildings, restaurants that are rated the best on the Cape, wonderful antiques shops and other places in which to stop and to browse. There are scenic harbors, hidden beaches and fine museums. Come along with us to the best of the Cape at our favorite time of year.

Getting There

Interstate 195 and Route 6 from the west, and Interstate 495 and Route 3 from the Boston area are the major auto routes to Cape Cod.

Bonanza Bus Lines serves the Cape. Small airlines fly into Hyannis.

Seeing and Doing

What is there to do on the Cape off-season? You may be surprised by the answers: beach walking and harbor exploring, dune climbing and shell hunting, kite flying and bird watching. There are also the more traditional sports, golf and tennis, biking and fishing and – when there's snow – cross-country skiing.

Shopping is super for gifts and gadgets, books and crafts, and art and antiques along Route 6A. The Cape Cod National Seashore and Provincetown beckon. And there are museums and historic sites, fun to visit when the weather is foul.

About Route 6A

Route 6A also is known as the Old King's Highway. It roughly parallels Cape Cod Bay for about 34 miles, crossing through seven communities from Bourne to Orleans. The route is believed to have begun as a Native American trail that stretched from Plymouth to Provincetown. As Colonial agricultural communities became more important on the Cape in the 1600s, this cart path became the major east-west thoroughfare for early settlers.

With the rise of maritime influence and activities in the 18th century, captains' homes and commercial enterprises emerged along the route. The collapse of the maritime industries in the late 19th century gave rise to a new focus on cranberry production. Residents planted shade trees along the road, many of which are mature today.

Route 6A is most scenic as it winds along the North Shore from Sandwich to Brewster. Golden trees arch above the road; century-old houses nestle by the side, picket-fenced and proper, their doorways decorated with bittersweet or vine wreaths. Antiques shops, boutiques, crafts and gift shops all hang out their shingles and as you mosey along, you'll likely find yourself stopping again and again.

First Stop: The National Seashore

Cape Cod National Seashore, South Wellfleet, (508) 349-3785. Although our focus is along Route 6A, almost everyone who visits wants to see Cape Cod's extraordinary natural resource – its ocean beaches and environs, which have been

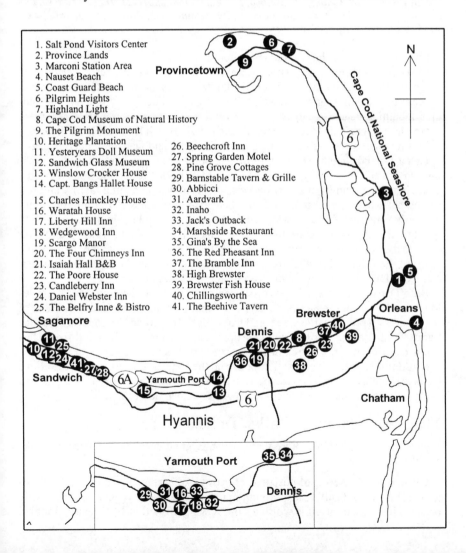

1. Salt Pond Visitors Center
2. Province Lands
3. Marconi Station Area
4. Nauset Beach
5. Coast Guard Beach
6. Pilgrim Heights
7. Highland Light
8. Cape Cod Museum of Natural History
9. The Pilgrim Monument
10. Heritage Plantation
11. Yesteryears Doll Museum
12. Sandwich Glass Museum
13. Winslow Crocker House
14. Capt. Bangs Hallet House
15. Charles Hinckley House
16. Waratah House
17. Liberty Hill Inn
18. Wedgewood Inn
19. Scargo Manor
20. The Four Chimneys Inn
21. Isaiah Hall B&B
22. The Poore House
23. Candleberry Inn
24. Daniel Webster Inn
25. The Belfry Inne & Bistro

26. Beechcroft Inn
27. Spring Garden Motel
28. Pine Grove Cottages
29. Barnstable Tavern & Grille
30. Abbicci
31. Aardvark
32. Inaho
33. Jack's Outback
34. Marshside Restaurant
35. Gina's By the Sea
36. The Red Pheasant Inn
37. The Bramble Inn
38. High Brewster
39. Brewster Fish House
40. Chillingsworth
41. The Beehive Tavern

preserved as a national park. The National Seashore, created in the early 1960s, stretches along the Outer Cape from the elbow that is Chatham to the fist that is Provincetown. The wildest beaches, the highest dunes and the oldest lighthouse on the Cape are within the limits of the national seashore. It is here that you go to see the ocean, to stand at the very end of the land, as it seems, and look out to sea.

The main information center is the **Salt Pond Visitors Center** in Eastham. Staffed by friendly, green-uniformed rangers, the center dispenses an amazing amount of information. Inside the contemporary wood building you might view a color slide display of how the Cape was formed or take in an exhibit on marine life. Special events like nature walks, movies, hikes and lectures are offered daily through October. You can pick up the official map here.

A second visitor center at **Province Lands,** closer to Provincetown, has an observation platform and offers exhibits and movies.

Salt Pond Visitor Center, off Route 6, Eastham. (508) 255-3421. Daily 9 to 4:30, to 8 in summer. Province Lands Visitor Center, Race Point Road, Provincetown,. (508) 487-1256. Daily 9 to 5, April-November.

Special features of the National Seashore include:

Marconi Station Area. This fascinating interpretive shelter describes the Marconi Wireless Station, the first in the United States, from which a message was successfully sent to England in 1903. There are a high ocean outlook and, in summer, a bathing beach.

Nauset Beach. This lengthy strand, reached via Beach Road in East Orleans, is a favorite place year-round. You can walk for miles and watch the open ocean.

Coast Guard Beach. The bathhouse and other manmade facilities at this bathing beach were swept away during the Blizzard of 1978. For summers since, shuttle buses have been run from a new parking lot. A shower, changing facility and rest rooms have been reconstructed at the beach. A few miles north, author Henry Beston's "outermost house" was also destroyed, sad to relate, in that storm.

Pilgrim Heights. Here are the highest dunes. People like to walk up and over them to the beach. A sign cautions correctly that it's a strenuous climb. In the same area are the Pilgrim Springs, from which the Pilgrims got their first fresh water, and Corn Hill, where they found corn hidden by Indians.

Bike Trails. The national seashore has three paved trails. Nauset Trail, 1.6 miles long, reached from the Salt Pond Visitors Center, is fairly easy, and so is Head of the Meadow Trail, two miles, reached from High Head Road, Truro. The Province Lands Trail, eight miles, has steep portions and sharp curves. Reach it from Herring Cove Beach parking area or Province Lands Visitors Center.

Highland Light. The oldest lighthouse on the Cape is located on the cliff above the beach and its strong beam can be seen twenty miles at sea. Henry David Thoreau said you could stand here and put all of America behind you.

Favorite Beaches, Walks, Drives

Outside the national seashore there are other great beaches and harbors, walks and drives. We like:

Cape Cod Museum of Natural History. Adjacent to the museum, the mile-long **John Wing Trail** leads through marsh and seashore vegetation to a lovely beach. The museum itself is worth a stop. A wing opened in 1987 nearly doubled the space available for exhibits, lecture rooms and the like. The whale exhibit includes the skeleton of a minke whale washed ashore at a Chatham beach in 1978. A bird room, mineral exhibit, turtle tank and weather station are other stops at this fun place, which is especially good for children. There's a good gift shop. *Route 6A, Brewster. (508) 896-3867. Monday-Saturday 9:30 to 4:30, Sunday 12:30 to 4:30. Adults $4, children $2.*

Sesuit Harbor, Dennis. A small harbor with picturesque sailboats, it has a nice stone breakwater where you can sit. Reach it via Bridge Street off Route 6A.

Rock Harbor, Orleans. Follow Rock Harbor Road to a working harbor with broad clam flats. There's something we love about this place; bring a steaming cup of coffee, sit and enjoy.

Yarmouth Port Boardwalk. Follow Centre Street from Route 6A to Homer's Dock Road to Gray's Beach. A wooden pier walkway stretches to Clay's Creek, with a lookout overlooking Bass Hole. Tidal pools, marine holes and nesting birds may be glimpsed. We recommend this spot for a picnic.

The Boardwalk in Sandwich. Sandwich also has a boardwalk, this one rebuilt in 1991-92 after an extraordinary storm hit the western part of the Cape. Individual planks were sponsored and bear sayings like "In Memory of Granny Dowden." To find the boardwalk, wend your way north through the center of Sandwich. Take Town Neck Road off Route 6A to Freeman Avenue.

Brewster's Punkhorn. In 1987, the town of Brewster acquired 800 acres of an area known affectionately as the Punkhorn, one of the last great tracts of undeveloped land on the Cape. Much of it is typical Cape woodland of pitch pine and mixed oak species, but the area is ringed by a necklace of ponds, old bogs and streams. Canoeists and fishermen can have a heyday here and hikers will note that the area was once the heart of Brewster's cranberry industry. Park at the Eagle Point Conservation area off Run Hill Road. The Brewster Conservation Department offers interpretive walks in the fall.

Getting High

The Cape is essentially flat, but you can be above it all, and in the clear air of autumn your view may be exceptional.

Scargo Hill Tower, Tobey Memorial Park, Dennis. Don't be put off by the graffiti inside this stone tower. Be turned on by the view across velvet-blue Cape Cod Bay, all the way to Provincetown's distinctive Pilgrim Monument. Scargo Lake, below, is a glacial gift. In the fall, there's a good view of the foliage.

The Pilgrim Monument. From the top of this 255-foot granite tower (an easy climb) you can see, on a clear day, down the Cape's forearm and across the waters of the bay toward Plymouth.

Town Hill, Provincetown. Daily, 9 to 7 in summer, to 5 in spring and fall. Adults $5, children $3.

The Sporting Life

Golf. The salt water keeps the Cape warmer than most of New England, and golfers love the long season. The **Dennis Pines Golf Course** off Route 134, run by the town, is a favorite and the 18th hole is all downhill.

Tennis courts are widely available, often adjacent to schools or town facilities.

Fishing for flounder, striped bass, blues and giant tuna is best from late August into November. You can surfcast from beaches, jetties, bridges or boats.

Biking is popular in the National Seashore and at **Nickerson State Park** in Brewster, which has two well-developed trails. **The Rail Trail** is a seventeen-mile bike path meandering through woods, marsh and cranberry bogs from Dennis to Eastham and the Cape Cod National Seashore. It can be reached in Brewster off Underpass Road and at Nickerson State Park. Bike rentals are available at both locations. People bike all around the Cape; but traffic is heavy along Route 6A.

Whale watching. The mid-Cape's only whale-watch excursion departs from Barnstable Harbor from spring through mid-October. **Hyannis Whale Watcher Cruises,** (508) 362-6088 or (800) 287-0374, located at Millway Marine, off Phinney's Lane in Barnstable, offers four-hour trips daily on a high-speed boat. Fares, $10 to $22.

The Inside Story

Three attractions in the fascinating town of Sandwich offer the opportunity for an entire museum day.

Heritage Plantation. The former estate of Charles O. Dexter is famed for its rhododendrons in spring, but there's much more. Proclaiming itself "a diversified museum of Americana," Heritage Plantation displays antique automobiles in a reproduction of the Shaker round barn at Hancock, Mass.; antique firearms and military miniatures in a military museum, and a large collection of Currier and Ives lithographs. Early tools, folk art and changing exhibits add to the experience. Walking the lovely grounds and picnicking are also fun.

Grove Street off Routes 6A and 130, Sandwich. (508) 888-3300. Daily 10 to 5, mid-May to mid-October. Adults $8, children $4.

Yesteryears Doll and Miniature Museum. A retired Army colonel and his wife collected the dolls while on tours of duty in Germany, Japan and at home. There are also dolls from France, an Edison phonograph doll of 1889 and a collection of nearly 50 dollhouses at this splendid museum, housed in a former church building. A unique group of German "Nuremburg kitchens" is fascinating. American dolls are being added all the time. The shop sells antique dolls, dollhouse furniture and other appropriate items.

Main and River Streets, Sandwich. (508) 888-1711. Monday-Saturday 10 to 4, mid-May through October. Adults $3.50, children $1.50.

Sandwich Glass Museum. Located in the center of the town's historic district, the glass museum of the Sandwich Historical Society houses one of the most complete collections of glass made by the Boston and Sandwich Glass Factory between 1825 and 1888. The priceless exhibit contains more than 3,000 examples. Note the extensive paperweight display and the wonderful punch bowl.

129 Main St., Sandwich. (508) 888-0251. Daily, 9:30 to 4. Closed in January. Adults $3.50; children, $1.

Historic Houses

Winslow Crocker House. In 1936, Mary Thacher, an avid collector of antiques, moved the house of a wealthy 18th-century trader, Winslow Crocker, to its present location in Yarmouth Port as a showcase for her antique furniture. The house is surprisingly elaborate, with rich paneling in each room. But the contents are what is important. Visitors see an extraordinary collection of fine pieces, including one of the earliest cradles made in America, and examples of many early styles of chairs. The house is owned by the Society for the Preservation of New England Antiquities.

250 Main St. (Route 6A), Yarmouth Port. (508) 362-4385. Tours hourly, noon to 4, on Tuesday, Thursday, Saturday and Sunday, June to mid-October. Adults $4, children $2.

Capt. Bangs Hallet House. A fine example of the Greek Revival style of architecture, this was built in the 1840s by a member of the Thacher family as an addition to a structure dating from 1740. It has been refurbished and furnished in a manner reminiscent of the lifestyle of a prosperous, 19th-century sea captain.

11 Strawberry Lane, On the Common, Yarmouth Port. (508) 362-3021. Sunday 1 to 3:30, June-October; also Thursday 1 to 3:30 in July and August. Adults $3, children 50 cents.

Other buildings of interest are the **Sturgis Library** in the center of Barnstable, which has among its collections a rare Bible brought to America in 1634 by one of Barnstable's first ministers; the **West Parish Church of Barnstable,** the oldest Congregational church building in the country, and the **Quaker Meeting House** off Spring Hill Road in East Sandwich, which has the oldest continuous Quaker meeting in the country.

Shopping

There's hardly a more scenic – or rewarding – outing for shoppers than along Route 6A between Sandwich and Brewster.

ANTIQUING is in season in fall. **Pflock's Antique Shop** in Brewster emphasizes copper and brass. **Kingsland Manor** is one of the most elegant places we've seen and it goes on and on. How about a scale model of the Titanic, encased in glass, for a cool $10,000? **Maps of Antiquities** in West Barnstable specializes in maps from the 19th century and earlier, as well as prints and books of places. Antique dolls are the specialty at **Dolores Gilbert Antique Dolls & Embellishments** at the Antique Center of Cape Cod, 243 Main St. (Route 6A) in Dennis. There are many more shops; discover your own favorites.

Parnassus Book Service in Yarmouth Port is one of a kind. Old (and a few newer) books are crowded into this big gray building at the edge of Route 6A; you can browse year-round at an open-air book stall. **Titcomb's Bookshop** on Route 6A in East Sandwich is another literary emporium with atmosphere galore. A wide staircase leads to the second floor where old books are shelved in wooden bookcases. On the main floor you'll find many books on the Cape (new and used), children's books, old magazines, cards and more.

ARTS AND CRAFTS are in plentiful supply along Route 6A. We like the selection at **The Lemon Tree** in Brewster, with lots of pottery and other unusual gift items. Next door, the **Cook Shop** offers all sorts of things for the kitchen, many of them European imports. The **Spectrum Galleries** in Brewster represents American artists and craftsmen and the selection is fine in almost all mediums. **The Handcraft House** in Brewster has a nice variety of arts and crafts.

Surf is super and beaches deserted in fall along Cape Cod National Seashore.

Everybody, it seems, is crazy about **Sydenstricker Glass** in Brewster, for it is always crowded. Window glass is fused together with colored paints to create unusual designs for bowls, plates, vases and paperweights.

Go to the source for some great pottery. We admire the work of Steve Kemp and his attractive shop at **Kemp Pottery** in Brewster. The stoneware, porcelain and black sand porcelain (made from Nauset Beach sand) pieces are amazingly affordable, too. We especially like the lamps. In Dennis, a visit to **Scargo Pottery** is an interesting experience. Harry Holl and his daughters – plus a couple of apprentices – hold forth in an oriental setting deep in a pine woods. Here you'll find wall art, birdbaths, whimsical teapots and cookie jars, and ornate birdhouses that look like castles. All are displayed beneath a roof with supports but no walls, so you are one with the outdoors.

Artists are everywhere. For an unusual experience, visit **The Underground Gallery** at 673 Satucket Road, Brewster, designed by Malcolm Wells, an architect who designs earth-covered solar buildings, which this is. Karen North Wells, a talented watercolorist, displays her work here. **Don DeVita's** art gallery is located in an interesting old town hall building on Route 6A.

MISCELLANY. Scandinavian country antiques and accessories of exquisite taste are found at **Design Works** in Yarmouth Port. Nearby, **The Garden Gate** has wonderful home and garden accents with an emphasis on dried floral wreaths, vases, botanical prints and other garden-oriented items.

The Weather Store on Main Street in Sandwich displays unusual and fascinating items for weather-watchers. You can pick up a hurricane watcher's graph and map, a fancy barometer; books on the weather, and other weather instrumentation. Also in Sandwich, on Jarves Street, is a fine decorating and gift store called **Madden & Co.** You'll find tasteful accessories for the home, cookbooks and gourmet foods.

The **Brewster General Store** remains in a time warp, although it's become a bit fancier as the years go by. Stop in for coffee and your Sunday newspaper and browse among the aisles for toys, kitchen knickknacks, cocktail napkins and other paper goods, corkscrews, glasses or almost anything you need or might want to give as a gift.

Choose your Halloween pumpkin at the **Tobey Farm Harvest Barn** in Dennis.

Where to Stay

This lovely old section of the Cape is increasingly blessed with good B&Bs. These are the accommodations of choice here for they suit the season and the surroundings. Some have fireplaced bedrooms, many have book-lined libraries or reading nooks, and most have pleasant innkeepers who serve good breakfasts before a day of exploration. For those who prefer more privacy, we include a few motels and inns. Accommodations are presented in geographical order, from west to east. All are open year-round or well into the fall.

Bed and Breakfasts

The Charles Hinckley House. Miya and Les Patrick created a romantic B&B with a gourmet flair in this 1809 Federal house. All four guest bedrooms, two on the main floor and two on the second, come with working fireplaces. While the beds are reproduction four-posters (three queens and a double), most furnishings are antique and include oriental rugs and wing chairs. Loveseats are set attractively before a fireplace in the parlor, magazines are spread on a sea chest between them, and a decanter by the window is filled with sherry. The house is named for the great-great-grandson of the last governor of Plymouth Colony, whose house it was. Miya, who also runs a catering business, makes great breakfasts – pancakes with strawberry topping the morning we stopped in. Fresh fruit, muffins, puff pastries and eggs in various styles are part of her repertoire. The Patricks like to cater to their guests on special occasions like anniversaries, and might stock the room with a bottle of champagne or deliver breakfast in bed.
Route 6A, Barnstable 02630. (508) 362-9924. Doubles, $119 to $149.

Waratah House. Set on five acres overlooking a tidal inlet from Cape Cod Bay, this B&B is far enough off Route 6A that you feel as if you're away from it all. Nancy and Garry Hopkins – he's an Australian and she grew up in West Hartford, Conn. – offer two rooms with private bath in their main house and two rooms in a cottage. The queen-bedded Blue Room on the second floor is a room in which actor Basil Rathbone stayed during the 1920s and his wife painted the ceiling and walls. The cottage is attractive and appeals to couples traveling together. It has one queen-bedded and one twin-bedded room and a fireplaced living room, kitchen and bathroom. The cottage rents for $165 for two people, $205 for four. A full breakfast is served, possibly cream cheese french toast with a fresh berry sauce.
4308 Main St., Box 6, Cummaquid 02637. (508) 362-1469 or (800) 215-8707. Fax (508) 362-7811. Doubles, $85 to $165. Open April to mid-December.

Liberty Hill Inn. Built as a private home for a shipbuilder in 1825, this Greek Revival-style house features an interesting elliptical staircase in the front hallway. There are five guest rooms, three on the second floor and a twin-bedded room on the first. Our room with kingsize bed on the third floor was spacious and the bathroom ample, but the steepness of the two staircases was a bit daunting. Guests have the use of a large, pleasingly decorated parlor. Breakfast is served at individual tables in the dining room. One day we had a quiche and the second day, an Irish apple pastry; both were quite tasty. Owner Beth Flanagan is a former actress who has written a book about the Cape's B&Bs and served on the local school board. Husband Jack is a very outgoing partner who signs notes about bathroom fixtures "Jack, the plumber." They team up with other innkeepers to offer innkeeping seminars two or three times a year.

77 Main St., Yarmouth Port 02675. (508) 362-3976 or (800) 821-3977. Doubles, $70 to $135.

Wedgewood Inn. Romantic getaways are offered by Gerrie and Milt Graham at this elegant B&B set up on a knoll overlooking the charming village. All six rooms have private baths and four have working fireplaces; understandably, the inn is popular in autumn and winter. Furnishings are somewhat formal but not stuffy. The house, built in 1812 for a maritime lawyer, has side porches for two main-floor suites, a built-in grandfather clock in the front hall, and handsome wood-work and moldings. Pencil-post beds in the rooms, floral wallpapers, wide-board floors and such touches as tea trays brought to the rooms in the afternoon contribute toward what Gerrie describes as an "elegant country" experience. Room 1 is the largest suite; in addition to its ample, fireplaced bedroom, there are a sitting room, a large bath and a porch with wicker furniture. Room 5, second-floor rear, has both a double and a single bed and a bathroom with a clawfoot tub that guests keep wanting to purchase. In 1997, the Grahams were planning to add three large fireplaced rooms, each with kingsize bed, TV, soaking tub and balcony or patio, in a rear barn. Gerrie serves full breakfasts at white-clothed tables.in the spacious dining room. Guests help themselves to cold cereal, yogurt, muffins and pastries from a sideboard, and then are served the main dish at their tables. French toast is clearly the favorite.

83 Main St., Yarmouth Port 02675. (508) 362-5157. Doubles, $115; suites with fire-places, $135 to $160.

Scargo Manor. Jane and Chuck MacMillan turned this wonderful-looking house into a B&B of note in 1996 and inspired compliments almost immediately. Two of the three accommodations are really suites with large bedrooms, sitting rooms and private baths. Jane's decorating taste is fabulous: the king suite has dark green painted floors, a canopy bed, a woodburning fireplace in the sitting room and a bold decor in green, red and blue. The queen suite offers a canopy bed and a sitting room with single daybed. The MacMillans hope to finish a couple more rooms on the third floor. Built in 1895, the house has high-ceilinged rooms on the main floor, where guests may use a fireplaced common room with TV, a large fireplaced dining room with one big table for breakfast, and an attractive screened porch. Jane offers a continental-plus breakfast, including cereal, fruit and baked goodies.

909 Main St. (Route 6A), Dennis 02638. (508) 385-5534 or (800) 595-0034. Fax (508) 385-3992. Doubles, $80 to $140. Open April-December.

The Four Chimneys Inn. Russell and Kathy Tomasetti have upgraded this B&B beautifully, with Russell doing most of the renovations himself. Eight attrac-tively wallpapered and well-appointed guest chambers, all with small TVs, are complemented by handsome private baths. They are named for plants or flowers of the Cape. Teaberry is particularly appealing, with green striped wallpaper and a small deck with wicker furniture. The high-ceilinged, main-floor common rooms, especially the fireplaced front parlor, are comfortable places in which to relax, as is the screened side porch. Kathy serves a continental-plus breakfast at a large dining-room table with a lace tablecloth.

946 Main St., Route 6A, Dennis 02638. (508) 385-6317 or (800) 874-5502. Fax (508) 385-6285. Doubles, $70 to $110. Open May-October.

Isaiah Hall B&B. Located on a quiet side street, this B&B comprises an 1857 farmhouse with five guest rooms and an adjoining barn/carriage house with six. Common rooms are comfortably cozy and a continental buffet breakfast is provided in the dining room, with seats for everyone at one large table. The rooms have an old-fashioned New England feeling and handmade quilts cover the beds, some of which are iron and brass. Bathrooms are private. Rooms in the barn also have patios and are somewhat larger than those in the main house. One room has a fireplace, and there's TV in a common room, A side porch is lined with rockers for relaxing.

152 Whig St., Dennis 02638. (508) 385-9928 or (800) 736-0160. Fax (508) 385-5879. Doubles, $78 to $112.

The Poore House. Randy Guy and Paul Anderson teamed up to run this attractively decorated B&B in what really was, at one time, the town's poor house. Then known as The Alms House, it sheltered the poor until the 1930s. Five rooms on the second floor have private baths and air conditioning. The Apricot Room, with a tomato-colored floor and a peach bathroom, and the Blue Room come with fireplaces. Randy serves a full breakfast in a large sunny parlor on the main floor. The house, bright and sunny, is reminiscent of a beach house from days gone by.

2311 Main St., Brewster 02631. (508) 896-2094 or (800) 233-6662. Doubles, $65 to $115.

Candleberry Inn. This big white house with dark shutters is a Federal-style house built around 1800 and situated nicely back from the highway on spacious grounds. Six guest rooms are handsomely furnished. All are air-conditioned and have private baths, and three have gas fireplaces. We particularly liked a front bedroom with dark green walls, a queensize four-poster bed and a lovely, old-fashioned white bedspread. Continental breakfast is served in a common room, and there's a quiet parlor. Innkeepers Jackie and Ed Czerniakowski came to the inn in 1992.

1882 Main St. (Route 6A), Brewster 02631. (508) 896-3300. Doubles, $75 to $98.

Inns

Daniel Webster Inn. An imposing red clapboard motor inn was named after the 19th-century orator, who stayed at a previous tavern on the site when he hunted and fished in the area. The lobby area conveys a dark, historic look, and the inn is popular for everything from Sunday dinner to a weekend getaway. No fewer than three dining rooms serve meals all day. The pub downstairs is a fun place to have Sunday brunch and maybe watch a football game on TV. Colonial decor in the 46 rooms includes some canopied beds, wing chairs, ruffled curtains and the like. Twentieth-century amenities are whirlpool baths and color TVs. For warm weather visitors, there are an outdoor pool and beautifully manicured gardens.

149 Main St., Sandwich 02563. (508) 888-3622 or (800) 444-3566. Fax (508) 888-5156. Doubles, $129 to $199, EP; $210 to $280, MAP.

The Belfry Inne & Bistro. A former rectory for Catholic priests has been turned into one of the more charming spots at this end of the Cape. Innkeeper Dawn Wilson even had the original belfry rebuilt when returning the house to its Victorian glory. Now you can climb into the tower. Eight guest chambers include three with gas fireplaces and a couple with whirlpool tubs. We especially like the rooms tucked up under the eaves on the third floor, one in pink and black with Alice-in-Wonderland murals on the walls. A full breakfast is included. There's a fireplaced pub, and a bistro restaurant on the premises serves prix-fixe ($29 to $35) dinners nightly except Tuesday. The menu might feature stuffed salmon wrapped in phyllo or grilled New York sirloin with garlic mashed potatoes.
8 Jarves St., Sandwich 02563. (508) 888-8550. Fax (508) 888-3922. Doubles, $95 to $165.

Beechcroft Inn. Celeste Emily and Bob Hunt have been working hard since 1995 to return this old inn to its full potential after being closed for a period. They managed an inn on Martha's Vineyard for two years before getting their own place. All ten guest rooms have private baths. Ours on the main floor had two twins pushed together to form a king but, alas, only a lamp on one side of the bed for reading. Full breakfasts for house guests and dinners for the public are offered in a pleasant dining room. French toast one day and an omelet the next were served with hot muffins. A fireside pub just off the main entrance way is inviting, especially on a chilly night, and two other common rooms are available for guests. There is a large TV in a den on the main floor.
1360 Main St. (Route 6A), Brewster 02631. (508) 896-9534. Doubles, $75 to $145.

— *Good Values* ———————————————————————

Spring Garden Motel. This weathered gray motel is set back from the highway and all eleven air-conditioned rooms have sundecks or patios to the rear overlooking a marsh. Most rooms are pine-paneled and contain two double beds, furnished with comforters, dust ruffles, designer sheets and pillow shams. There are two efficiencies and a two-room suite. Owners Marvin and Judy Gluckman provide a homemade continental breakfast in the lobby. Out back are interesting plantings, picnic tables and barbecue grills. There's a swimming pool, too.
578 Route 6A, Box 867, East Sandwich 02537. (508) 888-0710 or (800) 303-1751. Doubles, $53 to $75. Open April-November. In the fall, rates are as low as $45.

Pine Grove Cottages. Roger and Kathy Bumstead are the second generation to run this group of pine-paneled cottages, some built in the 1930s. "It's kind of like going back to Boy Scout camp," says Kathy with a laugh as she shows a visitor around the grove, which is set back from the highway and includes a swimming pool. Cottages range in size from a tiny duplex with the sink in the bedroom, renting for as little as $30 a night, to some with two bedrooms and a living room. Most have kitchenettes. Pets and children are welcome. While many of the cottages rent by the week in the summer, the owners will rent for the night if available, especially in fall.
Route 6A, East Sandwich 02537. (508) 888-8179. Doubles, $30 to $85. Weekly rates, $200 to $495. Open May-October.

Camping

Nickerson State Park off Route 6A, East Brewster. This is an exceptionally nice setting for campers. Tent sites are available until mid-October and facilities include drinking water, showers, flush toilets and sewer dumping. First come, first served.

Where to Eat

The Cape's restaurants offer something for everyone. You can snack on a clam roll or splurge on four-star French cuisine, and there's a lot in between. Yarmouth Port has more than its share of good restaurants and some of the best restaurants on the Cape are in Brewster. The restaurants are presented geographically in roughly the same order as accommodations, from west to east.

Barnstable Tavern & Grille. This black-shuttered, white clapboard inn is set back from the main street with a brick courtyard in front, where you can eat outdoors in good weather. The dining rooms, with light wood windsor chairs and mismatched tables, are cozy and welcoming. The appealing bar is a good place to have dinner while watching a football game – something we did early one Saturday evening. The menu lists appetizers like grilled portobello mushrooms, fried calamari and mussels marinara, plus Mideast specialties like spinach pie and hummus. Entrées include grilled salmon and swordfish, baked stuffed shrimp, grilled lemon pepper chicken, chicken and broccoli with pasta, and filet mignon. *3180 Main St., Barnstable. (508) 362-2355. Entrées, $10 to $20. Lunch daily, 11:30 to 5; dinner, 5:30 to 9 or 10; Sunday brunch.*

Abbicci. A low building beside Route 6A, formerly the Cranberry Moose, provides a sophisticated setting for a great meal. Abbicci, in Italian, is "ABC." Ancient maps of Italy have been reproduced in oversize scale on the walls of one dining room by the son of owner Marietta Hickey. San Pellegrino bottled water awaits on each white-clothed table; light windsor-style chairs give a clean, uncluttered look. There is nothing spare about the food, however, and the dinner menu is quite ambitious. Appetizers include oysters baked with spinach and pancetta, polenta with melted fontina and sautéed wild mushrooms, and meat-filled tortellini. Pastas ($16 to $19) might be linguini with littleneck clams and gnocchi in a gorgonzola cream sauce with toasted walnuts. Among entrées are zuppe di pesce (a seafood stew of lobsters, clams, mussels and shrimp), free-range chicken breast stuffed with mushroom duxelles, rabbit braised with a tarragon-lemon sauce and served with soft polenta, and pistachio-crusted rack of lamb. A wine list heavy on fine Italian and American wines includes a few less expensive selections. *43 Main St., Yarmouth Port. (508) 362-3501. Entrées, $15 to $27. Lunch daily, 11:30 to 2:30; dinner, 5 to 9; Sunday brunch.*

Aardvark. The big old gingerbread-trimmed house on the Main Street of Yarmouth Port, which looks as if it stepped out of *Hansel and Gretel,* has been home to several different restaurants, but the new Aardvark is earning praise from visitors and locals. It's open more or less all day, serving coffee and pastries in the early morning and then lunch and dinner. In the morning, a legion of different-flavored coffees is lined up in thermos carafes and the pastries look scrumptious. At lunchtime, you can get hot or cold sandwiches for $3 to $6; a typical hot sandwich being roasted eggplant with peppers, onions, broccoli, mushrooms and provolone. Soup or quiche and salad are other possibilities. In the evening, typical entrées, served with salad and seasonal vegetables, are pan-seared swordfish with pineapple and cranberry salsa, Mediterranean seafood linguini, and spicy jumbo shrimp with grilled portobello mushrooms, eggplant and grilled tomatoes over linguini. Kabobs of several different ingredients served on risotto and dinner tarts (grilled focaccia with a variety of toppings) are less expensive alternatives. A full bar is available.

Route 6A, Yarmouth Port. (508) 362-9866. Entrées, $13 to $19. Breakfast daily, 7 to 10:30, Sunday 9 to 2; lunch, Tuesday-Sunday 11:30 to 3; dinner, Wednesday-Saturday 6 to 9.

Inaho. The building that housed the former La Cipollina restaurant has become the home of a Japanese restaurant that was previously in Hyannis. Yuji Watanabe is the chef; his American wife, Alda, handles the front of the house. The Cape Cod cottage is startlingly spare and Oriental in style inside. Sushi and sashimi are featured as entrées, but you also can find chicken, salmon and beef teriyaki, several different tempuras and shabu-shabu ($36), a dinner for two cooked in a pot at the table with thinly sliced beef, vegetables and noodles, served with a dipping sauce. Appetizers include yakitori (broiled chicken on skewers), gyoza (pan-fried dumplings) and tako-su (octopus in a light vinegar dressing). Among entrées are several mixed plates; perhaps sushi, tempura, teriyaki and fruit.

Main Street, Yarmouth Port. (508) 362-5522. Entrées, $12 to $18. Dinner nightly, from 5.

Jack's Outback. If you don't mind a little ribbing along with your spare ribs, try this establishment, located "out back" behind a large parking lot in what appears, at first glance, to be a small A-frame house. Jack Smith, a local notable, keeps up a lively repartee with the clientele as he serves home-cooked specials for breakfast and lunch. The locals love it and don't seem to mind writing up their own orders, pouring their own soft drinks from a soda machine and clearing their own tables. About the only thing that is done for you is the delivery of the meal, but you're encouraged to throw a tip into the huge aluminum bowl by the cash register; when you do a cow bell is rung. Food items are written on placards and posted across the front of the restaurant. The day we stopped for lunch there were three soups – "cauliflower bisk," "minnie-stroney" and "toe mater cajun," plus several pita sandwiches ($2 to $5), including roast beef, veggie and ham. An excellent cold pasta salad of linguini, black olives, tomatoes, ham, chicken and cheese, dressed with a vinaigrette, was $3.95. Desserts look scrumptious, but beware, Jack can give you a hard time. "What happened to the diet?" he yelled at one woman as he was about to deliver a chocolate confection. For unsuspecting visitors things can be a bit unnerving, too. One couple, obviously not regulars, left their plates on the table when they got up to leave and Jack let them know the proper procedure in no uncertain terms. But for those who get into the spirit, this is a fun place.

Behind 161 Main St., Yarmouth Port. (508) 362-6690. Breakfast daily, 6:30 to 11:30; lunch, 11:30 to 3.

Marshside Restaurant. Locals like this restaurant and we do, too. Serving three meals a day seven days a week year-round, the Marshside is ready when you are. There's service at a small L-shaped counter in a rear corner, as well as at calico-clothed tables. Tiny white lights on the hanging plants add sparkle to the decor in the evening; lighting overhead is from Tiffany-style lamps. Everything from a frankfurter or a teriyaki burger to chicken florentine or shrimp scampi is available. The emphasis is on fresh seafood at rational prices. We enjoyed a dinner of broiled scallops, served with boiled red potatoes and a house salad with creamy dill dressing. Lunch is much the same as dinner with seafood platters, seafood rolls (shrimp, clam or scallop, $11) and burgers or sandwiches ($4 to $6). Desserts include apple pie, carrot cake and mud pie. Owner Mary Lou Goodwin seems to know what everyone likes. She decorates her restaurant with seasonal decor, which gets especially wild when Halloween rolls around. From servers to guests, everyone seems very comfortable here.
28 Bridge St. (near the junction of Routes 6A and 134), East Dennis. (508) 385-4010. Entrées, $11 to $15. Breakfast daily, 7 to 11:30; lunch, 11:30 to 5; dinner, 5 to 8 or 9.

Gina's By the Sea. Take Taunton Avenue down toward the beach and just before you reach the water you'll find Gina's. The small white clapboard restaurant with gray shutters and blue and white awnings has been on this site for more than 50 years. The original owner, Gina, has earned her heavenly reward; Larry Riley now handles the popular little spot where no reservations are taken and some are willing to wait up to two hours for a table. The pine-paneled bar with a few booths is decorated with baseball caps left by patrons; the interior dining room with fireplace and the enclosed sun porch are pleasant places to dine. Nightly specials such as lamb chops boursin supplement the northern Italian cuisine. Eggplant parmigiana, veal scaloppine a la milanaise, fettuccine alfredo and chicken dijon are among entrées. You might start with mussels marinara or shrimp cocktail. Pasta dishes include baked stuffed shells, spaghetti and ravioli for $10 to $14. Finish with Mrs. Riley's chocolate rum cake or cannoli.
154 Taunton Ave., Dennis. (508) 385-3213. Entrées, $13 to $18. Lunch and dinner daily in summer; dinner, Thursday-Saturday 5:30 to 9 in spring and fall.

The Red Pheasant Inn. People consistently praise the Red Pheasant, for the food is reliably good and the ambiance great. Behind an old red Cape Cod cottage is a long addition with a new entry and two cozy dining rooms. One is a long, porch-like area with white tablecloths and hanging plants. The interior room is separated by a low partition from a waiting area with sofas and chairs placed before a fireplace. Hurricane oil lamps, wall sconces and frosted glass lights make for subdued, intimate dining. The stuffed pheasant on the counter by the cash register is an acknowledgment, we suppose, of the restaurant's name. Chef-owner Bill Atwood Jr. features game among fall dinner entrées, perhaps braised pheasant with savoy cabbage, red wine and caramelized leeks or grilled venison with chanterelles. Grilled rack of lamb with fried red peppers and goat cheese ravioli and crisp vegetables was a wonderful recent offering, as was cedar-planked salmon. For starters, the signature dish is tuna pastrami, corned and smoked in-house and served with baby field greens and a green mustard-honey vinaigrette. Others include wild mushroom strudel, lobster and scallop lasagna, and chilled Wellfleet oysters and littlenecks served with lime and fresh fennel. There are three seatings for the popular Thanksgiving dinner.

905 Main St., Route 6A, Dennis. (508) 385-2133. Entrées, $17 to $24. Dinner nightly, 5 to 8:30 or 9; reduced schedule in January.

The Bramble Inn. Ruth Manchester's fame as a chef makes it imperative to have reservations at this pleasant inn, where diners are served in one of five attractive small dining rooms. We especially like the small room with the single table and eight Queen Anne chairs, although Ruth says the most requested tables are on the glassed-in front porch. The entrée price includes appetizer, salad and dessert. Ruth describes the food as continental and service as "fairly formal," but still likes to think of her guests as "having dinner in our home." Appetizers might be grilled oysters in prosciutto or grilled venison sausage served on a warm lentil salad. Entrées could be parchment-roasted breast of chicken served with lobster and champagne sauce, filet mignon with a roquefort cream, glazed onion and pear racine, and veal medallions with a mushroom, vermouth and mustard sauce, served with a sweet potato and parsnip hash. A selection of house-made desserts is offered.

Route 6A, Brewster. (508) 896-7644. Prix-Fixe, $44 to $51. Dinner nightly in summer, 6 to 9; fewer nights in spring and fall. Closed January to mid-April.

High Brewster. New owners Catherine and Timothy Mundy operate one of the most romantic restaurants on the Cape. Ensconced in an atmospheric 18th-century house located away from the main road, High Brewster oozes charm. Tables in the fireplaced keeping room, in two front dining rooms (which feel like living rooms) and a couple of especially popular tables out back opposite the bar (with high-back benches adding to their privacy) are set with white linens, gorgeous china and gleaming crystal. The prix-fixe four-course dinner includes a choice of appetizers such as pan-seared quail or chilled lobster with cucumber noodles, and an entrée like steamed lobster with spinach pasta or grilled duck breast with cranberry vinaigrette. Dessert could be fresh berry tart or crème caramel.

964 Satucket Road, Brewster. (508) 896-3636. Prix-fixe, $30 to $42. Dinner nightly by reservation, 5:30 to 9, Memorial Day to Columbus Day; Wednesday-Sunday in off-season. Closed January-March.

Brewster Fish House. Brothers David and Vernon Smith run this small and hugely popular spot, which they refer to as "a nonconforming restaurant." Julia Child ate here and liked it, we're told. Deep green formica-topped tables and bare wood floors are the backdrop for some inventive cuisine. Fish and nothing but fish is the order of the day, although there is the possibility of a hamburger or a chicken breast sandwich at lunchtime. "The lobster bisque is out of this world," says the hostess; fish chowder is also on the menu along with billi-bi, a mussel soup. Fried oyster and lobster salad rolls and a fish sandwich are offered. Luncheon entrées ($6 to $8) include grilled salmon with marmalade glaze, fried calamari, broiled cod with citrus butter and fish and chips. In the evening, appetizers could be a crab cake with a mixed fruit and pepper marmalade, dill and brandy-cured salmon, fried calamari, or steamed littlenecks and shrimp with white wine, fennel and garlic. Entrées might be baked bluefish with fresh rosemary, grilled sea scallops with sundried tomatoes and roasted garlic, and baked horseradish-crusted pollock.

Route 6A, Brewster. (508) 896-7867. Entrées, $12 to $17. Lunch daily, 11:30 to 3; dinner, 5 to 9:30 or 10; closed Monday in off-season. Closed December-March.

A Good Value

The Beehive Tavern. "An affordably priced Colonial tavern" is the descriptive phrase used by this informal restaurant. Dark wood booths and low lighting contribute to the tavern atmosphere. The all-day menu includes appetizers ($3 to $5) like a hummus and tabouli dip, baked stuffed quahog and baby back ribs. The special soup when we were there was chicken vegetable gumbo. French onion soup, chili and clam chowder are also offered by the cup or crock. Pastas ($8 to $10) include linguini with marinara or with white or red clam sauce. Among sandwiches are "The Bee's Knees," honey ham and swiss cheese, and "The Drone's Dilemma," honey ham and turkey with cheddar. Salads like caesar, greek, niçoise, and a hummus and tabouli platter are meals in themselves. Dinner entrées are $10 to $15, and the locally popular prime rib is a mere $12. Other possibilities are lobster pie (a house favorite), baked scallops, baked scrod, chicken teriyaki and chargrilled lamb chops. It's somewhat standard fare, but the price is right and the place is usually packed.

406 Route 6A, East Sandwich. (508) 833-1184. Daily from 11, weekends from 8; dinner, 5 to 9.

For A Special Occasion

Chillingsworth. Chillingsworth is the sort of place you'd select for a very special event. It is pricey and formal, and its contemporary French cuisine is considered tops in its class. In a restored 1689 house, Chillingsworth offers intimate, antiques-filled dining rooms, a greenhouse lounge and bar, and a gourmet food and gift shop. Chef-owner Robert "Nitzi" Rabin puts together a different menu nightly; his wife Pat works the front of the house and is the restaurant's pastry chef. The prix-fixe dinner varies, depending on choice of entrée. Appetizers might be grilled marinated shrimp on a red pepper pancake, or oysters and asparagus with spinach and lemon butter sauce. For autumn entrées, you might order seared duck breast with wild rice and grilled pineapple salsa, pan-seared sweetbreads with foie gras, rack and tenderloin of lamb with roasted tomatoes and fava beans, or loin of elk with celery root puree and red onion marmalade. In the greenhouse, where a less expensive bistro menu is served in the evening, entrées on the à la carte menu are priced from $9.50 to $21.50. To start, crab cakes with cucumber and lemon-chive sour cream or grilled pizza with four cheeses sound good. Main dishes could be grilled salmon with cucumber and tomato salad or lamb chops with risotto, beans and a fresh herb sauce.

Route 6A, Brewster. (508) 896-3640. Prix-fixe, $43 to $58. Lunch in summer, Wednesday-Sunday 11:30 to 2:30; dinner by reservation, Tuesday-Sunday, seatings at 6 and 9, weekends only in spring and fall. Closed after Thanksgiving to Memorial Day.

FOR MORE INFORMATION: The Cape Cod Chamber of Commerce, Hyannis, (508) 362-3225, provides information but tends to boost only its members. Some towns have individual tourist organizations; write to the town of your choice.

13 🍁 Fall

Stone wall fronts attractive campus of Pomfret School.

A Total Change of Pace

Northeastern Connecticut

A rolling, pastoral landscape crisscrossed by timeworn stone walls that stretch endlessly into the distance. Hill towns and mill villages brimming with history. Gracious Colonial and Victorian homes in which fascinating innkeepers lavish old-fashioned hospitality. And fall foliage creating a canopy above country lanes and wooded trails.

This is autumn in northeastern Connecticut, which lures visitors to a total change of pace.

Welcome to the state's forgotten corner, or the Quiet Corner, as it was designated in a tourist bureau contest. This is Connecticut off the beaten path, a place far removed from the Hartford, Worcester and Providence metropolitan areas that threaten to encroach on its far fringes like triple pincers.

The Quiet Corner wasn't always overlooked. Back in the 19th century, it was a fashionable resort area in the style of Lenox and Newport. Wealthy New Yorkers and Bostonians summered in Pomfret and Woodstock on vast country estates with dreamlike names like Gwyn Careg, Courtlands and Glen Elsinore.

By the 20th century, two distinct cultures had developed. One reflected the Yankee farmers whose livelihood depended on the corn, grain and apples that grew on the gentle hillsides; the other, the mill-centered industrial workers who lived within walking distance of the river that provided the power. The more prosperous farmers and mill owners mingled with the summer elite.

Today, the mills have gone and not many farmers are left. Newcomers with means and taste have followed in the footsteps of their 19th-century predecessors, imbuing the area with pockets of affluence. "The Street" in Pomfret carries much of the grace of a century ago. Substantial houses surround the picturesque commons in Brooklyn and Thompson and climb the hills of Putnam Heights. A low-key cachet is lent by Pomfret, the Rectory, Hyde and Marianapolis preparatory schools and the headquarters of Crabtree & Evelyn, one of the area's largest employers.

The weekend visitor can share in the good life here. You can stay in restored inns that once were the homes of the rich and famous. You can partake of bed and breakfast with the aristocracy in houses filled with family treasures. Your host may be an artist, a furniture-maker, a pediatrician, an interior decorator, an architect or a music buff. In no other New England area have we found the innkeepers and their facilities as a group so engaging.

Activities and sightseeing come quietly here. You will want to venture north into Massachusetts to visit Old Sturbridge Village, the region's leading tourist attraction and a restored New England village of the 1830s. But outside the museum grounds, you will be accosted by 20th-century commercialism. You'll likely be glad to return to the Quiet Corner, if only for another day or two. Here the essence of old New England lives on, quietly.

Getting There

The Northeast Corner is bordered on the northwest by Interstate 84. Interstate 395 cuts north-south through its eastern midriff. U.S. Routes 44 and 6 serve the area on an east-west axis.

The nearest major airports are in Hartford and Providence, R.I., which are roughly equidistant, depending upon what part of the corner you're in. Amtrak trains stop at New London and Mystic to the south, as well as at Hartford to the west.

Bonanza buses serve Danielson and Willimantic.

Seeing and Doing

Weathered barns and old stone walls in farm fields border the roads, evidence of the agricultural character of part of the region. Once-proud mills dominating the landscape of Putnam, Danielson and Killingly testify to another aspect. The biggest annual events are the Brooklyn Fair the last weekend in August and the Woodstock Fair on Labor Day Weekend. Both are among the nation's longest-running agricultural fairs. Fast becoming another tradition is a three-day Walking Weekend staged every October.

Enjoying the Countryside

Hill Towns and Mill Villages. A booklet of this name, prepared by the Association of Northeastern Connecticut Historical Societies, is a helpful adjunct for touring rural Woodstock, Pomfret, Brooklyn and Canterbury as well as the nearby mill towns of Thompson, Putnam, Killingly and Plainfield. We particularly enjoy "The Street" lined with academic buildings, churches and gracious homes in Pomfret, the Woodstock Hill green with a sweeping three-state view available behind Woodstock Academy, and the stunning Thompson Hill common on, yes, a hilltop. The hill towns are on quiet display along **Scenic Route 169,** which slices north-south through the heart of this region from the Massachusetts line to Canterbury. The buildings and land along both sides have been placed on the National Register. The 32-mile stretch is the longest officially designated scenic road in Connecticut and is one of fourteen "national scenic byways," as honored in 1996 by the U.S. Department of Transportation. It cited the route's location in "one of the last unspoiled areas in the northeastern United States."

Bicycling also is popular in this area, and the Northeast Connecticut Visitors District has prepared a helpful brochure with maps for ten distinct self-guided bicycle tours. Among the areas covered are Putnam Heights, Thompson, Pomfret-Woodstock, Canterbury-Scotland and Eastford-Ashford.

Heritage Corridor. The National Park Service was instrumental in developing the Quinebaug-Shetucket Rivers Valley National Heritage Corridor to preserve the region's rural character and protect it from encroaching development. Twenty-five area towns are cooperating to develop regional greenways and nourish historic and natural preservation. The corridor committee sponsors a **Walking Weekend** over three days each Columbus Day weekend in October. Experts guide upwards of 3,500 people on a total of about 50 walks, visiting mill towns, forests, farms, the Thompson Common, parks and more. One year there were even a bird walk, a fisherman's walk, a riverside botanical walk, a candlelight walk and a dog's walk (with adults on leash).

Mashamoquet Brook State Park. The 1,000-acre park also offers swimming, camping and an adventurous trail to the **Wolf Den,** where local Revolutionary War hero Israel Putnam killed the last she-wolf in northeastern Connecticut. Children can crawl inside and almost visualize Putnam stalking the beast in the cave. Another trail leads to a rock formation known as **Indian Chair.**
Route 44, Pomfret. (860) 928-6121.Trails open free, daily to dusk. Park fee on weekends in summer.

Pomfret Farms. The Connecticut Audubon Society offers several miles of hiking and nature trails on 147 acres of a little-known wildlife sanctuary near the intersections of Route 169 and 101. Weekend workshops on gardening and wildlife as well as guided bird walks are scheduled.
220 Day Road (off Route 169), Pomfret. (860) 928-4041. Open daily.

Historic Sites

Churches and Schools. The spireless **Old Trinity Church** in Brooklyn, the oldest Episcopal church (1771) now standing in the oldest diocese in the country, is open some summer afternoons but is used only once a year on All Saints Day. Modeled after Trinity Church in Newport and King's Chapel in Boston, it is a favorite of photographers. The gem of an interior is all bare wood, which remains unpainted. Other treasures are the Pomfret School chapel and the Tiffany windows in Pomfret's Christ Church. Also peek into the brick one-room **Quassett School** in Woodstock. The Pomfret and Rectory private schools occupy pleasant campuses.

Roseland Cottage. If the Quiet Corner has an "attraction," this is it. And its thrusting gables and vivid pink facade stand in colorful contrast to the otherwise Colonial character of the attractive New England village. Woodstock native Henry C. Bowen, a New York merchant and publisher, was into roses and the Fourth of

July. So he planted a formal garden with roses outside his summer house, upholstered much of its furniture in pink and named it Roseland Cottage. Such luminaries as Ulysses S. Grant, Benjamin Harrison, Rutherford B. Hayes and William McKinley came to the wild pink Gothic Revival mansion trimmed in gingerbread for his famous Independence Day celebrations. The house and its furnishings remain much as they were in the 19th century. The parterre garden, with 600 yards of dwarf boxwood edging, has survived since it was laid out in 1850. In the rear barn is the oldest extant bowling alley in a private residence; balls of varying sizes line the gutter. Victorian teas are scheduled some afternoons in summer and fall. More than 170 craftsmen and artists participate in a fall festival here the third weekend in October.

Route 169, Woodstock. (860) 928-4074. Wednesday-Sunday noon to 5, Memorial Day through Labor Day; Friday-Sunday through October. Adults $4, children $2.

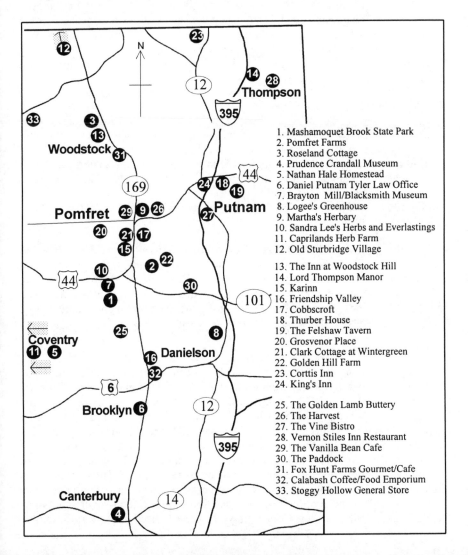

1. Mashamoquet Brook State Park
2. Pomfret Farms
3. Roseland Cottage
4. Prudence Crandall Museum
5. Nathan Hale Homestead
6. Daniel Putnam Tyler Law Office
7. Brayton Mill/Blacksmith Museum
8. Logee's Greenhouse
9. Martha's Herbary
10. Sandra Lee's Herbs and Everlastings
11. Caprilands Herb Farm
12. Old Sturbridge Village

13. The Inn at Woodstock Hill
14. Lord Thompson Manor
15. Karinn
16. Friendship Valley
17. Cobbscroft
18. Thurber House
19. The Felshaw Tavern
20. Grosvenor Place
21. Clark Cottage at Wintergreen
22. Golden Hill Farm
23. Corttis Inn
24. King's Inn

25. The Golden Lamb Buttery
26. The Harvest
27. The Vine Bistro
28. Vernon Stiles Inn Restaurant
29. The Vanilla Bean Cafe
30. The Paddock
31. Fox Hunt Farms Gourmet/Cafe
32. Calabash Coffee/Food Emporium
33. Stoggy Hollow General Store

Prudence Crandall Museum. The site of New England's first black female academy has a fascinating history to reveal. Asked to educate their children, Prudence Crandall ran afoul of townspeople when she admitted a black girl in 1832. They withdrew their children, so she reorganized the academy as one solely for the instruction of "young ladies and misses of color" until harassment and violence forced her to close. Now a museum and National Register landmark, the house is interesting for its architecture and changing exhibits.

Routes 14 and 169, Canterbury. (860) 546-9916. Wednesday-Sunday 10 to 4:30; closed mid-December to Feb. 1. Adults $2, children $1.

Nathan Hale Homestead. This rambling red house was built in 1776 by the father of the patriot who was captured by the British and hanged as a spy ("I only regret that I have but one life to lose for my country.") It served as the home of the Hale family until 1832 and offers a fascinating glimpse into life in the Revolutionary War era. Deacon Richard Hale held court here as a justice of the peace. The ten rooms are furnished as the Hales might have had them. A Revolutionary War Encampment on a July weekend brings together historic military groups, plus some "Indians," who stage battles, play music and camp out in tents the way it must have been done 200 years ago.

2299 South St., Coventry. (860) 742-6917. Daily 1 to 5, mid-May to mid-October, and by appointment. Adults $4, children $1.

Daniel Putnam Tyler Law Office. Amid the classic churches and homesteads of the Brooklyn Green historic district stands a statue of Israel Putnam, the local Revolutionary War hero. Hidden behind is the one-room country lawyer's office where Putnam's great-grandson practiced from 1822 to 1875. It is maintained by the Brooklyn Historical Society.

Route 169, Brooklyn. (860) 774-7728. Wednesday and Sunday 1 to 5, Memorial Day to Labor Day. Free.

Brayton Grist Mill & Marcy Blacksmith Museum. At the entrance to Mashamoquet Brook State Park, this example of a one-man mill operation survives from a time when water-powered grain mills were integral to every town. The milling equipment employed until 1928 remains in its original location. The fine blacksmithing tool collection belonged to three generations of the Marcy family.

Route 44, Pomfret. Saturday and Sunday 2 to 5, May-September. Free.

Antiquing

Antiquing around the Quiet Corner has long been popular in pockets like Coventry and Eastford, but a major concentration has emerged in downtown Putnam, which now proclaims itself "The Antiques Community of the Northeast." Putnam's antiques district began in 1991 when Jere Cohen restored the old C.D. Bugby department store at Main and Front streets into the **Antiques Marketplace,** renting space to 250 dealers on three floors and producing the largest group showroom in Connecticut. More than a dozen antiques stores quickly followed, stocking an incredible array of goods from tag-sale trivia to fine furniture. Three emporiums in the center of town dominate the scene and draw noted collectors and designers as well as dealers and common folk. On one floor of the 22,000-square-foot marketplace at 109 Main St., Jere Cohen shows the largest selection of antique Stickley furniture in New England at his **Mission Oak Shop.** Down the street, Greg Renshaw owns the 30,000-square-foot **Putnam Antique Exchange,** featuring architectural antiques, furniture, salvage items and other major pieces in a variety of period rooms and cubicles. **Jeremiah's Antique Shops** is all aclutter with odds and ends from various sources in a former drug store at 26 Front St. A handsome former bank building at 91 Main St. has been transformed into **Brighton Antiques,** full of beautiful furniture and accessories, some at rather substantial prices. **Wonderland Books** specializes in new and rare books devoted to antiques and collectibles. Old paintings and reproduction frames share space with a new cafe at **Arts and Framing.** British antiques and books, along with antiques and such hard-to-find British foods as haggis, bridies and salad cream, turn up at **Mrs. Bridges' Pantry.** Poke around town and find your own discoveries.

Heirloom Antiques in Brooklyn is considered one of the area's better shops. If you're into hats and vintage clothing, don't miss **Still Waters Antiques** in Eastford.

Horticultural Sites

Logee's Greenhouses. Push your way through the narrow paths past a jungle of greenery on all sides. On a cold day, seeing and smelling all the orchids and begonias among 2,000 kinds of exotic indoor plants in eight greenhouses will warm your innards. Although this is a thriving commercial enterprise, it's low-key and no one may know you're there. Joy Logee Martin, owner of the 100-year-old family business, is considered one of the great horticulturists in the country.

141 North St., Killingly. (860) 774-8038. Daily 9 to 4. Free.

Martha's Herbary. Martha and Richard Paul moved in 1995 from Hampton to this prime property at the main intersection of Routes 44 and 169 in Pomfret. They have herb gardens outside, and devote much of the main floor of their historic house to a stylish shop featuring herbal gifts and "accessories in and out of the garden." Unusual varieties of herbs, perennials, heirloom vegetables and flowers take precedence, as do workshops in herbal lore and decorating. Martha conducts gourmet cooking classes in her demonstration kitchen.

589 Pomfret St., Pomfret. (860) 928-0009. Tuesday-Sunday, 10 to 5.

Sandra Lee's Herbs and Everlastings. Herbs, perennials and dried flowers are featured at this 2.5-acre herb and plant farm. There are display gardens and a retail shop.

294 Hampton Road (Route 97), Pomfret. (860) 974-0525. May-July and September-October, Tuesday-Saturday 10 to 5, Sunday noon to 5.

Caprilands Herb Farm. Worth a side trip are the 31 theme gardens, shops, herbal luncheons and lectures offered by octogenarian Adelma Grenier Simmons at this herb farm known far and wide. Most visitors book far in advance for the daily luncheons, which start about 11 o'clock with herbal tea and canapés in the greenhouse. Following a noon lecture on herbal and seasonal topics by Mrs. Simmons, visitors move to her 18th-century farmhouse for punch and lunch, where herbs flavor every dish. Dessert and more tea are served afterward in the greenhouse.

534 Silver St., Coventry. (860) 742-7244. Herbal luncheon programs April-Dec. 24, $18. Grounds and shops open daily, 9 to 5.

A Side Excursion

Old Sturbridge Village. Just across the Massachusetts state line lies one of New England's most popular attractions, and most visitors to northeastern Connecticut take advantage. With great emphasis on authenticity, the 200-acre living-history museum re-creates a New England farming village of the 1830s. More than 40 restored buildings were relocated from various sections of New England. Costumed interpreters demonstrate life as it used to be. The meeting-house dominates the common, around which are craft shops, homes and a general store. Although Old Sturbridge is special any time, we like it best in the fall, particularly around Thanksgiving time, the traditional New England holiday. The cobbler and his apprentice turn out low black boots in the shoe shop, their Shaker-style wood stove offering a pleasant blast of warmth on a chilly day. The preacher in Richardson Parsonage polishes up his Sunday sermon, while a teacher in felt top hat and black cape gives lessons at the schoolhouse. Tinsmiths are at work on small coffee pots and pepper boxes that ultimately wind up in the village's large gift shop. You can eat at Bullard Tavern, where a cafeteria dispenses chowder, chicken pot pie and sandwiches. Or snack on cider and peanut butter cookies at the Grant Store and Bake Shop. Allow at least half a day to take it all in.

Route 20, Sturbridge, Mass. (508) 347-3362. Daily 9 to 5, late April to late October; Tuesday-Sunday 10 to 4 and some Monday holidays, rest of year. Admission (valid for two consecutive days), adults $15, children $7.50.

Shopping

South Woodstock seems to be the focus for the kind of stores that appeal to visitors. **Scranton's Shops,** a ramble of rooms in an 1878 blacksmith shop, is full of country wares from more than 70 local artisans. The array is mind-boggling, and we defy anyone to leave without a purchase. Nearby, the **Livery Shops** and **Garden Gate Florists** offer more small rooms given over to floral arrangements and local artisans who show their wares.

Other shoppers like **Cornucopia Crafts** for baskets, **Brunarhans Designworks** for wood furnishings, the **Woodstock Trading Post** for antiques and collectibles, **the David Lussier Gallery of Fine Art,** the **Woodstock Orchards Apple Barn** and the **Christmas Barn,** all scattered about Woodstock.

Hidden down a side street in downtown Putnam is a pleasant diversion from all the antiques shops. **Wade Paris Gallery** at 8 Livery St. looks like a bit of SoHo with its fine arts and crafts. We especially liked the handpainted tables and rockers and the stunning glassware.

Where to Stay

The Inn at Woodstock Hill. The heart of this full-service inn is the 1816 Christopher Wren-style home of Henry Bowen, whose shocking-pink Roseland summer cottage up the road is a landmark. Here are the main living room, a library, the morning/TV room and a small dining room, all outfitted with chintz fabrics, fine paintings, plush oriental rugs and tiled fireplaces. More Waverly floral chintzes accent the 22 guest rooms and suites, handsome and comfortable with

Thrusting gables and vivid facade mark Roseland Cottage.

reproduction antiques and wicker furniture, chairs and loveseats, thick carpeting and modern baths. All have television, telephones and air-conditioning. Six suites offer four-poster beds and fireplaces. A wing connected to a barn leads to a cozy lounge and two elegant dining rooms (see Where to Eat). Innkeeper Sheila Becks and her partner, chef Richard Naumann, serve a continental-plus breakfast. Warm mulled cider or lemonade await arriving guests in the afternoon.

94 Plaine Hill Road, Box 98, South Woodstock 06267. (860) 928-0528. Doubles, $75 to $100; suites, $110 to $150.

Lord Thompson Manor. This luxurious inn set on 42 secluded acres has been nicely transformed from what long was a novitiate for a Roman Catholic order and, before that, the summer retreat for the Providence mercantile family of John Gladding. Built in 1917, the classic stucco English manor house offers three small guest rooms with shared baths and four suites, the latter with full tile baths and three with working fireplaces. For sheer elegance, book the master suite, the epitome of the masculine Schumacher and Ralph Lauren horse and hunt motif. For romance, ask for the Morgan Suite, light and feminine with apricot walls, poofy curtains and a bathroom stocked with fine shampoos and lotions. Guests enjoy a 33-by-20-foot drawing room richly paneled in gumwood, an enormous sun porch outfitted in wicker, peach and chintz, and a downstairs billiards room with fireplace and TV. Innkeeper Jackie Silverston cooks popcorn twice a day for snacks and to offer with drinks from a bar in the manorial living room. She serves a full breakfast, from orange juice to fruit to Finnish or apple pancakes and waffles, on a dramatic breakfast porch with two walls of french doors to the outside. She also serves dinner by prior reservation for $35 a person. Some of the wait staff are singers and may perform a capella at breakfast or dinner. Known for hosting weddings and functions, this is a manor house without pretension and with a laid-back feeling.

Route 200, Box 428, Thompson 06277. (860) 923-3886. Doubles, $80 to $90; suites, $100 to $140.

Karinn. Karen Schirack and Ed Wurzel put seven years of work, money and artistry into transforming a wreck of a house into a grand B&B, with common rooms as photogenic yet comfortable as any we've seen. On one side of a grand foyer is a library with modern leather recliners that invite a long read. On the other are a parlor and a music room, where a leather sofa and leather chairs with otto-mans beckon guests to listen to music aficionado Ed Wurzel's majestic stereo system. The music room opens past a sunny, plant-filled area onto a side deck overlooking restored gardens. Beyond a skylit kitchen and a chandeliered dining room is a cozy, paneled barroom that dates back to the days this was the Old Pomfret Inn. Here you'll find board games and a TV with a library of tapes. Karen, who has a master's degree in interior design, has decorated in eclectic style, mix-ing antiques with a touch of oriental. Upstairs in front are a master bedroom with double bed, working fireplace, spacious bath and the oriental rugs and Thibault wallpapers characteristic of the house, and a double bedroom with fireplace and clawfoot tub, plus an adjoining single room with a fireplace. A twin bedroom and another double bedroom have private baths, and another single room can join the latter for use as a suite. The third floor has the potential for three more rooms, but the couple seem in no hurry. They serve a full breakfast, plus afternoon tea, wine and evening cordials.

330 Pomfret St. (Route 169), Pomfret 06259. (860) 928-5492. Doubles, $80 to $90; suites, $105 to $130.

Friendship Valley. Prudence Crandall, the Canterbury educator who was hounded out of town for teaching young women of color in her academy in the 1830s, named this Georgian-style country house Friendship Valley when it was occupied by one of her benefactors, abolitionist William Lloyd Garrison, and Helen Benson, who were married in the living room. Now the antiques-filled guest rooms are named for the five families to which it has belonged over its illustrious 200 years. Architect Charles Yates and his wife Beverly, transplanted Texans, bought the house on twelve wooded acres to run as a B&B. They offer five guest rooms, all with private baths and three with fireplaces. The prime accommodation is the new Prince Suite, transformed from a wood shed at the rear of the main floor, with a cathedral ceiling, queen mahogany rice poster bed, a jacuzzi tub and a private entrance. Four more bedrooms, one combinable into a two-bedroom suite, are located upstairs in the main house and convey a decidedly historic but comfort-able feeling, from the antique twin beds from France in the Wendel Room to the step-up queensize four-poster in the Benson. Guests enjoy two small front parlors, one a library and the other a fireplaced living room with TV hidden in a cabinet. Beyond are a formal dining room and a lovely sun porch overlooking the gardens. These are the settings for a hearty breakfast of juice, fruit plate and main course, perhaps eggs, quiche, pancakes or baked french toast. Beverly also offers tea and dessert in the afternoon or evening.

Route 169, Box 845, Brooklyn 06234. (860) 779-9696. Doubles, $85 to $125.

Cobbscroft. Tom and Janet McCobb grew up in Fairfield County and lived in nineteen houses – many in New York State – while he was with Xerox, but they chose this rambling white house almost up against the road for retirement. Tom is a watercolor artist of note, and his works adorn the white walls of an airy gallery-parlor. Off the reception-library are a double and single guest room joined by a bathroom, rented as a family suite. Upstairs are three more guest rooms with baths. Janet's charming stenciling enhances a front corner room with a four-poster bed and a chaise lounge. Over the living room is the bridal suite, a wondrous affair with windows on three sides, a working fireplace, loveseat, dressing table and a bed covered in frilly white linens. Two wooden chickens and a collection of lambs are among the country touches in the dining room, where guests breakfast on eggs, quiche or strata at a long table. In the afternoon, the McCobbs serve tea with cinnamon toast or fruit bread and offer a drink. Guests help themselves to brandy in the living room after dinner.

349 Pomfret St. (Route 169), Pomfret 06258. (860) 928-5560. Doubles, $65; suite, $80.

Thurber House. Another local artist, in this case the late T.J. Thurber, lived in this gracious house and the current owners, Betty and George Zimmermann, display several of his paintings on the walls. Elsie the cat parades across the wood floors and well-worn oriental rugs. Three second-floor guest rooms – one in back with a sunset view across stone walls and two in front – share two baths. All have working fireplaces, as do three rooms on the main floor, a cozy family room, a more formal parlor and a dining room with a mahogany table that can seat up to twelve. One of Betty's breakfast specialties is "fancy french toast." Guests also enjoy the view from the back porch.

78 Liberty Hwy. (Route 21), Putnam Heights 06260. (860) 928-6776. Doubles, $65 to $70.

The Felshaw Tavern. Terry and Herb Kinsman were the pioneers in the B&B business hereabouts, opening the doors to their restored 1742 tavern in 1982. He's a Yankee, she's a Southerner and the combination is fortuitous. Herb, a wood-worker of note, did most of the restoration himself. Craftsmen admire his building talents (reproduction furniture and rooms) and guests like the two uncommonly large bedrooms with working fireplaces and private baths. One with a queensize Mississippi rice-carved four-poster is full of fine French furniture. The other con-tains a remarkable Connecticut highboy that Herb built of cherry. Guests can watch TV in an upstairs sitting room paneled in wood. They also enjoy the keeping room/ library, where the remarkable ceilings are made of stained pine, and an adjacent living room full of oriental rugs. The Kinsmans serve a full breakfast in a sunny, cathedral-ceilinged breakfast room that Herb built from scratch. They offer tea or sherry in the afternoon. Guests may lounge on the European-looking terrace or enjoy the four-season garden with a fountain out back.

Five Mile River Road, Putnam Heights 06260. (860) 928-3467. Doubles, $80.

Grosvenor Place. Garfield and Sylvia Danenhower dispense comfort and Southern hospitality in a lovely beige house that has been in her family since it was built in 1720. They offer two large guest rooms with private baths, one adjoin-ing a single room that makes a family suite and the other a downstairs corner room with fireplace. A focal point of the main floor is the spacious dining room filled with silver, portraits and oriental rugs. The living room contains a collection of family pictures, next to a study full of books, a piano and a jigsaw puzzle in progress. Sylvia offers her guests tea or sherry upon arrival. She and her pediatrician-husband serve a breakfast of homemade muffins and rolls, sometimes supplemented on weekends by french toast from a recipe they acquired in Malaysia.

321 Deerfield Road (Route 97), Pomfret 06258. (860) 928-4633. Doubles, $75.

Clark Cottage at Wintergreen. Four light and airy guest rooms (two with private baths) and a family suite are offered by Doris and Stan Geary in their substantial gray Victorian house, part of the old Clark estate. Most coveted is the front corner room, which has striking green painted Italian furniture, including an incredible bedstead with an oval mirror in the headboard, set off against peach walls. Plush beige carpeting enhances a rear room with a sofa, twin beds and a porch for taking in the valley view. It forms a suite with an adjoining room with a brass bed and a wood stove in the fireplace. A full breakfast is served at a long table in the fireplaced dining room. Tea or drinks are served upon arrival.

354 Pomfret St. (Route 169), Pomfret 06258. (860) 928-5741. Doubles, $65 to $80.

Golden Hill Farm. A long, tree-lined driveway leads into the heart of a working farm complex that includes a few farm animals, hayfields and a fledgling B&B overlooking the Connecticut Audubon preserve. Owners Jim and Nancy Weiss converted a 1790 half Cape, formerly the assistant farm manager's house, into a two-bedroom guest house. The ground floor of the building, located 30 feet from their family residence, includes a small living room with beamed ceiling and fireplace, a galley kitchen and a bedroom with queensize poster bed, fireplace and a new bathroom. The upstairs has a second bedroom with twin beds and full bath. Each floor is booked separately, or the entire house can be rented for $140 a night. The Weisses provide the makings for an ample continental breakfast in the kitchen.

389 Wrights Crossing Road, Pomfret Center 06259. (860) 928-3351. Doubles, $75 and $85.

Corttis Inn. There's no other house in sight at this 1758 farmhouse, the focal point of a onetime dairy farm on 900 acres straddling two states. Herb Corttis, his wife Ginny and their two young children occupy his family homestead and put up guests in an apartment-like suite with a private entrance. It includes two bedrooms, a formal sitting room and a dining room with wood stove. The farm's 60 chickens furnish fresh eggs for the full breakfasts Ginny prepares for guests.

235 Corttis Road, North Grosvenordale 06255. (860) 935-5652. Suite, $100 for two, $160 for four.

King's Inn. Best of the area's motels scattered along I-395 is this recently remodeled, 41-unit establishment on two floors. Some rooms contain refrigerators, and one with a kitchen rents for $120. The nicely landscaped grounds include a pond and a pool. Rates include a continental breakfast, a shoeshine and a daily newspaper.

5 Heritage Road, Putnam 06260. (860) 928-7961 or (800) 541-7304. Doubles, $68 to $78.

Where to Eat

The Harvest. A longtime local favorite, The Harvest at Bald Hill, reopened in new quarters in early 1997 at a prime Pomfret location. Peter Cooper, a former chef at the Brown University faculty club in Providence, took over a 1795 house and built a substantial addition. The new establishment focuses on an open kitchen, an adjacent chef's table where the cooks offer the best food of the day for a fixed price, and a floor-to-ceiling wall of wines showcasing the Harvest's award-winning wine cellar at the entry. Around the periphery are a lounge, a grill room with a fireplace, a couple of fireplaced dining rooms seating 110, two dining porches, a cocktail terrace and a banquet facility. Peter described the elegant decor as "eclectic country – just like our food." The menus change seasonally to reflect the name and are similar in style to those at Bald Hill and its subsequent location, the Harvest at Wells Farm in Southbridge, Mass. For dinner, look for main courses range widely from garlic roast chicken to sirloin steak. Bouillabaisse, roast duck and veal marsala au gratin are perennial favorites. The emphasis on the harvest shows up spectacularly in the vegetable and bean sauté, the Pacific Rim vegetable grill and the roasted vegetable roulade Santa Fe. The grill menu offers light fare ($5.95 to $7.95) from a Tuscan lamb sandwich to a duck and asparagus crêpe. At lunch ($5.95 to $9.95), three of us enjoyed good french bread, a shared appetizer of gyoza (tasty Japanese dumplings), sautéed scrod with winter vegetables and two excellent – and abundant – salads, caesar with Thai chicken and tuna niçoise.

37 Putnam St., Pomfret. (860) 928-0008. Entrées. $14.95 to $25.95. Lunch, Monday-Friday 11:30 to 2; dinner, Monday-Saturday 5:30 to 9 or 10; Sunday, brunch 11 to 2, dinner 2 to 7.

A Rural Dining Fantasy

The Golden Lamb Buttery. Possibly Connecticut's most intriguing restaurant is run with verve and personality by Jimmie and Bob Booth. Jimmie, a former Lord & Taylor buyer, is in the kitchen; Bob is the affable host on this, his family farm. He prides himself on the extensive files with photos of diners that might reappear on their table in a lucite frame. He also treats them to little touches like matchbooks with their names imprinted and tales about the 1953 Jaguar convertible, the telephone booth and a totem pole ensconced in the great barn's waiting room. Weekend dinner here is an event, booked far in advance. The evening begins with a hayride through the fields as you enjoy a pre-dinner drink and the sweet voice of folksinger Susan Lamb. Then you pass through the tiny kitchen, probably to a friendly wave from Jimmie, to get to the small and candlelit dining rooms, which – for a barn – are rather elegant in a country way. The prix-fixe meal starts with appetizers, including some knockout soups Jimmie makes with herbs from her garden. There's a choice of four entrées, always duck and often salmon, châteaubriand and lamb. These are accompanied by six to eight vegetables served family style and, for us, almost the best part of the meal. Dessert could be lemon or grand marnier mousse. Add classical music or Susan Lamb's folksongs and a bottle of wine from Bob's well-chosen wine list for a fantasy-like experience. Lunch offers a sampling of Jimmie's cooking (entrées, $13 to $18, like seafood crêpes, salmon quiche or pork stew) without quite the evening magic.

Hillandale Farm, Bush Hill Road, Brooklyn. (860) 774-4423. Prix-fixe, $60. Lunch, Tuesday-Saturday noon to 2:30; dinner by reservation, Friday and Saturday, one seating from 7. Closed January-May. No credit cards.

The Inn at Woodstock Hill. Pink predominates in the pretty dining rooms at this inn, where German chef Richard Naumann presides over the kitchen. The restaurant, located to the side of the inn in a carriage house, contains a small dining room with banquettes draped in chintz and a long and narrow main dining room with windows onto fields and woods. Blue armchairs are at tables set with Villeroy

& Boch china. Dinner entrées vary from chicken piccata to filet mignon with green peppercorn sauce. Specials might be tuna steak with fresh basil, tarragon and dill or grilled breast of pheasant with juniper berry sauce. A few sandwiches and salads supplement a dinner-like luncheon menu, with entrées from $9 for spicy Thai chicken to $13 for filet mignon hunter style. One of us ordered the day's pasta off the appetizer list, a fine dish of ravioli stuffed with mushrooms and a sundried tomato sauce. The other sampled the chicken dijon sandwich topped with mushrooms, bacon and melted cheese, an ample plateful.

94 Plaine Hill Road, Woodstock. (860) 928-0528. Entrées, $15 to $25. Lunch, Tuesday-Saturday 11:30 to 2; dinner, Monday-Saturday from 5 to 9; Sunday, brunch 11 to 2, dinner 3:30 to 7:30.

The Vine Bistro. This contemporary American bistro enlivens downtown Putnam. Lisa Cassettari and Kim Kirker produced a stark white space accented with blond tables (dressed with white linens at night) and large, colorful paintings done by a local artist. Dinner fare ranges widely, from caesar salad (offered with grilled chicken or crab cakes) and pastas to more substantial fare, including veal marsala or piccata and "chicken d'vine" with artichoke hearts, tomatoes, black olives and mushrooms. Grilled salmon and rack of lamb might be among the nightly specials. Quite a selection of soups, sandwiches, salads and pastas, most in the $4.95 to $7.95 range, is offered at lunch. Our party liked the specialty vodka rigatoni, the appetizer of portobello mushrooms sautéed with spinach, roasted peppers, tomatoes, garlic and olive oil, and a generous sandwich of turkey, swiss and whole berry cranberry sauce. Tangerine sorbet served in a frozen tangerine and pumpkin cheesecake laced with cognac were winning desserts.

85 Main St., Putnam. (203) 928-1660. Entrées, $9.95 to $15.95. Lunch, 11 to 5; dinner, 5 to 9. Closed Monday. No smoking.

Vernon Stiles Inn Restaurant. Chef-owner Joe Silbermann's stagecoach tavern – built in 1814 – looks exactly the way a country inn ought to: with a fire blazing in the pub, three cozy dining rooms and a great picture of the inn made with what look to be pieces of tiles. The place was named for one of its more colorful landlords, who claimed that more stage passengers dined here every day than at any other house in New England. The continental menu is well regarded locally, and the historic ambiance is pleasing. Appetizers include brie with apricots and almonds, crab-stuffed artichoke hearts and escargots. Among entrées are broiled scrod, seafood casserole, lobster pie, grilled rosemary chicken, pork dijon, roast duckling, five versions of veal and filet mignon. The weekly "Stew and Story" sessions on Wednesday evenings are a winter tradition.

Route 193, Thompson Hill. (860) 923-9571. Entrées, $10.95 to $18.95. Lunch, Wednesday-Friday 11:30 to 2; dinner nightly except Tuesday, 4:30 to 8:30 or 9:30; Sunday, brunch 11 to 2:30, dinner 4 to 8.

The Vanilla Bean Cafe. Barry Jessurun – with siblings Eileen (Bean) and Brian and occasionally others of their family – runs this neat little cafe in a restored, cream-colored 19th-century barn. You order at a counter and your choice is delivered to one of the butcher-block tables with bentwood chairs inside or, on nice days, to the patio out front, where outdoor grill items also are available. Everything – even tuna steak and lamb kabob – is under $8.50 on the all-day menu, which includes chili, soups, great sandwiches and blackboard specials like gumbos, beef stew and quiches. We enjoyed the turkey sandwich which, the menu advised, is not "that awful turkey roll but the real thing," along with the half and half, a mug of assertive sausage and turkey gumbo and half a roast beef sandwich with the works. The desserts are decadent: rich brownies and hot fudge sundaes, perhaps, or you can order a milk shake, also listed under desserts, for $2.25. The dinner menu offers a large bean burrito, chicken teriyaki with vegetables, smoked mozzarella and basil ravioli, plus a number of specials (most under $10). Beers and wines also are available at this fun-loving, unpretentious place, where everyone from students to farmers in pickup trucks seems to hang out. It's also known for acoustic musical entertainment after dinner on Fridays and Saturdays, starting about 8.

Junction of Routes 169, 44 and 97, Pomfret. (860) 928-1562. Entrées, $5.25 to $11. Monday and Tuesday 7 to 3, Wednesday-Friday 7 to 8, weekends 8 to 8, later on music nights and in summer.

Local Color and Value

Stoggy Hollow General Store & Restaurant. For a dash of local color, the aroma of coffee and a bit of history, stop at this general store where food is a big attraction. Occupying a house built in 1836, it takes its name from the pegged shoes called "stoggies" made in the valley in the mid-19th century. The aura of the old days remains here as burgers, deli sandwiches, soups, salads and more are dispensed in huge portions at prices from yesteryear – $4.35 for chicken fillet on a bun or a tuna melt on an English muffin, $2.50 for a grilled cheese sandwich. Omelets, muffins and pancakes are the fare for breakfast, when Stoggy's hearty breakfast – two eggs, pancakes, homefries, breakfast meat, a bakery basket, juice and coffee – goes for $5.25. Dinner specials are offered nightly, along with quite a selection of beer and wine. There are tables in an expanded dining area inside or outside on the porch where you can watch a different world go by.

Route 198, Woodstock Valley. (860) 974-3814. Breakfast daily, 7 to 11, Sunday to noon; lunch daily, 11:30 to 5; dinner nightly, 5 to 9 or 10.

The Paddock. Everyone locally swears by the Paddock, a nondescript place beside the railroad track in downtown Dayville. One door at the front entry leads to the bar and the other to a small dining room where captain's chairs face formica tables set with red paper mats and patio candles. Crackers and bread sticks with a zippy cheese spread come with drinks, so you probably could skip the few appetizers, which are of the chilled fruit cup ilk. The $1.50 tossed salad is big enough for two. Go for the down-home main courses like broiled scrod, ham steak with pineapple, broiled pork chops, tenderloin tips en casserole, broiled scallops and shrimp scampi. Prices start at $5.95 for fish and chips with coleslaw (Thursday and Friday only); lobster casserole is highest. Prime rib is available Saturday for $12.95. The menu and the prices seldom change here, and everybody seems to know everybody else.

Route 101, Dayville. (860) 774-1313. Entrées, $5.95 to $15.95. Lunch, Tuesday-Friday 11:30 to 2; dinner, Tuesday-Saturday 4:30 to 9.

Light Bites

Fox Hunt Farms Gourmet & Cafe. This specialty food shop par excellence has expanded into a bakery, deli and cafe. An addition doubles its size and provides an espresso bar and tables for some of the goodies served up by partners Linda Colangelo, Laura Crosetti and Lisda Evripidou. Sandwiches ($5.50 to $6.50) include maple glazed turkey with swiss and cranberry, the house favorite. The diverse menu ranges from roast beef with cheddar and horseradish to smoked salmon with cream cheese and, our choice, country pâté with honey mustard. We also liked a warm croissant filled with chicken and red peppers. Among vegetarian offerings is one with goat cheese and sundried tomatoes. Dessert could be chocolate cheesecake or hazelnut-praline torte, accompanied by cappuccino or espresso. A deck out front with ice-cream parlor tables and chairs is used in good weather. The trio also own the adjacent **Fox's Fancy Old-Fashioned Ice Cream Parlor,** offering 24 flavors of ice cream, no-fat frozen yogurt and even no-sugar-added ice cream from April through October.

Routes 169 and 171, South Woodstock. (860) 928-0714. Cafe open Tuesday-Sunday, 10 to 5:30.

Calabash Coffee Company & Fine Food Emporium. The main floor of a 1762 house has been turned over to this casual new eatery. Owner Joel Rosenberg, who used to run a B&B, offers tables for two in three rooms, plus a few books, a few cards and a few specialty foods. Just opened at our 1996 visit, the kitchen was dispensing six sandwiches ($4.75) plus a changing daily special, perhaps smoked mozzarella with sundried tomatoes, radicchio and balsamic vinaigrette on a baguette with a side salad ($5.50). Muffins and bagels are available to go with your cappuccino and espresso. The pastries in the dessert case, among them lemon-coconut squares and pumpkin-ginger tort, looked luscious.

18 Providence Road (Route 6), Brooklyn. (860) 774-8263. Tuesday-Sunday 8 to 6, Thursday-Saturday to 8.

FOR MORE INFORMATION: Northeast Connecticut Visitors District, 62 Main St., Box 598, Putnam, CT 06260, (860) 928-1228.

14    Fall

Covered bridge is a landmark in the Woodstock area.

Vermont Cachet
Woodstock, Vt.

If ever a Vermont town were to be called chic (and how most Vermont towns would deplore the adjective), it would be Woodstock.

Its early stature as a winter resort area prompted it to be called, in a bit of hyperbole, "the St. Moritz of the East – without the Ritz." More recently, National Geographic magazine termed it "one of the most beautiful villages in America."

There's little question of its sophistication. This village of 3,500 obviously prosperous souls spreads out in serpentine valleys formed by meandering rivers against a backdrop of mountain greenery. Much of the village is listed in a historic district, which focuses on a broad New England green surrounded by stately residences and public buildings of the late 18th and 19th centuries. Nary a traffic light, a billboard, a utility pole, a fast-food chain nor a ramshackle building mars this pristine perfection.

Woodstock's prosperity can be traced to its early designation as the shire town of Windsor County back in 1778, before Vermont joined the Union. As the county seat and the early legal center of the state, it was settled by lawyers, doctors, bankers and tradesmen, among them George Perkins Marsh, the 19th-century Congressman credited with founding the Smithsonian Institution and the American conservation movement, and Frederick Billings, railroad magnate and local benefactor. As a stagecoach crossroads and later a railroad link, Woodstock attracted "rusticators" seeking the tonic of mountain air, and Woodstock's duality as a residential and resort community was forever joined.

Vermont's first golf course was established south of town around the turn of the century and the nation's first ski tow was installed on a cow pasture north of town in 1934. That same year, Laurance S. Rockefeller, grandson of John D., married localite Mary Billings French, granddaughter of Frederick Billings. Now Woodstock's largest landowner and employer, the Rockefeller interests buried the utility wires underground, provided a home and much of the stimulus for the Woodstock Historical Society, acquired and redesigned the golf course, bought and upgraded the Suicide Six ski area, bought and rebuilt the Woodstock Inn, opened the Billings Farm Museum, erected a multi-million-dollar indoor sports and fitness center, and gave the property and funding for the creation of Vermont's first national historic park.

The nearby hamlet of Quechee adds another dimension to the Woodstock area's mystique. Busloads of sightseers gape into Quechee Gorge, which its promoters tout as "Vermont's Little Grand Canyon" in the area's only venture verging on the honky-tonk. Among modern-day sophisticates, Quechee is better known as the home of the diverse Simon Pearce glass, pottery and restaurant enterprises.

Woodstock, the cradle of winter sports, is the town with three covered bridges, the town with five Paul Revere bells, the picture-perfect Currier and Ives village. Although it would deny the comparison, its polished sheen may be more reflective of Killington, the East's largest ski resort just a dozen miles up the Ottauquechee Valley, than by its rough-edged Suicide Six and the first rope tow in a cow pasture. Not that Woodstock is in any way glitzy. In the charming downtown area in summer, colorful flowers cascade from boxes once used for gathering maple syrup; in winter, large white Christmas lights bedeck the old-fashioned store facades. And in autumn, the fiery foliage provides color aplenty.

As Sen. Jacob Collamer, confidant of President Lincoln, once said: "The good people of Woodstock have less incentive than others to yearn for heaven." They've already found their portion of paradise. The visitor to Woodstock can share in it, too.

Getting There

Woodstock is located on U.S. Route 4 in east-central Vermont, 14 miles west of White River Junction and 31 miles east of Rutland. Interstate Routes 89 and 91 pass by a few miles to the northeast and east.

Bus service is provided by Vermont Transit Lines through White River Junction and Rutland. Although the Woodstock Railroad is long defunct, Amtrak serves the area daily via White River Junction and Windsor. Air service is offered by US Airways in Rutland and Delta Business Express in Lebanon, N.H.

Seeing and Doing

Woodstock is a place where you can be as active or as idle as you like. The autumn visitor can hike up nearby mountains, enjoy sports aplenty through the Woodstock Inn facilities and even ski at mammoth Killington, which for 36 years has been the earliest ski area to open in the East – the season's start on Oct. 4 in 1996 was not unusual. There are more sedentary pursuits as well, from cultural performances to museums and art galleries to great shopping.

Outdoor Recreation

Thanks to the early environmental interest here and Rockefeller funding, many of the Woodstock area's natural resources have been preserved and are accessible to the public. George Perkins Marsh, America's first conservationist, was born in a cottage on the slopes of Woodstock's Mount Tom. His family homestead was purchased in 1869 by Woodstock native Frederick Billings, lawyer and builder of the Northern Pacific Railroad, who reforested Mount Tom and Mount Peg, built carriage roads and developed Billings Farm, applying many of Marsh's conservation and land-use principles. The Marsh-Billings mansion is now occupied by Billings's granddaughter, Mary, and her husband, Laurance Rockefeller. Their home and 550 acres of surrounding gardens and woodlands, including Mounts Tom and Peg, have been given to the National Park Service for preservation as the new **Marsh-Billings National Historical Park,** paying tribute to Woodstock's and the nation's conservation efforts.

WALKING AND HIKING. Woodstock is blessed with a public trail system

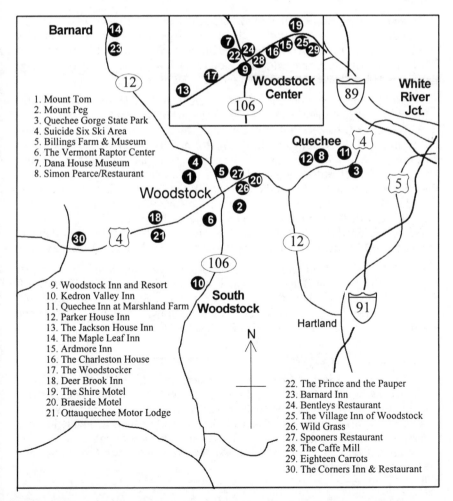

Barnard

Woodstock Center

White River Jct.

1. Mount Tom
2. Mount Peg
3. Quechee Gorge State Park
4. Suicide Six Ski Area
5. Billings Farm & Museum
6. The Vermont Raptor Center
7. Dana House Museum
8. Simon Pearce/Restaurant

Quechee

Woodstock

9. Woodstock Inn and Resort
10. Kedron Valley Inn
11. Quechee Inn at Marshland Farm
12. Parker House Inn
13. The Jackson House Inn
14. The Maple Leaf Inn
15. Ardmore Inn
16. The Charleston House
17. The Woodstocker
18. Deer Brook Inn
19. The Shire Motel
20. Braeside Motel
21. Ottauquechee Motor Lodge

South Woodstock

Hartland

N

22. The Prince and the Pauper
23. Barnard Inn
24. Bentleys Restaurant
25. The Village Inn of Woodstock
26. Wild Grass
27. Spooners Restaurant
28. The Caffe Mill
29. Eighteen Carrots
30. The Corners Inn & Restaurant

close to the village center, part of it on the hundreds of acres of Woodstock Inn & Resort forest lands. From the northwest edge of the village, footpaths ascend 550 vertical feet to the top of **Mount Tom,** where the hardy are rewarded with a bird's-eye view of Woodstock. The easier, 1.6-mile-long trail leaves from Faulkner Park on Mountain Avenue. The steeper Precipice Trail, whose upper sections cling to rocky catwalks, extends nearly a mile from the bridle trail beside River Street Cemetery. A 2.5-mile North Peak loop trail goes off the Precipice Trail. On the south side of the village, a narrow footpath loops its way from Golf Avenue 380 vertical feet up to the summit of **Mount Peg,** an open knoll overlooking the Ottauquechee River Valley, a one-mile hike. A longer trail to the Mount Peg summit covers 3.3 miles from the Woodstock Inn Sports Center. Three marked trails are on the grounds of the **Vermont Institute of Natural Science,** Church Hill Road. The **Appalachian** and **Long Trails** pass nearby.

Quechee Gorge State Park, Route 4, Quechee. Besides the 150-foot-deep gorge that some call Vermont's "little Grand Canyon," the park offers groomed hiking trails.

Guided **walking tours** of the village are scheduled three times weekly in season. Tours leave the information booth on the village green Monday, Wednesday and Saturday at 10:30; cost, $2.50. Guided **hiking tours** up Mount Tom, called "A Walk on the Wild Side," are led by the Woodstock Inn forester Tuesday mornings in season. Hikers leave at 9 a.m. from the inn's lobby; cost, $8.

SPORTS. For a fee, you can golf at the eighteen-hole **Woodstock Country Club,** designed by Robert Trent Jones Sr. on the site of Vermont's first golf course, or at the newer **Quechee Club** golf course in Quechee. The public also may use the facilities of the **Woodstock Inn's Health & Fitness Center,** where indoor swimming, indoor and outdoor tennis, squash, racquetball, croquet, aerobics, whirlpool, sauna and Nautilus equipment are available. Downhill skiing is offered at the inn-owned **Suicide Six,** on the back side of the Gilbert's farm pasture where Woodstockers installed the nation's first rope tow in 1934. Two of the East's premier ski resorts, **Killington** and **Okemo,** are each less than fifteen miles away. Some of the East's best cross-country skiing is available at the 60-kilometer **Woodstock Ski Touring Center,** a seasonal adjunct of the Woodstock Country Club.

RIDING. South Woodstock, home of the original 100-mile trail ride and center of the Green Mountain Horse Association & Youth Center, (802) 457-1509, offers many horseback riding trails. The Kedron Valley Stables, Route 106, (802) 457-1480, offers horse rentals, lessons and horse-drawn sleigh rides. Wagon and sleigh rides also are available through Billings Farm, 457-2221.

Trek with a Llama

Woodstock Llama Treks. For a change of pace, explore the hills of Woodstock in the company of the highly intelligent and sociable llama. Brian M. Powell, based next to the Red Cupboard Gift Shop three miles west of Woodstock, offers a variety of llama treks – breakfast, family, picnic lunch, early evening and romantic (music, flowers and a meal for two).
Route 4. (802) 457-2930 or 457-3722. Mid-May through October. Rates vary from $10 per person to $80 a couple.

Other Attractions

Billings Farm & Museum. This is both a working dairy farm and one of the country's leading agricultural museums. It keeps alive the spirit of Vermont's rural heritage, as evidenced by the purebred Jersey cows (imported from the Isle of Jersey) and Southdown sheep raised here since 1871. The livestock barns show Vermont dairying, past and present. Visitors also can see the horse barn, pet a calf in the nursery, and see the milk room and dairy barn. If you're here for the afternoon milking, you might get to milk a Jersey by hand. Farm animal programs are scheduled daily. Historic varieties of vegetables and herbs grow in the prolific heirloom kitchen garden. Exhibits depict farm life in the late 19th century, from the restored 1890 farm manager's house to the farm office and creamery. Such farm activities as cutting ice and firewood, making butter and cider, maple sugaring and even darning socks, as well as going to school and the general store and participating in community life, are imaginatively shown. Autumn special events include a harvest celebration, pumpkin day, activity weekends and wagon rides. An eight-minute audiovisual program, "A Thing Worth Doing," introduces the museum.

Route 12, just north of Woodstock. (802) 457-2355. Daily 10 to 5, May-October, and 10 to 4 weekends and holiday periods in November and December. Adults $6.50, children $3; family rate, $17.

The Vermont Raptor Center. If you've never felt you're being watched, you may well here. The birds of prey that you're supposed to be watching give the unmistakable feeling they are watching you. Bald eagles, hawks, owls, peregrine falcons and other birds of prey that have been injured in accidents are rehabilitated here to be released to live again in the wild. Birds that have been permanently disabled are on view in a series of huge outdoor flight enclosures connected by a gravel path and interpretive stations that make up the only living museum devoted to birds of prey in the Northeast. Among the more than 40 birds you're apt to see is Vermont's tiniest avian predator, the three-ounce saw-whet owl. Because raptors tend to be among the most elusive species to spot in the wilds, such a venue offers a good opportunity to observe these birds up close. The center is the highlight of the **Vermont Institute of Natural Science** headquarters, high on a meadow southwest of Woodstock. The complex includes a 77-acre nature preserve with self-guided trails, a beaver pond, a display area with live snake, turtle, bee and tarantula exhibits and a nature store.

Church Hill Road, Woodstock. (802) 457-2779. Monday-Saturday 10 to 4, also Sunday, May-October. Adults $5, children $1.

Dana House Museum. This rambling 1807 Federal-style house, its back yard yielding a prospect of meadows and Mount Tom, is the home of the **Woodstock Historical Society.** Built by Charles Dana, a prosperous dry goods merchant, it was home to several Danas who achieved national prominence. On display are paintings, furnishings, photographs, dolls, toys, tools, costumes and other artifacts that bring the history of Woodstock to life. Guided tours are available on the hour. At our visit, a special exhibit was entitled "Look Again: Woodstock Village Life, 1910 to 1965." The museum shop in the rear is full of country memorabilia.

26 Elm St. (802) 457-1822. Monday-Saturday 10 to 5, Sunday 2 to 5, May-October; also Thanksgiving weekend and December weekends. Free.

A Special Place

Simon Pearce. Be sure to stop at glass blower Simon Pearce's fascinating mill beside the Ottauquechee River. Simon Pearce left Ireland in 1981 to set up business in the abandoned flannel mill. The site is inspiring: a covered bridge, thundering waterfall, restored mill and classic Vermont houses all around. The interior has a fine restaurant (see Where to Eat) and a handsome shop offering glass, pottery and Irish woolens, all beautifully displayed, plus a second floor with seconds at 30 to 40 percent off. Downstairs is a glass-blowing area where you can watch Simon Pearce and eight associates turn out 120 pieces a day, a working pottery, the hydro station with enormous pipes from the river and a steam turbine that provides enough power to light the town of Quechee as well as serve the mill's energy needs (melting sand into glass, firing clay into porcelain and stoneware).The enterprise is growing all the time, opening retail stores (three locations in New York, one in Boston and others in Westport, Conn., and Princeton, N.J.), expanding its production capability with a facility in nearby Windsor and adding ventures (furniture, wooden bowls and brother Stephen Pearce's Irish pottery). We defy anyone not to enjoy, learn – and probably buy.

The Mill at Quechee. (802) 295-2711. Daily, 9 a.m. to 9 p.m.; glass blowers work weekdays.

Art Galleries

You can't miss the sculpture of a man walking five dogs, taken out to the sidewalk every morning, in front of the spectacular **Stephen Huneck Gallery** at 49 Central St. Animals (especially dogs and cats) are the theme of Vermont resident Huneck, one of America's hottest artists, who's known for playful hand-carved furniture, jewelry and sculpture. His flying dalmatian and angel-face cat pins and Christmas tree ornaments are affordable "mini-sculptures." The smallest pins start at $10, but you could spend up to $30,000 for a sculpture.

Gallery on the Green, One the Green, showcases some of the finest New England art and the works of more than 40 artists in six galleries. We can't go through Woodstock without stopping at **Woodstock Folk Art Prints & Antiques,** 6 Elm St., which displays many Woody Jackson cow prints and woodcuts of our favorite artist, Sabra Johnson Field, whose Tontine Press studio is in nearby East Pomfret.

North Wind Artisans Gallery is rather avant garde – we were struck by a papier-mâché flamingo, a mirror shaped like a face with hair on top and big earrings, and a torso of a nude male made of mesh.

The Vermont Workshop, 73 Central St., is said to be the oldest gallery in Woodstock, having evolved from a summer workshop established in 1949. Everything from woven mats and interesting lamp shades to wall hangings and cookware is for sale in room after room of great appeal.

Shopping

In Woodstock, **Woodstock Select Designs** displays fine handcrafts and gifts, from Shaker boxes to tapestry bags, framed silhouettes to door knockers, in a little house at 5 the Green. The **Christmas Treasures** shop has everything you might need to decorate. Check out the ever-changing and colorful pottery at **Aubergine,** a small but comprehensive kitchenware shop, where you might find a thermos full of chocolate-raspberry coffee to sample and dips to spread on crackers. We enjoyed some peach salsa at our latest visit. **Unicorn** sells handicrafts by New England artisans and clever cards, games and toys.

You can barely get through the aisles at **Primrose Garden,** there are so many silk flowers spilling from the shelves. We found several nice presents for gardeners here. The **Yankee Book Shop,** one of New England's better general bookstores, has a strong local-interest and regional section up front. Children's books are a forte at the newer and smaller **Shiretown Books.** The children dressed in flannel shirts sitting outside **The Vermont Flannel Co.** looked so real that we almost spoke to them. One of us admired the jewelry and the mini-birch-bark canoes at **Arjuna,** an international store "bearing antiques and adornments from as far away as Sumatra and as near as the Adirondacks." Across Elm Street from each other, **House of Walsh** and **Morgan-Ballou** offer classic apparel for the well-dressed Woodstock woman.

F.H. Gillingham & Co. at 16 Elm St. has the greatest variety of all. Run by the Billings family for 100 years, it's a general store, but a highly sophisticated one – offering everything from groceries, specialty foods and wines to hardware – and so popular that it does a land-office mail-order business. Here you'll probably find every Vermont-made salad dressing, candy, condiment and more. Owner Jireh Swift Billings's young son represents the ninth generation of the Swift family, dating to the 1600s. Next door is the **Village Butcher** where you can get a good sandwich, or maybe a bowl of lobster bisque or chili. There's a table full of maple sugar and maple syrup products.

The **Taftsville Country Store,** 155 years old, is an institution in tiny Taftsville, a blip in the road between Woodstock and Quechee. The things most people expect to find in a general store are in back. Up front are all kinds of upscale Vermont foodstuffs, from chutneys to cheddars.

In Quechee, shops seem to come and go on the three levels of **Waterman Place,** a 100-year-old restored house with a new glass atrium and elevator above Quechee village off Route 4. Antiques-related businesses are a strong point.

Shops of the variety that appeal to souvenir-hunting tourists are concentrated at **Quechee Gorge Village,** Route 4, next to the Quechee Gorge. Tour buses unload their passengers for a quick look at the gorge before they descend on the Antique Center (more than 450 dealers), the Arts & Crafts Center (220 artisans), the Country Store, the Christmas Loft, even a 1946 "Yankee Dinah." For those so inclined, the village may well be "the best of Vermont in one stop," as it's advertised. More to our taste along Route 4 are the **Fat Hat Factory, Etc.,** a small barn full of spirited hats and carefree clothing "for whatever shape your head's in," and Scottish imports at **Scotland by the Yard.**

Where to Stay

Inns and Resorts

Woodstock Inn and Resort. This is the full-service resort to go to if you want everything from sumptuous accommodations to the best recreational facilities. Situated near the heart of town, the inn sits majestically back from the green. The front faces a covered bridge and mountains, and the back looks across a pool and putting green and down the valley toward the resort's golf course and ski touring center. Other leisure facilities include its Suicide Six ski area, ten tennis courts and two lighted paddle tennis courts, an indoor sports and fitness center, and such attractions as sleigh rides, dogsledding and horseback riding. The inn was rebuilt by Rockresorts in 1969 after Laurance Rockefeller found the original beyond salvation. The interior contains a lobby warmed by a ten-foot-high stone fireplace around which people always seem to be gathered, a large restaurant, a cafe, a wicker sun room and lounge where afternoon tea is served, a suave gift shop and a comfy library paneled in barnwood. The 144 guest rooms are among the more luxurious in which we've stayed, with handmade quilts on the beds, upholstered chairs, three-way reading lights, television, telephones, and large bathrooms and closets. Walls are hung with paintings and photographs of local scenes. Many of the 34 deluxe rooms in the newer rear brick wing offer fireplaces, reading alcoves and double marble vanities in the bathrooms. An acclaimed Sunday brunch ($22.95) and a fancy dinner menu are offered in a large and glamorous dining room. More down-to-earth fare is served all day in the Eagle Cafe, transformed from the old coffee shop and more attractive than most in both decor and fare. Richardson's Tavern is as sophisticated a cocktail lounge and night spot as can be found in Vermont.

14 The Green, Woodstock 05091. (802) 457-1100 or (800) 448-7900. Fax (802) 457-6699. Entrées, $19.95 to $26.95. Lunch, 11:30 to 2; dinner, 6 to 9; Sunday brunch, 11 to 1:30. Doubles, $149 to $285, EP.

Kedron Valley Inn. This historic inn smack dab against a corner of the highway in the hamlet of South Woodstock has long been a favorite of the horsy set. Innkeepers Merrily and Max Comins have upgraded the accommodations as well as the dining room to suit their New York tastes, which some find unexpectedly both hip and laid-back. Accommodations include fourteen rooms in the three-story inn, seven in the old tavern building, and six out back in the motel-style log lodge rechristened the Country Cottages. Merrily's collection of beautiful antique quilts, which started with some from her mother's attic in Oklahoma, are a central feature of the decor. Rooms vary in size, and some have canopy or antique oak beds. All have private baths, TV sets and clock radios. Twenty have fireplaces or wood stoves. A collection of old bottles is over the mantel in the much-photographed corner Room 2, the innkeepers' favorite. We liked even better our tavern room, twice as big as the norm with three closets, beamed ceiling, bentwood rockers, a large bathroom, and a four-poster canopied bed with frilly sheets. Overnight guests get their choice of a full breakfast, served in the beamed dining room. The food is highly rated here, with selections from shrimp scampi on orzo pasta to loin of lamb with a shiraz demi-glaze. "Ours is Woodstock's only gourmet restaurant where casual dress is encouraged and there's a kid's menu," says Max. Dinner also may be served on an outdoor patio beneath a striped awning; its sides with screens and plastic can be rolled down and the interior heated to allow use well into the fall. Above the inn is a picturesque spring-fed pond for swimming and ice-skating. Lawn chairs are scattered about to take in the view of cows grazing on the hillside.

Route 106, South Woodstock 05071. (802) 457-1473 or (800) 836-1193. Fax (802) 457-4469. Entrées, $17 to $23. Dinner nightly, 6 to 9; closed Tuesday and Wednesday in the off-season. Doubles, $120 to $195, B&B.

Facing the green, Woodstock Inn is a major presence in town.

The Quechee Inn at Marshland Farm. This rambling white Vermont farm-house is handsomely situated against a backdrop of red barns across a quiet road from the Ottauquechee River as it heads into Quechee Gorge. Built in 1793 as the home of Vermont's first lieutenant governor, it provides comforts like modern baths and cable TV in all 24 spacious, elegantly appointed bedrooms. Reproduction Queen Anne furniture, wing chairs, hooked rugs and several queensize canopy beds convey the feeling of an earlier age. So does the beamed and barnwood great room, where tea and cookies are served in the afternoon, and the rustic, stenciled dining room for breakfast and dinner. The inn is large enough to be a focal point for activity: cocktails before a crackling fire in the lounge, summer get-togethers on the canopied patio, the Wilderness Trails Nordic Ski School in a small barn. The Vermont Fly Fishing School is based here, and guests have golf, tennis, swimming and skiing privileges at the private Quechee Club. Besides a full breakfast buffet, inn guests and the public may choose from a short but sweet dinner menu in the Meadows Restaurant. Recent offerings included seafood gumbo, Moroccan spiced breast of duckling and sliced Vermont lamb drizzled with balsamic syrup.

Clubhouse Road, Quechee 05059. (802) 295-3133 or (800) 235-3133. Fax (802) 295-6587. Entrées, $19 to $22. Dinner nightly, 6 to 9. Doubles, $180 to $240, MAP; suites, $240 to $260, MAP; deduct $40 for B&B.

Parker House Inn. A house-party atmosphere prevails in this inn run by ex-Chicagoans Walt and Barbara Forrester and their teenage sons. The red brick and white frame Victorian mansion with a steep mansard roof was built in 1857 by a Vermont state senator next to his mill (now owned by Simon Pearce) on the Ottauquechee River. Accommodations include four large, high-ceilinged guest rooms with private baths on the second floor, and three newer, less antiquey rooms with queensize beds and modern baths on the third floor. Guests share a small second-floor TV/sitting room and take breakfast downstairs in the sunny bar area (it's served outside on a pleasant wraparound porch overlooking the river in season). Walt, who enrolled at the Culinary Institute of America before switching careers, might prepare scrambled eggs with cream cheese and dill and homemade

sausage, pancakes with maple syrup or frittata. We liked his ample platter of bagels with smoked salmon, cream cheese and all the fixings. We also liked his
wide-ranging dinner fare, priced from $16.95 for curried chicken breast to $21.95
for Maine crab cakes atop a roasted red pepper coulis.

*16 Main St., Quechee 05059. (802) 295-6077. Dinner, nightly except Tuesday 5:30 to
9. Doubles, $100 to $125, B&B.*

Bed and Breakfasts

The Jackson House Inn. New innkeepers took over in 1997 to add luxury
rooms and a restaurant "to take this B&B to the highest level." Juan and Gloria
Florin, former Argentinians by way of Connecticut, were building a carriage house
with four luxury suites with jacuzzi tubs and wood stoves. Another addition was
under construction for a 45-seat dining room to serve dinner nightly to house
guests and the public. The Florins took over a B&B that guests already thought
was really special. "We're not going to change the B&B," Juan emphasized. "We're
just going to add to it." The most choice of the existing accommodations are two
third-floor suites with queensize cherry sleigh beds, Italian marble baths and french
doors onto a rear deck overlooking spectacular gardens and a pond. These and the
nine guest rooms are eclectically furnished with such things as antique brass lamps
on either side of the bathroom mirror, bamboo and cane furniture, a marble-topped
bedside table, an 1860 sleigh bed, Chinese carved rugs and handmade afghans
coordinated to each room's colors. The mirrored bathroom in the Francesca suite
was so sparkling it looked as if we were the first ever to use it. Each bathroom has
a glassed-in shower and hair dryer, but those are about the only modern touches
beyond the idea of luxury espoused by the innkeepers: elegant decor varying from
British Oriental to French Empire to old New England, a library where you can
curl up with a classic, an adjacent parlor in which champagne and wine are poured
and an elaborate buffet of hors d'oeuvres is set out at 6 o'clock, and a high-style
French menu in the $50 price range for a complete dinner. Breakfasts here have
always been extravagant, and the new innkeepers planned to continue their predecessors' menus and tradition. The first course might be bananas in cream or baked
apple with mincemeat in rum and wine. Croissants and muffins come next. Poached
eggs on dill biscuits with salmon and hollandaise sauce highlighted one of the best
breakfasts we've had.

*Route 4 West, Woodstock 05091. (802) 457-2065 or (800) 848-1890. Dinner by reser-
vation, nightly 6 to 9. Doubles, $150 to $165; suites, $195 and $250.*

The Maple Leaf Inn. Unable to find the perfect New England inn to buy,
Texans Gary and Janet Robison took the unusual step of building this Victorian-
style inn from the ground up in 1994 on a sixteen-acre wooded property north of
Woodstock. An architectural engineer by profession, Gary designed the inn on a
computer, and Janet scouted out antiques and reproduction Victorian pieces to fill
it. She also did the remarkable hand stenciling that embellishes each of the seven
guest rooms, five of them equipped with wood-burning fireplaces. Quite large and
luxurious, all have kingsize beds, bedside radio-tape deck combinations, telephones,
televisions in armoires, comfortable chairs and, in all but one of the bathrooms,
large whirlpool or soaking tubs. Guests enjoy a fireplaced parlor, a small library
full of travel books and artifacts from the couple's travels, a wraparound veranda
with a corner gazebo and a cheery dining room where breakfast is served by candle-

light at tables for two. Janet, a former elementary school teacher who coddles each guest as if he or she were the teacher's pet, offers such treats as buttermilk scones, baked bananas with a dab of Ben & Jerry's ice cream, and heart-shaped waffles or stuffed french toast. She also cooks light suppers by reservation in the off-season, serves a zippy cheese spread and crackers in the late afternoon and sends guests off with a personalized wooden Christmas ornament shaped like a maple leaf.

Route 12, Box 273, Barnard 05031. (802) 234-5342 or (800) 516-2753. Doubles, $100 to $160.

Ardmore Inn. The food and hospitality dispensed by owner Bill Gallagher and innkeeper Giorgio Ortiz are the subjects of raves in the guest book at this new B&B. Father Bill, as he's known to Woodstockers, bought the white Georgian Greek Revival house for his retirement from service as parish priest at Our Lady of Snows church across the street. Meanwhile, as an outlet for his Irish hospitality, he takes in overnight guests at Ardmore, which means "Great House" in the Irish tradition. Among its highlights are a solid mahogany front door, circular moldings around the original light fixtures on the ceilings, and recessed pocket windows screened with Irish lace curtains in the living room. The five bedrooms are painted in light pastel colors and outfitted with Waverly fabrics. A couple have fireplaces and one boasts a jacuzzi. All have private baths with marble floors. The biggest is Tarma, Irish for sanctuary, which has a kingsize bed, a loveseat facing a marble coffee table and guardian angels as night lights. Breakfast is served at an English mahogany banquet table inlaid with rosewood. Giorgio, the chef, gets creative with things like pumpkin pancakes, stuffed french toast and vegetable frittatas. Tea biscuits and cheesecake are offered with tea and cider on the rear screened veranda on pleasant afternoons.

23 Pleasant St., Woodstock 05091. (802) 457-3887 or (800) 497-9652. Fax (802) 457-9006. Doubles, $110 to $150.

The Charleston House. Sailing aficionados Barbara and Bill Hough from Maryland run this handsome 1835 Greek Revival townhouse, named for the hometown of its former owner. Listed in the National Register of Historic Places, it is elegantly furnished with period antiques and an extensive selection of art and oriental rugs. All seven comfortable bedrooms and a suite have private baths and most have queensize four-poster beds. The most deluxe are two in a new rear addition with jacuzzi tubs, fireplaces and TVs. One has a kingsize four-poster bed and its own patio. Breakfasts here are feasts. Among Barbara's specialties are chipped-beef eggs, puffed pancakes, a cheese and grits soufflé, and Charleston strata, an egg dish with sausage and apples.

21 Pleasant St., Woodstock 05091. (802) 457-3843. Doubles, $110 to $175.

The Woodstocker. Transformed from an apartment house, this B&B offers a mix of nine accommodations on two floors. They range from an efficiency with two double beds and a kitchenette to a traditional inn room with queen canopy bed to a couple of efficiency family suites, one with a living room with TV and another with a private balcony. All have private baths and most have queen beds. Guests share a living room with cable TV/VCR, games and puzzles, as well as a large indoor hot tub that's popular with hikers and skiers. Adding hospitality and warmth, new owners Tom and Nancy Blackford from Ohio offer tea or cider and banana bread or cookies in the afternoon. A buffet breakfast includes fresh fruit, home-made granola and a hot dish, perhaps cheesy baked eggs or strata, with bagels or English muffins.

61 River St. (Route 4), Woodstock 05091. (802) 457-3896. Doubles, $85 to $95; suites, $115.

A Budget/Family Choice

Deer Brook Inn. A year's hands-on restoration by Rosemary and Brian McGinty turned this 1820 farmhouse west of town into an attractive B&B, one that's particularly good for families. Country pretty in a simple Colonial style, five guest rooms have private baths with in-room vanities and king or queensize beds. All are nicely hand-stenciled by Rosemary, painted in cream colors with Colonial trim and have wide-board floors and the odd exposed beam. The McGintys, who have young children, serve a full breakfast including a main dish like featherbed eggs or baked apple pancakes. The food, good as it is, is almost upstaged by an unusual built-in bird feeder in the back window of the dining room. It attracts a bevy of birds that seem to be right in the room, where they can be observed pecking away at breakfast as guests enjoy theirs. Beyond the bird feeder is a pleasant back yard. Wicker seats on the front porch are good for watching the Ottauquechee River meander by.

Route 4, HCR Box 443, Woodstock 05091. (802) 672-3713. Doubles, $70 to $95.

Motels

The Shire Motel. The area's most appealing motel offers what owners Dot and Vince DiCarlo call the nicest rooms in town. Each different in size and decor, the seventeen accommodations on the new second floor look like inn rooms with four-poster beds, wing chairs and reproduction furniture, plus mini-fridges and double vanities. The white rockers on the common balcony in front of each up-stairs unit appeal, but the deal is sealed by the views out back onto the Ottauquechee River and across the meadow toward the mountains. The older rooms downstairs have french doors onto rear porches or decks for taking in the view. The best view of all is from the reading deck at the far end of the upstairs balcony, overlooking a curve in the river. Coffee is served here in the morning.

46 Pleasant St., Woodstock 05091. (802) 457-2211. Fax (802) 457-5836. Doubles, $68 to $95.

Braeside Motel. Billed as a motel with the charm of a country inn, this good-looking establishment occupies a pleasant hillside one mile east of town. Richard and Patricia Ploss offer twelve rooms with one or two beds and cable TV, but no phones. A pool is an attraction in season.

Route 4, Woodstock 05091. (802) 457-1366. Doubles, $68 to $88.

Ottauquechee Motor Lodge. Located along the Ottauquechee River four miles west of town is this twelve-unit motel. Rooms come with kingsize or two double beds, cable TV, telephones, full baths and coffee-makers. A three-room fireplace suite is available, too.

Route 4, Box 418, Woodstock 05091. (802) 672-3404. Doubles, $65 to $98.

Where to Eat

Among the options are the dining rooms at the four inns detailed above under Where to Stay. The dining experience at each is well regarded, but is of particular interest to house guests. Here we offer a few other favorites.

Fine Dining

The Prince and the Pauper. The addition of a cocktail lounge with the shiniest wood bar you ever saw has freed up space for more tables in what many consider to be Woodstock's best restaurant. Linen-covered tables in the expanded yet intimate L-shaped dining room are flanked by Hitchcock chairs or tucked away in high, dark wood booths that are the ultimate in privacy. Oil lamps cast flickering shadows on dark beamed ceilings. Chef-owner Chris J. Balcer refers to the cuisine as "creative continental" and changes the menu nightly. Meals are prix-fixe, not including dessert. Start perhaps with charred carrot soup, lobster ravioli, Vietnamese spring rolls or lamb sausage in puff pastry. The choice of six entrées might include the signature dish of rack of lamb in puff pastry, poached salmon with dill hollandaise and grilled veal chop with green peppercorn sauce. Homemade bread, house salad and seasonal vegetables accompany. Desserts include an acclaimed raspberry tart with white chocolate mousse served with raspberry cabernet wine sauce. The wine list has been honored by Wine Spectator. An interesting bistro menu, available for $9.95 to $14.95 in the bar, ranges from hearth-baked pizzas to grilled Maine salmon with soy-ginger sauce.

34 Elm St., Woodstock. (802) 457-1818. Prix-fixe, $34. Dinner nightly, 6 to 9 or 9:30; bistro to 10 or 11.

Simon Pearce Restaurant. This restaurant has as much integrity as the rest of Irish glass blower Simon Pearce's mill complex. The chefs all train at Ballymaloe in Ireland, and they import flour from Ireland to make their great Irish soda and Ballymaloe brown breads. The decor is spare but pure: sturdy ash chairs at bare wood tables, which are dressed with white linens at night. The brown and white tableware and heavy glassware are all made at the mill by Simon Pearce and his family. Large windows yield views of the Ottauquechee River, hills rising beyond. An enclosed dining terrace that can be opened to the outside is almost over the falls. The menu changes periodically but there are always specialties like beef and Guinness stew (which is delicious – for $9.25, a generous lunch serving of fork-tender beef and vegetables, plus a small side salad of julienned vegetables). Hickory-smoked coho salmon with potato salad (which one of us always orders) and the skewer of grilled chicken with a spicy peanut sauce are extra-good. The walnut meringue cake with strawberry sauce, a menu fixture, is crisp and crunchy and melts in the mouth. Cappuccino cheesecake and the homemade sorbets also are super. At night, dinner by candlelight might start with Maine crab cakes, cheese croquettes with tomato chutney or grilled chicken with spicy peanut sauce. Entrées could be sesame-seared tuna with wasabi and pickled ginger, chile-cured pork tenderloin with corn and black bean salsa, and grilled leg of lamb with garlic and rosemary. The wine list ranges widely and, naturally, you can get beers and ales from the British Isles.

The Mill, Quechee. (802) 295-1470. Entrées, $15.50 to $21. Lunch daily, 11:30 to 2:45; dinner nightly, 6 to 9.

Barnard Inn. Marie-France and Philip Filipovic from Quebec knew they had a lot to live up to when they purchased one of Vermont's finest restaurants in 1994. But they also had the credentials. The four-star Laurentian restaurant owned by self-taught Yugoslav chef Philip and his wife had been rated by the provincial government the best in Quebec. From their kitchen here comes the inn's longtime specialty, roast crisp duck, done as in the past and teamed with the inn's trademark potatoes, shaped and coated to look like a pear with a clove at the bottom and a pear stem on top. Philip has added more chicken dishes (one is stuffed with small vegetables and served with pickled ginger and turmeric sauce). Lamb is his trademark – we loved the noisettes wrapped in spinach mousse, as well as the rabbit tenderloin served with wild mushrooms, everything beautifully garnished and served on dramatic square plates. Dinner is à la carte. A good value is the five-course tasting menu we sampled for $33 each. The smoked salmon napoleon, a zucchini blossom with lobster and shrimp mousse, a salad dressed with balsamic and peanut oil, and the artist's palette of six intense sorbets made for one of the better meals of our recent travels. Service is friendly yet impeccable in four cozy dining rooms (one with a wood-burning fireplace) of the elegant, late-Colonial inn, whose owners now occupy the upstairs with their young family.

Route 12, Barnard. (802) 234-9961. Entrées, $19 to $28. Dinner, Tuesday-Sunday from 6; nightly in fall; closed Sunday and Monday in winter.

Casual Choices

Bentleys Restaurant. Local entrepreneurs David Creech and Bill Deckelbaum Jr. started with a greenhouse and plant store in 1974, installed a soda fountain, expanded with a restaurant catering to every taste at every hour, added a specialty-foods shop, and then developed the colorful Waterman Place with retail stores and a restaurant called **FireStones** with a wood-fired oven in a 100-year-old house along Route 4 in Quechee. The flagship of it all is the original Bentleys, a casual and often noisy refuge full of potted palms and Victorian decor. For lunch, we enjoyed a specialty French tart ($6.95), a hot puff pastry filled with vegetables in an egg and cheese custard, and a fluffy quiche ($5.95) with turkey, mushrooms and snow peas, both accompanied by side salads. From the dessert tray came a delicate chocolate mousse cake with layers of meringue, like a torte, served with the good Green Mountain coffee. Appetizers, salads, sandwiches and light entrées such as sausage crespolini and petite sirloin make up half the dinner menu. The other half offers more hearty fare like maple-mustard chicken and Jack Daniels steak.

3 Elm St., Woodstock. (802) 457-3232. Entrées, $15.95 to $19.50. Lunch, daily 11:30 to 3; late lunch, 3 to 5; dinner, 5 to 9:30 or 10; Sunday brunch, 11 to 3.

The Village Inn of Woodstock. This wildly colorful lavender inn with yellow trim has three equally colorful Victorian dining rooms with lavender walls and black floral trim. Floral overcloths top the white-linened tables amid carved oak mantelpieces, stained-glass windows and pressed-tin ceilings. The food situation became more interesting in 1996 with the arrival as chef of Stephen Mangasarian, former owner of Carpenter Street restaurant in nearby Norwich. He features such regional American dinner specialties as grilled salmon with balsamic vinegar and lemon juice glaze, braised lobster with lemon-thyme butter on corn pudding, roast poussin with braised vegetables and garlic sauce, and pan-seared scallops of venison with lingonberries. His Maryland-style crab and lobster cakes and a Vermont goat cheese tart with sundried tomatoes and figs make good appetizers. Dessert could be a warm raspberry tart that has your name on it. Besides the interior parlor/dining rooms and lounge, there's dining outside in season in the perennial gardens. On the chef's night off, innkeeper Kevin Clark cooks traditional Italian fare. Upstairs are eight guest rooms with private baths, one with a new jacuzzi tub in the room (doubles, $90 to $135).

41 Pleasant St., Woodstock. (802) 457-1255. Entrées, $16 to $21. Dinner nightly, 5:30 to 9 or 9:30.

Wild Grass. Multi-regional cuisine is the theme of this new restaurant on the lower level of a gallery/office complex on the east side of the village. Chef Paul "Shultz" Langhans, formerly of Simon Pearce and The Prince and the Pauper, offers a short dinner menu, from jerk chicken with sweet potato puree and wilted greens to cioppino served over linguini with garlic-rubbed crostini. Among the choices: pan-seared herbed Atlantic salmon with grilled polenta, "none-too-sober pork loin" marinated in juniper berries, garlic and cumin, and grilled steak marinated in soy and served with smoked wild mushroom jus. Start with mussels simmered in a broth of coconut milk, green curry, lemongrass and ginger, or scallops wrapped in smoked salmon with wasabi cream sauce. Finish with bread pudding with caramel sauce or pear galette with crème anglaise. The cream-colored decor with hunter green and mauve accents is sleek yet simple. Seating is at widely spaced bare pine tables inside an open dining room and bar. More tables are outside on a seasonal terrace beside Route 4.

Gallery Place, Route 4, Woodstock. (802) 457-1917. Entrées, $10.75 to $14.25. Dinner nightly, 5:30 to 9:30.

Budget Food and Lodging

The Corners Inn & Restaurant. The exterior is unassuming and the interior rather plain, for this is an old New England Inn, located seven miles west of Woodstock. But the values are unbeatable, and the food exceptional. Chef Brad Pirkey, son-in-law of the original longtime owners, has purchased the place and is back in the kitchen. His cooking talents transcend the type of restaurant it is, according to his loyal following, who can't say enough about his garlic bread as well as the caesar salad and the warm red cabbage salad tossed with walnuts and prosciutto, both medal winners in the Taste of Vermont competition. The fare is Mediterranean, with an emphasis on Italian. Dine by the fireplace and sample one of the fine pasta dishes, perhaps lobster ravioli or linguini with shrimp, chicken and clams. Other choices include salmon with raspberry glaze served over a pool of smoked salmon sauce, cioppino, chicken pancetta, roast duckling and veal with wild mushrooms. The mixed grill of chicken sausage, pork tenderloin and shrimp is served with Brad's acclaimed grill sauce. Cheese and crackers, fresh bread with rosemary-infused olive oil and mixed salads come with. The dessert tray might have apple strudel and white chocolate mousse in an almond cup with strawberry sauce. Upstairs are five simple guest rooms for overnight guests, with shared and private baths. All rooms come with continental breakfast, and families are welcome.

Route 4, Bridgewater Corners 05035. (802) 672-9968. Doubles, $35 to $45 weekends, $40 midweek. Entrées, $9.95 to $16.95. Dinner, Wednesday-Sunday 5:30 to 9:30.

Spooners Restaurant. The lower floor of the old Spooner Barn, built in 1850 at the east end of town, is now a handsome restaurant. It's all bare woods, dark greens and beiges, with bentwood chairs and inlaid tables in a modern greenhouse section, and velvet-covered benches from the old Woodstock Inn as well as booths made of old church pews in other sections. A classy bar centers the whole affair. Among the menu choices are grilled jumbo shrimp, barbecued chicken, prime rib, New York strip steak and steak kabobs, and there are many combinations (from chicken, shrimp and sirloin to "create your own"). The salad bar with home-baked breads is a meal in itself for $7.95. Starters are of the chicken fingers and mozzarella sticks variety. Desserts follow suit: mud pie, cheesecake and chocolate-amaretto mousse. Spooner's "select wine list" is short and affordable, and you can order a liter of the house white or red for $10.95.

Sunset Farm, Route 4, Woodstock. (802) 457-4022. Entrées, $9.95 to $15.95. Dinner nightly, 5 to 9:30.

For Special Interests

The Caffé Mill. Pop into this new cafe and espresso bar for a Vermont latte ($2.25), flavored with maple syrup and topped with whipped cream and crystallized maple sugar. Owner Tina Sheridan Palmer offers exotic coffees by the pound, as well as teas and lunches (and some delicious looking scones, popovers, cookies and the like). You might find carrot soup with ginger and orange, or panini (an Italian sandwich) with fried eggplant, fontina and tomato sauce. The attractive high-ceilinged, brick-walled cafe has windows onto Kedron Brook outside.

47 Central St., Woodstock. (802) 457-3204. Open daily, 7 or 5 or 6; weekend brunch, 9 to 3.

Eighteen Carrots. This natural-foods store has a deli section with baked goods, sandwiches, soups, salads and a few entrées of the day, to eat in or take out. Sandwich choices include mock tuna, tuna salad with tofu mayonnaise, free-range Vermont turkey, Mexicali spread, veggie pocket and more in the $2.99 to $3.99 range. Try the dairy-free 18 Carrot cake sweetened with Vermont maple syrup for dessert.

47 Pleasant St., Woodstock. (802) 457-2050. Open Monday-Saturday, 8 to 6.

Picnicking

Picnic spots abound, and you can probably find your own, as we did, along a dirt road traversing the north bank of the Ottauquechee River, just across from the covered bridge in Taftsville (at 194 feet one of the longest in Vermont). Less adventurous types should know about the **George Perkins Marsh Man & Nature Park,** a pleasant, shady spot with two picnic tables beside Kedron Brook at the foot of the Central Street bridge, right in the heart of Woodstock.

The Billings Farm & Museum also has a picnic area beside a brook, across the street from the museum entrance. On site, the dairy bar offers drinks, ice cream and a Vermont cheese and cracker lunch.

FOR MORE INFORMATION: Woodstock Area Chamber of Commerce, 18 Central St., Woodstock, Vt. 05091, (802) 457-3555.

15 🍁 Fall

World's oldest cog railway steams its way up Mount Washington.

A High Time

Mount Washington Valley, N.H.

If you stand in the center of North Conway's bustling Main Street and look north – admittedly a precarious venture, what with the bumper-to-bumper traffic – you can, on a clear day, see Mount Washington. The Northeast's highest mountain gives to the valley in which North Conway lies both its name and its spirit.

A rugged peak known for the perversity of its weather, Mount Washington symbolizes the challenge to hardy pioneers who forged roads through the rugged wilderness and settled towns in the valley. Not long after came sportsmen and travelers, for Mount Washington and its companion peaks in the Presidential Range are a real draw.

North Conway, the largest town in their shadow, has long been a center for serious sportsmen and tourists who sought the mountain air, the mountain scenery and the mountain challenge. When we first visited more than two decades ago, we saw hardy climbers wearing hiking shoes and knapsacks on almost every corner.

The hikers and sportsmen still come, but they're more apt to be found farther north – in Glen and Bartlett and Jackson, and at the Appalachian Mountain Club camp in Pinkham Notch.

North Conway has a new identity – as a serious center for discount shopping. Factory outlet stores line Route 16 south of town, forcing traffic to a crawl and often to a halt, especially on weekends in tourist season (summer, fall and winter). Canadians flock to the area for lower prices and taxes. Daytrippers from southern

New Hampshire and as far as Boston come in search of bargains. Fast-food stores on the strip cater to their needs.

Because Route 16 is the one main road north and south, there has been grumbling over the gridlock – even the police in town have taken to bicycles in summer to respond to calls more quickly. The age-old talk of a bypass around North Conway is ever in the news, but never seems to happen. It is needed.

There is still much to enjoy in the Mount Washington Valley, especially if you can avoid the commercial part of Route 16 (take West Side or Kearsarge roads as bypasses around). We love the vistas of high peaks afforded by driving along Route 302 and the Kancamagus Highway (Route 112), along Route 16 north of the village, and along the 16A and 16B loop roads through Intervale and the mountain village of Jackson.

Intervale, a picturesque spot off the main road, seems to have turned every other house into an inn. A quaint red covered bridge leads to Jackson, an alpine-style mountain town, where the houses are tucked into the hillsides and you put your car

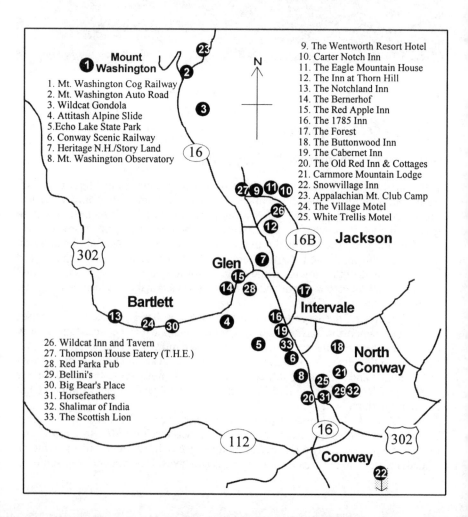

Mount Washington

1. Mt. Washington Cog Railway
2. Mt. Washington Auto Road
3. Wildcat Gondola
4. Attitash Alpine Slide
5. Echo Lake State Park
6. Conway Scenic Railway
7. Heritage N.H./Story Land
8. Mt. Washington Observatory

9. The Wentworth Resort Hotel
10. Carter Notch Inn
11. The Eagle Mountain House
12. The Inn at Thorn Hill
13. The Notchland Inn
14. The Bernerhof
15. The Red Apple Inn
16. The 1785 Inn
17. The Forest
18. The Buttonwood Inn
19. The Cabernet Inn
20. The Old Red Inn & Cottages
21. Carnmore Mountain Lodge
22. Snowvillage Inn
23. Appalachian Mt. Club Camp
24. The Village Motel
25. White Trellis Motel

26. Wildcat Inn and Tavern
27. Thompson House Eatery (T.H.E.)
28. Red Parka Pub
29. Bellini's
30. Big Bear's Place
31. Horsefeathers
32. Shalimar of India
33. The Scottish Lion

302

Glen

Bartlett

16

16B Jackson

Intervale

North Conway

112   16   302

Conway

into low gear to get around. It is also renowned for cross-country skiing; the Jackson Ski Touring Foundation has one of the largest trail complexes in the East.

Except for the towns, most of the area is part of the White Mountain National Forest, which protects it forever from despoilment.

Whether or not you climb them yourselves, getting up and down the mountains is one of the major diversions for visitors. The best-known way to do so is to take the Mount Washington Cog Railway, but you also can go up Wildcat in a gondola or down Attitash on its Alpine Slide. Now that the Conway Scenic Railway has added a train to Crawford Notch, riders on that trip have great mountain views, too.

Every season in the valley has its distinct flavor. In winter, skiers flock to the downhill areas: Attitash, Wildcat, Black, Cranmore and Bretton Woods. Cross-country skiers enjoy mile upon mile of trails, especially at Jackson.

In late spring the hardiest skiers tote their gear up and then ski down the Mount Washington snowbowl known as Tuckerman Ravine, where the combination of topography and climate holds the snow latest of all. Skiing Tuckerman is, for the skier, the ultimate Northeastern challenge.

Summer visitors have long been attracted to the White Mountains to escape the heat, and for more than a hundred years they've made innkeeping a way of life in the valley. The grand old dame of summer resorts is the Mount Washington Hotel at Bretton Woods in Crawford Notch. Even if you don't stay there, you'll want to stop in and look around.

Tennis courts and golf courses are plentiful. This is the season for hikes in the woods and picnics beside mountain streams.

Fall is short and shimmering and, for us, the best time of all. Unfortunately, we're not alone. Our first visit to the valley was on a late September weekend. Since then, whenever we think of foliage, we remember the Kancamagus Highway, a 34-mile stretch through the White Mountain National Forest from Lincoln to Conway. This is a true "high way" where the loveliness of leaf color is enhanced by the vistas over the mountains from frequent scenic lookouts.

In autumn, roadside stands are filled with cider, apples, pumpkins and New Hampshire maple syrup. Cord upon cord of wood is stacked by every house and hostelry and the smell of a wood fire greets you in the evening in virtually every inn, restaurant and lounge. The air is crisp, the sky blue, and the mountain peaks that are often obscured by clouds in other seasons are likely to be visible.

The best two weekends are the last in September and the first in October. Avoid Columbus Day weekend at all costs (no one else, it seems, does). After foliage season, the valley battens down the hatches and gets ready for winter in earnest. The holiday season is also a winner. Whichever time of year you pick, you'll love the valley.

Getting There

North Conway and the major towns of the Mount Washington Valley are located along Routes 16 and 302 in the midst of the White Mountain National Forest. Those approaching from the south can take Interstate 93 to Exit 32 and Route 112, the scenic Kancamagus Highway. Go east to Conway, then north into the valley on Routes 16 and 302.

The nearest major airports are in Boston and Portland, Me. Concord Trailways, (800) 639-3317, offers bus service from Boston to Conway, Glen and Jackson.

Seeing and Doing

Activities in the Mount Washington Valley focus on getting up and down, and hiking through, the mountains that surround it. Most people want to get to the peak of peaks – the summit of Mount Washington – the view that P.T. Barnum called "the second greatest show on earth." Mount Washington is particularly famed because of the wild weather reports issued from its observatory, which is manned year-round. The highest wind measured here set a world record, 231 miles per hour, on April 12, 1934. The lowest temperature was 47 below zero; the highest, a mere 71 above. So, if you're making the trip to the top, take suitable clothing.

Fishing, canoeing and white river rafting are other outdoor activities in the valley. A whole new clientele is drawn to the expanding array of factory outlets and discount stores in the area.

For families, there is everything from Storyland to the Conway Scenic Railway.

The Ups and Downs

Mount Washington Cog Railway. The most well-known and certainly the quaintest way to get to the top of Mount Washington is via the world's first cog railway, which has been operating along a 3.5-mile trestle-track since 1869. The average grade is 25 percent, although one particularly steep portion, known as Jacob's Ladder, rises at 37.4 percent. We have to admit driving to the summit via the auto road, but even if you don't actually ride the cog railway, a visit to the base station in Fabyan is a must. You can get great photographs as the feisty steam engine, billowing and snorting, disappears with its carload of passengers in a cloud of smoke. These are the only trains in the world still powered entirely by coal-fired steam. In the parking area is a display of the original railway engine, Old Peppersass. Depending on demand, up to eight trains a day can be run up the mountain. The trip takes a couple of hours, with a twenty-minute visit to the summit. The summit lodge contains a huge stone fireplace that is usually ablaze (and very welcome) as well as a neat dining area with old wood tables and windsor chairs for coffee, a sandwich or a snack. There's a souvenir shop with stuff like raccoon caps for the kids, little pine needle pillows that smell so refreshing, photographic placemats, T-shirts and a video of the cog railway for $24.95. Also on the site in a separate small building is a funky little museum with history on the cog railway and even a family of stuffed bears.

Route 302, Bretton Woods. (603) 846-5404 or (800) 922-8825. Trips daily by reservation, mid-April through October. Adults $35, children $24.

Mount Washington Auto Road. Opened in 1861, the eight-mile "Road to the Clouds" is used by cars and cycles. You can drive your own car (after which you can apply the bumper sticker, "This Car Climbed Mount Washington") or relax in a van driven for you. This was hardly our most frightening drive up a mountain, but it does have its dizzying moments; the average grade is twelve percent and there are frequent turnouts for taking photos or just taking in the view. The main reminder: pick a clear day or you may not see a thing. The trip takes about a half hour each way, and you should allow at least a half hour at the top.

Route 16, Pinkham Notch, Gorham. (603) 466-3988 or 466-2222. Daily, 7:30 to 6, mid-May to mid-October. Car and driver, $15; each passenger $5, children $3. Guided tours, 8:30 to 5; adults $20, children $10.

Wildcat Gondola. These enclosed two-person cars take riders on a mile-long trip to the 4,000-foot summit of Wildcat, the largest ski area in the valley. From the top you get a fantastic view of Mount Washington; there's a picnic area and some nature trails. Allow about one hour round-trip.
Route 16, Pinkham Notch. (603) 466-3326. Daily 10 to 4, late June to mid-October. Adults $9, children $4.50.

Attitash Alpine Slide. The Attitash ski area continues to expand with nearly an entire village of shops and restaurants at its base. You can take a scenic ride up the Attitash skylift, and follow it with a three-quarter-mile journey down the mountain in an Alpine Slide sled. Spectators can also ride the triple chairlift to visit the mountain's observation tower, with its 270-degree view of the White Mountains.
Route 302, Bartlett. (603) 374-2368. Daily 10 to 5 in summer, weekends until Columbus Day. Adults $7, children $5.50.

Mountain Biking. Lift-serviced mountain biking is available at Mount Cranmore via the Skimobile Express superquad. Other mountain biking options include a shuttle service to the White Mountain National Forest (departing from Attitash Bear Peak).

Walking and Hiking

When you head into the mountains, know where you are going and let someone else know, too. Pick up a guide to any of the many trails in the area and study it before you take off. The Appalachian Mountain Club's official guide to the White Mountains is a must for the serious hiker.

Trails lead off the road from many places in the White Mountain National Forest. Terrain varies from the mild and slightly sloping grades one finds on the ascent up North Conway's Black Cap Mountain to the wild and steep Huntington Ravine Trail, which requires lots of hand-over-hand maneuvering and is not for the faint of heart or ill-prepared.

The AMC Camp in Pinkham Notch is the center of hiking activities and offers many guided day and half-day hikes. There's good reading material and advice to be gotten here. Altogether, there are more than 1,200 miles of hiking trails in the White Mountains.

A tradition at AMC's Pinkham Notch Visitors Center is the Saturday evening lecture, a free program following the suppertime meal (adults $12, children $5). Call (603) 466-2727 for a schedule of programs.

International Mountain Equipment, Main Street, North Conway, (603) 356-7064, has a climbing school with guides who can teach you about ascending the rocky peaks safely and successfully. **Eastern Mountain Sports** is based in the Eastern Slope Inn on Main Street, (603) 356-5433. Check it out for outdoor gear for all levels of hiking and climbing. EMS also has a climbing school.

Cathedral Ledge, Whitehorse Ledge and **Diana's Bath** are hiking destinations reached from North River Road, one to two miles west of North Conway. The summit of **Cathedral Ledge** can be reached by auto – it's an easy drive and then an easy walk to get out to the ledge, which many rock climbers usually are ascending. We enjoyed sitting and watching them come up. The broad rocks are a fine place for a picnic, too. The views are spectacular.

Skiing

In season, **downhill skiing** can be pursued at Wildcat (the most challenging), Mount Cranmore (the oldest), Black Mountain (good for families) and Attitash (the trendiest). A bit farther west is Bretton Woods.

Cross-country skiing is sensational in Jackson, where 64 groomed trails offer 91 miles of touring around the village and in the White Mountain National Forest. There are any number of nifty inns or restaurants to stop at for lunch. You can even take the gondola to the summit of Wildcat and tour downhill via a twelve-mile trail to Jackson, 3,200 feet below.

Driving

Our favorite road for sightseeing is the Kancamagus Highway (Route 112). Others are Bear Notch Road from the Kancamagus Highway to Bartlett, Kearsarge Road from North Conway to Intervale and Route 16 north into Pinkham Notch. Crawford Notch Road (Route 302) is an old road passing mountain cascades and Crawford Notch State Park. Stop at the **Mount Washington Hotel** on Route 302 in Bretton Woods for a look around this beautiful old resort. Site of the Bretton Woods Monetary Conference of 1944, when representatives of 44 nations met here, the great white hotel with red roof keeps photos commemorating the event in the historic Gold Room off the huge lobby. A porch with a view of the Presidential Range stretches across the back of the hotel. You can have lunch at the hotel. The golf course is most impressive, as is the lobby with huge fireplaces and inviting settees.

On the Level

Echo Lake State Park, reached from West Side Road, North Conway, is picturesque. From one bank of its small lake you have a view of White Horse Ledge, sometimes with rock climbers scaling it. The large picnic grove is good for a midday repast in nice weather. There's swimming in summer. Admission, $2.50.

Conway Scenic Railway. The photogenic gold and white Victorian railway station behind North Conway's green is headquarters for steam train rides south to Conway, and north to Bartlett or – the most extensive trip of all, inaugurated in 1995 – on to Crawford Notch. You can ride in an enclosed coach or an open "cinder collector" car. The trip south to Conway takes about an hour. That to Bartlett can be taken at lunchtime or dinnertime and you can reserve a seat in the dining car, Chocorua. The meals, provided by the restaurant, Horsefeathers, have been terrific and we loved our lunch of cold plum soup and lobster salad on a croissant. The Notch trip takes five hours, leaving North Conway at 11 and returning at 4. Back at the station you'll find a snack bar, picnic tables and a gift shop specializing in railroad items. Trains run several times daily in summer and on weekends in spring and fall. A box lunch can be ordered for $7.50. You must reserve ahead for dining car and box lunches. The railway's **Polar Express** is a special holiday train inaugurated, with great success, in 1995. Departures are at 7 p.m. Friday through Sunday for several weekends prior to Christmas and children get to hear the wonderful story, "The Polar Express," as part of the experience.

Route 16, North Conway. (603) 356-5251. Conway trip: adults $8, children $5.50. Bartlett trip: adults $16.50, $25.95 with lunch and $39.95 with dinner; children about one-third less. Notch trip: adults $31.95, children $16.95. Polar Express, $15 and $10.

Heritage New Hampshire. Bob Morrell, whose reputation for wholesome, well-run enterprises seems deserved, is the inspiration behind this venture. A Bicentennial project, it provides a "you-are-there" approach to the state's history via dioramas, talking figures and costumed guides (some of them young adults from England whose accents are all the more authentic). Part of the fun is riding a vintage trolley from which you can trace 300 years of New Hampshire history by viewing a 120-foot-long mural, the largest outdoors in New England.

Route 16, Glen. (603) 383-9776. Daily 9 to 6 in summer, 9 to 5 in spring and fall; closed mid-October to Memorial Day. Adults $7.50, children $4.50.

Story Land. Located adjacent to Heritage New Hampshire, this is another Morrell family enterprise and is it popular! You can barely find a parking space during the summer or on fall weekends. This is an amusement park-like attraction where favorite storybook characters come to life via rides, shows and exhibits. You can attend the Farm Follies Show, take a ride on Space Fantasy, or visit a South of the Border town. Or how about riding aboard a pumpkin coach?

Route 16, Glen. (603) 383-4293. Daily 9 to 6 in summer, weekends to Columbus Day. Admission, including unlimited rides and entertainment, $15; under 4, free.

Mount Washington Observatory. This is a must, serving as headquarters as well as something of a historical museum for what goes on at the top of Mount Washington. Even if you prefer not to go to the top, you can find out about the weather observations and conditions, as well as pick up books and postcards about the Mount Washington Observatory. The observatory also holds symposiums and mounts exhibitions on various aspects of Mount Washington, and sponsors coach tours of the White Mountains on occasion.

Main Street, North Conway. (603) 356-8345.

Canoeing down the Saco River, golfing at the Wentworth Resort in Jackson and playing tennis at Mount Cranmore are other activities. You can rent canoes at several facilities in the valley. Among the local liveries are Canoe King of New England in North Conway, (603) 356-5280, which rents canoes for $15 per day, and the Joe Jones North Shop in Intervale, which also rents rubber rafts, (603) 356-6848. Saco Bound Inc. on Route 302 in Center Conway, (800) 677-7238, rents canoes and kayaks (about $25 per day) and teaches courses in whitewater canoeing. It also organizes trips on rivers and lakes in Maine and New Hampshire.

Covered bridges. There are two covered bridges in Conway. One crosses the Saco River and was originally built in 1890, then reconstructed in 1989. To reach it, take West Side Road north from Route 16 in Conway; the bridge is on the right a short way out of the village. The other crosses the Swift River and is also reached from West Side Road out of Conway. The bridge was restored in 1991. The area's most famous covered bridge is the so-called "Honeymoon Bridge" which enters Jackson from Route 16 as it crosses the Ellis River. This short and photogenic red bridge is the type often called a "kissing bridge."

Fishing. The Ellis River, which runs from Jackson to Glen paralleling Route 16, is stocked with brook and rainbow trout. The nearby Wildcat Brook is stocked with brook trout. The Saco River, which originates in Crawford Notch and runs through Bartlett to Conway, is stocked with brook, brown and rainbow trout and has many calm stretches, riffles and pools for casting your line.

Spotting animals. A good place for spotting deer and moose is the Deer Brook Road area, six miles west of Conway on the Kancamagus Highway. Park at the covered bridge parking lot, go through the bridge, and take the trail to your left. Brake for moose if you see one on the road. Do not feed the bears.

Shopping

The ever-increasing numbers of factory outlets are a great lure for some. Canadians who shop here for low prices, have helped the local economy enormously. There's no sales tax on clothing in New Hampshire. Among the names in North Conway discount stores: **Calvin Klein, Benetton, Banister Shoes, Liz Claiborne, Gorham, Polly Flinders, Eddie Bauer, Bugle Boy, J. Crew, Ralph Lauren** and **Patagonia. Anne Klein, Ellen Tracey** and **L.L. Bean** have factory outlet shops in the same small complex. We've found good bargains at **Banana Republic** on several occasions.

In the center of North Conway, the **Joe Jones Ski and Sport Shop** sells sporting goods for every season. **International Mountain Equipment** also draws the sportsman. **The Penguin** is a great gift shop with lots of ecologically-minded wares and stuffed penguins galore.

The **League of New Hampshire Craftsmen** has a large store in North Conway. The **Handcrafters' Barn** is a large, bright pink house that displays and sells items produced by many different craftspeople. **Yield House,** with its comfortable New England pine and maple furniture and accessories, is headquartered here. Its big showroom is on Route 16.

The **Jack Frost Shop** in Jackson is a preppy and expensive clothing and gift shop.

Where to Stay

You'd probably be happiest staying away from the commercial strip (Route 16) in North Conway, especially if your visit is during a busy season, although we've included a few particularly nice places for those who like to be in the middle of things. You also can stay in Jackson, Intervale, Glen or one of the other areas to the north. These are mountain towns where you'll smell the smoke from the wood fires in the inns and watch it curl from the chimneys on a frosty morning. For the most part we've selected personalized inns and guest houses, but we also offer you a couple of motels that are good values.

Jackson

This mountain village is traversed via a five-mile loop road, off which are located many first-rate inns and resorts.

The Wentworth Resort Hotel. Swiss-born hotelier Fritz Koeppel and his wife Diana, who hails from nearby Conway, own this resort hotel in the center of the village. The east side of the property is bordered by the scenic Jackson Falls of the Wildcat River; to the west, the resort is framed by the eighteen-hole Wentworth golf course. Built in 1869, the large sand-colored clapboard building with striped awnings has turrets and porches and the look of a settled resident of town, which it is. Since its restoration in 1983, it has also become an elegant place to stay. The 62 rooms in the main building and six cottages spread around the property come with private baths and French provincial furnishings. The rooms in the cottages are somewhat larger than the rooms we saw in the main inn, and several of them, with fireplaces, are quite elegantly decorated. Those in the main inn tend to be smaller and plainer. The fireplaced lobby is sedate in taupes and beiges. The Plum Room is a well-regarded dining room. Koeppel's experience with the Ritz-Carlton and Four Seasons hotel chains is standing him in good stead in Jackson.

Route 16A, Jackson 03846. (603) 383-9700 or (800) 637-0013. Entrées, $18 to $23. Dinner nightly, 6 to 9 or 10. Doubles, $135 to $235, MAP.

Carter Notch Inn. Jim and Lynda Dunwell, innkeepers in Jackson back in the '70s, left to enter the retail business. In 1995, the opportunity to fix up the house that had been the original owners' residence for the Eagle Mountain House next door lured them back into innkeeping. The white, pillared inn has been impeccably restored and its seven guest rooms are individually decorated in an uncluttered, comfortable, country style – with lots of crisp blue and white. Five rooms have private baths; two share. Jim is the innkeeper, making full breakfasts and doing most of the housekeeping chores, assisted by his mellow chocolate lab, Tucker. One of Jim's specialties at breakfast, which is served at a large table in the dining room off the spectacular green and white kitchen, is grand marnier french toast. He whips up pumpkin pancakes in the fall. There's a great porch out front and a deck in back for enjoying the countryside. Walkers like taking one of the ski-touring paths from here to Whitneys' Inn on the other side of Jackson.

Carter Notch Road, Jackson 03846. (603) 383-9630 or (800) 794-9434. Doubles, $59 to $99.

The Eagle Mountain House. The front porch of this imposing white clapboard hotel is longer than a football field, and a slew of dark green granny rockers is lined up along it, primed for the mountain view. Built in 1879 and totally rehabbed in 1986, the resort is busy in all four seasons, offering a nine-hole golf course, tennis courts and a heated outdoor swimming pool. There are also a health club with jacuzzi, saunas and exercise room. The old-fashioned lobby with a gorgeous patterned rug and, beyond, the Highfields dining room with its pressed oak furniture, speak of simple comforts. Part of a time-share resort, the 94 rooms, all with private baths, are furnished similarly in a pine country style. A buffet breakfast is available in Highfields; the Eagle Landing Tavern off the lobby is a pleasant spot for a drink. There's a fireplaced game room off the lobby as well.

Carter Notch Road, Jackson 03846. (603) 383-9111 or (800) 966-5779. Doubles, $79 to $129, EP; suites, $89 to $169.

The Inn at Thorn Hill. Innkeepers Ibby and Jim Cooper have been upgrading and redecorating the rooms here tastefully. "We cater to romance and the adult world," says Ibby. Designed by the architect Stanford White and built in 1895, the yellow inn with green trim holds ten guest rooms. The Carriage House next door adds seven more, and three cottages are ideal for those who seek privacy. The Carriage House was redone in 1996; its "great room" has comfortable furniture upholstered in plaid, a fireplace, and plenty of room for guests to spread out. Each room is decorated individually with something of a natural motif, such as butterfly wallpaper or a canoe bedspread. All have wall-to-wall carpeting and private baths.

A two-person jacuzzi and a working fireplace are found in the Forest View cottage. Rooms in the main inn are more Victorian in feel. The attractive dining room with hunter green carpet and walls and oak tables and chairs is renowned for its cuisine (see Where to Eat) prepared by chef Hoke Wilson, who returned to Thorn Hill after a few years elsewhere. The front porch with its wicker furniture is much photographed and painted; at our visit, a guest was working on a pastel of the porch and its mountain view.

Thorn Hill Road, Jackson 03846. (603) 383-4242 or (800) 289-8990. Fax: (603) 383-8062. Doubles, $150 to $275, MAP.

Crawford Notch

The Notchland Inn. Seven rooms and two suites in the main inn, and two more suites in the School House building out back, come equipped with wood-burning fireplaces, a particularly appealing aspect of this hostelry. Innkeepers Les Schoof and Ed Butler keep several other fireplaces, including one in the dining room where breakfast and dinner are served, fired up as well. Built as a private residence in the 1860s, the inn is a many-gabled stone house with gorgeous gardens and a wonderfully scenic stream out back, which has been dammed to make a pond. It is a destination in itself, more than twenty miles from the center of North Conway and surrounded by the White Mountains. Hikers and those who crave contact with nature especially enjoy it, but it's also favored for romantic getaways. Laura Ashley wallpapers and fabrics, thick carpeting, updated private baths and many decorator touches make the high-ceilinged rooms comfortable. Some rooms have wicker furniture; in others you'll find wing chairs for sitting in front of the fireplace. Several on the third floor have been expanded with large windowed dormers done so expertly you'd never know they were additions. Les and Ed were building another fireplaced suite in the main house – "our first jacuzzi room," said Ed, due to be on line in early 1997. A full breakfast and dinner are served to inn guests in an attractive wing that was once part of Abel Crawford's tavern, the oldest continuously used inn building (since 1790) in the North Conway area. The dining room with lots of windows adjoins a fireplaced sun room where guests like to lounge on chilly days. The Gustav Stickley room with games and magazines is a great gathering place; the map on the floor is of the White Mountain National Forest. Bring your own wine to dinner, which is available to outsiders by reservation. It's a two-hour affair with one sitting at 7:30.

Harts Location, Bartlett 03812. (603) 374-6131 or (800) 866-6131. Doubles, $170 to $230, MAP.

Glen

The Bernerhof. Long known for its dining, The Bernerhof also has attractive guest rooms on its second and third floors and some are positively elegant. Of nine guest facilities, six are "spa rooms" and two of these are suites. Spa rooms have king or queen beds, whirlpool tubs big enough for two, and interesting appointments. We liked Room 4 with its brass kingsize bed and a separate raised area in the bathroom for the spa tub, from which a shuttered opening looks out on the bedroom. Quilts on the beds add a homey touch. On the morning of a third night's stay, you're treated to a complimentary champagne breakfast in bed, a popular offering. A full hot breakfast is included in the rates. Innkeeper Sharon Wroblewski

Front porch at The Inn at Thorn Hill offers grand view of mountains.

has turned over the dining room (see Where to Eat) as a separate operation to a longtime chef.

Route 302, Glen 03838. (603) 383-4414 or (800) 548-8007. Fax (603) 383-0809. Doubles, $89 to $139.

The Red Apple Inn. This really is a motel, but one that is handsomely appointed. Out back is a nice outdoor area with playscape for children, picnic tables and swimming pool. Inside is a fireplaced game room and a dining area off the lobby for a complimentary continental breakfast of cereal and toast. Each of the sixteen rooms contains two double beds, phone and cable TV.

Route 302, Glen 03838. (603) 383-9680. Doubles, $79 to $109.

Intervale

The 1785 Inn. Owners Becky and Charlie Mallar are known for their dining room (see Where to Eat) and we're not surprised: the aroma of roasting lamb tantalized us on a rainy afternoon visit. The seventeen guest rooms in the inn, twelve with private baths, are simple and homey. All beds have white or off-white Martha Washington-style bedspreads, lending a not-unpleasing uniformity. Some of the furniture is painted in country style. A pool out back is nicely landscaped and surrounded by a white picket fence. There are a cozy living room with fireplace and a very dark and romantic lounge for drinks before or after dinner. Rates include a full breakfast served in the wraparound dining room with views of the mountains. The old portion of the inn, built in 1785 by Elijah Dinsmore, is one of the oldest buildings in the valley. Outdoors, relax in one of the redwood chairs and contemplate an extraordinary view of Mount Washington and the Presidential Range from an area next to the famed Scenic Vista.

North Main Street, Box 1785, North Conway 03860. (603) 356-9025 or (800) 421-1785. Doubles, $99 to $169.

The Forest. Nine rooms in the main house, two in a romantic stone cottage to one side, and one in another cottage out back form an interesting and inviting complex off the beaten track, on the alternate loop road that winds through Intervale. Lisa and Bill Guppy share innkeeping duties. He does breakfast, cooking hearty items like blueberry pancakes or cinnamon french toast. A pool and 25 acres of land are pluses in good weather. There are hiking and groomed cross-country ski trails, and tennis courts shared with the New England Inn next door. On Saturday afternoons in cool weather, Bill usually fires up the wood stove on the porch and puts out hors d'oeuvres. Rooms are furnished in comfortable, country style. The stone cottage has one romantic accommodation with a queen bed and a wood-burning fireplace. Gas fireplaces have been added to a couple of rooms in the main inn.
Route 16A, Box 37, Intervale 03845. (603) 356-9772 or (800) 448-3534. Doubles, $70 to $165.

North Conway

The Buttonwood Inn. No one just happens past this white inn, for it is off a dirt road that is off Hurricane Road at the north end of the village. But you will be rewarded if you find your way, for this is a good place to hang out and relax. The landscaping and flowers are exquisite and for warm-weather visitors, there's a very nice pool. Nine guest rooms, all on the second floor, are attractively and crisply decorated. Room 1 has a corner gas fireplace whose flickering flames can be enjoyed from the queen bed. The room has wide floorboards and a Colonial checked dark red valance to match the dust ruffle on the bed. Five rooms have private baths; four others share two. From the property hikers can easily get to the Black Cap trail, which, says innkeeper Peter Needham, "provides great rewards for little effort," or to the more demanding Kearsarge North Trail. Peter is the breakfast cook; specialties are "To Die For French Toast" and blueberry crumble french toast. His wife Claudia offers optional dinners for house guests on Saturdays in winter.
Mount Surprise Road, North Conway 03860. (603) 356-2625 or (800) 258-2625. Fax (603) 356-3140. Doubles, $70 to $160.

The Cabernet Inn. Built in 1842 as a Victorian cottage, the cabernet-colored clapboard inn was completely gutted and redone in 1992. Now there are ten guest rooms with queen beds, private baths and air conditioning. A handicapped-accessible, ground-floor room with double shower is particularly spacious and features a jacuzzi tub in the room. A comfortable game room has a fireplace and a large-screen TV. A full breakfast is provided in an attractive breakfast room with individual tables, and afternoon tea is set out on weekends. Sour-cream chocolate-chip cinnamon coffeecake is a specialty in the morning.
3552 White Mountain Hwy. (Route 16), North Conway 03860. (603) 356-4704 or (800) 866-4704. Doubles, $90 to $170.

The Old Red Inn & Cottages. Although right on the main drag in the middle of the commercial area, this is a place apart, a throwback to the old days with an early 19th-century inn and ten cottages. All are painted red with white trim and kept very nicely by owners Winnie and Don White. Winnie was previously involved in an herb business and hangs dried herb wreaths in most rooms; her outdoor herb garden is also fun for guests to check out. Five of the seven rooms in the main inn have private baths. We particularly like the suite with canopied queensize bed and adjacent kitchenette where you can breakfast in front of a picture window with a view of Mount Washington. The cozy and impeccably kept cottages are fun, too. They have one or two bedrooms, and a couple have kitchens. Winnie makes a full breakfast for everyone in the morning. Part is served buffet-style in the inn parlor, with the hot entrée served at individual tables in the exuberantly floral dining room adjacent. From the front porch of the inn, you can watch the goings-on of the village.

Route 16, North Conway 03860. (603) 356-2642. Doubles, $64 to $145. Closed November to April.

Cranmore Mountain Lodge. This white clapboard inn with red trim is set back from one of the bypass roads in North Conway on extensive grounds with a pond and pool. This allows you to stay away from midtown congestion and enjoy a quieter time, but also be close to the Mount Cranmore ski area. You can find traditional rooms, each with a private bath, in the main New England farmhouse inn; modernized rooms with private baths and color cable TV in the Barn Loft, and – for economy-minded outdoors enthusiasts and groups –four dormitory-style rooms with 40 bunks. A full country breakfast is included in the rates.

859 Kearsarge Road, Box 1194, North Conway 03860. (603) 356-3596 or (800) 356-3596. Fax (603) 356-8963. Bunks, $26; doubles, $89 to $99; two-bedroom suites, $170.

White Trellis Motel. If you want just a room – and aren't interested in a pool and other amenities – this squeaky-clean place on well-kept grounds along the main drag could be the ticket. The 22 rooms paneled in knotty pine have one double, two singles, or two double beds.

3245 N. Main St. (Route 16), North Conway 03860. (603) 356-2492. Doubles, $46 to $130.

Snowville

Snowvillage Inn. Located about six miles south of North Conway, this looks like the quintessential New England inn – all red with white trim and rambling, with a main inn plus two out-buildings with guest rooms. Approached by a rather steep road, it's situated 1,000 feet up Foss Mountain; from this perch you get fabulous vistas of the Presidential Range to the north. Especially good views are available from the charming, Bavarian-style dining room, run by Alain Ginistet, a French chef of note. Snowvillage feels as if it is far away from everything – and that's a measure of its appeal. For those who will sacrifice anything for a view, the room to request is the Robert Frost Room on the second floor of the main inn. Once a porch, it is a room with windows all around. All four guest rooms in the Chimney House, and a lobby as well, have wood-burning fireplaces. We also like the room over the dining room known as the Austrian-German room, which has a queen bed and a great view. Once a month on Fridays and Saturdays, innkeepers Kevin and Barbara Flynn sponsor "llama hikes" to the top of Foss Mountain. Llamas from a nearby farm carry a champagne lunch for a group of ten to twelve houseguests. Rooms come with a full country breakfast and a four-course candlelight dinner, which is also available to the public by reservation.

Box 68, Snowville 03832. (603) 447-2812 or (800) 447-4345. Fax (603) 447-5268. Doubles, $169 to $219, MAP.

A Special Place in Pinkham Notch

Appalachian Mountain Club. You don't have to be a member of the AMC to stay at this camp, which appeals to the hiker and backpacker and is often used by families. Located in the midst of the highest mountains, the camp is eleven miles north of Jackson. Trails lead from the busy base camp in all directions, including the summit of Mount Washington. Down vests, parkas and sturdy shoes are the fashion. The place really jumps in the summer and fall, so reservations are necessary. It is open 365 days a year and Christmas can be especially busy, too. Accommodations are bunk-style in spotless, rough pine-walled rooms in the Joe Dodge Lodge across from the A-frame building containing dining room, store and meeting rooms.

In the lodge are a fireplaced lounge with Appalachian-style furniture and a grand piano, perfect for singalongs; downstairs is the cozy Rathskellar, also with a fireplace. Meals are served cafeteria-style in the morning and family-style at dinner in the pine-paneled dining room with soaring roof and fantastic views from the huge window. There's also meal service throughout the day with a chance to purchase snacks, sandwiches, trail lunches and other food supplies.

Pinkham Notch Camp, Box 298, Gorham 03581. (603) 466-2727. Adult rates $35 to $47, including breakfast and supper; $20 to $29 for children, depending on whether you're an AMC member or not.

Camping

Camping is big in the White Mountains and favored sites are those in the **White Mountain National Forest.** Most are available from mid-May to mid-October, on a first-come, first-served basis. Call (800) 283-2267 between March 1 and Sept. 30 to reserve one of the primitive sites – no hookups – offered through the forest camping system. **Crawford Notch State Park** has 30 units in its Dry River campground, in a wonderfully scenic area twelve miles west of Bartlett on Route 302.

A Good Value

The Villager Motel. This good-looking, 29-unit red motel on fifteen wooded acres is away from the madding crowd, and offers a variety of accommodations at very competitive rates. There are queen units, king units, large rooms with two queen beds, efficiency apartments and even a couple of private cottages. All come with cable TV, air conditioning, refrigerator and full bath. Decorating is simple and pleasant. The Riverside Chalet, a private house beside the Saco River, offers a master bedroom, loft with a queen and two twin beds, fireplace and complete kitchen for $129 a night. The location, northwest of North Conway, is good for families who want to explore some of the mountains or special features like Storyland and Heritage New Hampshire with kids. Guests may swim in the pool or the Saco River in summer. Pets are accepted with prior approval.

Route 302, Box 427, Bartlett 03812. (603) 374-2742 or (800) 334-6988. Doubles, $49 to $76.

Where to Eat

Appetites are hearty in the mountains and so is the food. Breakfasts are usually bountiful; you'll probably like it that way, especially if you're planning a heavy day of touring, hiking, tennis, skiing or other energetic activities. Then you'll be ready for a big dinner at night.

The Favorites

Wildcat Inn and Tavern. Marty Sweeney, innkeeper with his wife Pam, oversees the kitchen at this restaurant, consistently rated tops in the area. It combines country charm and coziness with sophisticated dining at rational prices. The Wildcat's blue-gray building is located in the heart of Jackson Village. Three dining rooms offer an interesting mix of furnishings with creative placement of tables, homespun cloths and napkins, and soft candlelight in the evening. The emphasis at lunch is on salads and sandwiches, like one with apple slices on dark bread topped with camembert cheese. In the evening, there are two menus, one for the main dining room and the other for the tavern side, which is more casual and has two huge wood-burning fireplaces. A good selection of specials is available; we found the blackened red snapper with fresh fruit salsa to be excellent. The pea soup that evening was creamy and good. Entrées on the main menu include Wildcat chicken (stuffed with capicola ham and cheese, wrapped in puff pastry and topped with mustard sauce), loin of lamb with garlic-rosemary sauce and a baked lobster casserole topped with a pastry crust. A large salad like grilled chicken salad with avocado, bacon, tomatoes, blue cheese and eggs is a meal in itself in the evening. Sandwiches, salads and specials in the $6 to $9 range are served in the tavern. We liked the sound of the tavern turkey sandwich with avocado, bacon and melted cheddar, and the lobster benedict.

Jackson. (603) 383-4245. Entrées, $12.95 to $20.95. Lunch and brunch, daily 11:30 to 3; dinner nightly, 6 to 9 or 10; tavern from 4.

The Inn at Thorn Hill. With former Thorn Hill chef Hoke Wilson back in the kitchen, the food here is considered remarkably good. The dining room is quite pretty, with dark green walls, pressed oak furniture and pink tablecloths. The menu changes every couple of weeks. Typical appetizers might be grilled garlic and orange shrimp served on a zucchini carpaccio or broiled tomatoes with goat cheese crumbs, served with grilled vegetables. The house salad changes daily. Entrees might be grilled swordfish with a barbecued onion and beaujolais sauce, panfried scallops with mushrooms and grilled endive, and spiced tournedos of pork with tomatoes and figs. We remember fondly a dinner that began with cucumber soup, a basket of herbed sourdough bread and salads bursting with fresh goodies, served with mini-carafes of the house dressings – so good that we sampled them all. Main courses were twin filets of beef topped with pistachio-garlic cream and grilled quail on a bed of peanut and scallion couscous. Grand marnier parfait with blackberries and a chocolate velvet mousse were worthy endings.

Thorn Hill Road, Jackson. (603) 383-4242. Entrées, $17 to $20. Dinner nightly, from 6.

The Bernerhof. Home of the noted A Taste of the Mountains cooking school, the Bernerhof prides itself on its excellent dining room. Actually there are three rooms plus the Black Bear Pub, a dark and European-style bar. A black bear pelt adorns one of its walls. The most requested table for dining is a deuce in front of the bay window in one room, set off by itself, private and romantic. Among dinner favorites are such German-Swiss dishes such as wiener schnitzel, emince Zurichoise (Swiss-style julienned veal sautéed with mushrooms and onions in a white wine and cream sauce and served with roesti potatoes), and beef and cheese fondues. Also on the menu are smoked salmon pasta, roast duckling and Australian lamb tenderloin served with a mint and citrus vinaigrette. You can dine more casually in the pub, where entrées are priced from $7 to $10 and lots of pastas and sandwiches are available. A great selection of micro-brewed beers is offered. For dessert, try gingerbread with vanilla ice cream and butterscotch sauce.

Route 302, Glen. (603) 383-4414. Entrées, $15 to $19. Lunch daily in season, noon to 3; dinner, 5:30 to 9:30.

The 1785 Inn. The wraparound dining room at this inn yields views of the mountains all around. But you may be too absorbed in what's happening on the table in front of you to notice. Chef Peter Willis has earned an outstanding reputation for such dishes as sherried rabbit, curried chicken sautéed with shiitake mushrooms and sundried tomatoes and served over homemade pasta, and a veal rib chop with morel mushrooms in a butter sauce. For an appetizer, you might choose lobster imperial, blackened scallops with ginger-pineapple salsa or caesar salad for two, prepared tableside. On cool evenings, there's a wood-burning fireplace to snuggle up to.

Route 16 at the Scenic Vista, Intervale. (603) 356-9025. Entrées, $16 to $23. Dinner nightly, 5 to 9 or 10.

Thompson House Eatery (T.H.E.). This delightful spot is extremely popular with the locals as well as tourists. The old red farmhouse in which the restaurant is located dates from the early 1800s. There are three separate dining areas, plus an outdoor terrace in summer. Calico tablecloths in deep blue and pink are overset with burgundy placemats and topped with vases of fresh flowers. The cuisine of longtime chef owner Larry Balma has a sophisticated, original bent. As you enter, check the many specials listed on a blackboard. In the evening, the house salad arrives with what seems like a mini-salad bar of toppings in a muffin tin: raisins, sunflower seeds, walnut pieces, poppy seeds. Among the dressings for the good salads are cranberry vinaigrette and creamy dill. Entrées might be shrimp and scallops served on roasted leeks and fennel, chicken and sausage parmigiana, or lamb chops served with a cucumber, tomato and feta cheese relish. Lighter fare includes crab cakes, ham and asparagus melt and a meat loaf dinner ($7 to $8). At lunch time ($5 to $8), the "200 mile limit" is tuna salad on toasted English muffin bread with tomatoes and melted cheddar; "Larry's Bird" is grilled chicken breast served on a bed of greens with "lots of garden goodies." Notchland Dairy ice cream is served at the ice-cream bar out front.

Route 16A at 16, Jackson. (603) 383-9341. Entrées, $14 to $17. Lunch daily, 11:30 to 4; dinner, 5:30 to 10.

Hot and Hearty

Red Parka Pub. Located near the junction of Routes 302 and 16, the Red Parka Pub has proved enormously successful over 25 years. Locals love it, skiers flock to it and travelers return time and again. A young, spirited crew staffs the place, which has a menu in the form of a newspaper. An incredible array of beers is offered, and the bar is always jammed with drinkers and popcorn eaters. Here's where you'll find appetizers like spudskins, Buffalo wings, cajun popcorn shrimp and the Pub-Pub Platter, the last a sampler of spareribs, Florida-style shrimp, jack sticks, garlic bread and Buffalo wings, enough for four people at $13.60. Entrées include chicken or steak teriyaki, scallop pie, baked stuffed shrimp, prime rib and filet mignon. Among sandwiches are barbecued chicken, cajun chicken and the Sir Loin Burger. Everything on the children's menu is priced at $3.95. Desserts are delectable, from mud pie to a celestial cookie (a chewy peanut butter and chocolate chip cookie lightly heated and topped with vanilla ice cream and hot fudge).

Route 302, Glen. (603) 383-4344. Entrées, $10 to $17. Dinner nightly, 4:30 to 10.

Fun for Families

Big Bear's Place. Families love this casual spot and the kids are enchanted by all the stuffed bears that hang from the walls and perch on overhead beams. There is even one with a fishing pole. Chef Barry Williams and his wife Pam are in charge. The front dining room is non-smoking; out back is the fireplaced bar with lots more tables for dinner. The menu is eclectic, with "bear beginnings" like Buffalo wings, ribs, and smoked fish ($4 to $6); and "porridge and pies" such as clam chowder, black bean soup and chili. There are sandwiches and burgers, and entrées might include shrimp scampi, ribs and baked stuffed chicken. We found the penne pasta with chicken, broccoli and other vegetables delicious. Barry's meat loaf on Friday nights is one of the most popular dishes. Homemade desserts are the rule.

Main Street (Route 302), Bartlett. (603) 374-6950. Entrées, $9 to $13. Breakfast in summer and fall, 7 to 11; lunch on weekends in summer; dinner year-round, 3:30 to 9.

Horsefeathers. This fun, young-set spot is favored by college kids and families. The lines sometimes stretch out the doors on busy nights, as much because of the location in the heart of the village as for the food. But you can get almost anything you want, from a burger (beef or turkey) to country chicken pot pie. In fact, the menu is so extensive that it is spiral bound and you have to spend some time going through it. All the bar food is here, too, from "nasty nachos" to cheese-stuffed potatoes. Tempting entrées include margarita chicken, grilled with red onion and cilantro and served on spinach fettuccine in a te-quila-lime-jalapeño cream sauce. Typical desserts are mud pie, pecan pie with butter crunch ice cream and lemon bar explosion (with white chocolate mousse). Dining is on three or four different levels and we rather pity the wait staff who have to be running up and down all the time, but they're young and don't seem to mind.

Main Street, North Conway. (603) 356-2687. Entrées, $10 to $15. Daily, 11 to 10.

Ethnic Fare

Bellini's. Don't be put off by the bright pink exterior. Inside you'll get the best Italian food in the area, especially veal. The unusual decor includes a tiled floor of large black and white squares and a carousel horse mounted just inside the entrance.

The menu is basically divided between pastas and specialties, the latter including chicken and veal dishes, a "catch of the day," eggplant parmigiana and braciola. Clearly the pastas are featured, however, with everything from fettuccine carbonara to rigatoni, broccoli and shrimp.

Seavey Street, North Conway. (603) 356-7000. Entrées $10 to $16. Dinner nightly, from 5.

Shalimar of India. New in 1996, this Indian restaurant was getting good marks. The decor is rather plain in two dining rooms with lace curtains and little white lights edging beams and doorways. Chicken from the tandoori oven is a specialty among entrées. Also offered are many vegetarian specialties such as aloo mutter (fresh green peas in a spicy sauce with potatoes) or saag paneer (spicy spinach cooked with cheese). Lamb curry, shrimp korma (in a creamy sauce) and beef biryani (spicy chunks with basmati rice) are other possibilities.

27 Seavey St., North Conway. (603) 356-0123. Entrées, $7 to $11. Lunch, Monday-Saturday 11 to 3; dinner nightly, 5 to 10.

Miscellany

For lunch, you might try the **Jackson Bistro & Grocer** in the village of Jackson. This epicurean grocery store has a few tables out back for breakfast and lunch. You order at the counter up front and then the food is delivered to you – things like pâté sandwiches, panini, and caesar or fresh fruit salads.

A good breakfast spot is **Peach's** on Route 16 in North Conway, where peach-almond pancakes are a specialty. You can also get corned beef hash, oatmeal, eggs, homemade muffins and bagels.

The Scottish Lion, Route 16, North Conway, has a cozy pub where lots of single-malt scotches are poured and a popular dining room where the chef/owner offers Highland specialties like game pie and finnan haddie. Other entrees ($15 to $18) include seafood linguini, cioppino, beef wellington and foods from the Pacific rim (from several years spent in Hawaii).

The **Shannon Door Pub** in Jackson is highly favored by locals for its pizza and Irish entertainment.

FOR MORE INFORMATION: Mount Washington Valley Chamber of Commerce, Route 16, Box 2300-G, North Conway, N.H. 03860, (603) 356-3171. Lodging reservations, (800) 367-3364.

16 🍁 Fall

Mary Lou Estabrook Photo

Canoeist rides the rapids near covered bridge in West Cornwall.

A Country Sampler

Connecticut's Northwest Corner

"The Hidden Corner," New York magazine once called the Litchfield Hills section of Northwest Connecticut, touting its virtues as a place for city dwellers to make their second homes.

And hidden it is, this rural panoply called the Northwest Corner by its residents and the legions of weekenders and Sunday drivers who have headed here for years from across Connecticut and adjacent New York.

Less than two hours' drive northeast of New York City, the Litchfield Hills region is an unspoiled countryside with more state parks and public lands than any other area in Southern New England.

Much of the land not in the public domain is owned by wealthy residents and visiting New Yorkers, who have made this their weekend retreat. Over the years, world traveler Eugene Fodor settled outside Litchfield, the late artist-author Eric Sloane lived in Warren, playwright Arthur Miller and actor Dustin Hoffman live in Roxbury, actress Meryl Streep and the late writer Harrison Salisbury in Salisbury, Henry Kissinger in Kent, actress Susan St. James in Litchfield, designers Bill Blass in New Preston and Diane Von Furstenberg in New Milford, and politician James Buckley and opera singer Placido Domingo in Sharon.

The state parks and forests are relatively uncrowded and so are many of the inns, restaurants and shops that are supported by weekenders. This is a place for those who cherish nature, quiet times and a subdued sophistication.

Cows outnumber people, and more deer are claimed by cars than by hunters.

Litchfield County's 150,000 residents represent less than five percent of Connecticut's population but are spread across twenty percent of its land area. No town besides industrial Torrington and Winsted has more than a few thousand people.

What the truly rural Northwest Corner has most of, simply, are trees. They line the roads and hillsides and, while you'll see plenty of fall foliage up close, the longer vistas from roadsides and hilltops are infrequent and worth lingering over.

The foliage is best from Kent north and Norfolk west, according to those partial to the far Northwest Corner. The sugar and red maples and hickories dazzle amid the evergreens. Bright red barns dot the landscape, and orange pumpkins grace the

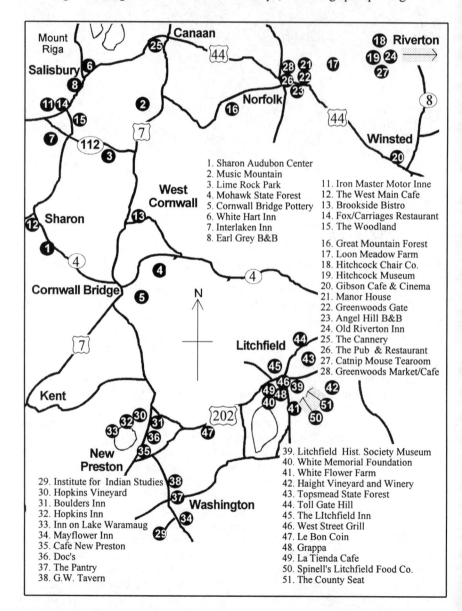

Mount Riga

Canaan

25

44

18 Riverton

19 24

27

Salisbury **6**

8

28 21

26 22

23

17

11 14

15

2

Norfolk

16

44

8

7

112

3

7

20

Winsted

1. Sharon Audubon Center
2. Music Mountain

West Cornwall

3. Lime Rock Park
4. Mohawk State Forest
5. Cornwall Bridge Pottery
6. White Hart Inn
7. Interlaken Inn
8. Earl Grey B&B

11. Iron Master Motor Inne
12. The West Main Cafe
13. Brookside Bistro
14. Fox/Carriages Restaurant
15. The Woodland

Sharon

13

12

1

4

16. Great Mountain Forest
17. Loon Meadow Farm
18. Hitchcock Chair Co.
19. Hitchcock Museum
20. Gibson Cafe & Cinema
21. Manor House
22. Greenwoods Gate
23. Angel Hill B&B
24. Old Riverton Inn
25. The Cannery
26. The Pub & Restaurant
27. Catnip Mouse Tearoom
28. Greenwoods Market/Cafe

Cornwall Bridge

4

N

4

5

Litchfield

44

43

45

7

46 39

49 48

40

42

Kent

41

51

50

32 30

31

33

36

47

202

New Preston

35

29. Institute for Indian Studies
30. Hopkins Vineyard
31. Boulders Inn
32. Hopkins Inn
33. Inn on Lake Waramaug
34. Mayflower Inn
35. Cafe New Preston
36. Doc's
37. The Pantry
38. G.W. Tavern

38

37

34

29

Washington

39. Litchfield Hist. Society Museum
40. White Memorial Foundation
41. White Flower Farm
42. Haight Vineyard and Winery
43. Topsmead State Forest
44. Toll Gate Hill
45. The LItchfield Inn
46. West Street Grill
47. Le Bon Coin
48. Grappa
49. La Tienda Cafe
50. Spinell's Litchfield Food Co.
51. The County Seat

doorsteps of almost every Colonial home and farmhouse. Against the blues of the lakes and skies on a crisp autumn day is a veritable rainbow of color.

The Northwest Corner embraces the estates of gentlemen farmers in Sharon and Norfolk, the remains of the early iron industry in Salisbury, the covered bridges and country stores along the Housatonic River, the Alpine inns around Lake Waramaug, the Indian ties of old Washington, the historic firsts of Litchfield, and the unrelenting quaintness of Riverton.

It's country fairs and flea markets, the Appalachian Trail, the sports-car races at Lime Rock, whitewater canoeing and camping in state forests. It's picnicking atop Mohawk Mountain, visiting a working forest or winery, strolling through the living history of Litchfield, watching Hitchcock chairs being made. And, of course, viewing the fall foliage in all its glory.

Be advised that the Northwest Corner is rather spread out – a collection of "pockets" that extend about 25 miles from end to end. Because even the residents don't often travel among them, we've dealt with each pocket individually. The whole makes up a patchwork country sampler.

Getting There

For a region so close to metropolitan areas, the Northwest Corner seems a bit inaccessible – which is fine with the natives. The only four-lane highway in the region is north-south Route 8 from Waterbury through Torrington and Winsted. Route 7 also winds slowly north-south; Routes 44 and 4 are main east-west roads. All are two-lane highways connected by county and town roads.

Bonanza Bus Lines serves western communities on a north-south axis along Route 7. Amtrak trains serve Danbury, Waterbury and Canaan.

Sharon, Salisbury and the Cornwalls

The homes are larger, the shops swankier and the restaurants more expensive the farther northwest you go. In this northwesternmost corner, the Hotchkiss and Salisbury preparatory schools and cultural attractions have drawn residents and weekenders for the good life.

Sharon epitomizes the region's quiet affluence. Historic estates line Route 41 south of town; some are the homes of the Buckley family and other "Tories" from Revolutionary days, giving the town a Yankee aristocratic flavor. More than 300 houses are a century or more old. The Clock Tower heads the long village green, where the marker says the land is "still much as it was laid out in the wilderness in 1739."

Just a few miles away is Cornwall, considered by some the most photogenic of Northwest Corner towns. Each of its sparsely populated hamlets grew separately among the hills along the Housatonic River.

Sharon Audubon Center. This is one of five National Audubon Society centers in the country. It's as marvelous for its abundant trees and pristine lakes as it is for wildlife (Canada geese, deer, beavers, otters and an occasional bear). A typically large old summer place houses a fine interpretive museum, a good shop and varied workshops. But "most visitors come to walk and to learn about the land and its inhabitants," reports the director. Half of the 684 acres form a natural sanctuary; the other half contain most of the eleven miles of self-guiding trails, two ponds and an herb garden.

Route 4, Sharon. (860) 364-0520. Daily 9 to 5, Sunday 1 to 5; trails open dawn to dusk. Adults $3, children $1.50.

Music Mountain. The oldest continuous chamber music festival in the United States was founded in 1930. Various string quartets from around the world present sixteen weekend concerts in the 335-seat Gordon Hall some Saturdays at 8 and Sundays at 3 from mid-June into September. Jazz and baroque concerts are staged on other Saturdays at 8. Concert-goers can picnic and stroll through the wooded grounds of the 120-acre hilltop refuge. Some of the houses occupied by staff are old Sears, Roebuck catalog prefabs.

Off Route 7, Falls Village (Box 303, Lakeville 06039). (860) 824-7126. Tickets, $15.

Lime Rock Park. Billed as "the road racing center of the East," this is the bucolic setting for sports car races on summer holidays and other weekends through mid-October. The track weaves through 350 acres around grassy knolls on a plateau beneath the hills. Actor Paul Newman has been known to race here. If that and the scenery aren't enough, there often are hot-air balloons and radio-controlled model airplanes doing their thing.

497 Lime Rock Road (Route 112), Lime Rock. (800) 722-3577.

FOLIAGE TOURS. Mount Riga is the generic name for a series of peaks stretching northwest from Salisbury to the Connecticut-Massachusetts-New York junction. Here you can hike the Appalachian Trail, swim or camp at South Pond, visit a restored stone iron furnace, climb Bald Peak or Bear Mountain, or drive (on dirt roads) across the scenic heights of Connecticut's highest area to Mount Washington in the Berkshires. The state and Mount Riga Inc., an association of 90 old-line Salisbury families who summer there, own most of the land, which you reach from Washinee Street, west off Route 44 at the Salisbury Town Hall.

Twin Lakes, just northeast of Salisbury off Route 44, is one of the most scenic places imaginable. Mount Riga and Canaan Mountain are backdrops for these two beautiful lakes dotted with homes and, on the east side off Twin Lakes Road, a public beach and boating area. A drive along Between-the-Lakes Road or an afternoon boat ride are good ways to enjoy the foliage.

Cathedral Pines, a centuries-old stand of gigantic pines near the foot of the Mohawk Mt. ski area, was reduced almost to rubble by a tornado. Drive along winding Essex Hill Road from the ski area access road to see the devastation, just as nature left it, and the regrowth. You come out of the spiked forest into an open field where cows graze; just beyond is Marvelwood School and Cornwall Center. An historic marker advises that writer Mark Van Doren "enriched many lives from his Cornwall home."

Mohawk State Forest atop 1,683-foot Mohawk Mountain in Cornwall is perfect for foliage viewing. Drive in from Route 4, past a couple of scenic overlooks with sweeping vistas to the west. About two and a half miles in is a wooden observation tower with 35 steep steps, which you can climb for a panoramic view in all directions.

RIVER EXPEDITIONS. Increasingly popular pastimes on the Housatonic River are canoeing, kayaking and rafting, both whitewater and flatwater varieties. On weekends from March through October, more than 400 canoes and kayaks have been counted in the 45-mile stretch from Sheffield, Mass., south to Kent – most concentrated in the twelve miles between Falls Village and Cornwall Bridge. The folks at **Clarke Outdoors** at 163 Route 7 in West Cornwall, (860) 672-6365, one mile south of the covered bridge, say there's no better way to view the foliage than from a canoe going down the river. Many canoeists take picnic lunches; family outings are popular, and you can get instruction, hire guides and obtain shuttle service back to your car. The standard trip takes three or four hours and canoes or kayaks can be rented by the day. Similar services are offered by **Riverrunning Expeditions,** Main Street, Falls Village, (860) 824-5579.

Cornwall Bridge Pottery. Todd Piker, the noted potter here, is helped by apprentices from everywhere. The showroom is lined with functional but beautiful and honest pottery, from tiny creamers to lamps and pots that seem too big to use for anything. Many are decorated with birds and fish. Early American, English Country and T'zu Chou are inspirations for Piker, who studied in England with the late Michael Cardew. The pottery behind his home is open daily. Upstairs above his retail showroom in West Cornwall is the **Covered Bridge Gallery,** a large space leased to craftsmen in a manner similar to an antiques center. We admired the furniture of Jonathan Gardner Steucek (a curly maple tea table was especially fine), handknit sweaters and mittens, and beautiful blown glass. Decoys, carved animals and some sensational amber jewelry caught our eye downstairs. New at the rear of the showroom is **Housatonic River Outfitters,** a full-service fly-fishing shop and outfitter. Proprietor Harold McMillan galvanizes interest in protecting the upper Housatonic as the premier trout river in New England.
    Route 7, one-half mile south of Cornwall Bridge. (860) 672-6545. Pottery, daily 9 to 5; West Cornwall showroom, Wednesday-Monday 10:30 to 5:30.

Room and Board

White Hart Inn. A wide white porch full of wicker and chintz fronts the venerable White Hart Inn, several times abandoned but now handsomely restored by Terry and Juliet Moore, owners of the Old Mill restaurant in nearby South Egremont, Mass. Given their track record, we knew the food would be first-rate, but the overnight accommodations turned out first-rate as well. The Moores have reduced the original 33 rooms to 26, all with private baths. Three are suites, six contain two double beds and most of the rest have queensize canopy four-poster beds. Mahogany reproduction furniture, TV sets in armoires and vivid floral wallpapers with matching comforters are the rule. The main-floor public rooms are showplaces, particularly the clubby Hunt Room with a library, bar and piano. In the convivial **Tap Room,** sandwiches, pizzas and light entrées are in the $7.50 to $15 range at lunch and dinner. Breakfast is offered in the airy **Garden Room,** where upholstered rattan chairs flank white faux-marble tables. A friend of the Moores did the paintings of fruits and vegetables that grace the walls of **The American Grill,** the serene and elegant main dining room with sponged walls of peach over green. Chef Robert Corliss features a contemporary American menu at affordable prices. For dinner, expect main courses like grilled medallions of monkfish with crabmeat and saffron sauce, garlic roasted chicken with soft polenta, and New York strip steak with mushroom ragoût. Start with grilled pizza, vegetable spring rolls or a pear, arugula and fennel salad with maytag blue cheese. Finish with a ricotta-lemon tart with honey-fig-caramel sauce.

The Village Green, Box 385, Salisbury 06068. (860) 435-0030. Doubles, $90 to $190, EP. Entrées $16 to $19. Dinner in Grill, Wednesday-Sunday from 5:30. Lunch daily in Tap Room, 11:30 to 2:30, weekends to 5; dinner nightly, 5 to 9:30 or 10:30.

Interlaken Inn. Built in 1973, this modern resort and conference center is situated around the corner from the Hotchkiss School between Long Pond and Lake Wononskopomuc (pronounce that! – accent second syllable), which give the inn and village their names. Guests may take out a canoe or rowboat or swim in the lovely clear lake; there's also a large heated pool. The main inn is contemporary with a slate floor and leather sofas in the lobby; its 55 deluxe motel-style rooms are crisply decorated. Sunnyside, a shingled rear building which is all that is left of the original New England inn on the site, has ten rooms with brass beds and fine antiques. Contemporary buildings contain seven one-bedroom townhouse suites, each with fireplace, kitchen, dining area and one and a half baths. Tennis, a sauna, a game room and golf privileges at Hotchkiss's nine-hole course are available. Breakfast is offered buffet-style. At dinner, continental entrées (from $14.95 for lemon sole meunière to $23.95 for rack of lamb persillade) are served in the stylish **Vineyard** dining room, with its wildly colorful purple chairs, purple napkins and large ficus trees strung with tiny white lights. In season, lunch and dinner are served outside near the pool on an awning-covered deck with wrought-iron furniture and globe lights. The lounge offers dancing at night.

74 Interlaken Road (Route 112), Lakeville 06039. (860) 435-9878 or (800) 222-2909. Fax (860) 435-2980. Doubles, $109 to $169, EP; suites, $265, EP.

Earl Grey Bed & Breakfast. The imposing Chittenden House on a hillside behind the Town Hall and town lockup has been opened as a B&B by well-traveled owners Patricia and Dick Boyle. He's a former art museum director in Philadelphia and still teaches at Temple University. They ran a B&B in Philadelphia and named it for a family cat. Retaining the name here, they share their home with guests in two antiques-filled bedrooms, both with private baths. One on the main floor with a queensize four-poster bed and a fireplace opens onto a private terrace. The other, upstairs, has an oversize sleigh bed. Patricia serves a full breakfast, perhaps apple pancakes or eggs benedict, at an antique marble table in her country kitchen. It opens into a living room furnished in contemporary style and a side porch.

9 Lockup, Box 177, Salisbury 06068. (860) 435-1007. Doubles, $135 and $150.

Iron Masters Motor Inne. This attractive, 26-unit motel is set back from the highway over the old Davis Ore Mine. Each carpeted unit has two double beds and all rooms have been refurbished with Ethan Allen furniture, Laura Ashley wallpaper and fabrics, and new bathroom fixtures. The stone fireplace in the lobby dates to the 18th century and is usually ablaze for a complimentary continental-plus breakfast, which is served at tables nearby. Guests enjoy swimming in a pool in a nicely landscaped garden area.

229 Main St. (Route 44), Lakeville 06039. (860) 435-9844. Fax (860) 435-2254. Doubles, $125 to $135.

Restaurants

The West Main Cafe. This intimate little cafe in a small house is the domain of talented young chef Matthew Fahrner and partner Susan Miller. They offer a short menu of tantalizing treats marked by bold Asian flavors. Expect appetizers like dynamite vegetable rolls with pickled cucumber salad, and sautéed oysters and leeks with black pepper brioche in garlic cream, both sensational. For lunch, we made a meal of these plus an Asian chicken salad piled high with wontons and peanuts, followed by a melt-in-the-mouth banana napoleon. Dinner brings such assertive fare as codfish with wasabi and orange-ginger sauce, Moroccan spiced salmon with curry and ginger, and grilled herb-encrusted pork loin with roasted garlic. Susan's refreshing desserts include bread pudding with currants and caramel sauce, ginger crème brûlée and chocolate silk ice cream. The 40-seat dining room is snug and simple, with white butcher paper covering the tables and glass service plates of assorted pastel colors. The rest of the color comes from the kitchen. *13 West Main St., Sharon. (860) 364-9888. Entrées, $15.95 to $17.95. Lunch, Thursday-Monday 11:30 to 2:30; dinner, Thursday-Monday 5:30 to 9 or 10. Also Wednesday in summer.*

Brookside Bistro. Country French food is featured in this true place with a great outdoor deck beside a waterfall. The L-shaped dining room is rich looking with green walls, rust-colored banquettes and heavy pine tables set with cloth mats. Proprietor Charles Cilona, a West Cornwall native who came home from California, patrols the front of the house. Chef Guy Birster from Dijon mans the kitchen, turning out a short menu of superb, unfussy dishes. Main courses at our visit were poached halibut with mustard sauce, steamed mussels, roasted poussin with portobello mushrooms, braised lamb shank with white beans, grilled ribeye steak with gorgonzola sauce and pommes frites and, for the vegetarians, eggplant terrine. That's all. You could start with escargots, brie en croûte, or one of four salads. The pastry case near the front door is laden with dessert treats: charlotte russe, tarte tatin, hazelnut cheesecake and chocolate pâté, among them. The wrap-around screened deck above the roaring brook is popular for lunch ($5.95 to $12.95), when the fare might be coq au vin or warm potato salad with marinated herring. *Route 128, West Cornwall. (860) 672-6601. Entrées, $11.95 to $16.95. Lunch, Wednesday-Saturday noon to 2, Sunday to 2:30; dinner, Wednesday-Saturday 6 to 9, Sunday 5:30 to 8.*

James Fox/Carriages Restaurant. The automobile theme of this restaurant in a onetime miner's cottage at the Iron Masters Motor Inne has been toned down by new proprietor James Fox, who attracted a culinary following from his earlier days at Fox & Fox Restaurant near Kent. He retained some of the glass tables inset with little car models, but eliminated the adult theme-park atmosphere. He then scattered oriental rugs on the floors of the two-story Carriage Room and the garden solarium. The food is highly regarded locally. Three versions of chicken are featured on the short dinner menu, which ranges from linguini with mussels posilipo to New York strip steak with mushrooms and onions. Appetizers include cajun and beer battered-shrimp, cheddar potato skins with spicy chicken wings, and vegetable spring rolls. You also can order a crisp-crust pizza, burgers or grilled chicken sandwich for $7.25 to $8.25. *227 Main St., Lakeville. (860) 435-8892. Entrées, $11.25 to $16.95. Lunch, 11:30 to 2:30; dinner, 5:30 to 9 or 10. Closed Tuesday.*

The Woodland. Once a coffee shop, this has been upscaled considerably and is locally favored for consistently good food. It's small and modern-looking inside, with beehive lights over the booths, interesting woven placemats, an abundance of fresh flowers and a small lounge. The artwork on the walls is done by the sisters of owner Carol Peters. Lunch salads, sandwiches and entrées cost $6.50 to $11.95 (for an open steak sandwich or sautéed fillet of sole). The roster of entrées expands at night, and some lunch items are available. A blackboard lists many daily specials – perhaps grilled swordfish with tabouli and caponata, shrimp and scallops on linguini, stir-fried imperial beef, and macadamia-nut crusted chicken with pineapple-mango salsa. Carol is the daughter of Anthony Peters, former owner of the Interlaken Inn, so she knows the hospitality business, and her brother Robert is the chef.

Route 41, Lakeville. (860) 435-0578. Entrées, $13.95 to $18.95. Lunch, Tuesday-Saturday 11:30 to 2:30; dinner, 5:30 to 9 or 10, Sunday to 8:30. Closed Monday.

Shopping

Salisbury offers a variety of shopping in a small area, which is fine for ambling around on a fall afternoon and for early Christmas shopping. Stunning ornaments and other must-have Christmas things are on display with decorative accessories and toys at **Garlande Ltd.,** a fabulous shop near the White Hart Inn. **House of Walsh** stocks the kind of men's and women's clothing that someone with a country home in this area would likely wear, plus a selection of gifts and accessories. **Riga Traders** is an amazing ramble of whimsical themed rooms carrying items related to golf, fly-fishing and children, among others – everything from home accents to folk art to sweaters and ties. Check out the ceramics, jewelry and stuffed animals at **Windemere,** an American crafts store in the Marketplace behind the bank. The place to pick up baked goods and dinner foods, from baguettes to crab cakes, is **Harvest Bakery & Prepared Foods** at 10 Academy St.; there are a handful of tables for eating, but many weekenders seem to take out. Across the street is **Amandari,** a one-of-a-kind shop stocking what it calls "small luxuries" made mainly of mahogany. Farther along Academy is **Pink Cloud Gallery,** where we admired the great wind socks and interesting clocks, one shaped like a lobster. **Habitant,** a good kitchen store in a house, is down Library Street.

Tea connoisseurs are in their element at **Harney & Sons,** which sells exotic teas by the bag or tin at the packing factory at 23 Brook St. John Harney, former innkeeper at the White Hart Inn, started a mail-order tea business in his family home across from the inn and now has quite an enterprise with a retail shop and tasting room (he makes it much more fun to taste different teas than we could have imagined); open daily 10 to 5 and Sunday noon to 5. For more than a taste, stop for traditional tea service at **Chaiwalla,** Mary O'Brien's tea house at 1 Main St. She offers soups, her famous tomato pie and open-face sandwiches as well as tea.

Shops seem to come and go in Lakeville, a mile away along Route 44. **Corner Clothiers** has suave apparel and **Horse 'n Around Ltd.** offers equine-related supplies. **April 56 Extreme Cookery** carries a potpourri of gourmet foods, Junior League cookbooks and original gifts; we liked the ceramic pie plates with lids topped with berries and apples. **Riga Mt. Coffee Roasters** has tables on one side and a living room with computers on the other for sampling the internet as well as many kinds of coffee. Light breakfasts, soups and five panini sandwiches ($4.50

to $4.75) are served, too. Home accessories, from candles to comforters, are featured at **The Linen Press.** Up the street is **Sweet Crewelty,** offering gourmet chocolates and local crafts.

Norfolk and Riverton

A wealthy summer colony since the completion of the Connecticut Western Railroad in 1871, the Norfolk area east of Salisbury along the Massachusetts border includes secluded estates and a lively summer music season that once gave it the title "the Lenox of Connecticut." Off the beaten track from anywhere, Riverton has become a destination since merchant John Tarrant Kenney gave up his West Hartford shoe store in 1946 and restored the old Lambert Hitchcock chair factory on its original site beside the Farmington River.

Great Mountain Forest. Windrow Road, Norfolk, (860) 542-5422. This working forest, west of Norfolk atop Canaan Mountain, is a treat for visitors. The 6,000-acre preserve is maintained with help from the Yale School of Forestry and the University of Hartford Environmental Studies Center. Enter from Wangum Mountain Road in Norfolk or, better, Canaan Mountain Road east of Falls Village. The roads through this experimental forest are lined with dozens of species – at some points, the markers come fast and furious on both sides and no matter how slowly you go, you'll miss some. Chinese imports, 90-foot hemlocks, the biggest black walnut trees you'll ever see, Douglas firs, oriental spruces and the King Boris fir are all there. Meadow sequoias are grown by the head forester from Chinese seed at the nursery.

Norfolk Chamber Music Festival. The Battell family endowed Norfolk with much of its character. The Norfolk Chamber Music Festival and the Yale Summer School of Music carry on the century-old tradition with summer concerts in the redwood-lined Music Shed on the hilly grounds of the Ellen Battell Stoeckel estate west of the village green. Up to two dozen concerts by the resident Tokyo String Quartet, the New York Woodwind Quintet, the Vermeer Quartet, the Norfolk Chamber Orchestra and others are given on Friday and Saturday evenings and some weekdays from late June into August. Concert-goers may picnic on shaded grounds beside a brook.
Ellen Battell Stoeckel Estate, Norfolk. (860) 542-5537 in summer, (203) 432-1966 from September-May.

Loon Meadow Farm. This twenty-acre working farm is home to many friendly animals, including horses that are called into service for hayrides, romantic moonlit carriage rides and winter sleigh rides. The service can be arranged direct or chartered through Norfolk B&Bs, whose innkeepers say the rides often prove to be a highlight of their guests' weekend. The owners also offer three B&B rooms with private baths in their 19th-century farmhouse.
41 Loon Meadow Drive, Norfolk. (860) 542-6085. Ride prices vary. Doubles, $95 to $120.

Hitchcock Chair Co. Factory Store. Hitchcock employees can be seen weaving, woodworking, rushing and stenciling behind the gift shop and furniture showroom. The authentic reproductions, sold at factory prices, start at around $50.

An antique original chair with its distinctive stenciled designs of flowers and fruits with handpainted outlines of gold can sell for up to $1,000.

Route 20, Riverton. (860) 379-4826. Monday-Friday 10 to 5, Saturday to 6, Sunday noon to 5.

John Tarrant Kenney Hitchcock Museum. Antique furniture from Hitchcock and other craftsmen is shown in the Old Union Church that Lambert Hitchcock helped build in 1829. A fifteen-minute movie, "America Be Seated," tells the early Hitchcock story. Chairs are attractively displayed; some hang in neat rows from the walls. You can view the fine stenciling and handstriping up close, and immerse yourself in other Hitchcock memorabilia.

1 Robertsville Road, Riverton. (860) 738-4950. Thursday-Sunday noon to 4, April-December. Donation.

Food and Flicks

Gilson Cafe and Cinema. Serious movie-goers flock to this cafe/theater/lounge fashioned from a 1920s movie house of grand proportions. They come from miles around to enjoy art, foreign and second-run films while munching sandwiches, salads, platters of veggies or pâté and brie, chili and desserts. Tiered, side-by-side seats for two, with small tables between, face a large screen. There's a full liquor license, and no one under age 21 is admitted on weekends. With admission at $4 and food in the $4.75 range, a couple can make a night of it for twenty bucks or so. The upstairs jazz lounge has been converted into a second movie venue.

354 Main St., Winsted. (860) 379-5108 or 379-6069. Movies, Tuesday-Sunday at 7, also Friday and Saturday at 9 or 9:30; doors open for dinner at 6.

Where to Stay

Manor House. This grand, Tudor-style manor home on five acres is run as an elegant Victorian B&B by Diane and Henry Tremblay, corporate dropouts from the Hartford insurance world. All eight guest rooms have private baths, one with a double jacuzzi and one with a double soaking tub. All are furnished with antique sleigh, canopy or four-poster beds covered with duvet comforters, European antiques and interesting decorative touches. Several have fireplaces and private balconies. The Tremblays are proud to show a prized collection of old prints by a local woman, which they acquired recently at an auction. The lovely and spacious main-floor public rooms are enhanced by Tiffany windows, cherry paneling and stone fireplaces. Very comfortable are the small library, the baronial living room with a gigantic stone fireplace, a sun porch with a wood stove, and two dining rooms in which the Tremblays serve full breakfasts. The herbs come from their garden and the honey from their beehives.

Maple Avenue, Box 447, Norfolk 06058. (860) 542-5690. Doubles, $90 to $190.

Greenwoods Gate. Pampering touches are everywhere in this striking white Federal home with four luxury suites for guests. They begin with the welcome card that greets you, continue through afternoon tea and pre-dinner wine and cheese, and end only when you leave (with a farewell bag of potpourri). Hospitality is lavished by retired hotelier George Schumaker, who found his B&B calling after twenty years at the top echelons of the Hilton chain. His elaborate suites are furnished with expensive antiques, lovely crafts and showy floral arrangements. The three-level Levi Thompson suite with a sitting area and spa-like bath with double jacuzzi is a coveted retreat for romance. A long and leisurely breakfast begins with wake-up coffee, continues with a buffet of fruit compote, pastries, granola and cereal, and culminates in a served entrée like eggs espagnole or cranberry-raspberry baked puffed pancakes.

105 Greenwoods Road East (Route 44), Norfolk 06058. (860) 542-5439. Doubles, $175 to $235; two-bedroom suites, $280 and $330.

Angel Hill Bed & Breakfast. Donna and Del Grilman, former owners of a small B&B nearby, moved up in the world when they opened this 1880 Victorian beauty on a hillside hugging the road but backing up to woodlands and a brook. They offer two main-floor bedrooms with fireplaces and queen canopy beds, two suites (one with kingsize bed) with whirlpool tubs, and a carriage-house apartment with a queen canopy bed, kitchen and a living room with a table for a candlelight breakfast that is an Angel Hill trademark. Each accommodation has private bath, robes, stereo players, candles and televisions if desired. Donna serves a sumptuous breakfast on the outdoor veranda, in a sunny dining room or by candlelight in guests' bedrooms beside the window or fireplace. Tea and sherry are offered in the living room or library at check-in. Guests relax in a Victorian gazebo, nap in a hammock under the pines, or stroll through the woods to the brook.

54 Greenwoods Road East, Box 504, Norfolk 06058. (860) 542-5920. Doubles, $110 to $150; apartment $150 ($475 by the week).

Old Riverton Inn. This inn opened in 1796 and was restored in 1937, but retains a stagecoach tavern atmosphere. Upstairs are twelve bedrooms of different sizes (some euphemistically called compact), all with private baths. The two front corner rooms are most desirable. A sitting area on the second floor contains Victorian furniture and antiques. The main dining room is furnished, of course, with Hitchcock chairs, beamed low ceiling and pretty bow windows. The food is traditional, with dinners in the $12.95 to $18.95 range. Lunch is popular with visitors to the Hitchcock factory and museum. There are also a cozy Hobby Horse bar and another dining room, the Grindstone Terrace, with a floor of grindstones quarried in Nova Scotia, glass tables and white iron chairs.

Route 20, Riverton 06065. (860) 379-8678 or (800) 378-1796. Doubles, $75 to $105. Lunch, noon to 2:30; dinner, 5 to 8:30 or 9, Sunday noon to 8. Closed Tuesday, also Monday from Columbus Day to Memorial Day.

Restaurants

The Cannery. Simple but stylish is this small American bistro that retained the name of its predecessor in which canning jars were the theme. Chef-owner William O'Meara, a Norfolk resident, presents a contemporary menu for dinner by candlelight. Main courses range from $16 for curried free-range chicken with sautéed pears and couscous to $20 for grilled sirloin with garlic and chive mashed potatoes and red pepper coulis. We liked the sound of the pan-seared duck breast with wild mushroom risotto and the grilled pork tenderloin sauced with Michigan dried cherries and cognac. Starters could be sautéed bay scallops with fresh pasta and sage butter or arugula salad with pinenuts, pancetta and shaved parmigiano-reggiano. Among desserts are orange-scented pecan tart with whipped cream, chocolate mousse terrine with raspberry sauce and pear-almond tart with caramel sauce. At our latest visit, Northwest Corner diners were anticipating the owner's acquisition of the landmark Village Restaurant on the green in Litchfield.

85 Main St., Canaan. (860) 824-7333. Entrées, $16 to $20. Dinner nightly except Tuesday, 5 to 9 or 10; Sunday brunch, 11 to 2.

The Pub & Restaurant. Crowded, casual and inexpensive – these are the attractions of this lively English-style pub in Norfolk Center, taken over and upgraded by David Davis, formerly co-owner of the famed Stonehenge restaurant and inn in Ridgefield. Sit at bare wood tables in jolly surroundings and select from a dinner menu of American and contemporary international cuisine that keeps getting better at every visit. Options run from seven kinds of burgers in the $7 range to grilled chicken, flank steak and specials like moussaka and poached salmon with watercress salad. The selection of 160 beers from everywhere is the most extensive in Connecticut.

Route 44, Norfolk, (860) 542-5716. Entrées, $12.50 to $15.95. Lunch, 11:30 to 5; dinner, 5 to 9 or 10. Closed Monday.

Catnip Mouse Tearoom. Lana Wells runs this neat little luncheon spot, with dark green wallpaper on which are baskets of flowers. The handwritten menu changes bi-weekly, with soups like lobster-broccoli bisque, salads and desserts. Sandwiches in the $6.95 range might be a Peter Piper, grilled ham and chicken with homemade pepper jelly, or the Italian Delight, homemade focaccia with prosciutto, artichoke hearts and basil mayonnaise, topped with melted mozzarella and served warm. Lana makes cinnamon, baked apple and pumpkin ice creams in the fall, or you might find white chocolate pecan pie. Everything is made from scratch, even the mayonnaise seasoned with herbs her garden, as well as the herbal teas.

Route 20, Riverton. (860) 379-3745. Lunch, Tuesday-Saturday, 11:30 to 2.

A Budget Choice

Greenwoods Market & Cafe. This is a small market and a deli/cafe, good for taking out or eating in at umbrella-covered tables on a rear deck overlooking the town meadow. Stop here for morning espresso and a pastry. The breakfast sandwich of egg, bacon and swiss cheese on a Portuguese roll gets the day off to a good start for $2.50. Owner Louis Salamone points to the sandwiches as good values ($3.75 each). Another lunch option is the deli salad plate: a choice of three plus a roll for $5.25.

32 Greenwoods Road West, Norfolk. (860) 542-1551. Monday-Saturday 8 to 6, Sunday to 3.

Shopping

In Norfolk, stop at the **Norfolk Artisan's Guild,** where 50 local craftsmen display their wares in a gift gallery on the main floor of the old Thurston Building. Just south at 515 Litchfield Road is **Hillside Gardens,** one of New England's outstanding perennial gardens, with more than 2,000 varieties of perennials abloom in twenty borders in a home garden setting. North of town, just across the Massachusetts line in Southfield, is **The Buggy Whip Factory,** housing antiques dealers, artisans, specialty shops and a small cafe.

Tiny Riverton has a short street of shops, in addition to the Hitchcock Chair Factory and Store around the corner. The **Riverton General Store** includes a country deli. **Gifts of Distinction** carries books, cards, new and old baskets and Carl Larsson prints. Stop at the **Village Sweet Shoppe** for ice cream or chocolate lace.

Lake Waramaug's Alpine Country

Nothing seems quite so European as sitting on the terrace of the Hopkins Inn for lunch or a pre-dinner cocktail and gazing down the hillside at the boats on Lake Waramaug. Named for an Indian sachem in this old territory, the lake reminds some of those in Austria and Switzerland, and the surrounding inns capitalize on it. Off in worlds unto themselves east of the lake are quaint New Preston, a hamlet of exotic shops, and picturesque Washington Depot and Washington, the former nestled in a valley and the latter perched on a hilltop.

For foliage-viewing, the narrow road that hugs the shore as it winds around the boomerang-shaped lake is a good way to see both lake and leaves. Lovely homes and manicured lawns mark the area, and three inns sit not far from water's edge. The nine-mile route is ringed by hills – when the water is calm, as it often is, the reflections of color are spectacular.

Mount Tom State Park in nearby Woodville is often overlooked. Right beside Route 202 is a 60-acre spring-fed pond for swimming; the excellent beach facilities include individual changing rooms. Picnic tables are smack dab on the shore and scattered along the hillside. A mile-long trail rises 500 feet to a tower atop Mount Tom. More good picnic tables are scattered along the tree-lined shore of **Lake Waramaug State Park.**

The hilltop village green in the postcard-perfect community of **Washington** is as classic as any in Connecticut. Large houses and prominent churches surround it, and off to one side is the Gunnery School's interesting campus. The **Gunn Historical Museum,** housed in a 1781 wooden structure near the green, is open Thursday-Sunday from noon to 4, free. It has a fine thimble collection, dollhouses, spinning wheels and western Indian baskets. Routes 109 and 45 east of Washington offer good panoramic views for foliage-seekers.

The Institute for American Indian Studies. Just southwest of town is the renamed American Indian Archeological Institute, a place dedicated to Indian relics and archeological digs. Some years back it made history when a team uncovered a fluted "clovis" spear point, which they say confirms Indians at the spot 10,000 years ago. A mastodon skeleton inside the contemporary museum shows the type of animal they would have hunted; there are arrowheads, early Indian pottery, sandstone dishes and dioramas of early Indian life. Also on the premises are an Indian longhouse, a simulated dig site and a specialized museum shop with handcrafted copies of items in the collection. A twenty-minute habitat trail takes the visitor through stages of geological and botanical development in Connecticut. *38 Curtis Road (off Route 199), Washington. (860) 868-0518. Open Monday-Saturday 10 to 5, Sunday noon to 5. Adults $4, children $2.*

Hopkins Vineyard. Behind the Hopkins Inn on land the Hopkins family has farmed for more than 200 years, Bill and Judy Hopkins started planting grape vines in 1979; they now have 35 acres of French-American hybrids, from which they produce nine varieties of wine. They converted their red dairy barn into an award-winning winery, where the visitor may taste and buy their products, including a superior seyval blanc. A winery walk extends to an addition, allowing visitors to view the new bottling and labeling room. An excellent shop sells wine-related items like stemware and grapevine wreaths and baskets, and on cool days a pot of mulled wine simmers on the wood stove. You can picnic with a $13.50 bottle of chardonnay in the small picnic area with a view of the lake below. You'll probably agree with the quotation printed on the Hopkins labels: "Where the air is like wine and the wine is like nectar." Wines are $6.99 to $16.25.

Hopkins Road, New Preston. (860) 868-7954. Daily 10 to 5, May-December; Friday-Sunday, rest of year.

CAMPING is particularly good in this area. **Lake Waramaug State Park** offers 88 sites in the woods and fields beside the lake, with a camp store, full facilities and a fine beach. **Housatonic Meadows State Park** in Cornwall Bridge has 104 sites in a heavily forested area beside the Housatonic River. **Macedonia Brook State Park** in Kent, known for its hiking along the Appalachian trail, offers 84 campsites. **Kent Falls State Park** south of Cornwall Bridge has twelve sites in open fields near the foot of the state's highest waterfall.

Room and Board

Boulders Inn. Innkeepers Ulla and Kees Adema of Fairfield County have made an already special place even more special. "This was supposed to be our retirement," kidded Ulla, who said her husband wanted a little B&B and ended up with this grand prize. Six bedrooms and suites in the shingled 1895 inn and eight in contemporary, fireplaced duplex guest houses up the hill in back are most comfortably furnished. A rear carriage house adds three choice, carpeted guest rooms with plush chintz seating in front of stone fireplaces. We like the inn's fireplaced and paneled living room with comfy sofas and wing chairs in splashy fabrics, a library corner with stereo tapes and a big Russian samovar from which tea may be dispensed in the afternoon. It has immense picture windows overlooking the lake; next to it is a small den with a TV. The dining room with its walls of boulders and a seven-sided addition with views of Lake Waramaug has a loyal following. The contemporary dinner menu might include Chilean sea bass with red pepper puree, sesame-crusted salmon with organic greens and wasabi potatoes, herb-roasted organic chicken with sweet pea sauce and grilled black angus strip steak. Start with a portobello mushroom and polenta tower with umberco cheese or wild game terrine with sweet and sour mustard sauce. But save room for a dessert like white and dark chocolate mousse in a tuile cup. The three-level outdoor terrace is perfect for cocktails and dining in summer. A hike up Pinnacle Mountain behind the inn reveals abundant wildlife and birds as you work up an appetite for a good dinner.

Route 45, New Preston 06777. (860) 868-0541 or (800) 552-6853. Fax (860) 868-1925. Doubles, $250 to $350, MAP; B&B available at times for $50 less. Entrées, $17.50 to $24. Dinner nightly except Tuesday, 6 to 9, Sunday from 4; Thursday-Sunday in winter.

Hopkins Inn. This pretty yellow inn is known more for its dining than its lodging – we often recommend it when we're asked where to take visitors for lunch out in the country. It does have eleven guest rooms (nine with private baths)

Mary Lou Estabrook Photo

Autumn scene in Northwest Corner.

and a couple of apartments, unexceptional but light and airy and furnished with country antiques as befits its origin as a summer guest house in 1847. For meals, its setting atop a hill overlooking the lake, with an outdoor dining terrace shaded by a giant horse chestnut tree, is spectacular from spring through fall. One dining room has a rustic decor with barnsiding and ship's figureheads; the other is more Victorian. Chef-owner Franz Schober is Austrian and always has Austrian and Swiss dishes on the menu. Dinner dishes are classics like wiener schnitzel and sweetbreads Viennese; wife Beth Schober says the roast pheasant with red cabbage and spaetzle is especially in demand in fall. Vegetables are always good; you may get something unusual like braised romaine lettuce. People love the strawberries romanoff and grand marnier soufflé glacé. The varied wine list includes half a dozen from Switzerland as well as several from Hopkins Vineyard next door. Franz designed the tile tables for the terrace and porch; he's also the inspiration for the striking copper and wrought-iron chandelier and lanterns that grace the terrace.

22 Hopkins Road, New Preston 06777. (860) 868-7295. Fax (860) 868-7464. Doubles, $61 to $71, EP. Entrées, $16.25 to $19.25 Lunch, Tuesday-Saturday noon to 2; dinner 6 to 9 or 10, Sunday 12:30 to 8:30; no lunch in April, November and December. Closed January-March.

The Inn on Lake Waramaug. From private home to village inn to boarding house for summer guests, this has grown since the 19th century into a destination resort with an indoor pool, whirlpool, sauna, lake beach, tennis court and 23 rooms. Five are in the main 1790 inn and the rest in two outlying guest houses that look rather like 1950s-style motels, but are comfortably outfitted with modern amenities and cable TV. Sixteen rooms come with working fireplaces. The staff keeps things busy for those who like lots of activity. The paddlewheeler Showboat takes guests on cruises around the lake. Three meals a day are served in peak season in the inn's dining rooms, on the terrace or at the boathouse beside the lake, where hamburgers are barbecued at lunchtime. The dinner menu features new American cuisine, from seared sesame-encrusted tuna to "grilled duck, two ways" to roast rack of New Zealand lamb.

North Shore Road, New Preston 06777. (860) 868-0563 or (800) 525-3466. Fax (860) 868-9173. Doubles, $209 to $229, MAP. Entrées, $16 to $21. Dinner nightly, 6 to 9, Sunday 5 to 8; Boathouse Cafe open noon to 8, Memorial Day to Columbus Day.

A Premier Country Hotel

Mayflower Inn. A long driveway winds up the hill to this inn hidden on 28 wooded acres above the campus of the Gunnery, the private school that used to own and operate it. New York owners Robert and Adriana Mnuchin poured big bucks into the inn's renovation and expansion in 1992, creating one of the premier English-style country hotels in America. The main inn holds fifteen guest rooms and suites of great comfort and style. Ten more are in two guest houses astride a hill beside a tiered rose garden leading up to a swimming pool. Furnishings are stately, even spectacular, mixing fine imported and domestic antiques and accessories with prized artworks and elegant touches of whimsy. The inn's main floor harbors an intimate parlor, an ever-so-British gentleman's library, an English-looking piano bar and three stylish dining rooms. Chef Christopher Freeman presents a changing menu of contemporary fare. The night's offerings might vary from roasted natural chicken with apple-pear ketchup to grilled pheasant breast and braised thigh on sage polenta. Start with roasted acorn squash soup with shaved aged goat cheese or grilled shrimp on a soba noodle salad with ginger shoyu vinaigrette. Finish with blueberry and raspberry crème brûlée or the Mayflower cookies, a tasty assortment including perhaps macaroons, thick butter shortbreads and chocolate chip for a cool $6.50. The setting for meals is exceptional, especially the outdoor terrace with its sylvan view of manicured lawns and imported specimen trees. The moneyed clientele who stay here are coddled to within an inch of their lives by a staff worthy of their Relais & Châteaux affiliation.

Route 47, Box 1288, Washington 06793. (860) 868-9466. Fax (860) 868-1497. Doubles, $240 to $395, EP; suites, $420 to $580. Entrées, $16.50 to $26. Lunch daily, noon to 2:30; dinner nightly, 6 to 9.

Restaurants

Cafe New Preston. Considered precious and pricey but very good is this pint-size newcomer run by Drew Stichter, a Pennsylvania chef of note who has cooked for the James Beard Foundation, and his wife Rebecca, who opened the Artiques Shop down the street. It's perfect for country-weekending city folks: snug with stone walls and bleached barnwood, twinkling white lights draped around a dried vine, and a huge, warming fireplace for chilly evenings. (In summer, folks spill out from the 30-seat interior onto tables on the front patio and even the asphalt. "That's the real cafe," volunteered a waiter; "the inside should be called `the grotto.") Anyway, the fare is a changing parade of contemporary Mediterranean cuisine. The dinner menu runs the gamut from pasta of the sun (angel hair tossed with garlic, roasted tomatoes, basil and chèvre) to lamb chops in dijon-rosemary breading. Pistachio salmon, veal and shrimp lemoni, cashew chicken, and pork and mango are typical choices. Start with roasted vegetable and three-cheese terrine or

peppered bourbon shrimp. Finish with pumpkin cheesecake or cranberry, pear and raisin tart. The lunch menu also ranges widely from $6 for spinach and endive salad to $12.50 for shrimp and scallop bouillabaisse. Who could resist the eggs rockefeller with smoked oysters on the weekend brunch menu?
18 East Shore Road (Route 45), New Preston. (860) 868-1787. Entrées, $14 to $21. Lunch, Wednesday-Sunday 11 to 4; dinner, Wednesday-Sunday 5 to 9:30; weekend brunch, 9 to 2.

Doc's. A favorite with both weekenders and residents is this roadside stand gone upscale. Adam Riess, a Californian who had just graduated from the University of Pennsylvania, opened the Italian cafe, pizzeria and bakery a few years ago and named it for his grandfather, a physician who summered on Lake Waramaug for 40 years. While he pursues graduate and culinary studies in New York, a team of chefs continues his tradition: dynamite pizzas in the $8 range, exotic salads and a smattering of robust pastas and entrées, among them sautéed salmon with pesto, roasted chicken with rapini and garlic and New York strip steak with wild mushroom sauté. The dessert chef produces a great ricotta cheesecake, panna cotta with raspberry sauce and pumpkin crème caramel. The setting is as gutsy as the food: hard green chairs at close-together tables covered with white butcher paper, their only adornments a bottle of olive oil and a big metal cheese shaker.
Flirtation Avenue at Route 45, New Preston. (860) 868-9415. Entrées, $13.75 to $17.75. Lunch in summer and fall, Friday-Sunday noon to 2:30; dinner, Wednesday-Sunday 5 to 9:30 or 10. BYOB. No credit cards.

The Pantry. Combining many functions, the Pantry is an elegant catering service, a food and gift store for gourmets, a glorified deli and a marvelous spot for late breakfast, lunch or tea. Amidst high-tech shelving displaying everything from American Spoon preserves to red currant or green peppercorn vinegars, cooking gadgets and serious equipment, you can lunch on innovative fare. On one visit the chef was dishing up a muffaletta sandwich ($5.95), that New Orleans favorite of salami, cheese, olive oil and olives, done up inside a loaf of bread, plus salads of watercress slaw, parsnips, Italian new potatoes and gingered carrots. You might try the salad sampler for $6.95 or game pot pie ($8.50). Soups like the curried cauliflower are heavenly. Desserts are to sigh over: among them, pear-almond torte, hazelnut dream roll, linzertorte and grapefruit soufflé.
Titus Road, Washington Depot. (860) 868-0258. Tuesday-Saturday, 10 to 6.

G.W. Tavern. Big bucks have been poured into renovations over the years at this restaurant of many changing names. But never more so, perhaps, than the latest in 1996 that transformed the late Bee Brook, a highly rated and rather fancy eatery, into a downscaled pub and tavern with an unlikely name. Fear not, however. The conversion by New York restaurateurs Reggie Young, the genial host, and Robert Margolis, the chef, has been done with style. The main dining room with vaulted skylight is now a tavern with an upscale Colonial look, oriental carpets on the floors and stunning murals of surrounding towns on the walls. The rear porch has been enclosed for year-round casual dining. The outdoor terraces beside the stream will continue to be put into use in summer. "Good, simple pub food" is featured by the chef. The dinner menu offers starters ($2.50 to $5.50) like mulligatawny soup, smoked and peppered mackerel, and venison sausage from

Nodine's Smokehouse in nearby Goshen. "Mains" start at $7.50 for a burger. Fish and chips, fresh cod, grilled salmon, roast duck, meatloaf, chicken pot pie and roast beef with yorkshire pudding are among the possibilities. Rice pudding and cherry pie are favored desserts. Incidentally, the initials in the name stand for George Washington, whose hatchet is carved in the sign out front.
20 Bee Brook Road, Washington Depot. (860) 868-6633. Entrées, $7.50 to $16.50. Lunch, Tuesday-Saturday 11:30 to 2:30; dinner, 5:30 to 10 or 11, Sunday 11:30 to 9:30. Closed Monday.

Shopping

The hilly hamlet of New Preston at the southeast end of Lake Waramaug is gaining retailers of note, most with an emphasis on antiques and accessories. **J. Seitz & Co.** is a small paradise of eclectic clothing and furnishings with an emphasis on the Southwest. Among other choices are **The Trumpeter** for "antiques of a man's interest," **Jonathan Peters** for fine linens and garden ornaments, **City House/Country House, Lou Marotta Inc.** for painted furniture, **Ray Boas, Antiquarian Bookseller** and **Black Swan Antiques.**

Washington Depot has a large and well-stocked bookstore, the **Hickory Stick Bookshop.** Authors, many of whom have homes in the area, are occasionally on hand to autograph their books. Orchids grow in pots and are pictured in frames at **The Orchid Gallery.** Find Canadian antiques, porcelain, painted boxes and such at the **Tulip Tree Collection,** women's sportswear at **Finula's** and gifts and jewelry at **Gracious Living.**

Litchfield

Considered Connecticut's finest example of a typical late 18th-century New England village, Litchfield is the place to which we take first-time visitors to Connecticut (we have relatives who make a beeline there almost every time they visit). You should, too, if you're in the area.

The entire center of the village settled in 1720 is a National Historic Landmark. While Williamsburg had to be restored, Litchfield simply has been maintained by its residents as a living museum. Most of the old homes and buildings are occupied.

The **Litchfield Historic District** is clustered around the green and along North and South streets (Route 63). The statuesque, gleaming white Congregational Church is said to be the most photographed in New England. Where else do a bank and a jail share a common wall as they do at North and West streets? The young attendant pointed them out proudly from the information center on the green. South Street is a broad, half-mile-long avenue where three governors, five state chief justices, six congressmen and two U.S. senators have lived. Landmarks include the birthplaces of Ethan Allen, Henry Ward Beecher and Harriet Beecher Stowe, plus Sheldons Tavern, where George Washington slept (he visited town five times). Sarah Pierce opened the first academy for the education of women in America on North Street in 1792.

The **Litchfield Historical Society Museum,** 7 South St., (860) 567-1041, is a good place to get your cultural bearings. It offers four galleries of early American paintings, decorative arts, furniture and local history exhibits. Its hours and admission price are the same as those of the Tapping Reeve House and Law School (see next), although this museum is open from mid-April to mid-November.

Tapping Reeve House and Law School. America's first law school (1784) is now a museum dedicated to Judge Tapping Reeve's life and times. You can visit both the house with its handsome furnishings and the tiny school with handwritten ledgers penned by students long since gone, including Aaron Burr, John C. Calhoun and 130 members of Congress.

South Street, Litchfield. (860) 567-4501. Tuesday-Saturday 11 to 5, Sunday 1 to 5, mid-May to mid-October. Adults $3 (includes admission to Litchfield Historical Society Museum).

White Memorial Foundation and Conservation Center. Litchfield resident Alain C. White and his sister Mary set up the foundation that established the state's largest nature center and wildlife sanctuary, and donated many other public lands in Northwest Connecticut. The 4,000 acres here contain 35 miles of woodland and marsh trails – much used year-round by hikers, horseback riders and, in winter, cross-country skiers. Almost every outdoor activity is available, including birdwatching from a unique observatory in which groups can watch birds undetected, and swimming at Sandy Beach along Bantam Lake, the largest natural lake in the state. The preserve is unusual in having both managed and wild natural areas within its boundaries. On one 30-acre lot known as Catlin Woods, which has been untouched for years, a forest road winds through giant hemlocks and white pines; elsewhere, a fully operating sawmill can be observed. The preserve with eleven ponds provides environments for all manner of animals and birds. A museum in a 19th-century mansion contains collections of Indian artifacts, 3,000 species of butterflies, live and stuffed animals, geology exhibits, and an excellent nature library and gift shop.

Off Route 202 two miles west of Litchfield. (860) 567-0015. Grounds open free, 24 hours a day, year-round. Museum, Monday-Saturday 9 to 5, Sunday noon to 4, April-October; 8:30 to 4:30 rest of year. Adults $2, children $1.

White Flower Farm. No relation to the White Memorial Foundation, this is one of the nation's more unusual nurseries. Famed almost as much for its literate catalog as for its nursery stock, it welcomes visitors to ten acres of display gardens and a sales center from which few go home empty-handed. More than 1,000 different flowers and shrubs are offered. The gardens are especially gorgeous in late spring and summer, and the begonia display in the greenhouses is viewed from July through September. Even non-gardeners will enjoy a visit here. The catalog appears under the pen name of Amos Pettingill and readers love it.

Route 63, Litchfield. (860) 567-8789. Monday-Friday 10 to 5, weekends 9 to 5:30, mid-April through October. Free.

Haight Vineyard and Winery. Housed in an English Tudor-style building, this is Connecticut's oldest farm winery, having produced its first chardonnays and rieslings in 1979 from fifteen acres of grapes planted by Sherman P. Haight Jr., longtime master of the hounds for the Litchfield Hunt. The Haight family take pride in their Covertside white and red prize-winners as well as their chardonnay and riesling labels. Visitors can take a self-guided vineyard walk through the 25-acre property and visit a large tasting room.

Chestnut Hill Road, Litchfield. (860) 567-4045. Monday-Saturday 10:30 to 5, Sunday noon to 5.

Topsmead State Forest. Often overlooked, this 511-acre preserve atop a knoll a mile east of Litchfield Center offers scenic views, picnic sites and trails for hiking and cross-country skiing. An English Tudor house that was once the summer home of the Chase brass family of Waterbury is opened for guided tours, Saturday and Sunday noon to 5, second and fourth weekend of the month, June-October.

Buell Road, Litchfield. (860) 567-5694. Grounds open year-round. Free.

Room and Board

Toll Gate Hill. This ancient-feeling inn actually is of fairly recent vintage, having opened in 1983 with six guest rooms, three dining rooms, a small tavern and a ballroom in a rural 1745 landmark house northeast of town. Four rooms and suites were added in 1986 in an adjacent "school house," and a new building with ten more rooms and suites and a lobby area was added to the rear of the property in 1990. Owner Frederick J. Zivic restored and furnished with taste the three-story house in which Capt. William Bull once took in travelers on the Hartford-Albany stage route. The bedrooms are done in custom fabrics and antiques; some have sofas, working fireplaces, goose down comforters and lighted mirrors. In the antiques-furnished dining rooms, owner Zivic offers a seasonal menu of what he calls "light, unencumbered" regional cuisine. The dinner fare ranges from roasted cod with horseradish crust to shellfish pie in puff pastry, a house favorite. We found the wine list interesting and fairly priced, the soups (like clam chowder with green chiles and tomatoes) creative, and our dinner entrées of sautéed scallops in a light beer sauce and broiled salmon with a tomato-chardonnay puree and warm chive ricotta excellent.

Route 202 (Box 39), Litchfield 06759. (860) 567-4545 or (800) 445-3903. Fax (860) 567-8397. Doubles, $110 to $140; suites, $175. Entrées, $18 to $24. Lunch, noon to 3; dinner, 5:30 to 9:30 or 10:30; Sunday brunch, 11:30 to 3:30. Closed Tuesday and Wednesday in off-season.

The Litchfield Inn. Local businessman James Irwin built from scratch this authentic – if austere-looking – Colonial-style structure back from the highway about a mile west of town. Starting with twelve guest rooms and an extensive dining and bar facility in 1982, the inn expanded in 1984 with a twenty-room addition; plans for another, much larger addition have been put on hold. Furnished in reproduction early American style, each room has private bath and color TV. Some have wet bars, and "highly decorated theme rooms" command top dollar. Several public rooms are studiously elegant. Ever-changing in an effort to find a niche, the restaurant operation was leased in 1996 to John Roller of the acclaimed Bistro Cafe in New Milford. He lightened up the menu for what he called **The Bistro East,** housed in the large and formal Benjamin Talmadge Room with wainscoted walls, hand-hewn beams and wide-plank floors. Entrées are in keeping with contemporary tastes: pan-seared catfish with lentil ragoût, grilled yellowfin tuna with Thai basil sauce, pan-seared chicken with roasted tomato vinaigrette, and gorgonzola-crusted New York strip steak. Lunches in the Terrace Room and lounge are more casual.

Route 202, Litchfield 06759. (860) 567-4503 or (800) 499-3444. Fax (860) 567-5358. Doubles, $105 to $165. Entrées, $13.95 to $17.95. Lunch daily, 11 to 2:30; dinner, 5:30 to 9:30; Sunday brunch, 11:30 to 2:30.

Restaurants

West Street Grill. The trendoids who pack this place at lunch and dinner seven days a week agree with the restaurant critics; the food is intensely flavorful and the sleek black and white digs stylish. Irish owner James O'Shea gives talented French chef Frederic Faveau from Burgundy free rein in the kitchen. He obliges with such dinner entrées as roasted codfish with a balsamic-shallot reduction, pan-seared chicken with a tomato-ginger coulis, and grilled leg of lamb with a lightly roasted garlic cream sauce. An autumn lunch began with a rich butternut squash and pumpkin bisque and the restaurant's signature grilled peasant bread with parmesan aioli. Main dishes were salmon cakes with curried French lentils ($10.95) and a special of grilled smoked pork tenderloin with spicy Christmas limas ($9.95). Indulge in dessert, perhaps an ethereal crème brûlée or a key lime tart. The food here is as assertive and colorful as the striking artworks on a brick wall near the front.

43 West St., Litchfield. (860) 567-3885. Entrées, $17.95 to $22.95. Lunch daily, 11:30 to 3, weekends to 4; dinner, 5:30 to 9:30 or 10:30.

Le Bon Coin. We've always been fond of this homey and unpretentious French restaurant out in the country. William Janega, who had previously run Le Parisien in Stamford, arrived in 1983 and has succeeded with tradition in an area where trends come and go. The two small dining rooms are most welcoming in the country French style. The front entry is decorated with wine casks, spigots and crate labels, and there are attractive stained-glass windows. Blackboard specials supplement a luncheon menu ($6.25 to $11.95) strong on such classics as assorted smoked fish niçoise, duck pâté flavored with cognac and port, sweetbreads in puff pastry, and a salad of warm chicken with mixed greens and cashews. At night, entrées include dover sole with mushrooms and artichokes, frog's legs provençal, pepper steak, lamb sauté and scallops of veal with basil and tomatoes. A plate of ice creams and sorbets, chocolate rice soufflé and crème caramel are among desserts.

Route 202, Woodville. (860) 868-7763. Entrées, $12.75 to $19. Lunch, Monday and Thursday-Saturday noon to 2; dinner, 6 to 9, Sunday 5 to 9. Closed Tuesday.

Grappa. The locals come to watch the weekenders at this offshoot of the trendy West Street Grill. Here all is contemporary Italian. A 650-degree wood-burning oven, with walls of brick and a floor of lava from Mount St. Helen's, produces more than a dozen versions of thin-crust pizzas ($8.95 to $13.95), from paella to roasted shrimp. There are novel starters, among them tender Greek-style octopus and grilled calamari with balsamic-mustard seed dressing. Pastas and main dishes might be homemade spinach ravioli with fresh sardines, cured codfish with confit of onions and tomatoes, a cassoulet of rock shrimp, lemon-garlic chicken and Tuscan-style flank steak. There's seating for a hundred in two dining rooms and a solarium, with spillover onto an outdoor patio in season.

26 Commons Drive (off Route 202), Litchfield. (860) 567-1616. Entrées, $9.95 to $14.95. Dinner, Tuesday-Sunday 5 to 9:30 or 10:30.

La Tienda Cafe. A green neon cactus beckons in the window of this two-room Mexican cafe. Colorful prints and rugs adorn the walls and cacti in small pots top the tables. A Mexican pizza ($5.95) was almost more than one could handle for lunch; an order of burritos ($7.95), one stuffed with chicken and the other with cheese and scallions, also was hearty and delicious. The all-day menu has four "north of the border" dishes, but why bother when you can feast on black bean soup, Arizona-style nachos (topped with ground beef), enchiladas, tostadas and such? Dinners run from folded tacos to seafood chimichanga.

Federal Square, Route 202, Litchfield. (860) 567-8778. Entrées, $7.95 to $14.25. Lunch, Tuesday-Saturday 11:30 to 2:30; dinner, Monday-Saturday 4:30 to 9 or 10, Sunday noon to 9.

Spinell's Litchfield Food Company. Doubled in size, this specialty foods shop, bakery and catering service has added tables for eat-in meals. It's run by Rick Spinell, former pastry chef at Brooklyn's famed River Cafe. Soups of the day could be tomato-bean-rosemary or mushroom-brie-onion. The foccacia sandwich with sundried tomatoes, goat cheese, roasted peppers, oil and vinegar ($6.95) and a three-salad combination plate are popular for lunch.

On the Green, Litchfield. (860) 567-3113. Daily, 8:30 to 6, Saturday to 7.

More than a Coffee House

The County Seat. This coffee house and cafe bills itself as "more than just a coffee house." It sure is. Occupying a prime corner space vacated by the old-line pharmacy, it's a veritable living room of sofas and banquettes, potted palms, ceiling fans and all manner of tables for enjoying soups and salads, pizzas and pasta, in addition to specialty coffees. An ice-cream bar dispenses ice cream in many flavors (spiced cranberry-apple sounds good for fall) and fruit smoothies. Gifts, confections, chocolates, musical entertainment and poetry readings – they're all here, and then some.

3 West St., Litchfield. (860) 567-8069. Sunday-Wednesday 7 a.m. to 9 p.m., Thursday to 10, weekends to midnight.

Shopping

Tony Litchfield, which clings to a vision of Connecticut more in keeping with its Colonial past than its sophisticated present, offers elements of both in its shopping area facing the broad green. (Only here would a proposal for a Talbots chain store generate months of controversy; **Talbots** won and now is a dignified presence among the locally owned stores and restaurants.) Also facing the green is **Workshop Inc.,** a boutique and gallery for the somewhat trendy, with Mexican and South American imports. We liked the straw hats and unusual handpainted silk earrings. **Hayseed** stocks terrific cards along with sweaters, clothing and jewelry. The suave **Barnidge & McEnroe** bookstore offers an espresso bar up front. **R. Derwin Clothiers** has two floors of timeless clothing for men and women.

Cobble Court, just off the green, has several small stores including the **Litchfield Exchange,** with handmade articles for infants and children, toys and linens, and homemade shortbread. **Kitchenworks** is a haven of cooking equipment and food-related gifts, and **Wildlife Landing** is full of accessories for nature lovers.

West of town is Litchfield Commons, a cluster of newish shops that come and go. Beyond along Route 202 is **House in the Country Ltd.,** where weekenders find furnishings for their second homes.

FOR MORE INFORMATION: Litchfield Hills Travel Council, Box 968, Litchfield, Conn. 06759, (860) 567-4506.

17 ❄️ Winter

Stowe Mountain Resort Photo/D. Curran

Fresh powder snow is heaven on earth for skiers at Stowe Mountain Resort.

Ski Capital of the East
Stowe, Vt.

Snow frosts the church spires, snug houses and pine trees that characterize the landscape of one of the country's oldest and most appealing ski villages. From many places in town and along the Mountain Road (Route 108) leading northwest, you can glimpse "the mountain" – Mount Mansfield, highest of Vermont's peaks, the one responsible for Stowe's destiny as a ski resort. Winter in Stowe has always been long and frigid and the Vermonters who lived here knew they had to play through it if they didn't want to hole up for half the year trying to ignore the chilly truth.

They accepted the challenge with verve. Back in 1921, Stowe's now-famous

Winter Carnival was born, mostly to give the locals something to look forward to in the post-holiday grip of snowy weather. In those days, the carnival was intended for town residents, but as its fame spread – and as skiing became a major sport here – tourists were drawn for the carnival.

In 1921, skiing hadn't really caught on yet in Stowe – or anywhere else. Skis were homemade, seven-foot wooden planks, and boots were the same as those worn for work on the farm. Boots were linked to skis by leather straps that allowed the heels to lift. A couple of long sticks made do as poles. It was makeshift, but it was a start.

Stowe became synonymous with the sport by the following decade. By 1934, trails had been carved down the steep slopes of Mount Mansfield and by 1940, a single chairlift had been installed to take skiers up. In the years to come, Stowe quickly became known as the Ski Capital of the East.

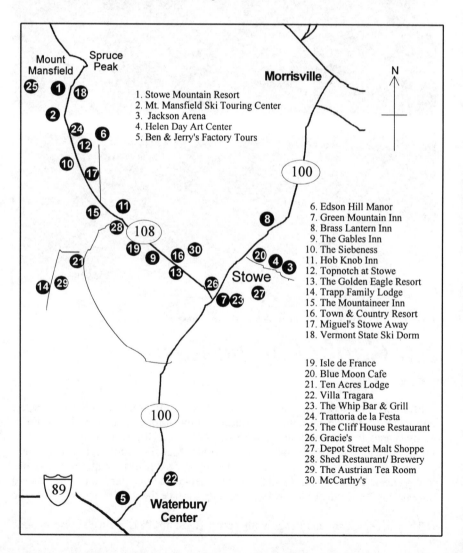

Mount Mansfield
Spruce Peak
Morrisville
N

1. Stowe Mountain Resort
2. Mt. Mansfield Ski Touring Center
3. Jackson Arena
4. Helen Day Art Center
5. Ben & Jerry's Factory Tours

100

108

Stowe

100

6. Edson Hill Manor
7. Green Mountain Inn
8. Brass Lantern Inn
9. The Gables Inn
10. The Siebeness
11. Hob Knob Inn
12. Topnotch at Stowe
13. The Golden Eagle Resort
14. Trapp Family Lodge
15. The Mountaineer Inn
16. Town & Country Resort
17. Miguel's Stowe Away
18. Vermont State Ski Dorm

19. Isle de France
20. Blue Moon Cafe
21. Ten Acres Lodge
22. Villa Tragara
23. The Whip Bar & Grill
24. Trattoria de la Festa
25. The Cliff House Restaurant
26. Gracie's
27. Depot Street Malt Shoppe
28. Shed Restaurant/ Brewery
29. The Austrian Tea Room
30. McCarthy's

89

Waterbury Center

Now, Mount Mansfield – with a gondola and a quadruple chairlift among other ways to whisk skiers to the summit – often opens before Thanksgiving, thanks to cold temperatures and abundant snowmaking capacity. Mansfield is still favored by experts, but across the way is the Stowe Mountain Resort's more recently developed Spruce Peak, perfect for beginners and early intermediates. The renowned Stowe Ski School has been teaching the sport since 1936.

In 1941, the von Trapp family of "Sound of Music" fame – fleeing Austria because of the war – arrived in Stowe and organized the Stowe Music Camp. In 1947, they began welcoming vacationers for overnight stays. Today, the showplace Trapp Family Lodge has 93 rooms in its main inn and another 100 chalets for time-share rental. It includes the oldest and most extensive of four cross-country ski centers in Stowe. And it is still family-owned. Johannes von Trapp is president of the corporation. His sister, Rosemarie, conducts sing-alongs a couple of nights a week, and the lodge's brochure endearingly relates the whereabouts of other family members.

The Austrian "gemütlichkeit" introduced to Stowe by the von Trapps has spread around the valley, and at Stowe as much as anywhere in this country, a festive Tyrolean atmosphere prevails in many lodges and restaurants.

In addition to skiing, outdoor enthusiasts can enjoy ice skating on frozen ponds or indoors at the Jackson Arena, snowshoeing, winter hiking, sledding, snowboarding and horse-drawn sleigh rides. Less active types may visit the municipal art center and library in town, check out the art and craft galleries, search for antiques or browse in the shops and boutiques for which Stowe is famed. Stowe is a particularly good destination for couples and families whose interests are diverse; skiers can spend a day at the mountain, while others poke around in town.

One of the nicest aspects of Stowe is the way growth has been moderated. As you approach the mountain itself on Route 108, you're not accosted by the commercialism and glitzy resort airs that prevail along "access roads" at other ski resorts. Instead, a swooping and curving road winds through a pine forest before it reaches the parking lot for Mount Mansfield and its low-key base lodge. The name Stowe is magic to skiers, and the town has accepted its designation with grace.

Getting There

Most visitors reach Stowe by automobile. The village of Stowe is located ten miles north of Interstate 89, the main interstate route through Vermont.

Major airlines fly into Burlington International Airport, about 30 miles to the west. A Stowe shuttle bus stops at major lodging establishments and takes skiers to the mountain.

Seeing and Doing

Of all the winter destinations in New England, Stowe is one where there's plenty to do. At the same time, the vacationer who wants simply to kick back and read by the fire is accommodated.

Downhill Skiing

Stowe Mountain Resort. The resort that makes Stowe the Ski Capital of the East offers downhill skiing on Mount Mansfield, the state's highest at 4,393 feet, and on the smaller Spruce Peak adjacent. All told, there are 47 trails, about one-fourth of them rated expert. Among them are the aptly named Nosedive and the legendary, double-diamond "Front Four" – the precipitous National, Goat, Starr and Liftline trails – each so steep that you can barely see the bottom from the top. Quite in contrast is the long and easy 3.7-mile Toll Road, part of the Stowe Auto Road that gives motorists access in the summer. The trails are reached via an eight-person gondola, a quadruple chairlift, eight double and triple chairlifts, and one poma lift. The vertical rise is 2,360 feet, one of Vermont's greatest. There are 480 acres and 39 miles of skiable terrain, 73 percent of it covered by snowmaking. Stowe claims the longest and highest night skiing terrain in New England.

Rental equipment is available at the mountain as well as from individual sports shops along the Mountain Road. **Snowboards** may be rented, too.

A variety of ski lessons is offered by the Stowe Ski School. Beginners take lessons at Spruce Peak, while more advanced skiers are taught on Mount Mansfield. Sessions lasting 90 minutes to two hours cost about $25. Private coaching is available for about $50 an hour.

5781 Mountain Road (Route 108). (802) 253-3000 or (800) 253-4754. Open daily, 8 to 4, mid-November to mid-April, weather permitting. Also night skiing, Wednesday-Sunday 4 to 10. Adult lift tickets $48, holidays $50; children, $28 and $30. Half-day, noon to 4, adults $34 and $37, children $19 and $22. Night, adults $20 and $22, children $16 and 18.

Cross-Country Skiing

Stowe is the home of one of the first cross-country ski centers in the country, the Trapp Family Lodge, rated by Ski magazine as one of the best in the world. It and three other centers combine to offer 150 kilometers of groomed and another 100 kilometers of back-country trails. Together they comprise the largest interconected trail system in the nation.

Trapp Family Lodge, Trapp Hill Road, (802) 253-8511 or (800) 826-7000, has 55 kilometers of groomed trails and another 45 kilometers of back-country trails. It offers a ski shop with rentals, instruction, and a cabin for lunch that is reachable only by skis.

Edson Hill Manor, 1500 Edson Hill Road, (802) 253-8954, includes 42 kilometers of groomed trails winding over 225 acres. Lessons and rentals are available.

Mount Mansfield Resort Cross-Country Touring Center, 5781 Mountain Road, (802) 253-7311, has 50 kilometers of trails. The cross-country center offers lessons, touring, telemark clinics, equipment rentals and repairs.

Topnotch at Stowe Resort, 4000 Mountain Road, (802) 253-8585, offers 25 kilometers of trails that connect to the Stowe cross-country link. A full-service ski center provides clothing and equipment for touring, back country and telemark skiing.

Other Active Pursuits

Ice skating is available in the center of the village at the **Jackson Arena,** (802) 253-4402. At least a couple of hours are scheduled daily for public skating, and evening skating is offered on Friday and Saturday nights. Skate rentals are available. Admission, $2.

Sleigh rides are offered through Charlie Horse Sleigh, Carriage and Wagon Rides, (802) 253-2215. By reservation, you can go on a romantic ride in a two-horse open sleigh day or night. Rates are adults $15 day, $18 night; children $10 day, $15 night. Sleigh rides are also offered at Edson Hill Manor, Stoweflake Inn, Stowehof Inn and Trapp Family Lodge.

Snowshoeing is popular. Guided tours are available through the Mountain Bike Shop (253-7919), Topnotch Resort (253-9649) and Umiak Outdoor Outfitters (253-2317).

Indoor swimming is available to the public (for a fee) at the swimming pools of the Golden Eagle Resort, Mountaineer Inn, Salzburg Inn, Topnotch Resort and Town & Country Motor Lodge. The pool at Topnotch (253-9649) is especially large and luxurious.

Indoor tennis courts are available at Topnotch Resort (253-9649).

Snowmobiling can be arranged through Nichol's at (802) 253-7239.

Green Mountain Club, Route 100, Waterbury Center, (802) 244-7037. This serious organization of outdoor enthusiasts, headquartered just south of Stowe, offers lessons and group tours in snowshoeing, cross-country skiing and winter hiking. Workshops and evening talks are scheduled.

The Stowe Winter Carnival

The king of winter carnivals, Stowe's annual extravaganza prevails for about ten days in late January or early February. Activities include a snow sculpture competition, snowshoe race, snow volleyball, dog sled races, telemark and downhill races, snow golf competition (in the snow, in costume), a 15-kilometer cross-country race and evening entertainment. In 1997, the 75-year anniversary was celebrated by resurrecting the sport of snow joring, which involves a skier being pulled by a horse.

Other Activities

The Helen Day Art Center. Located in a restored 1860 Greek Revival building in the downtown area, the art center offers changing exhibits, mostly by contemporary and Vermont artists. The comfortable **Stowe Public Library** is in the same building, and some hours overlap.

School Street, Stowe. (802) 253-8358. Art Center, Tuesday-Saturday noon to 5. Adults $2, students 50 cents.

Ben & Jerry's Ice Cream Factory Tours. The colorful headquarters building for Ben & Jerry's ice cream is a fun stop, especially for families. Tours are 30 minutes long and begin every half hour. Note: there's no production of ice cream on Sundays, but you can still take the tour. There is a big gift shop with Ben & Jerry souvenirs to purchase.

Route 100, Waterbury. (802) 244-8687. Daily, 9 to 5. Adults $1.50, children free.

Art Galleries. Of many in the area, we particularly like the **Blue Heron Gallery** on Route 100 in the center of town, where the works of popular Vermont artists Sabra Field and Stephen Huneck are shown, along with local artists' works.

The five-mile **Stowe Recreation Path,** a favorite of pedestrians and bicyclists in summer, is sometimes used by cross-country skiers in winter.

Shopping

Stowe offers many boutiques and shops and, thank goodness, none of those seemingly ubiquitous outlet centers. This is a great place to do your holiday shopping – or to get a head start for next Christmas.

Among our favorites: **Wildflower Designs,** a shop filled with unusual dried floral arrangements, candles, candlesticks, pottery and all kinds of flags and banners; **Dia north of Boston,** whose hand-loomed sweaters are incredible; **The Farmhouse Collection** for Simon Pearce hand-blown glass and pottery and other handsome crafts; **The Game Shop,** traditional and contemporary games from checkers to magic tricks, and **Stowe Forge & Stone Works** for architectural stone, hearthstones, birdbaths and wrought iron.

Shaw's General Store in the center of town is chock-full of Stowe stuff and general merchandise, from tasteful tees to shoes and boots. The **Stowe Kitchen Company** is a gourmet kitchen store with glassware, dishes, placemats and such. The gift shop adjoining the Austrian Tea Room at the **Trapp Family Lodge** displays nice items, especially Christmas ornaments, Trapp family books and music, jams and other specialty foods, including the lodge's famed linzertorte.

For ski and sports equipment, check out **Pinnacle Ski & Sports, Jim Shephard Ski Shop, Today's Edge** (overnight ski tuning and repairs), **Boots-n-Boards** and **Front Four Sports,** all located along Mountain Road.

Where to Stay

Lodging options in Stowe are great. You can find everything from a simple but homey motel room to elegant accommodations in pampering, full-service resorts. Many places have guest rooms with fireplaces. Several offer breakfast and dinner plans in winter. Often there are hot tubs, indoor pools and saunas. Here are choices in different categories.

A Country Lodge

Edson Hill Manor. A nearly mile-long country lane leads from the road to this lovely manor house, a true country inn owned by ex-Montrealers Eric and Jane Lande. The French Provincial style, brick and wood-beam manor, built as a country retreat in 1940, became an inn in the mid-1950s. Since its purchase by the Landes in 1991, it has come into its own as one of the most charming and relaxing places to stay that we know of – and an especially romantic choice for a couple wanting privacy and seclusion. Ten guest rooms in the manor house, which retains the flavor of a country home, are tastefully decorated and five have wood-burning fireplaces. All sixteen units in four newer carriage houses on a knoll across from the main house have fireplaces. Our spacious, pine-paneled abode in the carriage house came with a king bed, carpeting and two navy wing chairs beside a window with a good view of the grounds and mountains. We drifted off to sleep to the flickering of flames in the brick fireplace with raised hearth. The pine-paneled parlor in the main house has an understated elegance with oriental rugs on the floor, comfortable sofas facing the Delft-tiled fireplace and fine paintings on the walls. A handsomely decorated downstairs lounge is another space for relaxing. The Edson Hill dining room is highly regarded, and since the owners also own the Ten Acres Lodge in Stowe, guests have reciprocal dining privileges there. The 225-acre property includes stables and cross-country trails.

1500 Edson Hill Road, Stowe 05672. (802) 253-7371 or (800) 621-0284. Fax (802) 635-2694. Doubles, $110 to $170 B&B; $150 to $210 MAP.

An In-Town Inn

Green Mountain Inn. Built as a private residence in 1833, the Green Mountain Inn became a hotel not long afterward. It was restored for its 150th anniversary recently and continues to upgrade. Forty guest rooms are in the main inn and 24 in an annex to the rear. Several are considered "club rooms" with jacuzzis and fireplaces. Almost all have a canopied queen or kingsize bed, country quilts, TVs in armoires or wall niches and full baths. Wall stenciling and wainscoting add to the country inn feeling. The main-floor common rooms, especially the two front parlors, are gracious with oriental carpets and traditional sofas and chairs. There's a bustling quality to this place, for its lower-level dining spot, **The Whip Bar & Grill** (see Where to Eat), is popular with the public as well as house guests. The hotel's main dining room was being completely renovated when we were there.

Main Street (Route 100), Stowe 05672. (802) 253-7301 or (800) 253-7302. Fax (802) 253-5096. Doubles, $113 to $169 EP; suites, $159 to $309 EP.

Bed and Breakfasts

Brass Lantern Inn. An 1800 farmhouse and carriage barn north of town, this B&B has won an award for its restoration, most of which innkeeper Andy Aldrich did himself. All nine comfortable guest rooms with planked floors have private baths and are furnished with antiques and homemade quilts. The romantic Honeymoon Room has a reproduction Victorian queensize bed with heart-shaped headboard and footboard, two wing chairs and "frolic pillows" on the floor in front of a brick fireplace. Two other rooms have fireplaces and three have whirlpool tubs. An ell-shaped parlor on the main floor has a fireplace, a piano, a table with a jigsaw puzzle in progress and plenty of reading material. Andy serves a full breakfast in an attractive country-style dining room with individual oak tables and chairs, and a collection of baskets hanging from overhead beams. Among the offerings are fruit, warm breads and possibly a broccoli-mushroom quiche or "world famous apple crêpes." The outdoor deck yields great views of the mountain.

717 Maple St. (Route 100), Stowe 05672. (802) 253-2229 or (800) 729-2980. Doubles, $80 to $180.

The Gables Inn. For more than twenty years, Sol and Lynn Baumrind have run this friendly B&B halfway between village and mountain, constantly adding to and upgrading the facilities. Now they have thirteen rooms, all with private baths, in the main inn; four romantic Carriage House suites, and two spacious and luxurious Riverview suites in a separate farmhouse. Our Master Bedroom in the main inn had a canopied queen bed, fireplace and sitting area at one end. Carriage House suites offer cathedral ceilings, whirlpool tubs and fireplaces. Each of the Riverview suites occupies a full floor; that on the second floor has a dual fireplace that can be enjoyed in both the living room and king bedroom, plus a jacuzzi tub large enough for two. The Gables is famous for its breakfasts (included in the rates), which attracts the public as well. House guests can choose any menu item they want. A specialty is stuffed french toast made with raisin bread. The downstairs den is used for après-ski; the owners put out crockpots full of hot soup, hot hors d'oeuvres and crackers and cheese for hungry skiers, who BYOB. Dinner is also available in winter.

1457 Mountain Road (Route 108). Stowe 05672. (802) 253-7730 or (800) 422-5371. Doubles, $90 to $125; suites, $145 to $190.

The Siebeness. Longtime innkeepers Nils and Sue Andersen took over this B&B in 1973 and inherited the name, which means "seven 's's," from prior owners. The house is extremely comfortable, the kind of place to come back to after a hard day on the slopes and just settle in. The Andersens set up a BYOB bar in the large living room with a huge stone fireplace. Off the main room is a smaller TV room and library. A five-course country breakfast is served at individual tables in the breakfast room. In the main inn are ten homey bedrooms, all with private baths and duvets or quilts on the beds. New in 1996 were two fireplaced suites with TVs and refrigerators in a separate building out back.

3681 Mountain Road (Route 108). Stowe 05672. (802) 253-8942 or (800) 426-9001. Doubles, $90 to 135; suites, $170.

A Ski Lodge and Motel

Hob Knob Inn. Built as one of the country's first ski lodges, the Hob Knob has been run with care since 1965 by Debbie and George Rigby. He is a chef who oversees the dining room here (see Where to Eat). They offer seventeen units in the back building, which is more like a motel, and three fireplaced rooms with great mountain views in the front restaurant building. There is also a rustic cabin with fireplace and kitchen. All rooms have a king or two queen beds, private baths, TV and telephones. Those in the restaurant building have wood-burning fireplaces and one is a suite with kitchenette, handsomely furnished in light wood. The fireplaced lounge exudes après-ski conviviality, and another large stone fireplace in the dining room adds charm. Once settled in, you barely need leave, although you're free to try other restaurants as well. A full breakfast is included.

2364 Mountain Road (Route 108). Stowe 05672. (802) 253-8549 or (800) 245-8540. Doubles, $80 to $110; cabin $110; suite, $130.

Resorts

Topnotch at Stowe. This AAA four-diamond resort is perfectly suited to its Vermont environment and the low, contemporary building with lots of dark wood and stone and large picture windows manages to be luxurious but not glitzy. The main building, located up a driveway from the Mountain Road, contains all 92 guest rooms with a variety of king, queen and twin beds. There are also suites and townhomes. The main lounge, down a few steps from where you check in, with its floor to ceiling windows overlooking a snowy landscape, sofas and game tables and a glass center-of-the-room fireplace, is cheery. The spa with 60-foot lap pool is in one of the prettiest rooms we've seen. The 120-acre resort includes an equestrian center, a cross-country ski center, indoor tennis courts and hiking trails. Two restaurants, a cocktail lounge and cushy places to curl up with a book contribute to the total experience.

4000 Mountain Road, Box 1458, Stowe 05672. (802) 253-8585 or (800) 451-8686. Fax (802) 253-9263. Doubles, $198 to $300 EP; suites, $200 to $685; townhomes, $210 to $595.

Golden Eagle Resort. The Golden Eagle began life as a motel and wound up as a low-key resort. After the acquisition of the adjacent Alpine Motel, the complex has been expanded to include ten buildings on 80 acres. Owned and managed by the Hillman family, it has a friendly, "all in the family" feeling. The low, dark brown buildings are within a half-mile walk of town. The variety of accommodations appeals to families as well as couples. All ninety have private baths, televisions, telephones, comfortable chairs, refrigerators and coffeemakers. Fifteen or so come with fireplaces or whirlpool baths; some are one-bedroom suites, and others a single bedroom. Rooms have a king or two double beds. Tall Timbers, a free-standing chalet with two bedrooms, is a private sylvan retreat. A hearty breakfast is served in a fireplaced breakfast room near the main office. The resort features a fitness center with a 50-foot heated indoor pool, sauna and huge whirlpool. An outdoor pond is frequently the site of late-afternoon ice-skating parties with hot chocolate.

Mountain Road, Box 1090, Stowe 05672. (802) 253-4811 or (800) 626-1010. Fax (802) 253-2561. Doubles, $84 to $179; suites and apartments, $169 to $299.

A Place Apart

Trapp Family Lodge. Calling itself "a mountain resort in the European tradition," the Trapp Family Lodge is located high on a hillside with views over the town and countryside. The lodge, still run by the family that escaped Austria during World War II and whose story inspired "The Sound of Music," is a bit off the main roads of Stowe and seems a place apart. Of the 93 hotel rooms, 73 are in the main lodge and 20 in a separate facility across the road. It's more fun to stay in the main Tyrolean lodge for real Austrian atmosphere. Rooms have been redecorated recently in cheerful country prints and convey Old World charm, enhanced by the old black and white family photographs mounted on walls. All in the main lodge have balconies or private patios. Guests have use of a fitness center, heated indoor pool, sauna and the most extensive cross-country skiing area in Stowe. Full breakfasts and five-course, prix-fixe dinners are available in the main dining room and lunch in the separate **Austrian Tea Room** (see Where to Eat) with its view across the snowy fields. Tea is served in the fireplaced lounge in the afternoon and a light supper menu is available there as well.

42 Trapp Hill Road, Stowe 05672. (802) 253-8511 or (800) 826-7000. Fax (802) 253-5740. Doubles, $148 to $198 EP; $234 to $284 MAP.

Motels

The Mountaineer Inn. This especially attractive property is set back from the road, with 51 recently renovated rooms in a long building with two wings. The feeling is Austrian, from the Tyrolean-style tower on the exterior to the light wood furnishings in each room, the pieces painted with Austrian designs. Most rooms have two double or queensize beds and access to built-in ski closets in the corridor outside each. The central lobby with soaring glass windows and a raised-hearth fireplace is where guests pick up a continental breakfast. There are also a nice indoor pool and sauna. In winter, a restaurant operates on the premises.

Mountain Road, RR 1, Box 1410, Stowe 05672. (802) 253-7525. Doubles, $95.

Town & Country Resort at Stowe. About 45 rooms in four different buildings are available on this property, which also has an indoor and an outdoor swimming pool, sauna, game room and tennis court. Most rooms have a king or two double beds; several larger family rooms accommodate up to six people. The Carriage House restaurant offers house guests a complimentary full breakfast and optional dinner, and there's a Fireside Pub for a hot toddy or light snack.

876 Mountain Road, Stowe 05672. (802) 253-7595 or (800) 323-0311. Fax (802) 253-4764. Doubles, $85 to $120.

Special Values

Miguel's Stowe Away. The bedrooms above the Mexican restaurant by the same name are one of the bargains in Stowe. Six rooms have private baths and three share one bath. A large family room with king bed and two twins is perfect for a skiing family, while a small room with double bed and private bath might suit a couple. Rooms with shared baths have sinks in the rooms. Decorating is simple – mostly solid blue puffy bedspreads and plain walls. Rates include a full breakfast downstairs in the restaurant, and you can get a good dinner here, too (see Where to Eat). The pool table in the restaurant and a huge warming fireplace may entice you to while away a few hours. The bar is convivial, as well.

3148 Mountain Road, Stowe 05672. (802) 253-7574 or (800) 245-1240. Doubles, $50 to $65 (shared bath), $60 to $75 (private bath).

Vermont State Ski Dorm. The closest accommodations to Mount Mansfield – and the cheapest – are in this venerable ski dorm operated by the Vermont Youth Conservation Corps. The corps is a private non-profit organization that hires teenagers who work and study under adult leadership in park management projects on public lands in Vermont. The building was constructed in 1933 by the Civilian Conservation Corps to be used as a side camp while CCC members were working on Mount Mansfield and so has an historic connection with the mountain. Two large second-floor rooms hold 22 bunks for women, 26 for men. A country breakfast ($4) and a hearty dinner ($6) are offered in a good-sized dining room with picnic-style tables and chairs. There is also a large living room with huge fieldstone fireplace and chairs and sofas for lounging. You can walk easily from here to the Mount Mansfield base lodge, which is just beyond the parking lot across Mountain Road. There's a midnight curfew, and you must vacate the dorm daily between 9 and 4, which is usually no problem for skiers. Reserve two weeks ahead to be sure of a bed, although walk-ins are welcome (space permitting) up to 10 p.m. Hint: often this place is available during the Christmas holiday week when it is so tough, and expensive, to get accommodations elsewhere.

6992 Mountain Road, Stowe 05672. (802) 253-4010. Singles, $25.

Stowe/Brownell Photo

Mount Mansfield provides wintry backdrop for picturesque village of Stowe.

Where to Eat

Stowe offers a wide range of options, from quick snacks to sophisticated dining. Gourmets will find satisfying choices, although the emphasis is on "hot and hearty," especially during the ski season.

Fine Dining

Isle de France. Chef-owner Jean Lavina's food is acclaimed by those who dine at this elegant French restaurant. The chandeliered and mirrored main dining room – all white tablecloths and napery and deep rose accents – is quite formal, a "special occasion" room if ever there was one. More cozy and very popular is the lounge, known as **Claudine's Bistro,** where you can enjoy a limited selection of the same quality food at lower prices. We were happy to settle here on a cold winter night to enjoy the warmth of the wood stove and the conviviality provided by locals who all seemed to know one another. The lounge is a two-level space with rough plaster walls, dark wood trim, a three-tiered chandelier hanging from a high ceiling and floral cloths on the tables. Crisp, warm sourdough wheat bread arrived with our bottle of pinot noir, chosen from an award-winning wine cellar. Among bistro entrées, the night's special, trout amandine served with green beans and garlic-baked, stuffed potatoes, was piping hot and delicious. The filet mignon with béarnaise sauce came with a selection of fresh vegetables and rice. Other choices were poached salmon with hollandaise sauce, sole meunière and chicken forestière. In the main dining room, entrées include frog legs provençal, veal marsala, roast duck with orange or apple-flavored sauce, and medallions of beef with a creamy bourbon sauce. You can start with the classic French onion soup or escargots bourguignonne. For dessert, the meringue glacé, crème caramel and bananas foster come well recommended.

1899 Mountain Road. (802) 253-7751. Entrées, bistro, $11 to $14; dining room, $17 to $23. Dinner nightly except Monday, 6 to 9.

Blue Moon Cafe. This small, side-street storefront near the center of town holds probably the most inventive restaurant in the Stowe area. Chef-owner Jack Pickett, who made a name at Ten Acres Lodge before striking off on his own, oversees a kitchen that creates innovative combinations of food. Diners sit at white-clothed tables with mismatched chairs in the front window spaces or in a larger room at the back containing a service bar. Menus change every couple of weeks. Recent winter appetizers included Maine crab cakes with black bean salsa and chipotle sauce, grilled andouille sausage with sauerkraut and steamed blue potatoes, and wild rice galette with smoked trout, glazed leeks and dried cherry compote. Main-course choices were grilled tuna with avocado, tequila and lime sauce; marinated butterflied leg of lamb with winter squash puree, and sirloin steak with grilled portobello mushroom and sweet onion jam. Crème brûlée and homemade sorbets are among the desserts..

35 School St. (802) 253-7006. Entrées, $14 to $17. Dinner nightly, 6 to 9:30

Ten Acres Lodge. The dining rooms at this country inn, off by itself on a side road, are tranquil and pretty. It's the kind of refined atmosphere you'd choose for a quiet tête-à-tête or to take parents to dinner. A single slate blue candle in a handsome wrought-iron candleholder graces each beige-clothed table in three dining rooms. The lodge is owned by the same people as Edson Hill Manor and similar menus and prices prevail. Dinner appetizers might be a fresh spinach fettuccine, shrimp cocktail or vegetarian antipasto. For main courses, consider a grilled trio of salmon, tuna and swordfish, grilled free-range chicken breast, roasted rack of lamb or sautéed black angus filet mignon. Warm apple-pecan bread pudding or chocolate marquise might hit the spot for dessert.

14 Barrows Road. (802) 253-7638. Entrées, $17 to $22. Dinner nightly, 6 to 9.

Dining on High

The Cliff House Restaurant. Hop on the gondola from the parking lot at the base of the mountain to the Stowe Mountain Resort's deluxe restaurant at the summit, where the view, day or night, is fabulous. At night, you can watch skiers on the Gondolier, Stowe's new lighted trail below. The tables bear linens, fresh flowers and candles. Dinner is prix-fixe in four courses. You might start with rabbit pâté with tomato-golden raisin chutney or pan-fried crab cake on Boston brown bread with light curry sauce. A mixed green or caesar salad precedes the main course. Typical choices are grilled yellowfin tuna with a tomatillo salsa, roast duck with fruit chutney and grilled filet mignon with shiitake mushroom sauce. Dessert could be chocolate-chip cheesecake or hazelnut torte.

Atop Mount Mansfield. (802) 253-3665. Prix-fixe, $39. Dinner by reservation, Thursday-Sunday 5:30 to 9. Also Wednesday in summer.

Villa Tragara. Located six miles south of Stowe on the main approach route, Villa Tragara is consistently praised by the locals for superior Italian food. The white house situated above the road has several dining rooms with red-clothed tables and bentwood chairs. Starters include mussels marinara and woodland mushrooms sautéed with garlic, shallots, brandy and cream and served on grilled Italian bread. For entrées, there's a range of pasta, meat and seafood dishes. You might try seafood linguini, risotto sautéed with portobello mushrooms and grilled vegetables, rabbit braised with shiitake mushrooms, baby onions and prunes, or rack of lamb sauced with madeira wine. Entrées come with soup or salad, vegetables and pasta.

Route 100, Waterbury Center. (802) 244-5288. Entrées, $14 to $19. Dinner, Wednesday-Sunday in winter, 5:30 to 9:30, also Tuesday in summer.

Hot and Hearty

Hob Knob Inn. With nicely spaced tables dressed in green over red plaid undercloths and a huge stone fireplace at one end, the dining room at this – Stowe's first ski lodge – is festive and cozy. If you have to wait for a table, enjoy a drink in the fireplaced lounge, one of the most atmospheric around. Chef-owner George Rigby has been whipping up meals for some thirty years and knows what skiers like. The menu stresses beef – certified angus – and you can get a New York strip steak, filet mignon, ribeye or petite strip sirloin. Other choices include broiled salmon, shrimp scampi, roast duckling bigarade and chicken of the day. A mixed salad comes with entrées. Starters might be stuffed mushrooms, french onion soup and escargots bourguignonne.

2364 Mountain Road. (802) 253-8549. Entrées, $15 to $18. Dinner nightly except Tuesday, 6 to 9.

The Whip Bar & Grill. An impressive collection of antique buggy whips separates the plaid and wood dining room from the bar at this atmospheric spot on the lower level of the Green Mountain Inn. A garden dining room with an expanse of french doors looks onto a patio used in warm weather. The menus for both lunch and for dinner are large and varied. For lunch, you can have a club sandwich, crabmeat croissant, veggie melt or a Philly cheese steak for $6 to $10. There are also burgers, specialties like crab cakes or stir-fries, and an entire page of vegetarian specialties. In the evening, appetizers include artichoke dip with pita, steamed mussels and baked brie with walnuts and apples. You can still get a burger or a couple of sandwiches, and entrées like seared salmon, sirloin steak, barbecued baby back ribs and roast turkey. For dessert, how about blueberry-apple crumb pie, bread pudding with crème anglaise or the famous Sac de Bon Bon – a semi-sweet chocolate bag filled with a light chocolate mousse (for two).

Main Street. (802) 253-7301. Entrées, $10 to $20. Open daily, 11:30 to 9:30; Sunday brunch, 11 to 2:30.

Miguel's Stowe Away. "Authentic Mexican food" is featured at one of Stowe's more popular après-ski spots. The table for six in front of the large fireplace across from the bar is often taken by a group of ski instructors from the mountain, and all is convivial and cheerful. Appetizers include empanadas filled with chorizo, potatoes and cheese, and queso fundido (Vermont cheddar and jack cheeses baked with grilled lamb sausage). The menu lists "Tex-Mex Especiales" as well as Mexi-

can dishes like crab enchiladas, sweet and spicy shrimp with roasted garlic and chiles, chicken breast stuffed with cornbread and pecans, and grilled flank steak with cheese enchilada mole and cactus salad. For dessert, try a double chocolate torte, coconut flan, or light fried whole wheat dough served with honey butter.
3148 Mountain Road. (802) 253-7574. Entrées, $9.50 to $14. Dinner nightly, 5 to 10.

Trattoria de la Festa. The DeVito brothers (chef Antonio and Giancarlo, the sommelier) and partner Patricia Hammer, the pastry chef, bring a light-hearted attitude to their Italian restaurant, located to the rear of the Toscano Inn, a B&B. All three cut their culinary teeth in the Boston area, and their Stowe restaurant seems to have carved a niche for itself. Opera and other Italian music play in the background, the tables are dressed in red, and colorful lights are strung here and there. Pastas are the specialty. A special, spinach linguini with shrimp and vegetables, was good but very peppery and, unfortunately, overdone. Crusty bread and a good salad of mixed greens with a light vinaigrette dressing compensated. Other possibilities included lasagna Toscana, spaghetti puttanesca, fettuccine with fresh vegetables, and penne with ricotta cheese, broccoli and a cream sauce. Veal marsala and chicken parmigiana are also on the menu.
4080 Mountain Road. (802)253-8480. Entrées, $10 to $15. Dinner nightly, 5:30 to 10.

On the Casual Side

Gracie's. People love to hang out in this casual, cozy and dark refuge dominated by a large bar at one end and a huge brick fireplace at the other, with tiny white lights on the ceiling and tiered wood booths in between. Restaurateurs Susan and Paul Archdeacon named the place after their dog. Featured are "doggone good burgers" in different styles, but there's lots more. For lunch, sandwiches like the veggie special or the German shepherd (open-faced pastrami, coleslaw and swiss cheese) are offered along with entrées ($7 to $11) such as Marmaduke's meatloaf or pointer pot pies. At night, the "Neptune's Garden" section of the menu offers cashew-crusted salmon or swordfish, baked stuffed shrimp, and broiled or baked stuffed sole. Meat dishes include tenderloin tips, roast duck with a cranberry-red curry sauce or a sixteen-ounce steak served several ways. The evening menu also offers dinner-size salads and appetizers like nachos, marinated shrimp cocktail, conch fritters and batter-fried onion rings.
Main Street. (802) 253-8741. Entrées, $14 to $18. Lunch daily, 11 to 5; dinner, 5 to 11; late night menu, 11 to midnight.

The Shed Restaurant & Brewery. After a fire in 1994, one of Stowe's most popular restaurants was reconstructed, and a brew pub – brewing seven varieties of ales and beers – was added. The big red building has a couple of large fireplaced dining rooms in the front, and some light and airy greenhouse areas in back. There is incredible variety on the menu. You can try a grilled swordfish sandwich, a Greek or caesar salad, a veggie burger (one of the items the place is famed for, although ours was on the dry, tasteless side), Asian stir-fried noodles or a grilled gyro for lunch ($5 to $8). In the evening, entrées range from baked stuffed haddock and seafood strudel to prime rib and lamb bourbon. Chicken and broccoli scampi is a dinner specialty. Wash it all down with a selection from the Hall of Foam – amber ale, West Branch golden or a pale ale called the National in honor of one of the Front Four trails on Mount Mansfield. The lounge, with its popcorn machine, is a fun place to hang out.

Mountain Road. (802) 253-4364. Entrées $13 to $16. Lunch daily, 11:30 to 4:30; dinner, 5 to 10.

Depot Street Malt Shoppe. Take yourself back to the Fifties at this cleverly decorated – right down to the jukeboxes, ice-cream chairs and old Coca-Cola coolers – restaurant in the center of town. Locals rave about all the burgers ($4 to $5); we liked the sound of the patty melt on grilled rye with Russian dressing, onions and Swiss cheese. A hot dog, a chili dog, a western and a turkey club are among the possibilities. There's even a diet plate of chicken, tuna or egg salad and cottage cheese – just like some we remember from the Fifties. Fountain treats include cherry and vanilla Cokes, floats, ice-cream sodas, frappes and egg creams. A banana split costs $3.50. In the evening, one or two dinner specials appear on a blackboard.

Depot Street, near the Stowe post office. (802) 253-4269. Entrées, $10 range. Daily, 11 to 9.

For Lunch

The Austrian Tea Room. This brown-stained building across the road from the main Trapp Family Lodge overlooks a picturesque hillside where, on a snowy day, we enjoyed watching the shaggy Scottish highland sheep that graze there. Sit by one of the large windows to view the scene, or warm up next to the fireplace by the bar. Waitresses in dirndls serve the food, which we found to be quite good. One of us had a bowl of delicious mushroom, spinach and rice soup and a mixed salad with an orange-sesame-ginger dressing, while the other had an open-face turkey and asparagus sandwich with cheese sauce. The menu also lists several Austrian wursts, served with sauerkraut and potato salad, a braunschweiger liverwurst and onion sandwich, and entrées such as Hungarian beef goulash, shrimp and potato salad, and chicken caesar salad. You might have linzertorte for dessert. There is a good gift shop in the same building.

Trapp Hill Road. (802) 253-8511. Entrées, $6 to $10. Lunch daily, 10:30 to 5:30.

Breakfast Time

McCarthy's. This restaurant in a small shopping center is where the locals have come for breakfast since 1974, and the line is often out the door. A large open kitchen and a black and white tiled floor set the scene for selections ranging from waffles and omelets to breakfast sandwiches, oatmeal, granola and eggs any style. Prices are reasonable – $2.99 for a basic omelet, $3.19 for pancakes. Sides include scones, cinnamon rolls, sticky buns, muffins and pumpkin bread with cream cheese. A lunch menu with the usual kicks in around midday.

Mountain Road. (802) 253-8626. Daily, 6:30 to 3.

FOR MORE INFORMATION: The Stowe Area Association, Main Street, Box 1320, Stowe, VT 05672. (802) 253-7321 or (800) 247-8693.

18 ❄ Winter

Boston Harbor Hotel at Rowes Wharf is part of changing downtown skyline.

Big-City Splurge

Boston, Mass.

New England's hub is a wonderful place to weekend. No matter what your interests, Boston can satisfy. You want sports? There are the Celtics, the Bruins and the Red Sox. Interested in history? Visit the Freedom Trail, Old Ironsides, Bunker Hill. How about shopping? Find everything from designer suits to western boots. Culture? Consider the symphony, the art museums and the libraries.

Those of us who live elsewhere in New England are attracted to all of these options. But there are other lures: The soft red brick of Beacon Hill and the stately air of Back Bay. The busy waterfront. The Charles River. Boston conveys an elegance, an assuredness, a sense of place. Perhaps it's the age of the city that does it, with constant reminders of its heritage in a metropolis that is, at the same time, modern and vibrant .

Most of us – even first-time visitors – feel familiar with Boston. That's not surprising, since so much of Boston's history lives in our national heritage, so many of her moments are fixed in our memories. There is Revolutionary Boston (Paul Revere, Sam Adams and the Boston Tea Party) and there is Bulfinch's Boston (the glorious, gold-capped State House and so much of Beacon Hill's architecture). There are a taste of Boston (baked beans and brown bread and Boston cream pie) and a sound of Boston (the Symphony, the Pops and the 1812 Overture on the banks of the Charles River on the Fourth of July).

Boston is a city of the learned and the literate. The nation's first public school, the famed Boston Latin School, was founded here in 1635; a year later, Harvard opened its doors as the first institution of higher learning. Boston is home to the oldest public library supported by taxation in the country.

And now, for all of us who want to spend time in Boston, there are fine hotels and restaurants. Luxury hotels have risen on the city's waterfront and overlooking her public garden. Great chefs vie for star ratings in hotel dining rooms and chic restaurants, and food-loving visitors are among the beneficiaries.

The shopping is sensational. Prompted by the success of the Faneuil Hall Marketplace in the 1970s, the city has witnessed the building of the tony Copley Place, where you can shop at Neiman-Marcus and other noted emporia. Newbury Street remains the place for objets d'art, antiques and designer fashions. On Charles Street you'll find interesting antiques shops, greengrocers and leather goods.

Boston is not an inexpensive place to visit, if you want to do it right. So grab your wallet and your walking shoes and prepare for a splurge. Boston is *the* city in New England for the traveler.

Getting There

When George Washington visited Boston, he had to take the old King's Highway, Route 1. Today's traveler has an easier time of it. The Massachusetts Turnpike (I-90) leads directly into downtown from the west. Interstate 95 comes in from Maine and Rhode Island. Interstate 93 brings visitors south from Vermont and New Hampshire, and Route 3 is a fast route north from Cape Cod.

Amtrak trains serve Boston and commuter trains take suburbanites into the city from the west and north. Interstate buses serve the city at midtown terminals.

Most major airlines fly into Logan International Airport. A water shuttle takes air passengers to Rowes Wharf on the downtown waterfront.

Getting Around

Boston is an impossible city to navigate by car without fortitude, good humor and just plain luck. Even Bostonians seem puzzled by the traffic. Park your car at your hotel, underneath the Boston Common or at the Prudential Center and walk. Boston's subway (the "T") is the nation's oldest but far from its grubbiest and is a bargain. Four color-coded lines (blue, orange, green and red) take you almost anyplace you want to go. For extended stays, visitors can purchase a three- or seven-day Boston Passport for unlimited passage on the MBTA's four subway lines, trolleys and most bus routes. The three-day pass is $9; the seven-day pass, $18.

Taxis are expensive and not always easy to find. But they are sometimes necessary, especially when going to and from a restaurant in the evening.

Seeing and Doing

If a Bostonian were asked what a weekender should do in his city, he'd probably recommend attending a concert by the Boston Symphony Orchestra. He'd be sure to suggest a visit to the Museum of Fine Arts and another to the Gardner Museum with its flower-banked inner courtyard and chamber music concerts. He'd tell you to walk around Beacon Hill and to shop at Copley Place, Quincy Market and along Newbury and Charles streets. He'd probably urge a visit to the John F. Kennedy Library and perhaps the Boston Public Library.

He might not know you can visit a lavish Victorian townhouse in Back Bay, a Bulfinch residence in the West End or a fine house museum right on Beacon Hill.

A first stop for the culturally minded visitor is the Bostix Ticket Booth at Faneuil Hall Marketplace, (617) 423-4454. Tickets are available here for cultural events, including same-day, half-price tickets to commercial theaters. You also can pick up information about museums. Stop in and see the refurbished Faneuil Hall itself while here, and enjoy the shops of Faneuil Hall Marketplace.

Music

Boston Symphony Orchestra. The 1900 McKim, Mead and White building called Symphony Hall, with its columned facade and gilded interior, holds a warm and prideful place in the hearts of Bostonians. The renowned Boston Symphony Orchestra, under the baton of Seiji Ozawa, and the Boston Pops are at home here. The BSO is on in the winter and single tickets are devilishly difficult to come by. The Friday matinee is famous. Beacon Hill dowagers, retired gentlemen and suburban matrons hold most subscriptions and in the ladies room it sounds like old home week. We remember one concert when the older woman next to us began to cough. We slipped her a cough drop and at intermission she confided, "I've been coming to Symphony for 50 years and I've lived in dread that something like that would happen. You saved my life!" The acoustics are marvelous and the audience exceptionally well-mannered. A few special "rush seats" are available for Friday matinees and Tuesday and Thursday evenings, going on sale at 9 a.m. Friday and 5 p.m. the other days. It's one ticket to a customer and you'll have to vie with Boston's music and university students to get the $7 tickets.

Symphony Hall, Huntington and Massachusetts Avenues. (617) 266-1492.

Emmanuel Church, 15 Newbury St., (617) 536-3355. It takes about seven years to complete the entire cycle of Bach cantatas but they've done it at the Emmanuel Church, a city church that expresses much of its ministry through the arts, music in particular. This ecumenical church with an Episcopal base has a 10 a.m. service on Sunday, which is when you'll hear the Bach cantatas.

The New England Conservatory of Music, 290 Huntington Ave., (617) 262-1120. The conservatory has been in existence for more than 100 years and many musicians performing in the Boston area were trained here. The emphasis is classical, but other forms of music also are taught. More than 300 concerts a year are presented and it's likely you'll be able to find one when you're in town, especially on a Saturday night.

Tea and music. Visitors to the Museum of Fine Arts on Tuesday through Friday afternoons may want to head for the Evans wing for this Boston tradition. New England musicians play while you sip tea in the Ladies Committee Gallery. The cost is $2.

Art

Museum of Fine Arts. With its important collections, Boston's Museum of Fine Arts is a treasure. The West Wing by I.M. Pei with its skylighted gallery added amenities like a fine auditorium, restaurant and exceptional museum shop. In 1996, the Fraser Garden Court – the museum's largest courtyard – was re-opened following extensive renovation. Also new is the William de Kooning monumental bronze sculpture, *Standing Figure,* outside the West Wing entrance. We have always liked the Egyptian art, and who doesn't love the many French Impressionist paintings? The museum should be allotted plenty of time for browsing and, perhaps, a pause for a snack or a meal at its restaurant. It also presents an extensive series of concerts, films and lectures.

465 Huntington Ave. (617) 267-9300. Monday and Tuesday, 10 to 4:45, Wednesday-Friday to 9:45; Saturday and Sunday, 10 to 5:45. Adults $10, students $8. Wednesday evenings after 4, free.

Isabella Stewart Gardner Museum. Within walking distance of the Museum of Fine Arts, the Gardner is unique. Flowers, art and music were the passions of Mrs. Gardner, a New Yorker who was never fully accepted by the Boston society into which she married. She left her memorial in this replica of a Venetian palazzo, crammed with fine art objects and fascinating architectural and sculptural

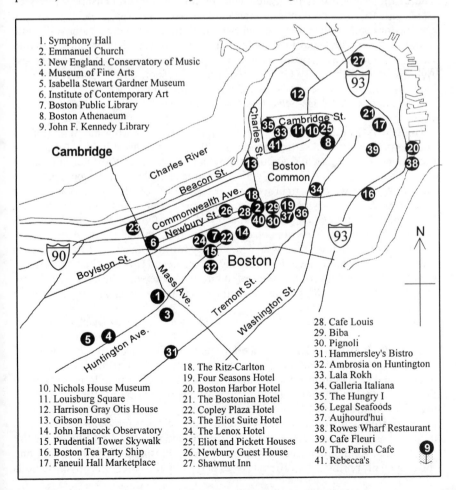

1. Symphony Hall
2. Emmanuel Church
3. New England. Conservatory of Music
4. Museum of Fine Arts
5. Isabella Stewart Gardner Museum
6. Institute of Contemporary Art
7. Boston Public Library
8. Boston Athenaeum
9. John F. Kennedy Library

10. Nichols House Museum
11. Louisburg Square
12. Harrison Gray Otis House
13. Gibson House
14. John Hancock Observatory
15. Prudential Tower Skywalk
16. Boston Tea Party Ship
17. Faneuil Hall Marketplace

18. The Ritz-Carlton
19. Four Seasons Hotel
20. Boston Harbor Hotel
21. The Bostonian Hotel
22. Copley Plaza Hotel
23. The Eliot Suite Hotel
24. The Lenox Hotel
25. Eliot and Pickett Houses
26. Newbury Guest House
27. Shawmut Inn

28. Cafe Louis
29. Biba
30. Pignoli
31. Hammersley's Bistro
32. Ambrosia on Huntington
33. Lala Rokh
34. Galleria Italiana
35. The Hungry I
36. Legal Seafoods
37. Aujhourd'hui
38. Rowes Wharf Restaurant
39. Cafe Fleuri
40. The Parish Cafe
41. Rebecca's

elements, most from the Medieval and Renaissance periods. Flowers, grown in greenhouses on the property, bank the exquisite interior courtyard. Musical concerts are scheduled many weekend afternoons in the handsome, tiled Tapestry Hall, a special atmosphere. Check the concert calendar at the museum desk or call 734-1359.

280 The Fenway. (617) 566-1401. Tuesday-Sunday 11 to 5. Adults $7, students $5.

Institute of Contemporary Art. Housed creatively in a renovated police station in the Back Bay area, this museum mounts changing exhibitions by contemporary artists.

955 Boylston St. (617) 266-5152. Wednesday-Sunday, noon to 5; also Wednesday and Thursday evenings to 9. Adults $7, students $4.

Libraries

Boston Public Library. The beautiful Italian Renaissance building designed by McKim, Mead and White in the 1890s has much to recommend it to the visitor. The central staircase is decorated with murals by the French artist Puvis de Chavannes (his only ones outside France) to represent the areas of poetry, philosophy, history and science. John Singer Sargent decorated the third-floor walls with murals dealing with Judaism and Christianity. In the second-floor Book Delivery Room are the Edwin Austin Abbey wall paintings depicting "The Quest and Achievement of the Holy Grail." From this room look down upon a sanctuary below – the cloistered courtyard with gardens and mosaic tiles.

Copley Square. (617) 536-5400. Monday-Thursday 9 to 9, Friday and Saturday 9 to 5.

Boston Athenaeum. Here on Beacon Street, not far from the State Capitol and behind a sooty and settled facade, are five floors of great books. Among the collections is the library of George Washington, for example. While the Athenaeum is a private shareholders' library, with shares traceable through Boston's patrician past, visitors are welcome to browse on the first two floors. It is an invitation to be accepted. At the desk where you check your parcels and coats, you're handed a large visitor's pass, which must keep with you as you walk around. There is an impressive amount of artwork on the second floor; in fact, it was the Athenaeum's collecting of art that eventually paved the way for the Museum of Fine Arts. On the main floor, with high windows looking out on the old Granary Burying Ground, are two grand reading rooms. We leafed through some periodicals, noted alumni magazines from most Massachusetts colleges and universities, and felt privileged indeed.

10½ Beacon St. (617) 227-0270. Monday-Friday 9 to 5:30, Saturday 9 to 4.

John F. Kennedy Library and Museum. Dedicated to the memory of America's 35th president, the library and museum was designed by I.M. Pei and opened in 1979. Within three months more than 170,000 people had streamed through the exhibition area, and the crowds have never ceased. Visitors watch a half-hour biographical film produced exclusively for the library, and can view excerpts from President Kennedy's televised press conferences, listen to his mother's recorded recollections of his early life, and watch a short film on the life of Robert F. Kennedy. A central exhibit, showing President Kennedy's desk and rocking chair, portrays the different roles played by the chief executive. Exhibits on his personal and family interests recapture the style and atmosphere of his presidency. The introductory film is particularly stirring; you will be moved by JFK's intelligence, vibrancy, sense of humor and the tragedy of his early death. Upstairs are manuscripts and letters of the writer Ernest Hemingway, donated by his widow. A certain stark grandeur is provided the building by its waterfront setting on the Boston campus of the University of Massachusetts.

Morrissey Boulevard. (617) 929-4523. Daily, 9 to 5. Adults $6, students 4.

The Way They Lived

Nichols House Museum. Henry James is reported to have said Mount Vernon was the most proper of Beacon Hill's streets. Few tourists seem to find their way to this house, attributed to Charles Bulfinch, located at the crest of the hill with a splendid view down the street. It's been a museum for some 30 years, willed as such by the unmarried Rose Standish Nichols, a gracious hostess and a landscape architect in her own right. You'll see Flemish tapestry from 1525, the parlor where Miss Nichols hosted afternoon teas and imitation embossed-leather wallpaper in the dining room. But the bookcase-flanked window seat on the third floor, with a glimpse of other brick facades on the street, is our favorite feature. The house is still in use as a neighborhood center and as headquarters for the Boston Council for International Visitors.

55 Mount Vernon St. (617) 227-6993. Tuesday-Saturday noon to 5, May-October; Monday, Wednesday and Saturday in winter. Admission, $4.

Louisburg Square, considered the gemstone of Beacon Hill, is reached from Mount Vernon Street, the equivalent of a block or two below the Nichols House. If the hill is icy, you'll appreciate the iron handrails to help you down. Gaslights lend atmosphere, as do the statues of Aristides and Columbus in the center. Caroling and a handbell concert make the square ring on Christmas Eve.

Harrison Gray Otis House. An appropriately grand location for the head-quarters of the Society of the Preservation of New England Antiquities, this brick Federal mansion is typical of the kind built after the Revolutionary War for well-to-do Bostonians. Charles Bulfinch designed it in 1796 for the Otises, a social couple who kept moving up; after this house they moved to two more Bulfinch-designed houses on Beacon Hill. This is Boston's once fashionable West End, now full of motels, parking lots and stores. But the house is magnificent and its position, jammed among less inspiring neighbors, sets it off to advantage. It has been carefully restored to the period. We love the red, yellow and green patterned carpet in the front parlor, the classic revival look to the dining room and the "with-drawing room" upstairs with its flowery, feminine touches. The Otises were great partygivers and their famous punchbowl is also on display. It was a family tradition to invite friends at 4 p.m. for a drink, possibly a precursor to today's cocktail hour. Otis was a Congressman, mayor of Boston, a land developer and the father of eleven children.

141 Cambridge St. (617) 227-3956. Tuesday-Friday noon to 5, Saturday 10 to 5; tours on the hour through 4. Adults $4, children $2.

Gibson House. Now for the Victorian period. This house in Back Bay was built in 1860 for a family whose bachelor son willed it in 1954 to the private

Gibson Society. He was Charles Hammond Gibson Jr., who kept the place just as it looked in its heyday. Our enthusiastic guide, a graduate student in local history at Northeastern University, said the gilt-embossed linen wallpaper in the foyer is original, and what a start! Check out the Bavarian carved wooden umbrella stand; you've never seen anything like it. The dining room, its table set with family china, is located to the rear of the house and looks out on the narrow lot. The four floors above are chock-full of original, incredible pieces, among them a velvet pet pagoda, a genuine hand-crank victrola, a stereopticon viewer and a magic-lantern slide projector. Even though the house has been open to the public for more than 35 years, it's a find.

137 Beacon St. (617) 267-6338. Tours, Wednesday-Sunday at 1, 2 and 3, May-October; Saturday and Sunday at 1, 2 and 3, rest of year. Admission, $4.

In case you wonder how high the society was in the neighborhood, the plaque across the street cites **152 Beacon St.** as the residence of Isabella Stewart Gardner before she moved to her museum on the Fenway. Once she left, the number was retired at her request.

A Boston Miscellany

Here are other favorite Boston stops.

Boston Common and the **Public Garden.** Boston Common is the oldest public park in the United States – as old as the city around it (1634). Across Charles Street from the Common is the beautiful Public Garden, where Swan Boats sail in the summer and ice skaters glide in winter. It is a lovely place to stroll through – hand-in-hand, of course. The parking garage under Boston Common (enter from Charles) has been newly renovated and brightly lighted and is a good place to park. It's also a bargain on Saturdays and Sundays, $5 all day.

The famed **Freedom Trail** begins at the Boston Common Information Center on Tremont Street, where you may obtain a brochure to guide you. The trail around downtown is about one and a half miles long and includes sixteen historical sites, all clearly marked.

First Night is Boston's creative approach to New Year's Eve. The entire downtown area, the Prudential Center and the Common feature events like puppet shows, jazz concerts, ballet and fireworks. The Boston Pops holds forth at Symphony Hall.

John Hancock Observatory. New England's highest manmade vantage point – the 60th floor of the John Hancock Tower – affords views of Boston and surroundings. There's also a presentation detailing the history of the Revolutionary War in Boston and changes that have occurred in the city's topography in the past two centuries.

200 Clarendon St. (617) 247-1976. Monday-Saturday 9 a.m. to 10 p.m., Sunday 10 to 10. Adults $3.75, children $2.75.

Prudential Tower Skywalk. Take the elevator to the 50th floor of the Prudential for a 360-degree view of Boston and the surrounding area. On a clear day you can see the White Mountains of New Hampshire.

800 Boylston St. (617) 236-3318. Daily, 10 to 10. Adults $3.50, children $2.50.

Boston Tea Party Ship & Museum. Here you combine a history lesson and a good time aboard a full-scale working replica of the Tea Party Ship, moored beside Harbor Walk across from Museum Wharf. Audio-visual presentations in the adjacent museum detail the ship's voyage, the taxing of the tea and the dumping overboard of the tea chests. Costumed guides are knowledgeable.
Congress Street Bridge. (617) 338-1773. Daily 9 to 5, March-November. Adults $6.50, children $3.25.

Boston Duck Tours. Brightly painted amphibious landing craft from World War II take Boston visitors on one of the most fun city tours imaginable, although unfortunately they're not available in winter. The 80-minute excursion by both land and sea includes about a half hour on the Charles River, with a spectacular view of the high-rises all around. From the Prudential Center, you wend your way through the streets of Boston and everyone on the sidewalks seems to wave. Our driver was a young guy with a sense of humor. "Quack, quack," he blared out at every intersection.
101 Huntington Ave. (617) 723-3825. Tours daily, 9 to 5, April-November. Adults, $18.

Shopping

Boston is a fabulous city for shopping, from bargains to books to boutiques.

The downtown department store area along Washington and Tremont streets is not the most elegant in the city, but a pedestrian mall called Downtown Crossing is flanked by **Macy's** (formerly Jordan Marsh) and **Filene's** department stores. The original **Filene's Basement** here is an institution. You may find $500 dresses from Neiman-Marcus going for a fraction of the original price. Brooks Brothers suits, men's quality shoes, children's items and more are discounted, depending on what the latest shipment is and how long the merchandise has been there. One of our friends bought her wedding gown here; we still smile to think of her struggling to try it on in the aisles (there are no dressing rooms). Incredibly, merchandise is returnable.

Faneuil Hall Marketplace, a comfortable walk from Filene's, has maintained its popularity as one of America's favored downtown renovations. Opened in 1976, it has attracted more than 150 merchants, restaurants and even a branch of the Museum of Fine Arts. Now the most visited of Boston's attractions, the marketplace has an information center where you can obtain a listing of the shops and stores and make your way among the North Market, South Market and Quincy Market. There are a fantastic kite shop, a coffee shop, boutiques for men and women, pushcarts with earrings, toys and jewelry, and all sorts of food shops for sandwiches, soups, chocolate-chip cookies and such. Adjacent to the marketplace toward the waterfront is the new **Marketplace Center,** with still more upscale shops. You can easily spend a day – and a bundle – around here.

At the other end of downtown in Back Bay, **Copley Place** is the trendy shopping mall anchored by **Neiman-Marcus. Tiffany, Ralph Lauren, Gucci** and **Brookstone** are all here. There's a lovely Dimitri Hadzi contemporary sculpture and waterfall near the center of the mall. Copley Place connects by skywalks to the new **Shops at Prudential Center,** offering Boston's best food court, more upscale shops and **Saks Fifth Avenue.**

Newbury Street has always been the place for art, antiques, furs, jewelry and designer clothing, and gets more fashionable (and expensive) all the time. Check out **Waterstone's Booksellers** at Newbury and Exeter streets, a three-story, British-owned emporium with frequent readings and book signings. At 175 Newbury, the **Society of Arts and Crafts** carries lots of unusual handmade pieces. **Vose Galleries**, a family-owned art gallery for years and years, is pleasant to visit and you don't feel as if you must buy something. **Gallery NAGA** at 62 Newbury has some of the most interesting art shows we've seen.

Charles Street is also a fun shopping street. **Helen's Leather Shop** is known for its quality handbags and one of the best selections of western boots in New England. The antiques shops on Charles are wonderful. **Blackstone's of Beacon Hill** at 46 Charles has some amazing and unusual gift items; we were smitten by some witches for Halloween. Not far from Charles on Beacon, you may want to stop in the **Bull & Finch Pub,** inspiration for the TV show, "Cheers," and a purveyor of T-shirts and other memorabilia with the Cheers logo.

Where to Stay

For a big-city splurge, we'd choose a hotel with class and taste. The classiest in Boston, for our money, are these:

The Ritz-Carlton. The grand dame of Boston's hotels, the Ritz-Carlton remains the ritziest. Understated elegance and an emphasis on personal service, with uniformed elevator operators who take the time to chat and afternoon tea that really is tea, are reminders of an era of gentility. Our room with kingsize bed, white French Provincial furniture, salmon and green floral draperies, bedspread and matching upholstered chairs and a view of the Public Garden (with ice skaters) was worth every penny. Breakfast in the room, wheeled in by an elderly and experienced waiter, was a memorable indulgence. It arrived on a white-clothed table with a single rose in a bud vase and coffee steaming in a silver pot. The 285-unit hotel (237 rooms and 48 suites) is the flagship of the Ritz-Carlton Hotel Company. The Ritz-Carlton Club, a concierge section on the three uppermost floors, offers such amenities as telephones in bathrooms, hair dryers, room refrigerators and weekday morning limousine service to select areas. Forty-four suites have wood-burning fireplaces. Try for one of the corner rooms, the "09" suites, which look out on bustling Newbury Street and whose fireplaced parlors have a view of the Public Garden. The second-floor **Dining Room** overlooking the Garden and the first-floor **Bar** are favorite gathering places for Bostonians, proper and otherwise. And tea at the Ritz, accompanied by harp music, is a cherished afternoon ritual.

15 Arlington St., Boston 02117. (617) 536-5700 or (800) 241-3333. Fax (617) 536-1335. Doubles, $285 to $335; suites, $340 to $840.

Four Seasons Hotel. This handsome hotel is nicely situated, opposite the Public Garden with a view of the gold-domed State House across the way. The brick facade is not extraordinary, but inside the feeling is sophisticated indeed. The open, spacious lobby leads to a main staircase and wonderful restaurants: **Aujourd'hui,** the main dining room (see Where to Eat), and the **Bristol Lounge,** where you can enjoy afternoon tea looking out over the Public Garden or choose from an all-day menu of lighter fare. The 288 rooms come in several categories, but all that we saw were spacious, traditionally furnished and enhanced by such amenities as hair dryers, plush robes, minibars, telephones in the bathrooms and –

Breakfast in the room is a weekend indulgence at The Ritz-Carlton.

if you dare – scales. For a splurge, consider the Presidential Suite, overlooking the Public Garden, with a balcony from which you might wave to your adoring throngs. The bathroom is marble, a grand piano graces its parlor, and Chippendale chairs are at a mahogany table in the dining room. It's yours for $2,850 a night. Guests also may enjoy a spa with lap pool (they'll provide a throwaway swimsuit if you forget yours), fitness center, masseuse, the works. No wonder that the American Automobile Association awarded the hotel and restaurant its five-diamond rating.

200 Boylston St., Boston 02116. (617) 338-4400 or (800) 332-3442. Fax (617) 423-2251. Doubles, $325 to $525.

Boston Harbor Hotel. This newish hotel on the waterfront is appealing – not only for the views of the harbor from nearly everywhere, but also for its elegant appointments and its location near Faneuil Hall Marketplace, the Aquarium and other fun destinations. Because the airport water shuttle docks here, there's always activity at the waterfront, and you can walk outside in a lovely promenade area. Nautical prints and fine art are hung in the public rooms. The floors are marble and the elevator walls are upholstered in brocade. The 230 rooms and suites are located on floors 8 through 16. Our oversize room had reproduction antique furniture, a sofa and an upholstered chair with good reading lamps in a sitting area, a kingsize bed and an enormous bathroom full of amenities from fine soaps to terry robes to a hair dryer. Breakfronts conceal the TV and a minibar. Soundproof windows that open and enormous towels are also pluses. A dark wood bar on the main floor and a lounge with piano overlooking the water are pleasant spots for a break from shopping or touring. The dining room on the second floor, **Rowes Wharf,** has dark wood walls, recessed lighting and a deep blue decor; its Sunday brunch buffet is legendary. Lunch and dinner, also highly rated, feature seafood in the contemporary idiom. The Rowes Wharf Health Club and Spa has a 60-foot-long lap pool, steam rooms and saunas, hydrotherapy tub and an exercise room with state-of-the-art equipment.

70 Rowes Wharf, Boston 02110. (617) 439-7000 or (800) 752-7077. Fax (617) 330-9450. Doubles, $280 to $400; suites, $390 to $590.

The Bostonian Hotel. Located across from the Faneuil Hall Marketplace, this smallish, deluxe hotel is quite special. Most of the 153 rooms on three floors are compact but beautifully decorated and equipped, all with bathrooms with deep tiled tubs, French soaps and thirsty towels. French doors open from many rooms onto tiny decorative balconies with wrought-iron rails and plants. Some rooms have fireplaces. The scene for all this elegance is set when you arrive via a dramatic circular driveway with marquee lighting overhead and enter the tasteful lobby where you check in at a period desk. An intimate cocktail lounge with piano is at one end. The gracious restaurant, **Seasons,** has served as a training ground for some of the city's best chefs.

Faneuil Hall Marketplace, Boston 02109. (617) 523-3600 or (800) 343-0922. Fax (617) 523-2454. Doubles, $245 to $355; suites, $450 to $625.

Copley Plaza Hotel. A refurbished elegance is apparent at the Copley Plaza, one of the city's classics, and the location is fortuitous, on Copley Square across from the deluxe shops of Copley Place. Opened in 1912, the Copley Plaza has hosted its share of prestigious Boston events, and President John F. Kennedy stayed here on his last trip to Boston in 1963. The hotel was designed by architect Henry Janeway Hardenbergh, who also designed New York's Plaza Hotel and the Willard in Washington, D.C. We love the **Plaza Bar** with its dark wood walls and subdued lighting, entered after walking through a vaulted passageway with a mosaic floor. The 365-room hotel had just been taken over by the Fairmont group when last we stopped in and changes were in the air.

Copley Square, Boston 02116. (617) 267-5300 or (800) 225-7654. Fax (617) 267-7668. Doubles, $280 to $350; suites, $375 to $1,800.

The Eliot Suite Hotel. Located next to the Harvard Club in Back Bay, this small hotel has been refurbished and made into an all-suites hotel. The Eliot Lounge is known to marathoners around the world, for it is the "in" place during the Boston Marathon. The 92 nicely furnished suites come with king, queen or two double beds, microwave, coffee maker, refrigerator, a stocked minibar and two televisions. French doors divide the bedrooms from the bathrooms, which are Italian marble. A warm and inviting family-owned hotel, the Eliot seems a quiet oasis from the moment you walk into its small but tasteful two-level lobby. A continental breakfast is served each morning in the hotel's private dining room. Dinner is available from room service, if you'd rather not go out.

370 Commonwealth Ave., Boston 02215. (617) 267-1607 or (800) 443-5468. Fax (617)536-9114. Doubles, $205 to $245; suites, $375 to $450.

The Lenox Hotel. This is another smallish, family-owned hotel that has been updated recently. The 222 guest rooms include seventeen corner rooms with wood-burning fireplaces. Corridors are wide and our room was a decent size, but we did find its faux-oriental furniture a bit tacky. We like the location at Copley Square: the Boston Public Library is across the street and the Newbury Street shopping district a block away. Room rates are quite good, especially in winter, when you may get a double for around $100. Corner rooms with working fireplace cost $235.

710 Boylston St., Boston 02116. (617) 536-5300 or (800) 225-7676. Fax (617) 236-0351. Doubles, $155 to $235; suites, $450.

Good Values

Eliot and Pickett Houses. Elegant and value-priced, these side-by-side brownstones atop Beacon Hill are located next to the gold-domed Massachusetts State House. Several rooms offer views of the Boston Common across Beacon Street. Owned by the Unitarian-Universalist Church Association, the houses were built in 1830 and served as private residences until 1940. The church association uses only about one-third of the twenty guest bedrooms, all but two with private bath, at any time. The rest are available for travelers. The attractive common parlor is comfortably furnished and a roof deck is pleasant in season. The high-.ceilinged guest rooms are furnished with one queensize or two double beds and the bathrooms have been updated recently. The traditional four-poster beds and mahogany tables and bureaus are not fancy but more than adequate. There's a TV in the common parlor. Breakfast is do-it-yourself, with cereal, fruit, bagels, English muffins and beverages available in a kitchen and several large tables available for eating. You'll need good directions to find this little street and there is no parking. You can leave your car in the Boston Common underground garage, which is about a ten-minute walk.
6 Mount Vernon Place (mailing address: 25 Beacon St., Boston 02108). (617) 248-8707. Fax (617) 742-1364. Doubles, $85 to $95.

Newbury Guest House. Here are three side-by-side, four-story brick and brownstone townhouses in the heart of the best shopping street in Boston, conveniently located to fine restaurants and points of interest. The large, marble-countered reception area is quite efficient, and there's a small common parlor. The 32 rooms are furnished in traditional fashion: mahogany queen sleigh beds, TV, a small table with two chairs and a sofabed. The bathroom we saw was small but adequate. Preferred rooms have bay windows looking out on Newbury Street. On the lower level, down a few stairs from the reception area, is an attractive breakfast area where you can select continental breakfast items from a buffet, and sit at one of several large tables to eat. The feeling here is of a small city hotel. Parking for a bargain $10 per day must be reserved in advance and isn't always available.
261 Newbury St., Boston 02116. (617) 437-7666. Fax (617) 262-4243. Doubles, $95 to $125.

Shawmut Inn. Here is a B&B of a different sort – located by the old Boston Garden or the new Fleet Center, where the Boston Bruins and Celtics play. This makes it a great choice for sports fans, but noisy whenever there's a game. Opened in 1995, it has an elevator from street level to the second-floor lobby with rooms located on the second, third and fourth floors. Furnishings are spare but new and clean and most bathrooms have tubs. There is a breakfast room where guests pick up juice, hot beverages, and muffins or Danish to take back to their rooms or eat at one of a few small tables. We stayed here on a weekend when the city was heavily booked and were awakened a couple of times by noise from a rowdy Bruins crowd. Parking is in a garage ($16 overnight) at the far end of the street. Once settled, you can take a cab or the T to get around.
280 Friend St., Boston 02114. (617) 720-5544. Fax (617) 723-7784. Doubles, $90 to $110.

Where to Eat

The home of the bean and the cod offers food for more sophisticated palates, too. Here is a sampling of choice places to eat.

Cafe Louis. Michael Schlow, who cooked in New York City before making his way to Boston, is chef at one of the most innovative and exciting restaurants in the center of the city. Located to the rear of the fashionable Louis of Boston clothing store (which is located in the old red brick former Museum of Natural History building), Cafe Louis is tiny but elegant with banquette seating along one wall, big high windows with a heavy swatch of drapery artistically arranged, and a black and white tiled floor. Walls are a deep mustard with burgundy trim and tables a dark marble, bare at lunchtime but covered with white cloths in the evening. You can enter either from the rear of the building – where there is free parking for a few cars ("How can you beat that?" asks Schlow) or valet parking – or through the clothing store, when it is open. We had lunch here on a brisk Saturday in autumn, with the shopping crowd swirling about. Crisp sourdough bread arrived in a specially forged metal "bread basket." One of us sampled the Asian fall salad with marinated salmon, spicy greens and peppers, dressed with a miso vinaigrette; the other was ecstatic with a shrimp and beet risotto, a magenta concoction thick with crunchy shrimp and enormously flavorful. Other choices ($10 to $18) included rare tuna served with braised tomato, eggplant and potato rings, and duck in a red wine sauce served with warm lentil and smoked bacon salad. Fabulous desserts include the best crème brûlée ever, served with a paper-thin caramelized sugar crust and fresh raspberries, a banana ice-cream sandwich and quince compote. At night, starters might be a seared breast of squab with a fig compote or tuna tartare. Typical entrées are Maine salmon with parsley potatoes and a mustard vinaigrette, grilled swordfish with creamy lentils and caramelized onions, and loin of venison with fall vegetables and truffled polenta.

234 Berkeley St. (617) 266-4680. Entrées, $19 to $33. Lunch, Monday-Saturday 11:30 to 3; coffee and dessert, 3 to 5; dinner, 5:30 to 10 or 11.

Biba. Celebrity chef Lydia Shire is at the helm of this trendy two-story establishment in the Heritage on the Garden shopping and residential complex across from the Public Garden. A bar seating 50 serves tapas and such on the main floor. Upstairs is the Biba Food Hall, with windows onto the Garden. Soft gold-yellow walls contrast with ceiling murals painted in bright patterns taken from Albanian carpets. Warm woods, white-clothed tables, chairs covered in deep green and huge bouquets of fresh flowers make for an interesting environment. An onion and green garlic soup in a roasted onion skin was offered the crisp winter day we had lunch here, along with such appetizers as a lobster pizza ("a Biba classic") and oven-roast pepper and bread salad. Entrées ($12 to $16) were equally inventive. One of us had the best lamb shank ever, flamed over fennel branches with baked lemony orzo. The other enjoyed a flaky tomato, potato and olive pissaladière, served with an abundant caesar salad. We made quick work of our basket of breads (the spectacular naan bread baked in the tandoori oven is both chewy and flaky), but had to forego dessert, among such possibilities as white chocolate crème caramel, peaches and cream ice-cream soda and bitter dark chocolate spoon cake. In the evening, entrées might be rib of beef salad with batter-fried beets, wood-roasted lamb or "young pig" preserved with anise and wood-roasted with peaches and prosecco. Everything is novel (some think too much so) and delicious, although a few complain about the noise level.

272 Boylston St. (617) 426-7878. Entrées, $25 to $32. Lunch, Monday-Friday 11:30 to 3; dinner nightly, 5 to 10; Sunday brunch, 11:30 to 3.

Pignoli. On the back side of the building in which Biba is located is Lydia Shire's sophisticated new Italian restaurant. The decor is dramatic as in her original, with huge wood and fabric light fixtures – shaped like blimps or, perhaps, pignoli nuts – floating overhead. Other whimsical touches refer to the "pig" in pignoli. For lunch ($11 to $14), try curry spaghetti with roast capon, pinenuts (there are those pignoli again) and raisins, sage fettuccine with wild mushrooms, or a grilled halibut chop. In the evening, prices go up to $20 or so for a dinner portion of pasta or rice, perhaps sweet onion risotto with roasted quail or rigatoni alla bolognese. Main plates could be lamb stew with roasted artichokes and tenderloin of beef with chestnuts and sweet potato, a hearty cold-weather meal. For dessert, consider Italian lemon crumb cake with peaches and wine or cassata, a rum-soaked sponge cake with sweet ricotta, pistachios and fruits. At the front is a good Italian bakery, the **Pignoli Bakery.**

79 Park Plaza. (617) 338-7500. Entrées. $24 to $28. Lunch, Monday-Saturday 11:30 to 2:30; dinner nightly, 5:30 to 10.

Hamersley's Bistro. Originally small and intimate, Hamersley's has moved across the street to a big brick building in a South End area that is gradually becoming gentrified. It now has large and comfortable digs, with three dining spaces decked out in yellow and dark green. Chef Gordon Hamersley produces incredible dishes from his open kitchen. We've enjoyed three items that have become signatures: the grilled mushroom and garlic sandwich on country bread as an appetizer; the roast chicken with garlic, lemon and parsley, an entrée, and the souffléd lemon custard, a dessert. Other appetizers might be duck liver mousse and smoked trout with mushrooms and spinach or a pie of shrimp, scallops and mussels. Entrées could be halibut cooked in rice paper with apples, bacon, sherry and sage; oven-cooked lamb khoresh with butternut squash, or roasted veal wrapped in bacon with capers and lemon sauce. Finish with a maple, walnut and pear tart or warm chocolate cake with coffee ice cream and espresso sauce. Wife Fiona Hamersley oversees a sophisticated wine list.

578 Tremont St. (617) 423-2700. Entrées, $20 to $32. Dinner nightly, 5:30 or 6 to 10.

Ambrosia on Huntington. A soaring corner space with huge windows looking out onto Copley Place is the setting for some of the more unusual dishes being served in Boston. Chef-owner Anthony Ambrose is the force behind the fusion cuisine – French Provincial with an Asian influence. Walls are pale yellow to peach in tone and there are classic architectural touches here and there. At lunchtime ($7 to $13), choose from sandwiches such as grilled pulled pig with Indonesian barbecue sauce or a grilled lobster and pancetta club, or try a pasta like sautéed mushroom saffron gnocchi with fresh tomato and basil oil. Also on a recent lunch menu was sushi-filled duck breast with sweet and sour orange cognac confit. In the evening, starters might be sautéed foie gras in coconut oil with fava beans, pan-fried lobster over a Breton crêpe and a salad of smoked salmon and English cucumber. Entrées could be salmon with a garlic-pecan crust served with chive mashed potatoes, a smoked pig chop with Japanese rice cake, or grilled veal chop with chanterelles and a cognac glaze. The wine list is superb.

116 Huntington Ave. (617) 247-2400. Entrées, $17 to $29. Lunch, Monday-Friday 11:30 to 2; dinner nightly, from 5.

Lala Rokh. This charming spot in a Beacon Hill townhouse has a new look and flavor – thanks to the brother-and-sister duo of Azita and Babak Bina, who are reviving the Persian cuisine of their heritage (they also own Azita's, a northern Italian eatery, in the South End). The three small rooms here are comfortably casual, with banquette seating along the side and Persian paintings and framed manuscripts on the walls. Azita says many of the menu items are from her mother's recipe file. A young and well-versed wait staff helps explain the unfamiliar fare. Think of foods with Mediterranean and mid-Eastern overtones. These are slow-cooked for the most part, often stewed, tender and flavorful. There are also several grilled items. Appetizers include mirza ghasemi (grilled eggplant served mashed with roasted garlic and tomato) or kotlet-e-gusht (breaded and sautéed ground beef with potato and turmeric). Salads could be fasle (mixed romaine, tomato, onion, cucumber and vinaigrette) and loubia sabz (string beans, pepper and dill with lime dressing). Five different styles of entrées include baghla (lamb shank with rice and fava beans), koofteh tabrizi (ground beef with herbs, dried plums, eggs, onions and barberries), and bademjan (chunks of beef with eggplant, grapes, saffron and tomatoes). One of the classic desserts is a Persian style baklava, softer and more moist than the Greek style. Lunch service was in the future.

97 Mount Vernon St. (617) 720-5511. Entrées, $13 to $16. Dinner nightly, from 5:30.

Galleria Italiana. Located near the theater district across from the Boston Common, this 50-seat Italian eatery offers breakfast and lunch cafeteria-style during the day. With chef Barbara Lynch in the kitchen, it comes into its own in the evening as one of the city's best restaurants. White cloths cover the tables for dinner and there's a vibrant, intimate quality to the experience. Antipasti include seared black-olive coated tuna over ligurian-style potato salad, sausage-stuffed quail over roasted apple polenta, and thinly sliced beef carpaccio with a creamy gorgonzola salad. For main dishes, try a pasta like fettuccelli with Tuscan-style bolognese sauce or ravioli stuffed with butternut squash and sage, or an entrée such as braised lamb shank with a shell-bean ragu or crispy duck with a butternut squash risotto cake. Finish with an almond-crusted quince soufflé with spiced quince sauce or a walnut crespelle pouch bearing spiced apples, sweet mascarpone walnut crème anglaise and cinnamon gelato.

177 Tremont St. (617) 423-2092. Entrées, $16 to $22. Breakfast and lunch, Monday-Friday 7 to 4:30; dinner, Wednesday-Saturday 5:30 to 10.

The Hungry I. We love the atmosphere of this restaurant along Charles street, especially when the weather is cold. It's one of the most romantic spaces in the city with wood-burning fireplaces in its main room, just below street level, and in two charming rooms upstairs. We had Sunday brunch one blustery day and settled in happily across from the fireplace in the main room, where dried herbs hang from beams overhead and patterned rugs are set atop deep green carpeting. Brunch items ($9 to $14) included Scottish woodcock (poached eggs on pumpernickel with welsh rarebit), curried lamb hash and Canadian bacon pancakes with cranberries and cinnamon. For dinner, you might start with the duck liver pâté served with a plum-mango coulis, chilled lobster and basmati rice pudding, or frog's legs with fresh ginger and water chestnuts. Entrées include braised rabbit with onions and capers, Canadian goose roasted with brandied prunes, and salmon baked with apples, chives, curry and cream. In warm weather, there's a small city garden in which to dine.

71½ Charles St. (617) 227-3524. Entrées, $23 to $29. Dinner nightly, from 6; Sunday brunch, 11 to 3.

Legal Sea Foods. People say this restaurant chain has the best and freshest fish in the city, and since 1981 its chowder has been served at the Presidential Inaugural lunch. The atmosphere is stylish yet fish-market casual, with paper placemats and tile floors. Well-known Boston chef Jasper White joined the corporation as executive chef in 1996 and was updating the menu. At lunchtime, sandwiches and specialties ($8 to $13) include shrimp dijon, Maine crabmeat roll, grilled or cajun salmon fillet, fish and chips, and bluefish with mustard sauce. Prices rise to $15 to $25 for dinner, which can be baked Boston scrod, broiled flounder, Portuguese fisherman's stew or grilled tuna with an herb marinade.

Locations including the Boston Park Plaza Hotel, 35 Columbus Ave., (617) 426-4444, and 100 Huntington Ave. (Copley Place), (617) 266-7775. Entrées, $15 to $25. Lunch daily, 11:30 to 2; dinner, 5 to 10.

Hotel Dining

Aujourd'hui. The location of this suavely elegant restaurant on the hotel's second floor, where a window table gives you a view of the Public Garden, is one of its many assets. Colors are soft and lights are low. Another plus is executive chef David Fritchey, a Culinary Institute of America graduate, who has been turning out superb food since his arrival in 1995. This is definitely a spot for a splurge, for a romantic tête-à-tête, for the celebration of a great event. But it will cost you. Dinner appetizers begin at $12 and main courses at $33. Start your extravaganza with sea scallops with a sweet potato and lobster glaze or a terrine of duck confit with spiced apple salad. Caviar is available – ossetra for $65 and beluga for $95. Main courses could be black bass with scallops, ratatouille and an asparagus sauce; veal tenderloin with pumpkin ravioli, and roasted squab with chestnut risotto.

Four Seasons Hotel, 200 Boylston St. (617) 338-4400. Entrées, $33 to $42. Lunch, Monday-Friday 11:30 to 2:30; dinner nightly, 6 to 10:30 or 11; Sunday brunch, 11:30 to 2:30.

The Bristol Lounge. Also at the Four Seasons Hotel, this is one of our favorite dining spaces in Boston. The expansive main-floor dining room has well-spaced tables and interesting seating, including sofas and loveseats. Warm neutral colors predominate, and a large fireplace at one end is a draw on cold evenings. Large windows look onto busy Boylston Street and across to the Public Garden. When snow falls outside, the view is magical. The all-day menu offers pastas, daily "homestyle" specials (chicken pot pie on Thursday; Maine crab cakes on Saturday) sandwiches like the Bristol turkey club and more substantial fare. Typical of the last are grilled salmon fillet, shrimp stir-fry and cornish game hen basted with honey and served with sweet potato pie. On Friday and Saturday nights, folks line up

before 9 for the lounge's famed Viennese Dessert Buffet (a choice of fifteen to twenty desserts – a plate of two for $8.75, four for $17.50).
200 Boylston St. Entrées, $18 to $25. Daily, 11:30 to 11:30; Viennese Dessert Buffet, Friday and Saturday, 9 to midnight; Sunday breakfast buffet, 10 to 2.

The Ritz-Carlton Dining Room. The second-floor Dining Room overlooks the Public Garden. With its gold and blue decor (down to the signature cobalt blue water glasses), it is serene and elegant. Hors d'oeuvres might be cannelloni of quail in truffle juice, gratin of mussels, and a compote of salmon and cauliflower cream. Typical soups are lobster bisque and coriander mussel. Entrées include lobster with whiskey sauce, veal medallions with roquefort sauce and beef tenderloin with truffle sauce. Finish with a hot apple soufflé, classic crêpes Suzette or bananas flambé. For a splurge, consider joining head chef Didier Rosa's dégustation table any evening except Monday. For $85, you can enjoy a four-course meal with selected wines. Just fourteen places are reserved each evening for this experience.
15 Arlington St. (617) 536-5700. Entrées, $29 to $43. Lunch, noon to 2:30; dinner nightly, 6 to 10; weekend brunch, 11 to 2:30.

Rowes Wharf Restaurant. This elegantly appointed, wood-paneled dining room overlooks Boston Harbor and is highly rated under executive chef Daniel Bruce. Especially famous for its Sunday brunch ($42), the dining room received a Best of Boston designation from Boston magazine. Typical dinner starters are lobster sausage over lemon pasta, charred venison carpaccio, wild mushroom consommé and salad of watercress and caramelized red onions. Entrées might be pan-roasted swordfish served with a turnip gratin, sea scallop lasagna with baby leeks and fennel herb-crusted rack of lamb with sage. Finish with honey crème brûlée, warm chocolate fondant cake or a trilogy of sorbets.
Boston Harbor Hotel, Rowes Wharf. (617) 439-7000. Entrées, $20 to $31. Lunch daily, 11:30 to 2; dinner, 5:30 to 11; Sunday brunch, 10:30 to 2.

Sunday Brunch

Sunday brunch is an institution in Boston, and most hotel dining rooms and many restaurants offer it.

Cafe Fleuri. The cafe in the Meridien Hotel presents a brunch that often has been voted the best in Boston. We found the skylit room with dark rattan chairs, deep rust banquettes and pink-clothed tables to be a luscious spot to devour the Sunday Boston Globe and the food. For $39 each, you can sample appetizers, hot foods, crêpes and desserts from many different stations. Waiters bring beverages and are good about refilling coffee cups. Soft jazz plays in the background, and there's a sophisticated, big-city feel to the experience. The hors d'oeuvre table when we were there offered pâtés, mixed fresh fruits, chicken liver mousse, rolls, bagels, herring in sour cream, cheeses and a nice selection of salads. Main dishes included eggs benedict, leg of lamb with rosemary, beef in brioche and a port wine sauce, veal medallions in pommery mustard sauce, chicken with tomatoes and basil, rice pilaf, scalloped potatoes and mixed vegetables. Crêpes of all sorts – served with ice cream or whipped cream and several intriguing sauces – were made to order. Among desserts were crème caramel, pecan pie, banana cake, chocolate layer cake and apple torte.
250 Franklin St. (617) 451-1900. Prix-fixe, $39. Seatings between 11 and 2.

Other favored brunch spots include the Four Seasons Hotel, Rowes Wharf at the Boston Harbor Hotel, The Bostonian Hotel and the Ritz-Carlton on both Saturday and Sunday.

A Value – With Verve

The Parish Cafe. Here's a place where you can sample creations of the best chefs in town for as little as $7.95. The cafe's co-owner, Gordon Wilcox, asked area restaurateurs to supply a sandwich recipe and the resulting menu offers twenty favorite concoctions of such chefs as Lydia Shire of Biba, Todd English of Olives and Tony Ambrose of Ambrosia. One of us chose the "Fig and Pig" sandwich created by Sean Simmons, chef/owner of the Parish, which was lip-smacking good – grilled focaccia bread filled with smokehouse ham, fig puree, whole figs, roasted peppers, roasted red onions and Danish fontina cheese. The all-day menu includes salads – also created by Boston chefs – and a few entrées, such as baked chipotle meatloaf, fish cakes with basmati rice and honey-soy marinated flank steak served with garlic mashed potatoes and cucumber salad. Desserts might be banana butternut crunch cake and chocolate hazelnut torte. In good weather, eat outdoors on the small sidewalk terrace in front and watch the passing parade. There is also a huge bar indoors. Takeout is available.

361 Boylston St. (617) 247-4777. Entrées, $9 to $14. Open daily, 11:30 a.m. to 2 a.m.

For Tea

The Ritz-Carlton. Afternoon tea in the second-floor parlor-lounge here is legendary. The room with its wing chairs, pie-crust mahogany tables, faded colors, floor lamps and wall sconces is perfect. A single red rose is on each table, and the waiters and waitresses all wear black jackets and ties. A harpist adds just the right touch. On a chilly late Saturday afternoon in January we enjoyed the leisurely pace, the warming tea and the passing parade; this is a place to see mothers with their young daughters in smocked dresses and patent leather shoes, and couples having tête-à-têtes. You can order full tea, light tea or à la carte. Full tea brings two tea sandwiches, a scone, tea bread and a fruit tart; light tea omits the sandwiches. The teas include Keemum, Lapsang Souchang, Harney's low caffeine tea, Darjeeling, Ceylon and India and Earl Grey's. You also can have sherry or coffee. Tiny fruit tarts and chocolate-covered strawberries are the finishing touches to a memorable experience.

15 Arlington St. (617) 536-5700. Light tea, $12.50; full tea, $16.50. Tea daily, 3 to 5:30.

Tea is also served in the **Bristol Court** at the Four Seasons Hotel and at the Boston Harbor Hotel.

On the Lighter Side

Rebecca's. Rebecca Caras's restaurant at the foot of Beacon Hill continues to be a favorite of locals and visitors alike. People gladly wait in line to be seated at one of the small square tables. There's a bakery counter where you can pick up goodies to go. The innovative menu offers such lunch items ($6 to $10) as spicy Maine crab cakes with a lemon chervil sauce, warm duck salad with spicy walnuts and a raspberry vinaigrette, and osso buco. Soups are always good, as are appetizers like steamed mussels in white wine, garlic and herbs or baked polenta with wild mushrooms and fontina cheese in an herb tomato sauce. For dinner, entrées might be roasted chicken with a sauce of caramelized onions, plum tomatoes and chardonnay or veal scaloppine with artichoke hearts and lemon fettuccine. On the brunch menu ($13 to $18), you may find an omelet with asparagus and boursin cheese, french toast with a compote of blackberries, raspberries and strawberries, and chicken livers with roasted shallots and mushrooms in a mustard demi-glace. Desserts are delectable, as are the muffins, scones and other bakery items.

21 Charles St. (617) 742-9747. Entrées, $14 to $22. Lunch, Monday-Saturday 11:30 to 4; dinner nightly, 5:30 to 11; Sunday brunch, 11 to 4.

Garden of Eden, 577 Tremont St., Boston, has great sandwiches and sweets. It is open Tuesday-Friday 7:30 to 7, Saturday and Sunday 8 to 6.

FOR MORE INFORMATION: Greater Boston Convention and Visitors Center, Prudential Plaza, Box 490, Boston, MA 02199, (617) 536-4100 or (800) 888-5515. A good book for background is *About Boston* by David McCord.

19 ❄ Winter

Skiers pause to enjoy view during run at Camden Snow Bowl.

Winter by the Sea
Camden-Rockland, Me.

Everybody thinks of Maine in the summer, when images of the crashing ocean, lobster dinners, wild blueberries and windjammer cruises come happily to mind.

But the section of coast from Rockland through Camden to Lincolnville calls to us in winter, too. The mountain backdrop behind Camden offers some spectacular winter scenery and the only downhill ski area in the East where you can glide down slopes while enjoying panoramic views of the Atlantic Ocean. The area also is good for cross-country skiing, ice skating and snowshoeing.

Camden's picturesque harbor is as appealing in the winter when touched with ice and snow, as it is in the summer when crowded with high-masted schooners. Actually, many of the boats are "shrink-wrapped" in a protective covering and remain in the harbor all winter.

Camden and neighboring Lincolnville, Rockport and Rockland don't close down for the winter, either. Many of their inns are at their coziest this time of year, with candles aglow in the windows and fires burning in parlors and guest rooms. Often, overnighters enjoy breakfast by the fireside.

Many restaurants remain open, dishing up hearty chowders and meals to warm your bones – those Mainers know how to stay warm in winter. The stores are open and uncrowded, offering a range of handmade crafts, antiques, gift items – everything to make browsing or holiday shopping a pleasure. There's even a store devoted to sweaters. Camden's annual "Christmas by the Sea" weekend in early December is becoming well-known.

Cultural opportunities abound. The Farnsworth Art Museum in Rockland shows one of the richest collections of work by Maine artists (especially the Wyeth family) in the country. The famous sculptor and collagist, Louise Nevelson, grew up in Rockland, and the Farnsworth has a collection of her works, too. An active theater group in Camden and chamber music concerts in Rockport add to the milieu. Good bookstores and libraries mean you won't have trouble finding a book to curl up with as the snow flies.

No, you don't have to go south to escape the doldrums of winter. You can head north for a winter weekend by the sea.

Getting There

Camden is about 190 miles northeast of Boston and 85 miles northeast of Portland. It is reached via coastal U.S. Route 1 and Interstate 95.

Greyhound and Trailways provide bus service. Major airlines fly into Portland International Jetport. Daily commercial air service is also available to Knox County Airport at Owls Head in Rockland.

Seeing and Doing

Outdoor Activities

In defiance of the chilly weather, people love to be outdoors in Maine. They've learned the best way to get through a long, cold, snowy winter is to ignore any discomfort and plunge in. You can, too.

SKIING. Camden Snow Bowl, John Street, Camden, (207) 236-3438. Ski Conditions (207) 236-4418. Just three miles west of town overlooking Hosmer Pond, Camden Snow Bowl has nine trails from beginning to expert. They are served by a 3,100-foot double chairlift and two T-bars (including the longest in the state at 4,100 feet). Major trails are equipped with snowmaking and lighting; night skiing is offered Tuesday, Thursday and Friday. The Ragged Mountain Ski School gives lessons for all ages and abilities. Lift prices are amazingly affordable, in the range of $15 to $20 for an adult all-day ticket. Two-hour ski passes are offered midweek. The area usually operates from mid-December to mid-March.

CROSS-COUNTRY SKIING. Ski touring is available on the rolling terrain of the golf course at the Samoset Resort in Rockland. Rental skis are offered at $15 for adults, $10 for children.

Skiers may use the ungroomed trails in Lincolnville of the Tanglewood 4-H Camp, (207) 594-2104, operated by the University of Maine Cooperative Extension Service. The camp is located north and west of Lincolnville Beach.

Cross-country ski lessons and tours are run by **Maine Sport Outfitters,** Route 1, Rockport, (207) 236-8797 or (800) 722-0826. This is a large sporting goods store specializing in skiing in winter and coastal sports in summer. Clinics and guided tours are offered on some Saturdays and Sundays, including a two-hour start-to-ski clinic. You can rent equipment from the store. The store also has five-hour ski tours introducing skiers to some of the area's most beautiful trails.

TOBOGGANING. The **Camden Snow Bowl** is the only area in Maine to have a public toboggan chute. The 400-foot-long chute takes you down the side of the mountain and out onto frozen Hosmer Pond. You pay on a per-ride basis. Bring your own toboggan or rent one at the Snow Bowl.

Big excitement is generated every winter with the annual **National Toboggan Championships** at the Snow Bowl, (207) 548-2645. The races attract tobogganers from throughout the East and Canada. In addition to the standard wood toboggans, a "development class" category has been added for those who want to construct their own toboggans. Costumes are worn by some of the competitors, as everyone goes out for a good time. Visitors can watch the event, and some get so revved up they decide to take part. Usually the festivities includes horse-drawn sleigh rides, dog sled races, ice skating and snow tubing. An annual Chili and Chowder Festival is part of the fun. The event is held on a weekend in late January or early February.

OTHER ACTIVITIES. Guided snowshoe tours are offered through Camden Hills State Park by Maine Sport Outfitters in Rockport. It also offers indoor clinics on paddling skills for **sea kayakers** in a high school pool.

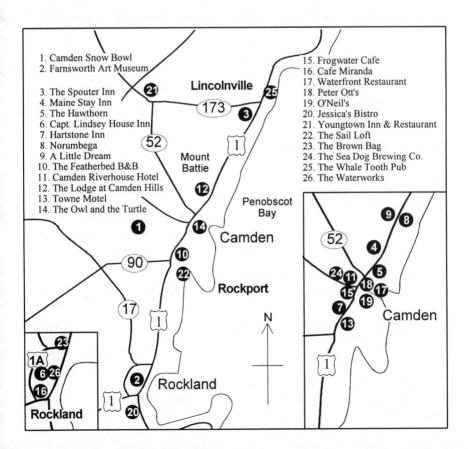

1. Camden Snow Bowl
2. Farnsworth Art Museum
3. The Spouter Inn
4. Maine Stay Inn
5. The Hawthorn
6. Capt. Lindsey House Inn
7. Hartstone Inn
8. Norumbega
9. A Little Dream
10. The Featherbed B&B
11. Camden Riverhouse Hotel
12. The Lodge at Camden Hills
13. Towne Motel
14. The Owl and the Turtle
15. Frogwater Cafe
16. Cafe Miranda
17. Waterfront Restaurant
18. Peter Ott's
19. O'Neil's
20. Jessica's Bistro
21. Youngtown Inn & Restaurant
22. The Sail Loft
23. The Brown Bag
24. The Sea Dog Brewing Co.
25. The Whale Tooth Pub
26. The Waterworks

Lincolnville
173
52
Mount Battie
Penobscot Bay
Camden
Rockport
90
17
N
Rockland
Camden
Rockland

Ice skating is available, when weather conditions cooperate, on Hosmer Pond at the base of the Camden Snow Bowl area. Other frozen ponds and lakes are sometimes used for skating, too.

Hiking may be enjoyed in late fall and early winter before the snow gets too deep. **Camden Hills State Park,** two miles north of Camden along Route 1, is a great place to hike in general, and the views over Penobscot Bay from the park are spectacular. Reach a trailhead by driving three miles west from Lincolnville Beach on Route 173.

Walking by the sea. Who doesn't like to walk along the water's edge, even in winter? You can find a patch of shoreline and easy walking at Lincolnville Beach, near the ferry dock for the Islesboro ferry. The harbor areas in Camden, Rockport and Rockland also are available.

The Islands. If you want to spend a day on a remote, quiet island out in Penobscot Bay, you can do so. Ferries run year-round from Rockland to Vinalhaven and North Haven, and from Lincolnville to Islesboro, as long as the water is not too rough.

Indoor Activities

Farnsworth Art Museum. Founded in 1948 by local businesswoman Lucy Copeland Farnsworth, this fine museum specializes in American art with a focus on art related to Maine. The Farnsworth has an especially rich collection of three generations of Wyeths, who have chosen it as the permanent repository of their works. The family of N.C. Wyeth summered for years in a house in nearby Port Clyde; Andrew and Jamie Wyeth also have had homes in Maine. The Pratt Memorial Methodist Church at Union and Elm streets behind the museum was being renovated to become The Wyeth Center. It was scheduled to open in 1998, the museum's 50th anniversary year.

Also featured is artist-sculptor Louise Nevelson, who grew up here before moving to New York City. A photo on the wall of one museum gallery shows her as the captain of the girls' basketball team at Rockland High School in 1916. She donated many of her works and personal papers to the Farnsworth and a major piece of sculpture, "Figure in a Blue Shirt," is on its lawn. The museum also has a good collection of works by American Impressionists, including Childe Hassam, John Henry Twachtman and Willard Metcalf.

The Olson House in Cushing, which Andrew Wyeth painted in many of his famous works including "Christina's World," is owned by the museum and open in the summer, as is the Farnsworth homestead to the rear of the museum. The museum gift shop is excellent.

325 Main St., Rockland. (207) 596-6457. Monday-Saturday 9 to 5; Sunday noon to 5; winter, Tuesday-Saturday 10 to 5 and Sunday 1 to 5. Adults $5, children $3.

CULTURAL OFFERINGS. Chamber music concerts presenting the Vermeer Quartet and guest artists are offered Thursday and Friday nights in July and August and monthly the rest of the year under the name **Bay Chamber Concerts,** (207) 236-2823. They are held at the Rockport Opera House.

Camden Civic Theatre, (207) 236-7595. Since 1972, the CCT has performed during the winter months at the historic Camden and Rockport opera houses. Shows feature local players.

ARTS AND CRAFTS STUDIOS. Many artists and craftspeople live in the area, and their works are shown in local shops and galleries. Among the more interesting: **Duck Trap Decoys,** creator of award-winning decoys, whose shop is one mile north of Lincolnville Beach. **Windsor Chairmakers,** whose reproduction furniture, including windsor chairs, may be seen in its showroom just north of Lincolnville Beach. **Anne Kilham Designs,** studio and showcase for the colorful paintings, posters and notecards of Maine scenes by Rockport artist Anne Kilham at 142 Russell Ave. And **Laurie Adams, potter,** whose work is displayed at her Camden studio.

Shopping

Shopping is in season year-round in the Camden-Rockland area. It culminates in "Christmas by the Sea," usually the second weekend in December, a festive time in the stores of Camden.

Bookstores beckon in winter. In Camden, we like **The Owl & The Turtle,** a major independent bookstore backing up to the harbor in the center of town; **ABCDef Book Shop** on Bay View Street, specializing in used and rare books, and **Meetingbrook,** a bookstore billed as "a place of collation and recollection at Camden harbor." It offers coffee and pastries and a fireplaced nook for reading spiritual and sensitive books from all faiths and ways of life. Also worth a stop is **Second Read Bookstore & Cafe** in Rockland.

Other stores to check out in Camden include **Unique One,** devoted to sweaters and knitting supplies; **Once a Tree,** filled with nothing but wood products, and **Wild Birds Unlimited.** Quite an array of eco-friendly items from clothing to toys to jewelry is offered at **Planet.** On Elm Street, **Kirsten Scarcelli,** a retail store for a Hallowell-based women's knitwear company, shows gorgeous clothing that's a bit pricey.

In Rockland, a new women's clothing store, **Caravans,** was attracting attention at our visit.

Some of the more than 30 antiques dealers in the area stay open in winter.

Where to Stay

Camden is well equipped with B&Bs, many of them having a particular appeal in the winter months with their cozy ambiance, fireplaces in guest rooms and hearty breakfasts. A new hotel and some motels are other options. Our favorites:

Bed and Breakfasts

The Spouter Inn. Catherine and Paul Lippman moved from Pennsylvania with their two sons to open this attractive B&B in 1989. Paul is a woodworker whose fine cabinetry is seen all around their seven-room inn. In the comfortable carriage house addition with three fireplaced guest rooms, the wood-beamed ceilings and wood floors testify to his abilities. We slept in a queensize four-poster bed in the Helmsman's Quarters in the carriage house and learned it had been made by Paul. The spacious top-floor Admiral's Quarters in the carriage house offers king bed, panoramic ocean views, sundeck and private bath with jacuzzi. Two guest rooms in the main house, including the Commodore's Suite, also come with fireplaces, as does one of the two front parlors. Breakfast is served family-style at a large table in the sunny, tiled breakfast room, where you get a good view of the water and the Islesboro ferry dock across the road. Paul does the main dish (dutch apple pancakes one day and eggs florentine the next when we were there). Catherine bakes muffins and delicious frosted sweet buns. Breakfasts here are so filling that you may not need to eat lunch.

U.S. Route 1, Lincolnville Beach 04849. (207) 789-5171. Doubles, $65 to $125 in winter; $75 to $175 in summer.

Maine Stay Inn. Peter Smith, a retired U.S. Navy captain, his wife Donny and her twin sister, Diana Robson, join forces in this welcoming B&B in the historic district just two blocks from the center of Camden. The Smiths traveled all over the world during his 37 years in the military, then returned to his native Maine. The innkeepers pour their hearts and souls – not to mention plenty of elbow grease – into the operation. Over the years, all eight lovely guest rooms have been given private baths, and two have gas fireplaces or stoves. Sponge-painted walls, stenciling, and a mix of antiques and more modern pieces lend character to the rooms. Wood-burning fireplaces warm up two front parlors. Many items from Peter's and Donny's travels – including a Fuji stick from one of his two ascents of Mount Fuji – are conversation starters. In the winter, all the breakfast cooking is done on a big old black stove in the well-equipped kitchen, and Gramma's Pancakes (made with molasses, sour cream and graham flour) get the day off to a good start. Coffee is available from 6 on for early risers. The wooded back yard of the house is laced with paths, set with benches and adjoins the 37 miles of trails at Camden Hills State Park. A "stitchery weekend" is always held in March and those attending make an embroidery item under the tutelage of an instructor.

22 High St., Camden 04843. (207) 236-9636. Fax (207) 236-0621. Doubles, $75 to $125 (20 percent less in winter).

The Hawthorn. Having tired of the corporate rat race, British-born Nick Wharton and his wife Patricia from Texas took over this beautiful yellow inn in the historic district in 1995. Their nine guest rooms and a suite are located in the main house or in a carriage house out back, and many rooms offer great harbor views. Three carriage house rooms have gas fireplaces, TVs and VCRs and two have double jacuzzis. Jillian's Room in the main house is a two-room suite with separate living room and four-poster queensize bed. The Turret Room in front is light and airy with one queen and one twin bed and wicker furniture, including a chaise set next to the turret windows, from which you get a good view of Mount Battie and the setting sun. Full breakfasts are served in a fireplaced dining room. They might include crème caramel french toast or "bodacious turkey."

9 High St., Camden 04843. (207) 236-8842. Fax (207) 236-6181. Doubles, $80 to $175. Closed in February.

Capt. Lindsey House Inn. Ken and Ellen Barnes, who are skippers of the Stephen Taber schooner in summer, converted the offices of the city water company in downtown Rockland into an in-town B&B in 1995. Nine rooms have been decorated with dramatic wallpapers and bedspreads and outfitted with televisions, usually hidden in armoires. Terry robes are hung in bathrooms, and bedrooms have comfortable chairs, good reading lights and mostly king or queen beds. On the main floor, a welcoming parlor with fireplace is done in dark greens and ma-

Sculpture attracts attention on lawn outside Farnsworth Art Museum.

roons; off it is a tiny library. Continental breakfast, served in a pub-style room, consists of fresh breads, granola, yogurt and beverages. Among the many package plans are romantic Valentine's Day, wine tasting. murder mystery and learn-to-draw weekends. The next-door restaurant/pub, The Waterworks (see Where to Eat), is also owned by the Barnes family.

5 Lindsey St., Rockland 04841. (207) 596-7950 or (800) 523-2145. Doubles, $95 to $160

Hartstone Inn. This high, mansard-roofed Victorian inn is presided over with warmth by Sunny and Peter Simmons. Eight guest rooms on second and third floors are light and airy. All have private baths and two have fireplaces. We loved the thick terry towels served up in the bathroom of our high-ceilinged, third-floor hideaway. Guests enjoy a quiet fireplaced parlor. Breakfast is served at individual tables near the fireplace in a dark green breakfast room. Among Sunny's specialties are a mushroom and ham frittata, homemade corned beef hash, and baked eggs served over minced ham, cheese and chives – a delicacy for which guests constantly request the recipe. In winter, guests may enjoy a special consisting of two nights' accommodation, two breakfasts for two and one dinner for two for a bargain $185. The fireside dinner is served by candlelight in the dining room; guests provide their own wine.

41 Elm St., Camden 04843. (207) 236-4259. Doubles, $75 to $125; in winter, $60 to $90.

Norumbega. Working fireplaces in five guest rooms, the dining room, a living room and even on the staircase landing help make this majestic mansion overlooking the ocean quite cozy in the winter. The turreted stone and wood building just north of the harbor area was built in 1886 by Joseph Stearns, a Maine native who invented the duplex telegraphy system. Staying in this choice B&B today is definitely an indulgence. The main-floor common rooms have parquet floors, elaborate woodwork, a grand piano, and comfortable sofas and chairs. Complimentary wine and hors d'oeuvres are served every evening and the kitchen is always open to guests for fresh chocolate-chip cookies and coffee, tea or hot chocolate. The thirteen accommodations range from the merely elegant to a couple of enormous suites. The most exotic is the Penthouse, with a lace-trimmed bed, nicely furnished sitting area, three-sided fireplace and a huge bathroom with a circular whirlpool tub for two. Wintertime brings special murder mystery weekends –what a perfect environment for them!

61 High St., Camden 04843. (207) 236-4646. Fax (207) 236-0824. Doubles, $195 to $450; in winter, $135 to $295.

A Little Dream. The first night that Joanne Ball and Bill Fontana spent in their new house during one cold January stretch, they awakened to a snowscape that painted everything below them, all the way to the harbor, in white. "It was like a little dream," said Joanne, who decided to give that name to their five-room B&B. Decorated in exuberant Victoriana are five large guest rooms, two of them in the carriage house behind the main, turreted house, which rests high on a hillside across the street from Norumbega. Guests at the lacy, doll-and-toy-filled B&B gather around a fireplace in the parlor after enjoying a gala breakfast at a table topped with a white cloth and tied with satin ribbons at each corner. The scent of rose petal potpourri fills the house and all sorts of Victorian accents are found: high-button shoes, beautifully made old hats and dresses, even a birdcage. For the holidays, Joanne goes all out and rooms are garlanded and bowed even more than usual.

66 High St., Camden 04843. (207) 236-8742. Doubles, $100 to $140.

The Featherbed B&B. Ted Skowronski and Michelle Painchaud came from New Jersey to the Maine coast to open an art gallery, framing shop and a two-room B&B just south of Camden. Michelle sponge-painted the bedroom walls and decorated in pastel colors. Renovations in 1997 produced a private bath for each room. Guests are surrounded by down in the queensize featherbeds, which promise warmth even on the coldest Maine nights. Full breakfasts (waffles, pancakes and such) are joint projects, according to the innkeepers, who serve in a dining room with a corner cupboard. Contemporary art is on display in the living room, where the fireplace may be lit for guests in the evening.

705 Commercial St. (Route 1), Rockport 04856. (207) 596-7230. Fax (207) 596-7657. Doubles, $80.

A Small Hotel

The Camden Riverhouse Hotel. Camden's first hotel, opened in 1995, is small, tastefully furnished and located back from the main road near the headquarters of the MBNA credit corporation, whose new Northeast operations center is located in Camden. The 36 rooms are outfitted with traditional mahogany furnishings, green and burgundy floral bedspreads and draperies, and large TV sets. Most have two queen beds, although those on the third floor have kingsize beds, plus microwaves and refrigerators. Two rooms offer balconies and jacuzzis. Continental breakfast is served at individual tables in a pleasant second-floor breakfast area. Facilities include a small oval indoor pool with jacuzzi and an exercise room.

11 Tannery Lane, Camden 04843. (207) 236-0500 or (800) 755-7483. Fax (207) 236-4711. Doubles, $149 to $209; in winter, $79 to $139.

Perfectly Private

The Lodge at Camden Hills. Twenty modern, motel-style units in seven buildings are set back from the highway in a wooded setting, assuring privacy and, in some cases, offering distant bay views. The property is located a mile north of Camden and offers an away-from-it-all feeling for those who prefer to have a self-contained unit to do their own thing. Several suites contain a queensize bed, sitting room with wood-burning fireplace, efficiency kitchen and full bath, some with jacuzzis. All units have TVs, in some cases two. A few guest rooms offer two doubles or one queen bed, a refrigerator and a private deck. A cottage has a queen bed, jacuzzi, kitchen, fireplace and private deck with bay views.

Route 1, Box 794, Camden 04843. (207) 236-8478 or (800) 832-7058. Fax (207) 236-7163. Doubles, $110 to $225; off-season, $75 to $175. Open weekends only in winter.

Budget Choices

Towne Motel. This two-story motel sits sidewise on a small lot. Rooms are small (those on the first floor smaller than the second) but adequate with a double and a single bed or two doubles. Downstairs, bathrooms have a stall shower only; upstairs there are tubs. Owners Hal and Barbara Smith from Connecticut offer a complimentary continental breakfast in the office.

68 Elm St. (Route 1), Camden 04843. (207) 236-3377 or (800) 656-4999. Fax (236-0075. Doubles, $89 to $99; in winter, $55 and $65.

The Owl and the Turtle. Three guest rooms, all with some sort of harbor view, are located directly above the bookstore by the same name in downtown Camden. The pleasant, paneled rooms come with private baths, televisions and telephones. Two have queen beds; one has twins. Continental breakfast, including homemade muffins or breads, is taken in the room. There is no common room, but there is an outdoor deck for each room to use in season. And there's a bookstore full of reading materials below.

8 Bayview St., Camden 04843. (207) 236-9014. Doubles, $75 to $90; in winter, $45 to $55.

Where to Eat

Top Ratings

Frogwater Cafe. Little white lights twinkle in two bright storefront windows year-round, signaling a festive atmosphere at this highly rated new restaurant. All is bright (a little too bright for dinner) and whimsical inside with wall art that looks like windows to the blue-skied outdoors, and a door painted to make it appear that a cow is looking out. Homespun napkins and placemats in pastel plaids top light wood tables. A variety of innovative dishes is offered. Appetizers include wild mushroom strudel made with three types of mushrooms, and crab and artichoke hearts baked in puff pastry. For main dishes, try haddock stuffed with rice pilaf and mushrooms and served with a shallot-vermouth cream sauce, double-cut pork chop baked with a parmesan crust or mussels florentine with mussels, scallops and shrimp served over linguini with a spinach-parmesan cream sauce. Our party sampled the sea scallops baked with tomatoes, potatoes and fresh mozzarella and the sliced duck in a raisin-marsala sauce, both excellent. Tossed salads in a basil vinaigrette or parmesan pepper dressing came with. For dessert, we shared a chocolate concoction, made with macadamia nuts and coffee cream of some sort, big enough for four.

31 Elm St., Camden. (207) 236-8998. Entrées, $9 to $14. Dinner nightly, from 5:30. Closed Monday in off-season.

Cafe Miranda. Chef Kerry Altiero and his wife, Evelyn Donnelly, offer an innovative and extensive menu at this colorful, funky looking place on a downtown side street. More than 40 entrées emerge nightly from a tiny kitchen visible from most of the tables, and especially so from the four seats located at a counter next to it. Tables are bright with Caribbean-colored placemats and napkins, and the intimate space is happily boisterous when filled with diners. Menus change frequently and a wood-fired brick oven is used to make a pizza or two each day. Appetizers might be roasted butternut squash with mushrooms, "uptown blinis" (sautéed potato and zucchini cakes served with sour cream and spicy apple chutney), and portobello mushroom and onions roasted with blue castello cheese. Entrées include grilled salmon with a coconut-corn curry and Indian spices and served with yellow rice, rack of pork ribs with plum hoisin sauce and Chinese noodles, filet mignon kabobs with barley risotto, and almond chicken with mushrooms, pickled cucumber and chutney. For dessert, you could have pumpkin pie, frozen lemon mousse pie or trifle made with kahlua-soaked cake pieces, white chocolate sauce and peaches. A select wine list is offered.

15 Oak St., Rockland. (207) 594-2034. Entrées, $10 to $15. Dinner nightly from 5:30. Closed Sunday and Monday in winter.

Tried and True

Waterfront Restaurant. Head for this venerable restaurant beside the harbor near the center of town if you want to see the water. On a rainy Saturday in early winter, we managed to snag a table in the new, waterfront alcove on the bar side. A huge brick, two-sided fireplace means that you can sit by the fire in either the bar or the main restaurant if you wish; in summer, most opt for the outdoor terrace under big awnings by the water. Lunch offerings ($7 to $10) range from burgers to crab cakes; from baked brie in phyllo pastry served with seasonal fruits and French bread to a boiled lobster dinner. We tried the day's special, lamb stew served in a "crock" of bread. Ample green salads with a choice of dressings came with. At night, lobster and mussels sauté, seafood newburg, broiled scallops over wilted greens, a roasted vegetable pasta and grilled chicken served with polenta are all possibilities. The three-salad plate with smoked salmon, grilled chicken and pasta is a meal in itself.

Waterview Square off Bay View St., Camden. (207) 236-3747. Entrées, $10 to $24. Lunch daily, 11:30 to 2:30; dinner, 5 to 9.

Peter Ott's. This dark-walled restaurant with bare wood tables has quite a following among the locals. It is named for a native of Germany who settled in Rockport in the early 1770s and opened his home as a tavern. Today's appetizers include sea scallops wrapped in bacon; stuffed mushroom caps, and cajun popcorn. Light meals ($6 to $11) might be fried crab cakes, pasta primavera and caesar salad with grilled chicken. Entrées highlight premium angus beef, including two sizes of sirloin steak, a teriyaki sirloin and sirloin steak dijonnaise. Other possibilities include boneless salmon fillet with lemon-caper sauce, a pan-blackened seafood sampler with red onions and peppers, and pepper-crusted pork tenderloin with a brandy cream sauce. Diners enjoy a large salad bar (included with all entrées, and $6.60 à la carte). Gingerbread with ice cream and warm butterscotch sauce might be on the dessert menu.

12 Bay View St., Camden. (207) 236-4032. Entrées, $14 to $23. Dinner nightly, from 5:30. Closed Monday and Tuesday in winter.

O'Neil's. Another local favorite is O'Neil's, an Italian restaurant that stays open through the winter, pleasing residents and visitors alike. The decor is simple: bare wood tables and chairs. Front and center is a wood-fired oven for the featured pizzas: perhaps topped with chicken, Italian sausage and fresh basil. The "blue" pizza contains roasted beets and tomatoes, toasted walnuts, garlic and blue cheese. A wood-grilled burger goes for $7.95 and you can get a "big plate" Italian country salad (greens with rotisserie chicken, pancetta, roasted tomatoes, calamata olives and gorgonzola) for $11.95. Among appetizers are Maine crab cakes and bruschetta topped with marinated tomatoes, basil and parmesan. Special entrées might be grilled swordfish or sirloin, planked salmon, chicken breast parmesan or baked potato gnocchi with artichoke hearts and basil.

31 Bay View St., Camden. (207) 236-3272. Entrées, $14 to $17. Dinner nightly, from 5:30.

Jessica's Bistro. Swiss chef Hans Bucher presides over the kitchen at this popular restaurant, which styles itself a "European bistro." Opened in 1989, it is pleasantly ensconced in an old house set up high off the street, painted gray with burgundy trim. Diners enjoy the intimacy of several small dining rooms where they eat at mahogany tables set with beige placemats. Hans considers his menu international with "a little bit of everything." Veal Zurich (medallions in a creamy mushroom sauce) is a house favorite, as are tournedos topped with gorgonzola, mushrooms and shallots. Scallops, shrimp, fresh seafood, breast of duck and lamb provençal are usually on the menu, along with several pasta dishes. A house salad of mixed greens is dressed with a creamy Swiss vinaigrette for which people are always requesting the recipe. Favorite desserts are crème brûlée and tirami su.

2 South Main St., Rockland. (207) 596-0770. Entrées, $11 to $19. Dinner nightly except Tuesday, 5 to 9:30.

Youngtown Inn & Restaurant. Manuel Mercier, who hails from Paris, and his wife Mary Ann are the proprietors of this country establishment four miles west of Camden center along a scenic road that passes Lake Megunticook. Fires burn in the bar and one of the smaller dining rooms, seating twenty, while the main dining room is warmed by a wood stove. Guests dine à la carte or prix-fixe for $30. Chef Manuel describes his food as French/American and includes local game such as pheasant or rabbit, seafood from the nearby coast, and such popular entrées as rack of lamb or salmon in a potato crust. Corn chowder with lobster and lobster ravioli are among the acclaimed appetizers. Dessert soufflés of many varieties, including grand marnier, are a specialty. Should you want to settle in for the night, the big white inn with black shutters has six guest rooms, all with private baths. The Merciers take the holidays seriously and serve Thanksgiving dinner as well as dinners on Christmas Eve, Christmas Day and New Year's Eve. Then they close for the month of January to rest.

Route 52, Lincolnville. (207) 763-4290. Entrées, $14 to $23. Dinner nightly, 6 to 9. Closed Sunday and Monday in off-season.

Ambiance Beside the Harbor

The Sail Loft. When winter winds start to howl, diners are drawn to The Sail Loft for its cozy ambiance, including two fireplaced dining rooms; not to mention the views of Rockport harbor from its window tables. Pine-paneled walls and small wood tables, each with a surface varnished to a high sheen and dotted with homespun placemats, convey an old-fashioned feeling. So does the atmospheric cocktail lounge, which resembles the "below decks" area of a wooden ship. The extensive menu is big on lobster, from lobster stew to lobster salad plate (at $28.50, the highest-priced item). For lunch ($6 to $10), you can order fish and chips, lobster newburg, crabmeat and lobster quiche or a chicken club sandwich. Dinner entrées include platters of broiled or fried fish, Penobscot Bay scallops, chicken pasta primavera and roast duckling with raspberry sauce. Among desserts are hot Indian pudding, southern pecan pie, ice cream puff with hot fudge sauce, and old-fashioned bread pudding with whiskey sauce.

Public Landing, Rockport. (207) 236-2330. Entrées, $10 to $24. Lunch, 11:30 to 2:30; dinner, 5:30 to 8:30; Sunday brunch, noon to 2:30. Closed Tuesday and Wednesday, January-March.

For Breakfast and Lunch

The Brown Bag. Four sisters own this bustling bakery and restaurant that serves breakfast and lunch. You order at a counter and try to find a booth or table in the adjoining room to wait until your name is called over a loudspeaker. For breakfast, oatmeal with applesauce, raisins and nuts; croissants in various flavors; pecan sticky buns; giant muffins, and omelets are possibilities. Lunch fare ($2 to $7) ranges from cold sandwiches to hot (perhaps grilled ham with havarti cheese, capers and artichoke hearts), lentil burger and a daily special. On the way out, why not stop for a cinnamon biscuit or a giant chocolate chip-oatmeal-raisin nut cookie at the bakery?

606 Main St., Rockland. (207) 596-6372. Breakfast daily, 6:30 to 11, Sunday to 2; lunch, Monday-Saturday 11 to 4.

Pub Grub

Seaside taverns can be cozy in inclement weather. Here are three to try:

The Sea Dog Brewing Co. Located in an old mill building beside the Megunticook River, the Sea Dog is known not only for its brews but also for its food and its view of a waterfall in the old mill stream. Good sandwiches and appetizers are offered day and night. In chilly weather, the lobster stew, chili, french onion soup, fried haddock sandwich or crab cakes with honey-mustard sauce make a good lunch ($5 to $9). In the evening a selection of tavern dinners is available. Quaff your thirst with one of seven regular brews, including Penobscot Maine pilsener, Windjammer ale, and Old Golly Wobbler Brown Ale, or one of three weekly specials. Got a sweet tooth? Order Reese's peanut butter pie. There's live music on Thursday, Friday and Saturday nights in winter, nightly in the summer. *Mechanic Street, Camden. (207) 236-6863. Entrées, $7 to $14. Lunch daily, 11 to 2; dinner, 5 to 9:30.*

The Whale's Tooth Pub. An old red brick house attached to a modern restaurant addition is the site of this pub, favored in cold weather because of its roaring fire. Cozy chairs and tables and booths provide good sightlines to the hearth, and you can order goodies like onion soup or seafood chowder in a bread loaf, fish and chips, or steamed mussels. Need something heartier? How about prime rib, sirloin steak, surf and turf, crab cake platter; or grilled swordfish? *Route 1, Lincolnville Beach. (207) 789-5200. Entrées, $8 to $20. Dinner, Wednesday-Friday 4 to 10, Saturday and Sunday noon to 10.*

The Waterworks. The location of this casual restaurant was once the eight-bay garage for the Camden-Rockland Water Company. Renovations added a huge stone fireplace to give the atmosphere of a pub. A long bar runs along one wall, and wood tables (which remind one of the big tables at the Hofbrau Haus in Munich) line the other wall. Brews from Maine microbreweries are on tap and many bottled beers are available. Dining options range from starters like a basket of sweet potato chips served with sour cream or warm pretzels with mustard to meat loaf, fish and grilled vegetable sandwiches ($5 to $7). You can also get shepherd's pie, a bread bowl stew or beef and stilton topped with a puff pastry crust. After 5, "supper" can be penne pasta with pesto; a half barbecued chicken; New York strip steak; roast turkey, or pork loin. *Lindsey Street, Rockland. (207) 596-7950. Entrées, $7 to $14. Daily, 11 to 10; Sunday from noon.*

FOR MORE INFORMATION: Rockport-Camden-Lincolnville Chamber of Commerce, Public Landing, Box 919, Camden, ME 04843, (207) 236-4404.

20 ❄ Winter

Early homes have been restored along Benefit Street's "Mile of History."

A Haven of History

Providence, R.I.

"For freedom of conscience the town was first planted,
Persuasion, not force, was used by the people.
This church is the oldest, and has not recanted,
Enjoying and granting bell, temple and steeple."

The inscription is on the bell atop the first Baptist church in America. It tells something about this city and this church founded in 1636 by Roger Williams, who started here more than 350 years ago the thrust for "soul liberty" and individual freedom that now prevails across the land.

The words cannot fully convey the legacy of Roger Williams, who fled the tyranny of Massachusetts Puritanism and named his settlement at the head of Narragansett Bay "in commemoration of God's providence." Nor can prose adequately describe the charms today for the visitor to this rags-to-riches city that calls itself – with a curious mixture of hometown pride and inferiority – "New England's Best Kept Secret."

Increasingly recognized beyond its borders, its treasures of history, architecture, arts and letters are appropriate for an over 350-year-old university town. Lately, this long-sleepy town that had a reputation for flamboyance and tackiness is acting like the second largest New England city that it is.

The views of the skyscrapers through the ivied gates of Brown University give it something of the look of Boston. The spotlighted State Capitol dome could be

Washington's. The restored townhouses, close-in mansions, gaslight-type lanterns and statued squares lend the air of Philadelphia. The East Side's nearly perpendicular hills could be San Francisco's. The parks, promenades and bridges along the revived downtown riverfront lend the cosmopolitan air of Venice or Amsterdam.

All this is on a compact, human scale. Providence is unusual in that most of its historic, cultural and sightseeing attractions are within walking distance of downtown.

In the vanguard of the restoration movement, the city was among the first in the nation to attempt to save an entire neighborhood. The preservation of College Hill on the East Side began 40 years ago and is still unfolding on its steep, tree-lined Colonial streets with providential names like Benefit, Hope, Benevolent and Power.

Today, College Hill is a lively mix of historic residences and institutions, including top-ranked Brown University with its world-class libraries and the Rhode Island School of Design with its outstanding art museum. Benefit Street's "Mile of History" has more than 200 notable homes dating back to early Providence, when this was *the* street (it still is). At the foot of College Hill are the restored South Main and North Main street areas, where the city was born along the Providence River. Boutiques and restaurants have sprung up amid old buildings. And everywhere there are churches, whose spires give this part of the city a classic New England look, as befits its religious heritage.

The downtown area has regained vibrancy with the opening of the Rhode Island Convention Center and the Westin Hotel. They anchor the $143-million Capital Center project, the most ambitious urban renewal project in America. Rivers have been relocated and eight graceful new bridges built to open up the downtown riverfront. Waterplace Park with its cobblestone riverwalks and amphitheater is alive with musical events, arts festivals and even ESPN's Extreme Games. At our latest visit, final approvals had just been granted for Providence Place, a downtown mall with nationally known anchor stores and movie theaters.

This is a city of rarities, firsts and superlatives: America's first enclosed shopping mall (1828). A national park. The world's second largest unsupported dome. A bus tunnel under College Hill. New England's largest city park and zoo. The country's first department and dry goods stores. Two of its oldest banks.

Not only is Providence a city of firsts. It's a city of today, especially in its restorations and restaurants, both of which receive national recognition. The mix is intriguing for a weekend visitor, especially in winter when the colleges are in session and the city seems particularly vibrant.

Getting There

Interstate highways ring Providence and cut around the downtown area from all directions. But this is not an easy city in which to drive unless you know exactly where you're going (we've managed to get lost almost every time we've been in Providence). One-way streets, dead-ends and unmarked expressway entrances are a visiting motorist's nightmare. If you stay downtown, park your car and walk.

Amtrak trains from New York and Boston stop at a new railroad station at the edge of downtown. The restored Union Station facing Kennedy Square has been converted to new uses. Local buses converge on Kennedy Square, which is now a busy transit center. The bus station for Greyhound and Bonanza lines is nearby.

An eye-catching new terminal complex recently doubled the passenger space at Green State Airport, which is served by major airlines. More frequent flights serve Boston's Logan International Airport, an hour's drive north of Providence.

Seeing and Doing

Rhode Island's capital city is one of the most historic in the United States. The oldest section of town is the riverfront area along North and South Main Streets. Roger Williams and his 17th-century colonists built their homes, shops and churches on the hill rising sharply up the east bank, an area now known variously as College Hill and the East Side.

In the 18th century, the town's leading citizens were the four Brown brothers (John, Joseph, Nicholas and Moses), merchants and entrepreneurs whose funds helped build Brown University and one of the nation's most powerful business dynasties.

During the 19th century, the commercial center moved westward across the Providence River to Weybosset Point, and the river and nearby portions of its tributaries, the Moshassuck and Woonasquatucket, were covered over by a 1,145-foot-wide bridge, the world's widest. Immigrants settled to the west in Victorian homes in Elmwood and Federal Hill. By the 20th century, Providence was one-third foreign born, and another third were children of immigrants. The ethnic ties of these groups remained stronger here than elsewhere; some neighborhoods still possess a foreign air.

With the flight to the suburbs in the 20th century, only College Hill retained its aura as a Yankee enclave, proud and aloof. Even that was endangered by university expansion in the mid-1950s, at which time John Nicholas Brown founded the Providence Preservation Society to preserve the past as "an asset for the future."

Now, old Providence has been preserved and the new downtown revitalized. The National Register has designated 26 historic districts in Providence, which retains more intact Colonial and early Federal buildings than any other city in America. Lately, the rivers that few realized were there have re-emerged. Train tracks were moved and the rivers relocated to flow freely under picturesque new bridges beside walkways and gardens. They will connect eventually with the soon-to-be-renovated Old Harbor area near India Point Park.

Everything is nicely detailed on a brochure and map designating key historic and cultural sites along Providence's new Banner Trail, available from the visitor information center in the pavilion building facing the pond in Waterplace Park.

History and Architecture

Benefit Street "Mile of History," College Hill. Here is the most impressive collection of original Colonial homes in America. It is an extraordinary, lived-in mix of 18th- and 19th-century residential and institutional treasures – more than 200 on tree-lined Benefit Street with its imitation gaslights and brick sidewalks, and more on cross streets. Benefit Street, surely one of America's most distinctive thoroughfares, is eminently walkable – and that's the best way to see and savor it. The Providence Preservation Society, 21 Meeting St., (401) 831-7440, has brochures for self-guided walks ($1) and guides group tours by reservation. Ninety-minute walking tours leave the society headquarters daily at 10 in summer. Tours cover Benefit Street, portions of College Hill, the restored South Main Street area and the new Waterplace Park.

Among the highlights: Architect Joseph Brown designed the 1773 **Market House** at the end of Market Square and his own **Joseph Brown House** (1774) along one side at 50 South Main. The house was occupied in the 19th century by the Providence Bank which he founded, the oldest in New England. Next door is the gold-domed **Old Stone Bank** building, once the Providence Institute for Savings, one of the nation's first. The huge red brick **County Court House** (1933) is considered the largest Republican structure of its style in the world. Buses cut through the East Side Bus Tunnel to Thayer Street.

Old State House Area. An open "parade" leads from North Main Street up the hill to the **Old State House,** 150 Benefit St., and is surrounded by structures that rank among the city's oldest (the **Cushing houses,** 1737 and 1772). The state house is where Rhode Island became the first colony to declare its independence from England on May 4, 1776. Now housing state preservation offices, it was the seat of government and social life until the new Capitol opened in 1900. A block

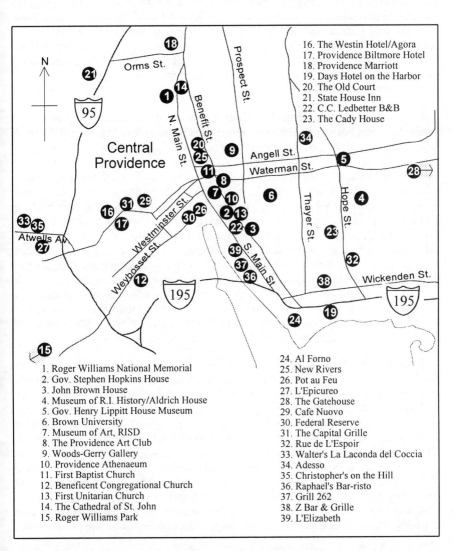

16. The Westin Hotel/Agora
17. Providence Biltmore Hotel
18. Providence Marriott
19. Days Hotel on the Harbor
20. The Old Court
21. State House Inn
22. C.C. Ledbetter B&B
23. The Cady House

1. Roger Williams National Memorial
2. Gov. Stephen Hopkins House
3. John Brown House
4. Museum of R.I. History/Aldrich House
5. Gov. Henry Lippitt House Museum
6. Brown University
7. Museum of Art, RISD
8. The Providence Art Club
9. Woods-Gerry Gallery
10. Providence Athenaeum
11. First Baptist Church
12. Beneficent Congregational Church
13. First Unitarian Church
14. The Cathedral of St. John
15. Roger Williams Park

24. Al Forno
25. New Rivers
26. Pot au Feu
27. L'Epicureo
28. The Gatehouse
29. Cafe Nuovo
30. Federal Reserve
31. The Capital Grille
32. Rue de L'Espoir
33. Walter's La Laconda del Coccia
34. Adesso
35. Christopher's on the Hill
36. Raphael's Bar-risto
37. Grill 262
38. Z Bar & Grille
39. L'Elizabeth

south is the **Brick School House,** built in 1769 as the city's first free school; now it is the home of the Providence Preservation Society's Revolving Fund. Across the street is **Shakespeare's Head** (1771), a restored garden and a house where Benjamin Franklin's apprentice, John Carter, published the Providence Gazette. On Benefit Street to the north are the 1810 **Sullivan Dorr Mansion,** an outstanding example of Federal architecture designed by John Holden Greene and once home of the leader of the Dorr Rebellion for universal voting rights; the **Sarah Helen Whitman House** (1783-92), home of the poet courted by Edgar Allan Poe, and several houses built by the founder of Providence's Gorham Silver Company.

Roger Williams National Memorial. This four-and-a-half-acre plot is being developed for passive recreation around the site of the original 1636 settlement. National Park Service rangers preside over a small visitor center with exhibits and a three-minute slide show describing the life of the city's founder, a park with gardens, and a shrine around the site of the spring that supplied Williams's water and was the true beginning of the colony. Several blocks east and almost straight up on Congdon Street is **Prospect Terrace,** site of the Roger Williams memorial statue. It yields a panoramic view of downtown Providence.
282 North Main St. (401) 521-7266. Daily, 8 to 4:30.

Governor Stephen Hopkins House. Owned by the state and administered by the National Society of Colonial Dames, this is the dark red clapboard home of the ten-times governor of Rhode Island, first chancellor of Brown University and a signer of the Declaration of Independence. Governor Hopkins added the main part of the house in 1743 to the original two 1707 rooms. He became a Quaker after he married his second wife and the home reveals his simplicity of heart. Here is the four-poster in which George Washington slept, the wig stand on which he rested his wig and a decanter set he presented to his host. On display are the owner's spectacles, his baby cap and shoe buckles. Guides point out the children's room with a trundle bed, an old cradle with a cloth doll, a tiny chair used by tots to learn to walk as they held onto the back, and the weasel (a wool winder that popped every 40th revolution – hence "Pop Goes the Weasel"). Beside the house is a typical 18th-century parterre garden designed by a Hopkins descendant and centered by a sundial with a Hopkins quote: "A garden that might comfort yield."
15 Hopkins Street at Benefit Street. (401) 884-8337. April-December, Wednesday and Saturday 1 to 4, and by appointment. Free.

John Brown House. The first great mansion in Providence was built in 1786 for John Brown, China trade merchant, slave trader, privateer and patriot. George Washington was entertained here, John Quincy Adams called it "the most magnificent and elegant private mansion that I have ever seen on this continent." An outstanding example of late Georgian architecture, it is now a house museum with nine rooms and a priceless collection of Rhode Island cabinetmakers' furniture. The most prized piece is Joseph Brown's Goddard-made nine-shell desk and bookcase. Visitors see a video show giving a good overview of early life in Providence before they are guided on hour-long tours through the three-story museum, now owned by the Rhode Island Historical Society. You can tell that John Brown really weighed 300 pounds in his later years by his capacious waistcoat spread on one of the beds. The third floor displays collections of early dolls, silver and pewter, most of it the family's, as well as goods brought back from the Orient by neighbor Edward Carrington. The carriage house garage has John Brown's robin's-egg-blue chariot, the earliest coach made in America (1782).

52 Power St. (401) 331-8575. Tuesday-Saturday 10 to 4:30, March-December; weekends only, rest of year. Adults $5, children $2, families $12.

Museum of Rhode Island History at Aldrich House. The 1822 Federal-style mansion, home of the Nelson Aldrich family, was donated by heirs of Winthrop Aldrich, ambassador to Great Britain, and is now the Museum of Rhode Island History. Exhibitions change about twice yearly and are generally excellent. One called "Harboring History: The Providence Waterfront" included a lecture series and boat tours. We like the wrought-iron benches under the huge copper beech tree at the side of the house, where groups may picnic by appointment.

110 Benevolent St. (401) 331-8575. Tuesday-Saturday 11 to 4, Sunday 1 to 4. Adults $2, children $1.

Governor Henry Lippitt House Museum. A red-brick Italianate mansion built in 1865, this is considered one of the most complete, authentic and intact Victorian houses in the country. The high-Victorian interior includes richly carved woodwork, colorful stenciling, faux marble and stained-glass windows.

199 Hope St. (401) 453-0688. Tuesday-Friday 11 to 4, Saturday 1 to 4, April-December; winter, by appointment. Adults $4, children $2.

Arts and Letters

The educational heritage of Brown University and the creative influence of Rhode Island School of Design (RISD, locally called Riz-D) have left their marks on Providence, particularly on College Hill.

Brown University, head of College Street, College Hill, (401) 863-2378. The nation's seventh oldest, Brown was the Baptist answer to Congregationalist Yale and Harvard, Presbyterian Princeton and Episcopalian Penn and Columbia. Graduates still process down the hill to the First Baptist Meeting House for commencement exercises, although the university shed its Baptist ties in 1938 and then entered a period of rapid expansion. The original **University Hall,** patterned by Joseph Brown after Princeton's Nassau Hall, houses the administration at the head of College Street today. The admissions office is located in the 19th-century Italian villa-style **Corliss-Brackett House** (ask to see the Victorian bathroom) at Prospect and Angell streets, where students start guided campus tours on most weekdays and Saturday mornings from September to December.

Brown Libraries. The huge **John D. Rockefeller Jr. Library** at 10 Prospect St. houses the university's general collections. Next door at 20 Prospect is the old **John Hay Library,** now home of the university archives and special collections. Foremost here is the McLellan Collection of Abraham Lincoln memorabilia – two small upstairs rooms with 700 Lincoln manuscripts, busts, portraits and even a lock of his hair. The curator considers the collection one of the finest in the country. The Lownes History of Science Collection is said to be the largest botanical collection anywhere. Open Monday-Friday 9 to 5; free. The beaux arts **John Carter Brown Library** across the quadrangle is a world-renowned repository of early Americana, furnished like a "gentleman's library" with huge hanging tapestries at either end. Manuscripts starting from the 15th century were shown in glass cases when we were there. The casual visitor may be bored, but the scholar will find such national treasures as Thomas Paine's original manuscripts for *Common Sense* and eight editions of Christopher Columbus's 1493 letters. Open Monday-Friday 8:30 to 5, Saturday 9 to noon; free.

Museum of Art, Rhode Island School of Design. One of the nation's outstanding small art museums is operated by one of its leading art and design schools. From mosaics and other treasures of ancient Greece and Rome to a fine collection of oriental art (don't miss the exquisite robes given to the museum by Lucy Truman Aldrich) to an outstanding selection of works by French artists (Monet, Degas, Manet, Cezanne and Matisse, among many) to changing exhibits, there is a bit of everything among the more than 70,000 works here. The famous bronze of Balzac by Rodin is one of the museum's prized possessions. The adjoining Pendleton House, housing American furniture and decorative arts, is the earliest example of an American wing in an American museum. Here is the Lucy Truman Aldrich collection of 18th- century porcelain figures, wonderfully displayed in cabinets lighted from inside. The new Daphne Farago wing contains two large contemporary galleries and frees up space elsewhere for a permanent gallery for the museum's Gorham silver collection, a recent gift of the Providence-based Textron Inc. A nifty museum shop has jewelry, posters, dolls, postcards, stained-glass medallions, notes and cards.

224 Benefit St. (401) 454-6500. Tuesday-Saturday 10:30 to 5, Thursday noon to 8, Sunday 2 to 5; summer, Wednesday-Saturday noon to 5. Adults $2, students 50 cents; admission by donation on Saturday.

The Providence Art Club. This 1790 brick-veneered house within easy walking distance of the RISD Museum has harbored the nation's second oldest art club (1880) with its parlors and private dining rooms for more than 100 years. A spacious upstairs gallery holds changing exhibits by a membership involved in everything from oils to photography.

11 Thomas St. (401) 331-1114. Monday-Friday 10 to 4, Saturday noon to 3, Sunday 3 to 5; free.

Two buildings down the street is the unusual 1866 Norman-Breton **Fleur de Lys Building,** former studio of Sidney R. Burleigh, dean of Rhode Island artists in the early 1900s. The Greek Revival building at 5 Thomas St. was long the headquarters of the Providence Water Color Club. Off "Artist's Row" but within walking distance is the **Bell Gallery** in Brown University's contemporary List Art Center, 64 College St., with changing exhibits throughout the school year.

Woods-Gerry Gallery. An Italian Renaissance-style mansion designed by Richard Upjohn houses RISD student galleries. Three sculptures, a towering copper beech tree and thick plantings of rhododendron grace the lawns and terrace overlooking Providence. Maintained as an important example of the city's 19th-century architecture, the three-story mansion devotes its stripped-down main floor to changing exhibitions. The student and faculty works are worth viewing.

62 Prospect St. (401) 454-6141. Monday-Saturday 11 to 4, Sunday 2 to 5; closed Wednesday and Thursday, mid-February to June. Free.

Providence Athenaeum. One of America's oldest subscription libraries is housed in this 1838 Greek-Doric temple-style building, which was the center of Providence's early intellectual and literary life. Many valuable books are shelved in its alcoves, within which Edgar Allan Poe wooed local poet Sarah Helen Whitman. The rare book wing has original Audubon elephant folios and changing art exhibits. Books are for members only, but the rare book displays and art exhibits are open to visitors.

251 Benefit St. (401) 421-6970. Monday-Friday 8:30 to 5:30, Saturday 9:30 to 5:30, Sunday 1 to 5; closed weekends in summer. Free.

The Churches

Like the cathedrals of Europe and the missions in California, Providence's churches can be destinations. What better way to spend a Sunday morning in this city of churches?

First Baptist Church, 75 North Main St. Members from as far away as Newport belong to the oldest Baptist congregation in America, established in 1638 by Roger Williams. Designed by architect Joseph Brown, it opened in 1775 "for the publick worship of Almighty God; and also for holding Commencement in." Its 1,300 seats represented one-fourth the population of Providence at the time; it's still filled to the rafters for Brown University's commencement. John D. Rockefeller Jr., who taught Sunday school here as a Brown undergraduate, provided funds in 1957 to renovate and strengthen the building. The woodwork was restored to the original Meeting House color, a restful sage. Note the Waterford crystal chandelier, given by Hope Brown upon her marriage in 1792 in memory of her father; it has gone from candles to gas to electrified miniature lights. The striking 185-foot spire was based on designs for the steeple of St. Martins-in-the-Fields, London. Free self-guided tours are available Monday-Friday 9 to 3:30. Tours are given by members after Sunday services at 11 (at 9:30 in July and August); our guide was an erudite drama professor from Brown.

Beneficent Congregational Church, 300 Weybosset St. Also called Round Top Church for its landmark copper dome, this is the city's oldest church (1809) west of the Providence River. It resembles the Custom House Building in Dublin and is one of America's earliest Greek Revival buildings. The church has had only ten ministers since its founding in 1743 and is known as the "house of ecumenicity." The first sermon by a Universalist was preached here in 1773, the first by a Methodist in 1791 and the first by a Roman Catholic bishop in 1962. The crystal chandelier – a feature of many Providence churches – came from Austria, and the splendid organ was given by Mr. and Mrs. John D. Rockefeller Jr. in memory of her mother, Abby Pierce Aldrich. Open Monday-Friday 8 to 4, Saturday and Sunday 9 to 1.

First Unitarian Church, 301 Benefit St. Local architect John Holden Greene built this stone church, third on the site, in 1816 and considered it his best work. The always-liberal congregation was officially Congregational but affiliated with the Unitarian movement and changed the name to reflect its leanings in 1953. You can climb your winding way up the steeple (by appointment with the sexton) for a good view of the city and of the largest bell ever cast in the foundry of Paul Revere.

Interior features are a three-tiered chandelier and the shallow oval dome, decorated with graduated panels, of Bulfinch inspiration.

The Cathedral of St. John, 271 North Main St. This Georgian building with Gothic trim, detail and tower was built by John Holden Greene in 1810 after the 1722 King's Church structure was demolished. Under the 18th-century altar is a replica of an ancient Saxon cross set in a stone from Canterbury Cathedral; the 1816 Waterford chandelier is striking. The Episcopal congregation now is racially mixed. The adjacent burial ground contains graves of famous Rhode Islanders. Open Monday-Friday 9 to 4, Sunday 8:30 to 11:30 (tours following services).

Other churches of note: **Grace Church** (Episcopal), serene amidst the hubbub of Westminster Street, was designed in 1846 by Richard Upjohn. The earliest Gothic Revival church in the country, it has buttressed walls, a towering spire and a dark interior lighted by fourteen unique memorial windows. Another Upjohn church, **St. Stephen's** at 114 George St., is described as "Smoky St. Steve's" by the irreverent because it's so high Episcopal. Outstanding stained glass and a large chapel with windows onto the huge carved-wood sanctuary mark this Georgian edifice surrounded by Brown University. The basilica-size copper dome of **First Church of Christ, Scientist,** at Prospect and Meeting streets is a landmark visible across the city. The Unitarian church sexton says it has an even better view than his.

An Urban Retreat

Roger Williams Park. One of the pleasant surprises of Providence is this 430-acre haven of greenery – the largest city park and the best zoo in New England. It's a real urban park, well-maintained and a place on the way up. We know East Siders who rent paddleboats on Sunday afternoons from the restored Victorian Dalrymple Boathouse and lose themselves along the meandering lagoons – "you go with the hordes and end up thinking you're out in the country," says one. The 900-animal zoo contains penguins, polar bears, sea lions, pink flamingos and a new African plains exhibit where elephants, zebras, giraffes and cheetas roam in a natural habitat. The new Marco Polo Trail through three acres of "Asia" combines culture, animals and history in one of the first interactive biopark exhibits of its kind in the country. The **Museum of Natural History and Planetarium** and the Rose, Japanese and Hartman outdoor gardens are considered fine. Near the park entrance (follow the signs and the statues) is the restored 1773 **Betsy Williams Cottage,** last occupied by a descendant who deeded part of the land in honor of the city's founder. Besides miles of walks, waterways and driveways, the park has a Carousel Village with a replica of a Victorian carousel, a train ride, and a small amusement area with an indoor pony ring.

950 Elmwood Ave. Exit 17 off I-95 south. (401) 785-9450. Park daily, 7 a.m. to 9 p.m., free; zoo, daily 9 to 6, adults $5, children $2.50; greenhouses and Carousel Village, daily 11 to 5.

Shopping

Downtown Providence was getting a much-needed retailing revival with **Providence Place,** an upscale, 150-store mall being built atop a 4,000-car parking garage between the Westin Hotel, the State Capitol and I-95. It will include three big-name anchors, Macy's, Lord & Taylor and Nordstrom, as well as a twenty-screen movie theater and restaurants.

Rhode Island State Capitol, as seen from rear of house on Benefit Street.

Meanwhile, downtown shopping has been largely confined to The Arcade at 65 Weybosset St., built in 1829 as the nation's first indoor shopping mall. It reopened in 1980 with three floors of specialty shops and restaurants connected by balconies with cast-iron railings and topped by a block-long skylight. Many of the nicest shops have gone, and the main floor is now mostly fast-food eateries, where most of Providence seems to line up for a quick weekday lunch.

The major shopping areas are the malls in Warwick and, an exceptional destination, the upscale shops at The Village at Garden City Center in suburban Cranston.

Thayer Street has college-type shops and two good book stores beside each other – the **College Hill Book Store** and the **Brown University Book Store.**

At 297 Thayer, **Oop!** is a contemporary gift gallery like few others – colorful, funky and avant-garde. Because of the strength of RISD, the shop carries the works of more than 100 regional artists, from handblown vases to decorated boxes. The magnets of movie starlets on an old refrigerator door weren't exactly contemporary, but typified the flair of this unusual emporium. Later, we found displays of its wares in glass showcases in the downtown lobby of Citizens Bank, testifying to their quality.

Wayland Square on the East Side is the center of old-line shops for clothing, gifts and such, among them the **Opulent Owl** (one of our favorite gift shops anywhere), **Dorothy Williams** for lovely apparel, **T.W. Rounds Co.** for leather goods, the **Cheese Shop** and **Books on the Square**.

The historic forge beside the Seekonk River at 6 Richmond Square houses **Simple Pleasures,** a little treasure of a place that looks like a garden cottage. It enchantingly displays goods from Italian scarves and French fragrances to scented soaps and chocolate topiary, all billed as "clever chaos – a state of mind." We thought everything here was unique.

You'll also find several contemporary stores along South Main Street, including **Social Expressions** for greeting cards and stationary, **Nature's Comfort** for shoes and boots, and **Comina,** for international gifts and crafts. Art galleries and antiques shops are proliferating along four blocks of nearby **Wickenden Street**.

Where to Stay

Chain motels are concentrated south of Providence in the Warwick area and east of the city (a shorter drive) in Seekonk, Mass. For a city weekend, however, you probably will want accommodations in or near downtown.

Downtown Hotels

The Westin Hotel. Built by the state as part of the new Rhode Island Convention Center complex, this is New England's fanciest hotel outside Boston. From the striking, 25-story-high gabled roof that denotes its Neoclassic presence on the Providence skyline to the majestic four-story lobby rotunda with its marble floor and columns, this hotel exudes class. Each of the 363 handsomely appointed rooms and suites come with kingsize or two double beds, at least one easy chair with ottoman, a spacious writing desk, two telephones, a minibar and a TV tucked away in an armoire. They are decorated in contemporary European style to reflect the interior of a Newport mansion. The top of the line is the Executive Club Floor with a lounge for afternoon hors d'oeuvres, continental breakfast and upgraded services. Above it all are three suites overlooking the city. Guests enjoy a health spa with indoor pool beneath the dome atop the rotunda building. The Library Lounge off the lobby rotunda is the ultimate in plush surroundings. Take the long escalator up to the second-floor lounges, which include a sports bar and a jazz room. The elegant **Agora** restaurant (see Where to Eat) was named one of America's best new restaurants by Esquire magazine. Less lofty fare is offered in the **Arbor Cafe,** which has a breakfast buffet, a buffet or à la carte lunch, and a short dinner menu from $9.95 for chicken cordon bleu to $14.95 for sirloin steak.

One West Exchange Street, Providence 02903. (401) 598-8000. Fax (401) 598-8200. Doubles, $130 to $195.

Providence Biltmore Hotel. An early feather in Providence's cap, this restored downtown hotel appears a bit dowdy lately in comparison with its brand-new neighbor across the plaza. The imposing brick dowager opened in 1922 to a special trainload from New York, a 50-piece band and a sea of roses, but fell on hard times and closed in 1973. It reopened with great fanfare in 1979 after local business interests renovated it for $15 million. It later was taken over by the Omni chain and since has become a Grand Heritage hotel. At the top of the three-story lobby you can see the wonderfully ornate, original gilt ceiling, and the crystal chandelier and palm trees remind one of the Plaza in New York. The original 500 bedrooms have been converted into 217 comfortable, large and deluxe rooms, done in soft and soothing colors. Most have kingsize or two double beds, plus armchairs and sofas in elegant sitting areas, with TVs hidden in armoires. We liked the huge closets and the bathrooms with separate dressing areas and vanities. The Presidential and Vice Regal suites are some of the largest we've seen – each impeccably outfitted with antiques, two bathrooms, dining room, living room and kitchenette. (The price? If you have to ask, you won't be staying). **Stanford's Restaurant** on the main floor serves three meals a day in a pleasant setting with a tiered lounge. The vaguely continental menu offers ten entrées from $15.95 for island-grilled pork chops to $24.95 for filet mignon aux duxelles.

Kennedy Plaza, Providence 02903. (401) 421-0700 or (800) 294-7709. Fax (401) 455-3050. Doubles, $144 to $219; weekend packages, $89 and up.

Providence Marriott Hotel. A multi-million-dollar renovation in 1996 was creating a new entrance, expanding the lobby and upgrading guest rooms at this motor hotel built in 1974. Like others of the chain, it's good for families, with a large indoor-outdoor pool, game room, sauna, whirlpool and exercise equipment. The 345 rooms on six floors are ordinary size, nicely decorated and have queen or kingsize beds. Some have a view of the nearby State Capitol or face onto the landscaped pool area. The lobby is especially welcoming. **Stacy's Sea Grille Restaurant** offers three meals a day. It's a long walk to downtown, but buses pass every fifteen minutes.

Charles and Orms Streets (Exit 23 off I-95), Providence 02904. (401) 272-2400 or (800) 937-7768. Fax (401) 273-2686. Doubles, $159 to $179; weekends from $89.

Value Beside the Water

Days Hotel On the Harbor. Opened in 1989 just east of downtown, this 136-room cross between a Days Inn and something more grandiose is a welcome addition to Providence accommodations. The six-story hotel faces the spruced-up harborfront park, from which the East Bay bicycle path originates on its fourteen-mile trek along the shore to Bristol. A seasonal cocktail terrace takes advantage of the view. Rooms come in four configurations – two doubles, queensize, kingsize and king deluxe with whirlpool tub. The decor is pleasant in green and beige, with light pine furniture. We regretted that our room with two double beds had only one easy chair, and that was clear across the room from the TV set. The only drinking glasses were white plastic Days Inn cups. But we appreciated the quiet of our digs on the side facing Providence Harbor (not so quiet are those on the other side right next to I-95) and the price was right. A small health center includes a jacuzzi. Three meals a day are served in the **India Point Cafe.**

220 India St., Providence 02906. (401) 272-5577. Doubles, $90 to $115.

Bed & Breakfasts

The Old Court. You can stay on historic Benefit Street and relive today the Providence of yesteryear, thanks to the conversion of an 1863 Episcopal church rectory into an elegant B&B. Owners Jon and Carol Rosenblatt, who also own a series of small East Side restaurants, spared no expense in the restoration. Italianate in design, the Old Court has ornate mantelpieces, plaster moldings and twelve-foot-high ceilings. Each of the ten guest rooms with private tiled baths is decorated differently. Some have brass beds, some four-poster, and most have exotic wallpapers. The Eastlake Room is done with Eastlake furniture. Lace curtains and old clocks convey a feeling of the past; air-conditioning and telephones are concessions to the present, and a couple of rooms have television. Because there is no common room, the Old Court seems like a small hotel. A full breakfast is served in a pink breakfast room, graced with an oriental rug and fresh flowers. The specialty is crêpes, but the day's menu might dictate eggs, pancakes or french toast. A new two-bedroom suite in a house across the street is available for long-term guests at $160 a night.

144 Benefit St., Providence 02903. (401) 751-2002. Fax (401) 282-4830. Doubles, $135.

State House Inn. Creature comforts are well provided in this rooming-house-turned-B&B in a residential area just across I-95 from the State Capitol. Frank and Monica Hopton have furnished their ten guest rooms in a vaguely Colonial style typical of her (Parker) family's three B&Bs on Nantucket. Two rooms have canopy beds and two have fireplaces; all contain TVs, telephones, king or queensize beds topped with quilts or comforters and an overstuffed, comfy chair. Hooked rugs or carpets cover the maple floors that are original to the house. Stenciling and wreaths are scattered here and there. The main floor harbors a small guest parlor and a bigger, fireplaced dining room where the full breakfast might include quiche, french toast or blueberry pancakes.

43 Jewett St., Providence 02908. (401) 351-6111. Fax (401) 351-4261. Doubles, $99 to $109.

C.C. Ledbetter Bed & Breakfast. There is artistry in Clare "C.C." Ledbetter's B&B, which occupies an historic house with a big side yard and garden in the heart of the East Side historic district. The artistry is reflected in C.C.'s amazing collection of paintings and photographs, her choice of colors (vivid green and apricot for the guest living room), and in the dhurrie rugs, Delft tiles and handmade quilts gracing four guest rooms that share two baths. A new bedroom created from storage areas at the rear of the third floor has a private bath, king bed and view of the downtown skyline. The spacious third-floor front room running the width of the house contains a queen bed and an exercise machine, typical of the home-like touches in this much-lived-in house. Each room is decorated in eclectic style and has a small television. C.C., who raised three children in Montana before moving back East in 1988 and deciding to settle in Providence sight unseen, serves a continental-plus breakfast of fruit, choice of juices, cheese, bagels, homemade breads or English muffins.

326 Benefit St., Providence 02903. (401) 351-4699. Doubles, $80 and $95. No credit cards.

The Cady House. The owner's eclectic collections of folk art are everywhere evident in this imposing 1839 residence with pillared entrance on College Hill. Their offspring gone, Anna Colaiace and her husband Bill, a radiologist, offer three much-decorated Victorian guest rooms with queen beds and private baths. A side suite contains a daybed with trundle bed in the living room and sturdy armoire and dresser in the bedroom. A rear bedroom has a luxurious settee in a windowed alcove and a giant bathroom with clawfoot tub, separate shower and a circular stand holding a multitude of plants. Guests enter a front bedroom through the bathroom to find a spacious room with sofa and tiled fireplace. The wild wallpapers throughout "are my interpretation of Victorian," says Anna, who did the decorating herself. A former caterer, she serves an ample breakfast of eggs, frittata or french toast on the weekends (continental during the week) in a formal dining room opening onto a delightful screened porch. The porch overlooks a curved terrace and showy gardens on a triple lot. Folk art and sculptures continue in the lower garden. The couple's two dogs are much in evidence.

127 Power St., Providence 02906. (401) 273-5398. Doubles, $75; suite, $75 to $90.

Where to Eat

Little more than a decade ago, the Mobil Guide did not list a single restaurant for Rhode Island's capital city, and on one dining foray we nearly were reduced to writing about the downtown McDonald's. That situation has happily changed, and Providence now claims some of the best and most interesting restaurants in New England. Lamentably, some of the most popular do not take reservations – we know folks who have driven from Boston and faced two-hour waits for dinner.

Gourmet's Choice

Al Forno. Moving from tiny quarters on Steeple Street to two floors of a renovated 19th-century stable near the waterfront, owners Johanne Killeen and George Germon have generated national publicity and turnaway crowds for their innovative northern Italian cuisine. Their followers love the pizzas done over the open fire with ever-changing toppings, they love the salads dressed with extra-virgin olive oil and balsamic vinegar, they love the pastas bearing such goodies as grilled squid and spicy peppers, and they love the grilled items done on the wood grill using fruitwoods and even grapevines from Sakonnet Vineyards. They also don't seem to mind long waits for a table. Pizza done over the grill in the main-floor kitchen open to the bar is the signature dish ($11.95). With a crackly thin crust and different toppings every day (ours had tomato, onion, gorgonzola, chicken, tarragon and tomato coulis), it is sensational. Choices include pastas (how about one with ground sausage, walnuts, currants and grilled shiitakes?) and grills and roasts, perhaps grilled chicken sausages with lemony split peas and mixed greens, and grilled veal tenderloin with roasted peppers and onions. The choucroute garni includes three of the fattest sausages you ever saw topping mild and not-salty sauerkraut, accompanied by wide noodles sparked with fresh coriander. The skirt steak is seared right on the coals and served with wilted watercress and a green chile sauce. The exceptional desserts include pineapple granita with chocolate-glazed candied pineapple and mascarpone cream-filled chestnut crêpes with persimmon and caramelized pears. The special tarts for two are $12.95 – on the menu that changes daily you might find one of cranberry-walnut or fresh quince. We tried the lemon soufflé version, which was ethereal. Portions are huge and we saw many others leave, as we did, with doggy bags. This is food at its gutsiest. Tables are covered with sheets of paper, the wine is poured into stemless glasses like those used for vin ordinaire in the south of France, and the jolly atmosphere is just right. The owners, both RISD graduates, are artists and restaurant designers as well as highly inventive cooks; their cookbook, *Cucina Simpatica,* is available for $25.

577 South Main St. (401) 273-9760. Entrées, $15.95 to $23.95. Dinner, Tuesday-Saturday 5 to 10. No reservations.

Fine Dining

New Rivers. The intimate space where Al Forno got its start is now the sophisticated setting for ex-Bostonians Bruce and Patricia Tillinghast, he in the kitchen and she out front. A striking picture of red pears glistening against a dark green wall sets the theme for an American bistro and contemporary international fare that some consider the best in the city. Fresh nime chow spring rolls and smoked trout are favorite starters, or you can share a Thai sampler of nime chow and chicken satay on vermicelli noodles. You can order light: a burger on a Portuguese sweet roll with garlic mashed potatoes and mixed green salad, garlic chicken or mushroom polenta ($11.95 to $16.95). Or you can sample one of the innovative main dishes, perhaps grilled brook trout on baby mustard greens, grilled pork tenderloin marinated in Jack Daniels, or Jamaican jerk beef with oven-fried sweet potatoes. Available as side dishes are exotica like spiced lentils with East Indian spices and baked rattlesnake beans with cumin, cilantro and chipotle. Walnut torte with a spice-poached pear and maple cream, a fruit tartlet in a delicate pastry shell or praline ice cream might top off your meal.

7 Steeple St. (401) 751-0350. Entrées, $14.95 to $19.95. Dinner, Tuesday-Saturday from 5:30.

Pot au Feu. No less an authority than Julia Child is partial to Bob and Ann Burke's long-running success – 25 years in 1997 and the first five-star rating granted by Rhode Island Monthly magazine reviewers. A country French bistro in the basement contains old dark beams, brick and fieldstone walls, steel tables and a zinc bar. You can snack on pâtés, soups, snails, omelets, salads and crêpes or feast on entrées like bouillabaisse or Pot au Feu stew of beef and chicken (dinner entrées, $15.95 to $19.95). Upstairs, a pleasing L-shaped room houses an excellent classical French restaurant called the Salon. Decor is sophisticated with lacquered black chairs at white-linened tables against a backdrop of wall panels painted black and gold. Here you can have a five-course dinner for $28.95 to $36.50, a great value, or order à la carte. Executive chef Sean Dutson offers about fifteen main courses ranging from traditional to contemporary. On the night we dined we were celebrating a double birthday and each ate enough for two. Fond memories of escargots bourguignonne and clams épinard dance in our heads, as do thoughts of the mushroom soup, the salad with fresh mushrooms and cherry tomatoes, the French bread served from a huge basket with sweet butter, the pink roast lamb, the tournedos au poivre, the crisp vegetables, the hazelnut tart, the espresso. Memories are a bit blurred by a couple of the best martinis we've had and a bottle of La Cour Pavillon Medoc – well, it was a birthday! If we lived in Providence, we might celebrate every one here.

44 Custom House St. (401) 273-8953. Entrées. $18.95 to $26.50. Lunch, Tuesday-Friday noon to 1:30; dinner, Tuesday-Saturday 6 to 9 or 9:30; bistro open daily, lunch 11:30 to 2, dinner 5:30 to 10 or 11.

Agora. The culinary star of the new Westin Hotel is a favorite of the national food media for its sophisticated fare and magnificent setting. The view is of the new Waterplace Park with the domed state capitol in the background. The 75-seat dining room has the look and intimacy of an East Side mansion. Formally clad tables are flanked by floor lamps and mohair-covered armchairs in the Chippendale style. Dark brocade walls are hung with fine oil paintings, a barrel-vaulted gold ceiling glistens overhead and floor lamps are placed all around. Weekenders' choice would probably be the settees with side-by-side seats facing the view. Casey Riley, former sous chef at the acclaimed L'Espalier in Boston, imparts a lightheartedness to a kitchen that might otherwise be staid. From his custom-built wood-fired rotisserie come grilled Atlantic salmon with ginger and cashews, aged beef tenderloin with green chile relish and Australian venison with huckleberry fumé. Menu choices may be as straightforward as local codfish, lobster or scallops without embellishment. Or they may be complex, as in tangerine-glazed yellowfin tuna with confit duck potstickers, fire-split chestnuts and caramelized ginger or Languedoc cassoulet with sausages, braised chard, sekel pear and roasted Vermont pheasant. Starters might be a wood-grilled pizza of lobster and native chèvre or a soup of three potatoes (Maine blue, native sweet and Yukon gold with roasted garlic and aged cheddar). Six flavors of soufflés are among the extravagant desserts. The wine list offers considerable range at reasonable prices.

One West Exchange St. (401) 598-8011. Entrées, $15 to $28. Dinner, Monday-Saturday 5:30 to 10:30.

L'Epicureo. Some of the best food in town comes from the kitchen of this sophisticated, small restaurant that evolved from Joe's Quality Meat Market. It's a European bistro with New York flair, in the words of chef Tom Buckner, co-owner with his wife Rozann. The walls have a mahogany leather look created by a local artist, the wood paneling is mahogany and ash, and Italian marble and granite dress the service counter in front of the partially open kitchen. Oil lamps outfitted with tiny shades top the white-linened tables. Tom credits his food expertise to his twenty years in the famed meat market of his late father-in-law, Joseph DiGiglio. Start perhaps with a wood-grilled portobello mushroom over garlic-braised spinach, or crespelle stuffed with black tiger shrimp and spinach topped with gorgonzola sauce and toasted pinenuts. Among main courses, consider lobster ravioli in a brandy-shallot cream with wood-grilled scallops, roasted breast of chicken with porcini-stuffed tortellini, or seared pork loin with roasted red onion and gorgonzola butter. Desserts include a special tirami su over espresso crème anglaise, hot fruit au gratin, ice creams and granitàs.

238 Atwells Ave. (401) 454-8430. Entrées, $16.95 to $25.95. Dinner, Tuesday-Saturday 5:30 to 9 or 10.

Tops for Atmosphere

The Gatehouse. This chic new East Side restaurant occupies a restored gatehouse on the banks of the Seekonk River. As we lunched at a window table on the enclosed porch, we had the feeling of being on a cruise ship with the waves rippling by. The lobster club sandwich ($12.95) was enhanced with avocado and rémoulade sauce, and a grilled chicken sandwich with creole salsa on a homemade bulkie roll ($7.95) proved to be a hefty, knife-and-fork affair. Both came with an unusual sweet-potato salad, a house signature that turned out to be surprisingly tasty and not at all sweet. At night, the place shimmers with the moon reflecting off the river and the glow of brick walls, candlelight and fascinating paintings of old Providence scenes all around. The contemporary menu lists such main courses as blackened yellowfin tuna, coriander-crusted salmon fillet, roast duck with a pumpkin spice gravy and grilled filet of beef with lobster bordelaise sauce. Dessert choices included raspberry-chocolate pudding cake, hazelnut layered torte with coffee buttercream and chocolate ganache, and espresso crème brûlée. The lower level includes an ultra-elegant, Victorian-style lounge and a great canopied dining porch open to the river. Sunday brunch beside the river is popular here. In

1996, owner Henry Kates opened a second restaurant called the Cheeky Monkey in downtown Newport.

4 Richmond Sq. (401) 521-9229. Entrées, $17.95 to $24.95. Lunch, Monday-Friday noon to 2:30; dinner, Monday-Saturday, 5:30 to 10; Sunday brunch, 11 to 3.

Cafe Nuovo. A stylish newcomer along the revived downtown riverfront, this is an offshoot of Capriccio, a glamorous traditional Italian restaurant in the city's financial district. The tables of choice are those on the outdoor terrace beside the riverwalk in season. Views of water and skyline also are sensational through soaring windows that make up one side of the angular dining room off the rotunda of the new Citizens Bank tower. Sleek rust-red chairs and banquettes flank white-clothed tables set with votive candles and fresh flowers. From a semi-open kitchen comes trendy fusion fare presented in the architectural style, as in a signature dessert called espresso chocolate towers, so named because it arrives looking like two towers. Main courses could be ginger-crusted salmon, creole pork tenderloin topped with littleneck clams, wood-grilled black angus sirloin and angel-hair pasta with sesame shrimp tempura and Asian vegetables. Oak-grilled oysters with a trio of dipping sauces and a towering portobello napoleon with a sprig of rosemary as a steeple are typical appetizers. For lunch ($6.50 to $11.50), try the Cuban black bean soup and perhaps the house-cured salmon galette, a Mediterranean pizza, yellowfin tuna burger or grilled paillard of chicken.

One Citizens Plaza. (401) 421-2525. Entrées, $16.50 to $24.95. Lunch, Monday-Friday 11:30 to 3; dinner, Monday-Saturday 5 to 10:30 or 11.

Federal Reserve. The owners of Pot au Feu took over an abandoned downtown bank building, spiffed up the Victorian gothic interior and made another culinary splash in this breathtaking space, a block wide and upwards of three stories high. Stained-glass crests of international banking families and an ornate frieze with hand-molded ornamentation on the ceiling set a swank backdrop for steak and seafood fare billed as Rhode Island regional cuisine. The extensive menu, enclosed in an oversized replica of a $1,000 Federal Reserve bill, starts with jonnycakes, stuffed quahogs and clam fritters for appetizers. Main dishes run the gamut from broiled scrod to black angus ribeye steak. Favorites include the Rhode Island lobster bake, a New England clam boil, a "pilgrim feast" of cornish game hen, prime rib and a sampler of buffalo and beef steaks. The mixed grill here might be "a gaggle of sausages" – wild boar, venison and pheasant over herbed linguini and sautéed broccoli rabe, at our visit. Popular with tourists as well as the downtown banking crowd, lunch ($6 to $13) brings a scaled-down version of the dinner menu, as well as sandwiches and "high rollers" in pita bread.

60 Dorrance St. (401) 621-5700. Entrées, $12 to $25. Lunch, Monday-Friday 11:30 to 3; dinner, Monday-Saturday 5:30 to 9, weekends to 11; Sunday brunch, 11 to 2.

The Capital Grille. All is dark and elegant in the style of a British men's club in this establishment owned by local restaurant impresario Ned Grace, who first made nearby Hemenway's into a shrine for seafood. This is his sanctuary for steaks. Only the beams and ceiling are original in this, once the boiler room of the old Union Station; the rest shows what deep pockets can buy. Hobnob with the pols as you feast on the finest steaks (aged on premises), chops and roasts, priced mainly in the twenties, except spit-roasted chicken for $15.95. This is dining of the grand old school: cold shellfish platter and beluga caviar among appetizers, french onion soup and caesar salad, and sides of potato (baked, $3.25) and vegetables (asparagus with hollandaise, $5.75). Fresh strawberries with grand marnier is the signature dessert. Success here has spawned new Capital Grilles in Boston, Washington, D.C., Detroit and Miami.

1 Cookson Place. (401) 521-5600. Entrées, $15.95 to $26.95. Lunch, Monday-Friday 11:30 to 3; dinner nightly, 5 to 10 or 11, Sunday 4 to 9.

Ethnic Eateries

Rue de L'Espoir. Originally a Left Bank-type bistro in the university area, this neighborhood place has changed to an international menu, and now is French in name only. But longtime owner Deb Norman retains her following with an inexpensive, with-it dinner menu featuring entrées like roasted salmon with pistachio-orange crust, a "duet" of duck breast and sea scallops served with two sauces, and wood-grilled sirloin marinated in ginger and served with green chile-curry sauce. Mix and match some of the small plates: perhaps lobster madeira crêpe, Thai crab cakes, crispy calamari with sweet pepper relish and grilled chiles rellenos with mango salsa. Some of the specialty salads, among them niçoise, roasted salmon or duck and caesar with grilled chicken or shrimp, are meals in themselves. For lunch, the grilled scallops and tomatoes on a bed of greens has a nippy citrus-thyme vinaigrette, pan-sautéed mussels are served with a champagne sauce on a bed of wilted greens, and from the dessert tray we recall a memorable charlotte malakoff (lady fingers, whipped cream, nuts, kirsch and strawberry preserves). A large selection of beers is available, as are interesting wines. The unusual tables are made of quarry tiles, copper pans and plants hang from the pressed-tin ceiling, and abstract art accents the walls sponged in navy and cranberry colors.

99 Hope St. (401) 751-8890. Entrées, $13.95 to $19.95. Breakfast, Tuesday-Friday 7:30 to 11, weekends 8:30 to 2:30; lunch, Tuesday-Sunday 11:30 to 2:30; dinner nightly, 5 to 9 or 10:30.

Walter's La Locanda del Coccia. Loosely translated as "the inn of the clay pot," this convivial establishment with warm Mediterranean decor is the latest home of local chef Walter Potenza and his celebrated food prepared in terra cotta pots in the ancient Etruscan manner. He cooks pastas, chicken, seafood and rice in clay pots in a stone oven, then serves pot and all atop oversize pewter service plates delivered to the table. The technique imparts earthy flavors to several concoctions (each $14) detailed on the menu, among them chunks of fresh snapper baked with potatoes and kale, and farfalle with sliced chicken and prosciutto. Other main dishes range from a sauté of shrimp and shiitake mushrooms to pan-seared beef filets served on braised radicchio and ricotta-filled tortellini. Start with the lavish antipasti displayed on a table near the entry. Finish with cranberry-pecan tart or a sponge cake with flambéed strawberries. In late 1996, Walter opened **A Pranzo,** a takeout spot for Italian country food at the Arcade in downtown Providence.

265 Atwells Ave. (401) 273-2652. Entrées, $13 to $16. Lunch, Tuesday-Friday noon to 2:30; dinner, Tuesday-Saturday 5:30 to 10.

Cafes and Bistros

Adesso. This old garage just off Thayer Street has been converted by David Drake into a swinging, sophisticated California cafe and pizzeria that's a favorite of East Siders. It's noisy and fun, with its gray oilcloth tablecloths, heavy European cutlery rolled up inside white linen napkins and neon signs on the walls. The back room is like a greenhouse, with skylights and huge windows; the new rear lounge is dark and intimate. The food is consistently terrific. From the open mesquite grill and wood oven come interesting pizzas – $7.75 to $9.75 at lunch, $9.95 to $13.50 at dinner. Sweet Italian sausage with mozzarella, asparagus with pancetta and barbecued chicken with smoked gouda and cilantro are some. For lunch, we tried a marvelous pizza with lamb sausage, roasted red and yellow peppers, mozzarella, wild mushrooms and a madeira sauce. We also sampled delicious grilled squid with a salsa of red peppers, onions and black olives, served with grilled zucchini, potatoes and snap peas, followed by a pear bread pudding with bourbon sauce. At dinner, start with grilled shrimp with a melon, red pepper and fresh mint concassé, order something from the mesquite grill like grilled warm duck salad with radicchio, grapefruit, orange and grand marnier or grilled pork loin stuffed with pancetta and garlic, and end with a refreshing trifle with plump blackberries and strawberries or imported white peaches with champagne sabayon, orange sherbet, raspberry sauce and crushed amaretti. Strong coffee is served in stainless steel cups, and the sleek chrome and glass salt and pepper grinders are so handsome that we bought a pair for $25. A pizza chef from Spago in Los Angeles helped open this place in 1987; Adesso means "now" in Italian and it remains up-to-date indeed.

161 Cushing St. (401) 521-0770. Entrées, $13.95 to $23.95. Daily, 11:45 to 10:30, Sunday from 4:30. No reservations.

Christopher's On the Hill. How's this for diversity? Christopher Turner, a former chef from the French restaurant Pot au Feu, cooks a blend of French, Italian and Mediterranean cuisine with subtle Asian influences in what he calls an American bistro with a look of the American Southwest in the Italian heart of Federal Hill. A wood-fired oven and grill take up most of the tiny kitchen, which serves two large and comfortable dining areas in the rear as well as a lounge up front. The food is taken seriously here, but the atmosphere is pleasantly unpretentious. Expect main courses like bouillabaisse, grilled jumbo shrimp with grilled vegetables and saffron rice, boneless breast and confit of duck, sirloin steak sauced with a garlic-dijon demi-glace, mushroom risotto and oriental stir-fries. Good starters are any of the half dozen shellfish appetizers, from steamed mussels to clams casino, or the sashimi-style yellowfin tuna served over an arugula and baby greens salad. Crème brûlée and white chocolate bread pudding are favored desserts.

245 Atwells Ave. (401) 274-4232. Entrées, $15.95 to $19.95. Lunch, Tuesday-Friday 11:30 to 2; dinner, Tuesday-Saturday 5:30 to 9:30.

Raphael's Bar-risto. In 1985, then 27-year-old Raphael Conte opened a smart Italian restaurant in the boiler room of one of Providence's old jewelry factories along Pine Street. In 1992, the space was usurped by Johnson & Wales University, so Raphael – a bit older and wiser – moved to a more central location with a more casual ambiance. A long bar, big windows onto South Water Street, sponged yellow walls and a black ceiling distinguish the noisy, two-level space. So do a couple of paintings of sensuous nudes above the end of the bar, and the hip clientele of what one observer described as muscled body-builders and their sweet young things. The consensus is that the food is better than the ambiance, and the prices are pleasant.

A wood grill in an open kitchen produces a with-it menu of pizzas, pastas (how about black ravioli stuffed with crabmeat and vodka-flashed shrimp?) and main dishes like pork chops with garlic mash and grilled veal chop with portobello mushroom sauce. Desserts run from zuppa inglese to tirami su. In 1996, Raphael opened a suburban location – same name, style and menu – at 5600 Post Road in East Greenwich.

345 South Water St. (401) 421-4646. Entrées, $11.95 to $19.95. Dinner, Tuesday-Saturday from 5.

Grill 262. There's a dark lounge with an angular bar on the main floor of this new American brasserie, which claimed the first humidor in Rhode Island (and an early bourbon and cigar dinner to go with). Head upstairs for some innovative food prepared in an open kitchen and served with style. The decor is pleasant in blue and white, with window tables overlooking the Providence River. Peripatetic chef Jim Ridgeley, formerly of Al Forno and lately of the Clarke Cooke House in Newport, offers a contemporary menu. Start perhaps with Maryland crab cakes, clam-corn fritters or grilled sweet Italian sausage with potato salad. The frisée salad is tossed with pancetta and a roasted egg. Main courses range from a mixed grill of three sausages (chicken, turkey and garlic, each with its own accompaniment), to wood-grilled tenderloin medallions with plum ketchup.

262 South Water St. (401) 751-3700. Entrées, $14.75 to $20.75. Dinner, Monday-Saturday 5 to 10:30.

How 'Bout a Zangwich?

Z Bar & Grille. Young people are partial to this new bistro hot spot transformed from the former Cafe at Brooke. Close-together tables in the two-level dining area are covered with white butcher paper. Beyond a large skylit bar is a rear courtyard popular for outdoor dining in season. Blackboard specials supplement the concise all-day menu. Appetizers, salads, pizzas and "Zangwiches" are featured. Half an open-face chicken on garlic crostini with a bowl of the day's soup makes a quick lunch for $5.50. More substantial fare for dinner might include grilled veal with portobello mushrooms or a special of pan-seared scallops with tomatoes, scallions and grilled corn tossed with fusilli. Desserts are prepared by an award-winning pastry chef.

244 Wickenden St. (401) 831-1566. Entrées, $8.95 to $16.95. Daily, 11:30 to 11.

Coffee and Beverage Houses

Coffeehouses and brew pubs have burst into the Providence limelight lately.

The 200 block of Wickenden Street is the ne plus ultra of the coffee scene. Its funky apex is the **Coffee Exchange** at 207, where the walls are covered to the last inch with flyers and posters, and folks lounge on the side deck on any sunny day the temperature is above freezing. Close by are the **Cafe Internet & Deli** and **Cafe Tugo.** You can get coffee with bagels **at Lox 'n Lox of Bagels,** and espresso with sandwiches called zoggers at **Cafe Zog.** Elsewhere, you can have a coffee with dessert at **Pastiche** on Federal Hill (see below), coffee with liqueur at **L'Elizabeth** or with a movie at the **Cable Car Cinema** cafe on South Main Street, coffee with poetry/music/antiques at **Cav** in the Jewelry District, and coffee with art at **California Coffee** on the East Side.

The **Union Station Brewery,** 36 Exchange Ter., produces specialty ales, lagers and stout in a section of the old Union Station, along with some snacks and light fare to go with. More award-winners emanate from **Trinity Brewhouse,** across from the Providence Civic Center at 186 Fountain St. The chicken pot pie there is also highly touted.

Tête-à-Tête Treats

L'Elizabeth. Here's the most romantic spot imaginable for a tête-à-tête coffee or drink. It has a true European feeling, with the look of a salon where there are different groupings of sofas and chairs, and is very dimly lit at night. No meals are served, but tea and pastries in the afternoon (always L'Elizabeth's torte cake with raspberry, apricot and chocolate, or maybe chocolate mousse pie) are about $6. Espresso, cappuccino, international coffees, hot toddies and a large selection of single-malt scotches and liqueurs are available. *285 South Main St. (401) 861-1974. Daily from 3 to midnight or 1 a.m.*

Federal Hill

An entire book could be written on Federal Hill, a tight little enclave of ethnic eateries. Lately, the stress on heavy Neapolitan cuisine has been broadened with the likes of L'Epicureo and Walter's La Locanda del Coccio, the international Christopher's on the Hill, the Japanese outpost **Fuji,** and the authentic, inexpensive **Mexico.** Traditionalists still dote on the **Blue Grotto, Camille's Roman Garden** and **Cassarino's.** Visitors mix with regulars at old kitchen tables in **Angelo's Civita Farnese,** an unlikely-looking spot where you roll up your sleeves for family-style food like Mama really did make.

We like best the new action around the piazza and fountain at DePasquale Square, where you can lunch on an Italian tuna sandwich ($5.50) or one of prosciutto, fresh mozzarella and tomatoes, and fine imported desserts at **Caffe Dolce Vita.** Or partake of an exotic homemade dessert (perhaps toffee-walnut torte or lemon mousse cake, $2.95 a slice) with cappuccino or caffe latte beside the fireplace at **Pastiche,** a bakery and gourmet dessertery par excellence around the corner at 92 Spruce St. Pick out dinner to go from a remarkable selection at **Tony's Colonial Food Store** at 311 Atwells Ave., which for decades has purveyed the finest of Italian foods. We enjoyed our chicken cutlets, broccoli rabe and garlic breadsticks at home after a long day in Providence. The new **Roma** across the street is equally fun to browse in, and has a small cafe at the side. **Scialo Brothers Bakery** at 257 Atwells has terrific muffins, breads and pastries. **Constantino's Venda Ravioli** sells absolutely wonderful pastas and sauces. We tried the cheese ravioli with wild mushroom sauce and it was heavenly.

The natives are right when they think they have a touch of Europe here.

FOR MORE INFORMATION: Providence/Warwick Convention & Visitors Bureau, One West Exchange Street, Providence, R.I. 02903, (401) 274-1636 or (800) 233-1636.

21 🌷 Spring

HERE
On the 19 of April
1775
was made
the first forcible resistance
to British aggression.
On the opposite Bank
stood the American Militia
Here stood the Invading Army
And on this spot
the first of the Enemy fell
in the War of that Revolution
which gave
Independence
to these United States.
In gratitude to GOD
and
In the love of Freedom
this Monument
was erected
A.D. 1836.

Monument marks historic site at Old North Bridge.

Writers and Revolutionaries

Lexington and Concord, Mass.

Lexington and Concord. Just say the words and your patriotic blood stirs. As little as any American may know about his country's history, he or she has usually heard of the Battle of Lexington and Concord, which literally started the Revolutionary War the morning after Paul Revere's ride.

The battle was April 19, 1775, and because of it the two towns northwest of Boston are linked irrevocably. They take an understandable pride in that past. Not only do they stage re-enactments and parades each year to commemorate the events of the famous battle, but they've also preserved, for the visitor and for themselves, precious reminders of their feisty resistance to the British.

Proud and protective as they are of their past, however, Lexington and Concord are thriving Boston suburbs whose residents work in sophisticated 20th-century industries.

Their shops are tasteful, their homes gorgeous and their residents savvy. Their traffic can be horrendous at rush hour; Route 128, which rings Boston and swings close to Lexington, is infamous. Still, there is a sense here not only of preserving the past, but of living comfortably with it. And there is more to it than the Revolution.

In Concord, there are the writers. Possibly the richest town of its size in America in terms of literary output, it was home to Ralph Waldo Emerson, Henry David Thoreau, Nathaniel Hawthorne and Louisa May Alcott – all at the same time.

That was in the mid-1800s, and the writers found in this gently wooded town an inspiring atmosphere for their ideas. Happily, the homes and famed literary sites of the Concord authors are preserved and opened to the public as shrines.

And there is the Concord grape. Ephraim Wales Bull started with a wild lambrusca grape and wound up with the purple variety that is so widely used today. His house on Lexington Road, known as the "Grapevine Cottage," is noted with an historic marker. A descendant of the original vine still survives.

In a way, much of the area is a shrine. You have the sense when you are there of walking on hallowed ground.

Students of early American architecture are delighted by the many fine examples of 18th- and 19th-century homes in both Lexington and Concord. It is a joy to view them at any season of the year.

Still, we're inclined to agree with the woman, a Thoreau scholar, who urged us one January day to "come back in the spring to Walden Pond; it's best then."

We've been back in the spring and we agree. There are lilacs in Lexington and dogwoods in Concord; there is the soft spring green not only at Walden, but in all of the parkland and wooded areas preserved as Minute Man National Park. There are the April celebrations for Patriots Day (including the nearby Boston Marathon). There are sun-softened days for canoeing on the Concord, the Sudbury and the Assabet rivers, which converge in Concord. This is the time to walk in the hillside hush of Sleepy Hollow Cemetery, where the authors lie.

A spring vacation from school is a good time to bring your children along, for we've never yet seen kids who didn't love to hear stirring stories of battles, to practice with their own make-believe muskets or to take home a souvenir tri-cornered hat.

In these times of uncertain national spirit, we can go back to Lexington and Concord, lest we forget.

Getting There

Lexington and Concord are located about twenty miles northwest of Boston and are easily reached by major automobile routes. Route 2, the Mohawk Trail, which crosses Massachusetts from west to east, goes right through Concord. Lexington is located near Route 128, the inner beltway around Boston. Concord and Lexington are linked by Route 2A, the Battle Road followed by Paul Revere on his famous Midnight Ride.

Trains run between Concord and Boston's North Station on the Boston & Maine line. Buses follow Route 2 from western Massachusetts to Acton and West Concord.

Most major airlines, domestic and international, serve Boston's Logan International Airport.

Seeing and Doing

Food for thought takes precedence over the bodily sort when you're in Concord and Lexington. The battle that started the American Revolution is commemorated by a Massachusetts state holiday, Patriots Day, on the Monday closest to April 19. That's also the day of the famed Boston Marathon. Lexington and Concord stage special events.

In addition to Revolutionary War sites in both towns, Concord is renowned for its literary lights and landmarks. Other special places, not specifically connected with revolutionaries or writers, are also worth a visit.

Revolutionary Sites

Start in Lexington, which is where the British did, early on that chilly April morning more than 200 years ago. Appropriately, Lexington's common is known as Battle Green, and this is where it all began. Some 800 troops marched onto the green to be met by a tiny band of 50 Minutemen. When they refused to disperse as ordered, the British opened fire, killing eight and wounding ten. The others scattered and the British went on to Concord's North Bridge.

The Chamber of Commerce Visitors Center, in a Colonial house just off the green at 1875 Massachusetts Avenue, is open daily 9 to 5 (shorter hours in winter).

The **Minuteman Statue** on the Battle Green, erected in 1900, was done by the Boston sculptor, Henry Hudson Kitson. The base is rough fieldstones, raising the statue to a symbolically appropriate height.

Lexington Historical Society Houses, 1875 Massachusetts Ave., (617) 862-1703. The society operates three historic houses on or near Battle Green. All are

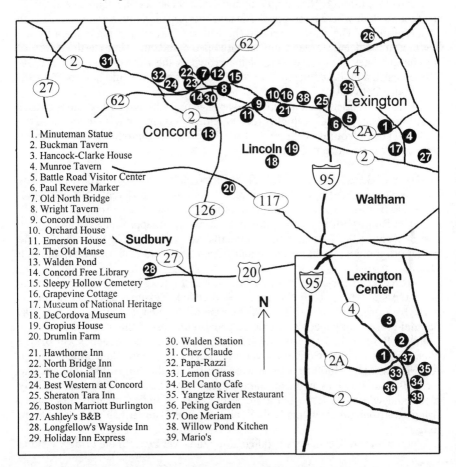

1. Minuteman Statue
2. Buckman Tavern
3. Hancock-Clarke House
4. Munroe Tavern
5. Battle Road Visitor Center
6. Paul Revere Marker
7. Old North Bridge
8. Wright Tavern
9. Concord Museum
10. Orchard House
11. Emerson House
12. The Old Manse
13. Walden Pond
14. Concord Free Library
15. Sleepy Hollow Cemetery
16. Grapevine Cottage
17. Museum of National Heritage
18. DeCordova Museum
19. Gropius House
20. Drumlin Farm

21. Hawthorne Inn
22. North Bridge Inn
23. The Colonial Inn
24. Best Western at Concord
25. Sheraton Tara Inn
26. Boston Marriott Burlington
27. Ashley's B&B
28. Longfellow's Wayside Inn
29. Holiday Inn Express

30. Walden Station
31. Chez Claude
32. Papa-Razzi
33. Lemon Grass
34. Bel Canto Cafe
35. Yangtze River Restaurant
36. Peking Garden
37. One Meriam
38. Willow Pond Kitchen
39. Mario's

open mid-April through October, daily 10 to 5, Sunday 1 to 5. Adults, $4 each house, children $1; combination ticket, $10.

Buckman Tavern, across from the Green at 1 Bedford St., dates from 1710 and served as the rendezvous for the Minutemen before the April 19 battle. Among the bullet holes lodged in the structure is one that marred the front door during the first shots of the Revolution. The interior today appears much as it did in 1775. The original seven-foot-wide taproom fireplace and a portrait of John Buckman, the tavern proprietor, are of interest.

The **Hancock-Clarke House** at 36 Hancock St. is where Paul Revere alerted Samuel Adams and John Hancock during the night of April 18, 1775, that the British were coming. The house, built around 1698, served as the parsonage for the Rev. John Hancock, grandfather of the Revolutionary statesman with the famous signature. At the time of the battle, Hancock and Adams were visiting the Rev. Jonas Clarke, another minister, here. The house contains furnishings and portraits owned by the Hancock and Clarke families.

The **Munroe Tavern** at 1332 Massachusetts Ave. was used as headquarters and as a hospital by the retreating British after their surprise defeat in Concord. Dating from 1695, the house also was visited by George Washington in 1798 when he was traveling through New England, and visitors can see the southeast room on the second floor where he stopped. The tavern is kept as a museum of home life in Colonial times. The gardens around the Munroe Tavern are maintained by the Lexington Field and Garden Club, and are open at the same times as the tavern, at no charge. They show flowering plants grown in the Boston area before 1830. There is also a modest collection of old garden roses that would have been available in the Colonial period.

All around Battle Green are stellar examples of 18th- and 19th-century houses and churches, and a walk is highly recommended. You might want to look in at the **Old Burying Ground** at the rear of the First Parish Church behind the green, where the oldest stone is dated 1690.

Minute Man National Historical Park, Battle Road, (617) 862-7753. The name is a misnomer for this "park" is really a number of different sites, exhibition areas and historic markers commemorating the famous battle. Among them:

Battle Road Visitor Center, Route 2A, Lexington, approximately half a mile east of Route 128. A 22-minute film details the events leading to the battle, and ranger programs and exhibits highlight it. Open daily, 9 to 5:30, mid-April through October.

Paul Revere Marker, a short distance down the road toward Concord, designates the site where Revere's famous ride ended. Revere was forced from his horse by a group of six British soldiers. One of the men traveling with him, Dr. Samuel Prescott, escaped and carried the alarm the rest of the way to Concord.

North Bridge Unit off Monument Street, Concord. The wooden North Bridge over the slow-moving Concord River is a source of pride for Concordians and all Americans. About 400 Minutemen were waiting for the 200 British soldiers who arrived about 7 o'clock in the morning on April 19. The Americans were not only ready and willing to fight, but their observances of Indian methods, especially firing from behind trees, made them able as well. The British retreated before long.

When we visited, canoeists paddled along the river beneath the bridge, visitors picnicked nearby and a couple in Colonial dress answered questions – an entrancing scene. Park rangers lecture periodically.

Concord's historic **Minuteman Statue,** sculpted by Daniel Chester French, is on the path just beyond North Bridge. The statue is engraved with a stanza from the Ralph Waldo Emerson poem, "Concord Hymn:"

By the rude bridge that arched the flood
Their flag to April's breeze unfurled
Here once the embattled farmers stood
And fired the shot heard round the world.

At times, federal park service employees dress in tri-corner hats, breeches and buckled shoes and engage visitors in a discussion of the events of the 18th century. Sculptor French is buried in Concord in Sleepy Hollow Cemetery, the final resting place of most of Concord's literary greats.

A museum at the **North Bridge Visitor Center,** (508) 369-6993, is on the hill above the North Bridge and can be reached by footpath or by car from Liberty Street. Open daily, 9 to 5:30.

Wright Tavern, 2 Lexington Road, Concord, (508) 369-9609. Near Monument Square in Concord center, this was where the British commanders Col. Francis Smith and Maj. John Pitcairn made their headquarters while the British occupied Concord. It now houses the Concord Chamber of Commerce and an unusual gift shop (see Shopping).

Concord Museum. If you have time to visit only one museum in Concord, this should be it. A large expansion in 1991 added considerable space for changing exhibitions and orientation theater. A splendid diorama of the fight at Concord's old North Bridge heightens the visitor's understanding of the event. You'll also find one of the two lanterns that were hung in the spire of Boston's Old North Church on the night of Paul Revere's ride. Fifteen period rooms, arranged in sequence from 1680 to 1860, vividly depict the growth and evolution of one of America's most significant early communities. From the stark "keeping room" to the Empire Parlor, the decorative arts and domestic artifacts, either owned by Concord-area residents or made by Concord craftsmen, are attractively displayed. The study of Ralph Waldo Emerson, furnished as it was at the time of his death, came from his house across the street. The Thoreau Room contains the bed he made, the flute he played at Walden Pond, his spyglass, walking stick and snowshoes. Alcott memorabilia includes a copper kettle used by Louisa when she was a nurse in the Civil War. A replica of Thoreau's cabin used at Walden Pond was constructed in 1996 on the grounds.

200 Lexington Road, Concord. (508) 369-9609. Monday-Saturday 9 to 5, Sunday noon to 5; slightly reduced hours January-March. Adults $6, children $3.

Patriots Day Events

Lexington, Concord and the State of Massachusetts have had trouble getting their acts together to celebrate the famous day. A few years ago, the state moved the traditional anniversary of the battle to the Monday closest to April 19 for a three-day holiday. Things got confusing, however, because Lexington and Concord had always celebrated the event on the actual anniversary and were reluctant to change.

For a while, one town was celebrating on the 19th and the other was going with the state, which made it impossible for the visitor to do both in one day. To be sure of what is going when you plan to visit, check with the local Chambers of Commerce after January.

What happens?

Lexington re-enacts the original battle with the British on the Battle Green at 6 a.m.; natives say this is the most fun of any of the celebrations. A small local parade follows in which Girl Scouts, Boy Scouts and other civic groups participate. In the early afternoon, a larger parade with floats, marching fife and drum corps units, town officials – the works – makes its way down Massachusetts Avenue for a couple of hours.

Concord has a spirited parade that usually begins around 9 a.m. at the North Bridge. Groups gather and march into the center of town. One of the civic clubs sometimes sponsors a pancake breakfast until noon.

The Literary Legacy

Concord's literary heritage is incredibly rich and, as you walk around town, it's easy to imagine the 19th-century writers feeling at home here. The very air seems rarefied. The old homes are beautiful but not pretentious, and the nearby hills and woods were places in which the writers might ponder the issues of the world and the age. Concord today is not so different from the Concord of Emerson, Hawthorne, Thoreau and the Alcotts; one imagines them resting in peace in Sleepy Hollow Cemetery.

Orchard House. The Alcott family came here in 1857 when Louisa May, author of *Little Women,* was already in her mid-twenties. Her father, Bronson, a great friend of Emerson's and one of the Transcendentalists of the early 19th century, spent a year having two early 18th-century houses on the site joined together and renovated. The Alcotts lived here for twenty years; the house became the setting for *Little Women,* the most widely published children's book in the world. Guided tours show the house and grounds. We like Louisa's "mood pillow," a sausage-shaped pillow on the living room sofa; the author would let the rest of the family know when she was not in good spirits by putting the pillow in a certain position and they would leave her alone. Upstairs are costumes used by the Alcott girls (then young women) when they gave their famous plays. Louisa's sister, May, was an accomplished artist who had a studio in the house; the visitor may view some of her works. Outside is the **School of Philosophy,** a barn-like structure for the school started by Alcott and Emerson in 1879. Great thinkers of the day studied and spoke here; the spirit is continued in summer evening events sponsored by the school. In front of the house are the fruit trees from which it took its name.

399 Lexington Road (Route 2A), Concord. (508) 369-4118. Monday-Saturday 10 to 4:30, Sunday 1 to 4:30. April-November. Reduced hours rest of year and closed in January. Adults $5.50, children $3.50.

Emerson House. This great white house was Ralph Waldo Emerson's home from 1835-1882 and contains a wealth of family memorabilia. The study is a replica since the genuine articles are across the street at the Concord Museum, but there's plenty of authenticity here among the books, personal effects and furniture.

Since the family furnishings were always retained in the house, this is much the way it was when the great philosopher lived here with his wife and four children and assorted relatives and friends, including, at times, Henry David Thoreau.

Cambridge Turnpike, Concord. (508) 369-2236. Thursday-Saturday 10 to 4:30, Sundays 2 to 4:30, mid-April through October. Adults $4.50, children $3.

The Old Manse. This was the home of Concord's early ministers, including the Rev. William Emerson, grandfather of Ralph Waldo, who was here on April 19, 1775. Ralph Waldo Emerson also lived here at various times. Here also Nathaniel Hawthorne brought his bride, Sophia Peabody. The house is marvelously restored and filled with original furnishings from several generations of descendants of Mrs. William Emerson. Charming mementos of the Hawthorne residency are the inscriptions on several window panes, cut by Sophia's diamond ring. The Hawthornes called the house "their Eden" and referred to each other as Adam and Eve in their early nuptial bliss. Set far back from the road, the house was the inspiration for Hawthorne's *Mosses from an Old Manse*, which he wrote on a tiny board desk in an upstairs bedroom.

Monument Street, next to the North Bridge, Concord. (508) 369-3909. Daily except Tuesday 10 to 5, Sunday 1 to 5, June-October; weekends only, mid-April to May 31. Adults $4.50, children $2.50.

Concord Free Library. This is quite a library – not only a lovely building, built in 1873, but a repository for collections by the Concord authors in special cabinetry in the lobby. Busts of the authors, four by Daniel Chester French, are here, as is a case containing Thoreau's surveying instruments and pieces of the original cabin at Walden Pond. The oak-paneled reading room provides just the right atmosphere for scholarly research. There's a fine diorama of old Concord, a collection of editions of Walden in many languages and, of course, works of Emerson, Alcott and Hawthorne. Upstairs in a balcony art gallery are changing exhibits.

Junction of Main Street and Sudbury Road, Concord. (508) 369-5324. Monday-Thursday 9 to 9, Friday 9 to 6, Saturday 9 to 5, Sunday 2 to 5 except summer.

A Walk with Thoreau

Walden Pond. Follow the white-circled Ts on the trees, an easy walk along the edge of Walden Pond, to the site of Thoreau's cabin. Thoreau lived here for two years from 1845 to 1847, producing the classic work, *Walden*. The site, rediscovered in 1945, is marked by a circle of stones. Nearby is the plaque with Thoreau's famous words on his reasons for the experiment: "I went to the woods because I wished to live deliberately, to front only the essential facts of life, and see if I could not learn what it had to teach and not, when I came to die, discover that I had not lived." The area is now a state reservation. Concord kids swim off the dock at the entrance to the spring-fed pond; we encountered some skinny dippers in a cove as we walked the path to the cottage site one warm May day. The swimming is seasonal, but you can walk to the cottage site anytime. There's a reproduction of Thoreau's cottage – fully furnished – next to the parking lot across the road from the pond. The Thoreau Society operates a gift shop in a small building near the parking lot.

Route 126 (Walden Street), a half mile south of Route 2, Concord. (508) 369-3254. Daily, dawn to dusk. Parking, $2.

Sleepy Hollow Cemetery. Concordians like to stroll with their friends or their dogs through this large, hilly cemetery near the center of town. Enter the main vehicle gates (the second set of stone and wrought-iron gates from the center of town) to reach Authors Ridge and you can find the graves of the Thoreau family, the Alcotts, the Emersons, the Hawthornes and sculptor Daniel Chester French, whose stone says he left us "a heritage of beauty."
Bedford Street (Route 62), Concord. (508) 371-6299. Daily, 7 to dusk.

Other Sights

The **Grapevine Cottage** at 491 Lexington Road, Concord, was the home of Ephraim Wales Bull, who planted the seeds of a wild lambrusca grape found growing on the hillside. After three generations it became, in 1840, the famous Concord grape. The house is privately owned; you can stop at the gate outside to read the plaque and see the small grape arbor by the side of the house. Many Concord families chauvinistically grow the Concord grape in their yards.

Museum of Our National Heritage. This Bicentennial gift to the nation from the Scottish Rite Freemasons is unusual in that they generally put their money into hospitals and medical centers. The sprawling brick place (four galleries, two atria, a large auditorium) has presented all sorts of changing exhibits, from one on Amish quilts to a major one from the British Library on Sir Francis Drake. The museum has only two permanent galleries, one devoted to the heritage of revolutionary Lexington, "Let It Begin Here," and another to the history of the Masons, of which Benjamin Franklin was a member. Special auditorium events are scheduled frequently on Sunday afternoons. A large gift shop contains wares from other museums, such as Old Sturbridge Village, in addition to its own items. The contemporary building somehow fits into Colonial Lexington quite comfortably.
Marrett Road, Lexington. (617) 861-6559. Daily 10 to 5, Sunday noon to 5. Free.

DeCordova Museum. Given the questionable taste and worth of his private collection, the art museum that honors Julian DeCordova is not only a monument, it is almost a miracle. In DeCordova's turreted hilltop mansion, the museum presents the art of living New England artists – the only museum in the country to so concentrate. The exhibitions are generally very good. The museum uses the stunning 35-acre site well for summer band concerts in an open-air amphitheater and several other special events, and for displaying contemporary sculpture. It is a great place to stroll or picnic.
Sandy Pond Road, Lincoln. (617) 259-8355. Tuesday-Thursday 10 to 5, Friday 10 to 9, Saturday and Sunday noon to 5. Adults $4, children $3.

Gropius House. This interesting structure was built in 1937-38 by influential architect Walter Gropius, director of Germany's Bauhaus School. He ordered components from catalogs and stores to create a house blending the Bauhaus principles of function and simplicity with New England traditions. Some of its art and furnishings came from the Bauhaus workshops in Germany.
68 Baker Bridge Road (off Route 126), Lincoln. (617) 227-3956. Wednesday-Sunday noon to 5, June to mid-October; also first Saturday and Sunday of the month, rest of year. Adults $5, children $2.50.

Relive a Memorable Canoe Trip

South Bridge Boat House. A spring trip to this area really ought to include a canoe trip down the Concord, Assabet or Sudbury rivers (they all come together here). Such a trip – only a longer one – was immortalized by Thoreau in his first published book, *A Week On the Concord and Merrimack Rivers.* You can paddle to North Bridge, a trip we found especially scenic and fun on a warm spring day. Or you can go off for more than twenty miles of water travel. Rent a canoe from the boat house, a beehive of activity on a sunny spring or summer day.

Main Street, Concord. (508) 369-9438. Tuesday-Friday noon to 6, weekends and holidays 9 to 6, April-October.

Drumlin Farm. Part of the Massachusetts Audubon Society, whose headquarters is across the street, this 220-acre New England farm with animals is a delight for youngsters. There are walking and hiking trails, a picnic area, a wildlife sanctuary and the animals, mostly of the barnyard variety. What is really special for adults here is the gift shop, one of the best conservation and nature-oriented ones we've seen. Family programs and usually hayrides are scheduled every weekend.

Route 117, Lincoln. (617) 259-9807. Tuesday-Sunday 9 to 5. Adults $6, children $4.

Shopping

Lexington is about twice the size of Concord in terms of population, but has about half as much interesting shopping from our point of view. It is a more urban area, and more closely allied to the spirit of Cambridge and Harvard Square than to the country towns to the west, with which Concord is identified. The diversity of population results in several ethnic restaurants, especially Asian.

The **Candy Castle** on Massachusetts Avenue and **Steve's,** an ice cream and light lunch spot, are places hard to pass with young children. The latter carries unusual toys. **Goodies to Go** is a gourmet deli with luscious baked goods; it sells wonderful scones from Concord Teacakes in Concord, but makes most of its own baked goods and salads. At the **Coffee Connection** you can buy from a wide selection of coffees and teas or stop for a cup of cappuccino or espresso and a homemade muffin or croissant. The Swiss chocolatier, **Lindt,** opened a chocolate emporium in late 1996 on Mass Ave. **Decelle's** is a beloved downtown store with clothes for everyone in the family at discounted prices, including lines like Liz Claiborne and Jones, New York.

Wilson Farms, south of Lexington center on Routes 4 and 225, purveys produce, cheeses and seasonal items. People come from far and away for top-notch fruits and vegetables, including fresh herbs in wintertime. You'll also find frozen pies and gourmet items.

In Concord, check out the **Wright Tavern,** Monument Square, which is not only an historic building but a good place to browse. The five downstairs rooms are operated as the Tri-Con Shop, a non-profit shop run by the women of Trinitarian Congregational Church. Actually, the building is owned by the Unitarians; talk about ecumenism! One of our favorite rooms is the one with paper and party goods, but you also can get your child a tri-corner hat in the room devoted to historically oriented souvenirs. China, pewter, brass and table goods are also sold.

The pewter is magnificent at **John Anthony's** pewter shop in the basement of The Colonial Inn. You can buy mugs that say Concord or, if you want to break the bank, a lovely coffee and tea service. There are also great gifts, not all pewter, like baskets and teddy bears, and a nice selection of cards.

The **Concord Depot** on Thoreau Street stocks quilts, pottery, placemats and napkins, toys and paper goods, all of the highest quality. Across the street, **Spice & Grain** has more kinds of tea for sale than we've seen under one roof. The **Mary Curtis Shop** in Concord, one of the best gift shops we've seen, carries local New England crafts, plus special items like opals from Australia. **The Concord Shop** is the last word in kitchen shops. **Concord Hand Designs** has interesting dried flower arrangements and wreaths. Gourmet goodies can be found at **The Cheese Shop.** **The Concord Bookshop** on Main Street is a good place to buy reading materials.

In West Concord, you can visit a couple of unusual factory outlets. The **Potting Shed** is the outlet for Dedham Pottery, manufacturers of that very special crackle glaze pottery with bunnies on it. We bought a plate for deviled eggs, with the dearest bunny sitting in the center, and used it for an Easter Sunday brunch with friends. At the outlet we also found a new pattern, the Concord Grape.

Also in West Concord is the outlet store for a mail-order business called **bear-in-mind.** This is the ultimate shop for the teddy bear lover, and you can buy not only bears but T-shirts, aprons, books and more with bears on them.

Concord Teacakes in West Concord serves scrumptious currant scones. You can eat here: coffee and pastries for breakfast and sandwiches, pizzas and other goodies for lunch. **The West Concord 5&10** is a rare breed of store, selling everything from oil paints to ant poison. A very well-organized place it is, too.

Where to Stay

It used to be that you could scarcely find an old house turned into an inn in the area, but the situation is improving. Concord has a couple of B&Bs in addition to the Colonial Inn in the center of town. Longfellow's Wayside Inn in South Sudbury is within striking distance. Lexington hasn't a single venerable inn right in town, but several local residents offer from one to three guest rooms in their homes. There are a couple of good motels in the Lexington area.

In Concord

Hawthorne Inn. Dating from 1870, this pale pink stucco house with lavender and deep pink trim is on the Battle Road. If its location didn't recommend it, the fine furnishings and warm hospitality of its innkeepers – Gregory Burch and Marilyn Mudry, husband and wife – would. Since we first stayed here, the inn has been updated, redesigned and redecorated so that each room is a treasure. All seven rooms, three on the main level and four on the second floor, have private baths. Six have double beds, one of which uses a handmade linen tablecloth as a canopy; one has maple twin beds that were originally rope beds. Most are covered with quilts made by Marilyn. Furnishings include items from the Sheraton, Federal and Victorian periods; bare wood floors are polished to a shine. We like the bay window and fireplace in the Emerson Room, and the black wallpaper with honeysuckles and the red bathroom in the Walden Room. Guests enjoy a common room where there's frequently a fire in the hearth. Gregory is an artist whose stunning contemporary pieces adorn the walls throughout. Marilyn serves homemade breads and fresh fruits for continental breakfast, taken at a long table in the dining room. "People love the pound cake that we make," says she. Sometimes there are cookies at check-in, if the couple's three children haven't reached the cookie jar first.

462 Lexington Road (Route 2A), Concord 01742. (508) 369-5610. Fax (508) 287-4949. Doubles, $110 to $175.

North Bridge Inn. The six guest rooms on the second and third floors of this center-of-town B&B are large and well-appointed. Four have kitchens; the others, kitchenettes. All have updated private baths and decor, different in each room, is crisp and restful. You enter a small lobby with striking large black and white tiled floor, off which is the breakfast room where such goodies as baked pancakes or an egg casserole start the day. All beds are queensize and telephones and television are standard. On the third floor is a suite whose bathroom has a footed tub and a stall shower; in the bedroom are two comfortable wing chairs.

21 Monument St., Concord 01742. (508) 371-0014. Fax (508) 371-6460. Doubles, $129 to $159.

The Colonial Inn. Deep gray with white trim and dating from the early 1700s, this inn meets the expectations of those who want an early American inn, on a village green, with an old-fashioned dining room. There's even tea served in the afternoon. German-born innkeeper Jurgen Demisch took over the hotel after much experience with the Omni hotel chain and has completed upgrading. Most of the 60 air-conditioned rooms are furnished with a period look and have four-poster beds, wide floorboards and beamed ceilings; all come with private baths, telephones and television. Those in the main inn are a bit larger and more elegantly appointed than the seven in the adjoining Prescott Wing, which are decorated in country style. John Thoreau, grandfather of Henry David, lived in that part of the inn that houses the offices and the Thoreau Room. The main dining room, with beamed ceilings and wooden columns, is cozy, with lamps flickering on wood posts. Tablecloths are white and napkins a Colonial blue; the chairs are a comfortable captain's style with rust-colored leather seats. Traditional New England and continental specials are featured at dinner nightly. The Village Forge lounge is just the place to order a hot toddy.

On the Green, Concord 01742. (508) 369-9200 or (800) 370-9200. Fax (508) 369-2170. Doubles, $99 to $195.

Best Western at Historic Concord. This member of the chain has some extra amenities including an outdoor swimming pool, a fitness facility with hot tub, and a complimentary continental breakfast which – due to the small size of the lobby – you're encouraged to enjoy in your own room. All 106 rooms are equipped with cable TV. The location is a couple of miles west of the center, directly next door to the restaurant, Papa-razzi (see Where to Eat).

Route 2 at Elm St., Concord 01742. (508) 369-6100. Fax (508) 371-1656. Doubles, $75 to $95.

In Lexington

Sheraton Tara Lexington Inn. Conveniently located between Concord and Lexington, this attractive, two-story motel's 119 rooms have been renovated recently. Although close to an exit from Route 128, the site is wooded and private. Most rooms contain two double or queensize beds and reproduction period furniture. A simple lobby with Chippendale-style loveseats is quite pleasant. There's an exercise room and an outdoor pool. The **Cracker Barrel** restaurant on the premises offers three meals a day in an attractive wood-paneled lounge or a handsome adjoining dining room with dark wood tables, Queen Anne-style chairs and fireplaces. The dinner menu ($13 to $17) stresses classic foods like baked onion soup, prime rib, a pot pie of the day and, in the tavern, a hot roast beef sandwich.

727 Marrett Road, Lexington 02173. (617) 862-8700 or (800) 843-8272. Fax (617) 863-0404. Doubles, $155 to $235; weekends, $89 to $139.

Boston Marriott Burlington. Located just north of Lexington on Route 128 near the Burlington Mall, this nine-story, 419-room hotel has outdoor and indoor pools, an exercise room and sauna. On site are a restaurant, **Allie's American Grille,** and a lounge. Each room has a cable TV with in-room pay movies and there's a 31-room concierge level with further amenities.

Routes 128 and 3A, Burlington 01803. (617) 229-6565 or (800) 371-3625. Fax (617) 229-7973. Doubles, $170 to $174; weekends, $84 to $104.

Ashley's Bed & Breakfast. Joan and Fletcher Ashley offer two rooms with private baths in their large and striking, 1950-built contemporary home in an unusual neighborhood of contemporary homes in Lexington. The Ashleys raised four daughters here, and now have time and space to take guests. One room is on the main floor, seemingly off in its own wing. A large room with queensize bed, it's decorated in sunny contemporary style in oranges and yellows. A slightly smaller room at the end of a hall on the second floor has a double bed, modern furniture and a very private feeling. Both rooms have their own TVs. Joan serves a full breakfast in her kitchen in the morning. The house was featured in 1988 on "This Old House," the PBS television special. The grounds, full of rhododendron and other flowering plants, are especially attractive in spring. The Ashleys have a conservatory-greenhouse with built-in goldfish pond.

6 Moon Hill Road, Lexington 02173. (617) 862-6488. Doubles, $80 to $100.

Value Oriented

Holiday Inn Express. This 200-room motel has been taken over by Holiday Inn and was being upgraded. The rooms were all to have burgundy wall-to-wall carpeting, traditional-style mahogany furniture, and two double beds or one queensize. Thirty two-room efficiencies were being constructed in early 1997. A small outdoor pool is available in warm weather. Lodging includes a buffet continental breakfast taken at small tables in the lobby.

440 Bedford St., Lexington 02173. (617) 861-0850. Doubles, $79.

Nearby

Longfellow's Wayside Inn. America's oldest inn, or so it claims, has ten guest rooms with a mix of king, queen, double and twin beds. They are decorated in Colonial style and proudly boast no TV or radio, and they tend to be booked far in advance. Henry Wadsworth Longfellow spent a night in one of the rooms, then wrote *Tales of a Wayside Inn*, but no one seems to know exactly which room he used. The pleasure of staying here is enhanced by the Colonial dining room (see Where to Eat) and the Martha Mary chapel on the grounds, where you're likely to witness a wedding, since more than 400 are held here annually. The Ford Foundation restored the inn, the oldest section of which is the Old Barroom, dating from 1702. Now it is operated by a non-profit trust. Antiques and charm abound and the rates include a full breakfast.

Wayside Inn Road, South Sudbury 01776. (508) 443-1776. Fax (508) 443-2312. Doubles, $120.

Where to Eat

Dining Favorites

Walden Station. This fun restaurant in an old fire station is one of those BPBW (brass, plants, brick and wood) places, but it's a pleasant environment and the firefighting theme is not overdone. You can enter from the rear (directly from a municipal parking lot), where an old red fire engine marks the spot, or from busy Walden Street. The narrow restaurant contains a bar in the center, with dining areas at either end. The all-day menu is nicely varied. We enjoyed the thick, spicy turkey gumbo soup with bits of Louisiana hot sausage. Chicken caesar or almond shrimp salads are lighter entrée options ($7 to $9) and you can always get an eight-ounce Walden burger. Other sandwiches include the Vermonter (roasted turkey breast topped with homemade stuffing and an orange-cranberry relish served hot with turkey gravy), grilled vegetable and brie on sunflower bread, and flank steak with garlic dressing on a bulkie roll ($5 to $8). After 5, entrée specials include striped sea bass with wild rice, veal gruyère and fusion pork (sautéed tenderloin slices with sage, apples and walnuts, served over garlic-rosemary linguini). Because it's smack in the middle of Concord's shopping district, Walden Station tends to be crowded at lunchtime.

24 Walden St., Concord. (508) 371-2233. Entrées, $12 to $16. Daily, 11 to 11.

Chez Claude. Claude Miquel, the chef-owner of this charming little French restaurant ensconced in an old red house, maintains his popularity in the area more than 25 years after opening. Striped floral wallpaper in one of the three dining rooms and plain white linens, with a single white candle on each table, provided a pleasant atmosphere one chilly Friday evening for dining on classic French fare. Among the hors d'oeuvres, you might try escargots bourguignonne, Claude's home-made country meat pâté or french onion soup. Such classic entrées as frog's legs in garlic butter, coq au vin, roast duck with orange sauce, crêpes filled with shrimp, scallops and lobster, and châteaubriand for two are available. The price includes starch, vegetable, salad and coffee. Dessert possibilities are crème caramel, poire belle hélène, strawberries romanoff and almond pie. At lunchtime, typical dishes ($8 to $10) are chicken livers, shrimp salad and breast of chicken in a champagne-mushroom sauce.

5 Strawberry Hill Road (Route 2A), Acton. (508) 263-3325. Entrées, $13.50 to $19. Lunch, Tuesday-Friday noon to 2; dinner, Monday-Saturday 6 to 9:30.

Papa-razzi. One of a small Boston-based chain, this popular trattoria and bar offers creative Italian cuisine. The setting is fun, with black and white Associated Press photos of celebrities all over the walls, and there is sometimes live entertain-ment on weekends, usually contemporary jazz. There's a great fireplace to cozy up to on chilly evenings. Pizzas, pastas and salads make up most of the menu. Spaghetti alla bolognese and fusilli con pollo are two standards. Pizzas are of the gourmet variety. One is topped with goat cheese, sundried tomatoes, mozzarella, basil and marinated roma tomatoes.

768 Elm St., Concord. (508) 371-0030. Entrées, $12 to $16. Daily, 11:30 to 10 or 11.

A Colonial Experience

Longfellow's Wayside Inn. This is the kind of Colonial dining spot that everyone gets into the mood for once in a while. Hordes of visitors seem to get into the mood on nice weekends and the place is usually mobbed for Sunday dinner. The menu changes daily but generally includes tried-and-true favorites like your grandmother used to make. For cocktails, how about a Coow Woow, called "America's first mixed drink" and made with rum, or a Stonewall, a "Revolutionary War favorite," made with gin? Believe it or not, Wispride cheese and crackers is offered among appetizers at lunch. Others are New England clam chowder, apple cider, frosted fruit shrub, cranberry juice, fresh fruit cup with sherbet and marinated herring. For lunch ($8 to $12), you might select yankee pot roast, chicken pie, fried scallops, stuffed fillet of sole or New En-gland boiled dinner. Among dessert selections are deep-dish apple pie with spiced whipped cream, baked Indian pudding, strawberry shortcake, parfaits, pecan pie and custard pudding. Complete dinners are in the $17 to $22 range, except for baked-stuffed or boiled lobster. Other choices might be poached salmon with hollandaise sauce, filet mignon, prime rib or jumbo baked shrimp. The food is consistent, and people return again and again to enjoy it in the exceptional surroundings. The dining room is simply and honestly furnished; bare wood floors, gold cloths and napkins, and floral china convey a sense of the old days. We prefer the cozy Tap Room with two fireplaces, brown and white checked tablecloths and less din.

Route 20, South Sudbury. (508) 443-1776. Table d'hôte, $17 to $29. Lunch, Monday-Saturday 11:30 to 3; dinner, 5 to 9, Sunday noon to 8.

Lemon Grass. Nothing but praise is heard for this Thai restaurant in the center of town. Fan-back rattan chairs and tables with white tablecloths and bright green placemats occupy a bright open space with soft pink walls. At lunchtime, you can start with Siam rolls (crispy spring rolls served in a white turnip sauce) or chicken or beef satay. Hot and sour shrimp soup, chicken coconut soup and a large list of "rice dishes" – from chicken pineapple to beef panang (sautéed sirloin in a Thai curry with lemon leaves, mushrooms, basil leaves and walnuts) are in the $6 to $8 range. In the evening, consider beef basil (pan-fried with mushrooms, green peppercorns, fresh basil and green peppers and onions) or duck sautéed in curry and vegetables. Noodles and fried rice are offered, as are vegetarian dishes..

1710 Massachusetts Ave., Lexington. (617) 862-3530. Entrées, $9.25 to $13.95. Lunch, Monday-Friday 11:30 to 3; dinner, Monday-Saturday 5 to 9:30.

Bel Canto Cafe. This second-floor Italian restaurant on the main street is a warren of bright spaces. Red basket-weave chairs are set at tables topped with bright printed tablecloths. Bel Canto's offers pizzas, calzones, panini, pastas and dinner-size salads. You can have a spinach and broccoli pizza or one with sliced prosciutto, mushrooms, ricotta, parmesan and mozzarella. Grilled portobello mushroom over angel-hair pasta is $10 and nothing else is more than that.

1709 Massachusetts Ave., Lexington. (617) 861-6556. Entrées, $7.95 to $10. Monday-Saturday 11 to 10, Sunday noon to 10.

Two Chinese Landmarks

The Yangtze River Restaurant. For more than twenty years, this Chinese restaurant has been commanding loyalty from its followers, among them members of the area's Asian population. The food is Szechwan-Mandarin on one side of the menu, Polynesian on the other. Beyond an off-putting bar just as you walk in, the decor is rather contemporary with lots of wood and plants. High ratings by Boston's restaurant critics are displayed prominently. Among the Chinese offerings are house specials, including General Tsao's chicken with watercress, sesame beef with broccoli, hunan shrimp with black bean sauce and hunan lamb. Other items include all the regulars plus plum-flavored duck or peking duck ($28). A lunchtime buffet for $5.95 weekdays is appreciated by business people; at night, a dinner buffet is $10.95. You also can order from the regular menu.

25 Depot Square, Lexington. (617) 861-6030. Entrées, $9 to $14. Daily, 11:30 to 9:15 or 10:15.

Peking Garden. This is Lexington's *other* Chinese restaurant, offering Mandarin-Szechwan cuisine. A large establishment, it nevertheless seems serene inside, beyond the two stone lions who guard the entrance. A buffet lunch is offered Monday-Friday for $5.25 and for dinner from Sunday-Thursday for $10.50. In addition to the usual dinner dishes, look for whole tea-smoked duck ($20) and peking duck ($28).

27 Waltham St., Lexington. (617) 862-1051. Entrées, $7 to $11. Daily, 11:30 to 9:30 or 10:30.

Lighter Fare

One Meriam. Sandwiches, salads and soups are served up in this small, bustling restaurant conveniently located near most of the historic sites around Battle Green. Popular for breakfast and lunch, the restaurant is bright and open with cane chairs at wood tables. The menu is quite ambitious, considering the size of the place, and you can get breakfast – from pancakes to omelets – all day long. Sandwiches, soups and salads in the $5 to $7 range are offered at lunchtime. *1 Meriam St., Lexington. (617) 862-3006. Monday-Friday 7 to 3, Saturday 8 to 3.*

Willow Pond Kitchen. This low gray roadside building with a huge beer sign over the entrance may not look promising, but it is. Locals not only crowd the large parking lot but enthusiastically recommend the place. Old wooden booths, muskets mounted on beams, a TV over the bar and a counter where you can get a quick bite contribute to a down-home air. The walls and ceiling are pale green and the curtains change periodically, but somehow it all works, even the plastic ketchup bottles on the tables. Seafood is a draw and you can get whole fried clams or baked shrimp pie off the dinner menu. A hamburger is about $2.50, a BLT $2.45 and a grilled cheese, $2.15. Other favorites are beef stew, franks and beans, chili, homemade bread pudding and pecan pie, all at reasonable prices. Beer and wine are available. *Lexington Road (Route 2A), Concord. (508) 369-6529. Entrées, $8.50 to $12.50. Monday-Saturday 11 to 11, Sunday 1 to 11.*

Other possibilities include **Dabin,** a new Japanese-Korean restaurant on Muzzey Street in the center of Lexington, and **Aesop's Bagels,** a large bagel emporium on Massachusetts Avenue, Lexington, where 24 varieties of bagels include "super cinnamon" and "apple crunch." You can also get soup and bagel sandwiches during midday.

Cheap at the Price

Mario's. Here is a restaurant the family will love and that's kind to Dad's wallet. Locals crowd in for lunch every day so that there is usually a short waiting line. The atmosphere harkens back to the 1950s: big murals of Italy on the walls, red checked tablecloths, dark wood captain's chairs, and good aromas of traditional Italian fare like chicken or eggplant parmigiana, spaghetti or shells with meatballs, and pizzas that do not try to be gourmet (toppings like meatball and onion, anchovy, salami). There's no booze, but you may bring your own. The most expensive item on the menu is veal parmesan served with a side of spaghetti, $8.95. *733 Massachusetts Ave., Lexington. (617) 861-1182. Entrées, $5.95 to $8.95. Daily, 11 to 10.*

Afternoon Tea

The Colonial Inn. The Colonial Inn serves a five-course tea ($16.95) consisting of a choice of teas, pâté de foie gras with warm toast, dainty sandwiches of salmon, cucumber and chicken, homemade scones served with strawberries and whipped cream, and cakes and pastries. Colonial tea with teas, scones, pastries, berries and cream is $10.50 and a light tea may be had for $7.95. *On the Green, Concord. (508) 369-2373. Tea by reservation, from Tuesday-Thursday and Saturday 2:30 to 5; Sunday 3:30 to 5:30.*

FOR MORE INFORMATION: Concord Chamber of Commerce, Wright Tavern, 2 Lexington Road, Concord 01742, (508) 369-3120. Lexington Chamber of Commerce Visitor Center, 1875 Massachusetts Ave., Lexington 02173. (617) 862-1450.

22 🌷 Spring

Cornelius Vanderbilt's Breakers occupies grand site along the ocean.

Waterside Riches

Newport, R.I.

Fabulous mansions from the Gilded Age, the Newport Jazz Festival, the America's Cup races – all have given Newport a cachet perhaps unmatched in the Northeast.

The combination of water and wealth make Newport probably the single most varied town in New England. Here in one roughly ten-mile-square area are seashore, history, architecture, culture, affluence, shops and restaurants in both variety and quantity that would be the envy of cities many times its size.

As an early seaport dating to 1639, Newport contains more pre-Revolutionary houses than any other in America. Most are restored, signed and lived-in, some are open to the public, and all are a delight to view on walking tours through the Point or Historic Hill.

The wealth of history was enhanced during Newport's second heyday following the Civil War. The Astors, Vanderbilts, Morgans and other leading families built their summer "cottages" near the ocean along Bellevue Avenue, creating a society resort unmatched for glitter and opulence. Now opened to the public, America's largest collection of what Europeans would call palaces can keep a visitor enthralled (and occasionally appalled) for several days.

What links both eras of Newport's history and makes it so engaging for today's visitor is, of course, the water. Newport is at the southern tip of Aquidneck Island,

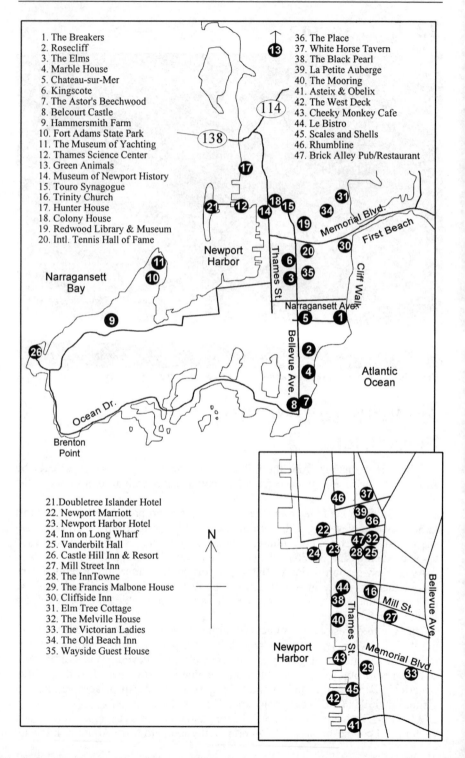

1. The Breakers
2. Rosecliff
3. The Elms
4. Marble House
5. Chateau-sur-Mer
6. Kingscote
7. The Astor's Beechwood
8. Belcourt Castle
9. Hammersmith Farm
10. Fort Adams State Park
11. The Museum of Yachting
12. Thames Science Center
13. Green Animals
14. Museum of Newport History
15. Touro Synagogue
16. Trinity Church
17. Hunter House
18. Colony House
19. Redwood Library & Museum
20. Intl. Tennis Hall of Fame

36. The Place
37. White Horse Tavern
38. The Black Pearl
39. La Petite Auberge
40. The Mooring
41. Asteix & Obelix
42. The West Deck
43. Cheeky Monkey Cafe
44. Le Bistro
45. Scales and Shells
46. Rhumbline
47. Brick Alley Pub/Restaurant

114

138

Newport
Harbor

Narragansett
Bay

Thames St.

Narragansett Ave.

Bellevue Ave.

Memorial Blvd.

First Beach

Cliff Walk

Atlantic
Ocean

Ocean Dr.

Brenton
Point

21. Doubletree Islander Hotel
22. Newport Marriott
23. Newport Harbor Hotel
24. Inn on Long Wharf
25. Vanderbilt Hall
26. Castle Hill Inn & Resort
27. Mill Street Inn
28. The InnTowne
29. The Francis Malbone House
30. Cliffside Inn
31. Elm Tree Cottage
32. The Melville House
33. The Victorian Ladies
34. The Old Beach Inn
35. Wayside Guest House

N

Newport
Harbor

Thames St.

Mill St.

Bellevue Ave.

Memorial Blvd.

surrounded by water on three sides. The restored waterfront areas off America's Cup Avenue and Lower Thames Street are great for browsing, shopping and viewing sailing ships and fishing vessels. Out Ocean Drive are today's mansions – large homes (some strikingly contemporary) showing that Newport hasn't lost its glory – and the rocky shoreline is good for fishing, hiking or bicycling expeditions. Just east of town are excellent beaches for swimming and surfing.

There is much to keep you busy. Tour the mansions along the newly repaved and restored Bellevue Avenue, walk the Cliff Walk, bicycle the Ocean Drive, visit old Touro Synagogue and Green Animals topiary garden, take the self-guided history tours, savor the seafood, browse through the shops, ogle the yachts, swim in the ocean and revel in all that is Newport.

But note: as an old, island city, Newport wasn't built for large numbers of visitors. In summer and on weekends, the town is jammed. The streets are narrow and many are one-way – you can find yourself going in circles, so you will want to leave your car, particularly in the downtown area, which is eminently strollable anyway. Also, for a resort of such magnitude and despite so many accommodations, Newport is not able to keep up with the demand at peak periods. So book far in advance, or pick an off-season weekend, say in December, when the town decks itself out for Christmas in style, or better yet in spring, when the azaleas and rhododendron burst forth in all their glory.

Getting There

Its watery location has cut Newport off from main highway access. Bonanza Bus Lines serves the city direct, arriving at the Gateway Visitor Information Center at 23 America's Cup Ave. Amtrak serves Providence, and major airlines fly into the Green State Airport in Warwick, south of Providence. Most visitors arrive by car, taking the Jamestown-Newport Bridge from the west ($2 toll) or Routes 114 and 138 from the east. And, of course, you can arrive on your own yacht – what better way to savor the waterside riches of Newport?

Seeing and Doing

The Mansions

Nowhere in this country can such a concentration of palatial mansions be found, and few visitors fail to take in at least one. Tops in popularity is Cornelius Vanderbilt's Breakers, first leased to the society in 1948 by his daughter – half a century later, more than five million people have gone inside to gape.

Most mansions are strung along **Bellevue Avenue,** paved with concrete and lined with brick sidewalks, gas lights and utility poles with a period look. A parade and three days of parties and concerts marked the rededication in 1992 of Bellevue Avenue, a once-a-century event. The mansions have since been illuminated by floodlights at night.

Whether or not you like the ostentatious manner in which the four hundred lived, it must have been a fabulous era when a hostess could give a ten-course dinner party for more than 100 dogs belonging to friends (the dogs came in party dress to dinner at the Marble House). It's hard to believe the mansions were occupied only two months of the year and were considered summer cottages. The "cottage" we like best – and one that is often skipped – is the early Victorian Kingscote, which is smaller and not so overwhelming.

The Preservation Society of Newport County, 424 Bellevue Ave., (401) 847-1000. Six mansions are under the auspices of this organization, which also operates the 1748 Hunter House in the Point section and Green Animals topiary farm in Portsmouth.

All mansions are open for guided tours, daily 10 to 5, May-September; the Breakers is open Saturdays until 6 in July and August. The Breakers, Marble House and Rosecliff are open daily from 10 to 5 in April and October, also the Elms in October, while the others are open weekends only. Marble House, The Elms and Chateau-sur-Mer are open most of December and weekends and most holidays from 10 to 4 in November and January-March.

Prices for the Preservation Society facilities: The Breakers, adults $10, children, $3.50. The Elms, $7.50 and $3. Marble House, Chateau-sur-Mer, Rosecliff and Kingscote, each $6 and $3. Combination tickets good for all six plus Hunter House and Green Animals topiary farm are $35.50 for adults, $10 for children; mansions only, $28 and $8.

The Breakers, Ochre Point Avenue at Ruggles Avenue. Richard Morris Hunt, the architect who designed many public buildings, modeled Cornelius Vanderbilt's residence after a northern Italian palace. Built in a mere two years (1893-95), it was an extravagant place for a man described as quiet, kind and a pillar of his church – ironically, he was disabled by a stroke in 1896, was unable really to enjoy his summer home, and died in 1899. Tour highlights are the lower and upper loggias (from the upper you can, on a clear day, see the Elizabeth Islands far out to sea), the 45-foot-high Great Hall, an immense tapestry on the landing of the grand staircase (softly illuminated by a stained-glass ceiling), a magnificent 42-by-58-foot dining room, and a music room totally executed in Paris and shipped to this country. Upstairs, the bedrooms are comparatively modest, but the bathtubs had a choice of fresh or salt water. Also on view are the kitchens and butler's pantries, an area bigger than most houses. The fully equipped Breakers Stable and Carriage House, open on weekends from Memorial Day to Labor Day ($3.50), shows Vanderbilt memorabilia, including the famous coach Venture.

Rosecliff, Bellevue Avenue. Rosecliff's romantic reputation wasn't hurt by the fact that "The Great Gatsby" wooed Mia Farrow here. The house was designed by Stanford White to resemble the Grand Trianon of Louis XIV in Versailles, and finished in 1900 for Mrs. Hermann Oelrichs, an heiress whose father made his fortune in Virginia City as one of a partnership that struck the Comstock Lode. She was considered one of the three great hostesses of Newport and is said to have spent $25,000 each summer on perfume to fill the light fixtures. The living room could double as a ballroom – at 80 by 40 feet, it was the largest in Newport and was the scene of many lavish balls. The grand staircase is graceful, heart-shaped and appropriately romantic looking. Rosecliff is sometimes rented for various functions; we enjoyed cocktails on the terrace during a New England press convention some years ago and felt elegant indeed.

The Elms, Bellevue Avenue. Built in 1901 for coal baron Edward J. Berwind by Philadelphia architect Horace Trumbauer in the classical style of 18th-century France, this palatial structure is considered one of the finest homes in America, partly because of its balanced architectural plan. It doesn't exactly have a lived-in look; in fact, the Elms is more like a museum, with some furniture on loan from the Metropolitan Museum. The conservatory is perfectly charming, bright and cheerful, with a marble fountain, statues in the corners and a gigantic marble urn. As befits a coal baron, Mr. Berwind had tracks for a coal car under his house; the car could be pushed out to the road where it would be filled with coal, thus ensuring no unsightly coal delivery on the property. He also generated his own electricity. The grounds are thought to be the finest of the Newport mansions, with a sunken garden, marble teahouses, fountains, and labeled trees and shrubs.

Marble House, Bellevue Avenue. Considered the most sumptuous of the "cottages," Marble House was completed in 1892 for William K. Vanderbilt and designed by Richard Morris Hunt. All the original Louis XIV furnishings are here, the ballroom is practically covered in gold, and this is where the party for all the dogs was given. It's modeled after the Petit Trianon at Versailles.

Chateau-sur-Mer, Bellevue Avenue. The original villa here was built in 1852 but was extensively redone by Richard Morris Hunt twenty years later. William Wetmore, who made a fortune in the China trade, was the first owner. His son, George Peabody Wetmore, a Rhode Island governor and senator, inherited it, and his daughter Edith lived here until her death in 1968. It is considered a fine example of lavish Victorian architecture and, although the interior is quite dark, at least it feels lived in. A collection of Victorian toys enchants younger visitors.

Kingscote, Bellevue Avenue. A picturesque cottage in the Gothic Revival style, Kingscote is one of the very early summer residences remaining, having been built in 1839. A McKim, Mead and White dining room was added in a new wing in 1881. We think it is one of the nicest rooms of all the mansions, decorated with Tiffany glass tiles and stained-glass panels of dahlias. Since one of the two owners of the house was in the China trade, there's a fabulous collection of Chinese export ware. The house was left to the Preservation Society in 1972, with most of its furnishings intact. It looks lived-in and thoroughly livable.

Several other mansions are open to visitors under private ownership:

The Astors' Beechwood. Built in 1851 as an Italian seaside villa, this was purchased in 1880 by the William Backhouse Astors, at the time the richest family in America. Mrs. Astor coined the phrase "the 400," because that's how many her ballroom in New York could hold. In 1890 she took $2 million, went to the Continent and had sent back to her mansion a music room from France, a dining room from an English manor house, and a ballroom that is a replica of one in a Viennese palace. Mrs. Astor had 281 diamonds in her stomacher and looked like a walking chandelier, according to our tour guide. The house is the most recent to be restored and opened to the public; the owners have tracked down many of the original furnishings.

580 Bellevue Ave. (401) 846-3772. Daily 10 to 5, May-October, 10 to 4 in November-December, Friday-Sunday in February-April. Adults $8, children $6.

Belcourt Castle. The summer home of Oliver Hazard Perry Belmont and his wife, the former Mrs. William K. Vanderbilt, was built at a cost of $3 million by (who else?) Richard Morris Hunt in the style of Louis XIII's palace. Since 1956, the castle has been the home of the Tinney family and a place to display their

2,000 art treasures and antiques from 33 countries. There's a fine collection of stained glass and a golden coronation coach that weighs four tons – imagine what that would be worth these days! Costumed guides take you around, and you can stay for tea.

657 Bellevue Ave. (401) 846-0669. Daily, 9 to 5, Memorial Day to mid-October; 10 to 5 in spring and fall; 10 to 3, December-March. Adults $6.50, children $2.

Hammersmith Farm. With much more of a country feeling than most Newport mansions, Hammersmith Farm also has one of the nicer settings – across the island on a hill next to Fort Adams, overlooking 50 acres of farmlands and meadows beside Narragansett Bay. The late Jacqueline Bouvier Kennedy Onassis spent childhood summers in this airy, 28-room, shingle-style home. President Kennedy used one of the second-floor rooms as the summer Oval Office. Tour guides are well-versed in anecdotes about the Kennedys and the Auchincloss family, owners of Hammersmith since the late 19th century, until it was sold to a group of businessmen in 1978 and opened to the public. Caroline and John Jr. summered here too, Caroline with her famous pony Macaroni.

Don't miss the beautiful tiled fireplaces in almost every room, the fabulous flower arrangements, the glimpse of monogrammed linen in Mrs. Auchincloss's bedroom (her bed is turned down to show it) and, our favorite, the huge deck room, where surely a crowd of grownups and children could find their own spaces.

The grounds are worth a stroll, with formal gardens created by Frederick Law Olmsted. Trees and shrubs are labeled. A small gift shop is in the old children's playhouse, with a greenhouse attached. As well as plants, seedlings and bulbs, you can buy the book, *One Special Summer,* by Jackie and her sister Lee about a trip they took to Europe as young girls, plus oriental china, and pickles and jams. The shop is especially heavy on all sorts of candy, some in fancy boxes.

Ocean Drive. (401) 846-7346. Tours daily 10 to 5 (to 7 in summer), April to mid-November. Adults $7, children 3.

Things to Do

There is so much to see and do in Newport that it would take many days and more space than we have available to cover everything. Free local publications like *Newport This Week* and *The Pineapple Post* can clue you in to timely events.

TOURS. The **Newport Trolley** departs from the Gateway Visitor Center at 23 America's Cup Avenue on the hour daily from 10 to 3, June-September, and makes sixteen stops at Newport's leading attractions. You can hop on and off as many times a day as you want for $5 (children, $2). **Viking Tours of Newport,** 847-6921, sponsors a variety of daily bus tours, also departing from the Visitor Center, and lasting from 90 minutes to four hours. It also offers one-hour harbor cruises six times daily from Goat Island Marina on its 140-passenger Viking Queen. Several enterprises rent tape cassettes for driving tours of Newport, available at the Visitor Center. Harbor tours and sailboat cruises are provided by any number of boats around the downtown wharves. The **Old Colony & Newport Railroad,** 624-6951, runs one-hour train excursions along the Narragansett Bay shore Wednesday, Thursday and Saturday at 11, 12:30 and 2 in summer (adults $5, children $3), plus a three-hour excursion to Green Animals topiary garden in Portsmouth, Sunday at 12:30, May-November (adults $6, children $3).

Oceanside Attractions

The Cliff Walk. For an intimate look at the crashing ocean and also at the backs of the mansions, the three-and-a-half-mile Cliff Walk is a must. In late spring, wild roses lend their fragrance to the salty air. You can get onto the walk at several points; many people start at the foot of Narragansett Avenue, where you walk down to the ocean on the Forty Steps. When we did the walk some years ago, we found the first couple of miles easy because it was well maintained, but the latter part unkempt and difficult (and we had torn stockings to show for it). we hear this section has been upgraded.

Ocean Drive. This should not be missed, whether you go by car, bike or moped (the latter two can be rented from several places). With the possible exception of the Park Loop in Maine's Acadia National Park, the ten-mile drive is like nothing else on the East Coast. It offers spectacular scenery, rocky points with crashing surf, views of many privately owned mansions and striking contemporary homes, the fabled Bailey's Beach where the 400 swam (and still do), and refreshing ocean breezes. The lovely Brenton Point State Park is along the drive and a favorite of sunset-watchers; you can park free and welcome spring with a picnic on the rocks.

Fort Adams State Park. Named for President John Adams, the fort was begun during the Revolution and is one of the largest seacoast fortifications in the country. Near the start of Ocean Drive, the hilly point juts into the bay and provides as good a vantage point today for yacht-watching as it did for soldiers defending their country. Tours of the fort and period garrison drills are offered in the summer. The park also offers picnicking, swimming and fishing.

Fort Adams Road off Harrison Avenue. (401) 847-2400. Daily during daylight hours; parking, $2.

The Museum of Yachting. Housed in a 19th-century granite building on a point at the end of Fort Adams, this museum showcases the history of yachting and yacht racing. Costumes, memorabilia, photos, paintings and models trace the history of sailing inside what was once an Army mule barn. The fascinating photo exhibit called "The Mansions and the Yachts" focuses on the sailing roles of the Vanderbilts, Astors and Morgans ("while the women were here for the social life, this is what the men did," our guide explained). The Small Craft Gallery displays old wooden boats beneath a model of the boat that won the first America's Cup perched near the ceiling. The small museum, designed to appeal to laymen as well as sailors, gives a feeling for this aspect of Newport's heritage, and the hilly waterside site is spectacular.

Fort Adams State Park. (401) 847-1018. Daily 10 to 5, mid-May through October. Adults $3, family $6.

Thames Science Center. After 70 years near the Thames River in New London, Conn., this moved into the bigtime with a location beneath the Marriott Hotel not far from Newport's Thames Street. It also dropped its former emphasis on children and nature in favor of contemporary technology, with a stress on digitalized communications, global navigation and computer mapping. High-tech

computers are everywhere, and one tracks by satellite the local airport shuttle bus, which was moving at precisely seventeen miles an hour in a busy section of Middletown when we tried to find it. Many walk-in programs of interest to visitors take place on weekends. A large science store offers toys and tools for the mind.
77 Long Wharf. (401) 849-6966. Monday-Wednesday 10 to 6, Thursday-Saturday 10 to 9, Sunday noon to 5. Adults $2, children $1.

Green Animals. The topiary is terrific at Green Animals, which is run by the Preservation Society just north of Newport. On view in the gardens are 80 trees and shrubs sculpted into shapes of a donkey, bear, ostrich, horse and rider, camel, mountain goat and the like. The animals are formed of California privet; the geometric figures and ornamental designs of golden and American boxwoods. The charming small estate that slopes toward Narragansett Bay also includes dahlia and vegetable gardens, espaliered fruit trees, a grape arbor, and a gift and garden shop where you can buy plants, pottery and forms to make your own topiary.
Cory Lane off Route 114, Portsmouth. (401) 847-1000. Daily 10 to 5, May-October. Adults $6, children $3.

BEACHES. The Newport area has plenty of places where you can stretch out on the sand. Of course, the water is rather chilly except in July and August. **King Park** on Wellington Avenue in town is on the sheltered harbor with green lawns for sitting, a raft with slides, free bathhouses and swings; it's a good beach for children. Another family-oriented site is **Gooseberry Beach,** a private-public beach along Ocean Drive just west of Bailey's Beach; it charges $5 for parking on weekdays, $10 on weekends. **Easton's Beach,** also known as First Beach, is a three-quarter-mile-long strand from the Cliff Walk at Memorial Boulevard to the Middletown line. It was restored and raised onto piers following the destruction caused by the tidal surge from Hurricane Bob in 1991. The amusement area includes bumper boats and mini-golf. Beach admission is $5 per vehicle weekdays, $10 weekends. Just beyond Easton's are **Second Beach** and **Third Beach** in Middletown. Third Beach offers the island's best windsurfing.

A Wealth of History

Newport has more than 400 buildings dating from the Colonial era, more than New York, Boston and Philadelphia combined. All are within walking distance of the Gateway Visitor Center. A few places not to miss:

The Museum of Newport History. Newly housed in the stately 1762 Brick Market, the museum of the Newport Historical Society provides an overview of varied aspects of local history in interactive displays on two floors. Pick up a telephone speaker to hear about religious history. View the locally made Goddard-Townsend furniture on display in a middle-class parlor, not far from a printing press that belonged to Benjamin Franklin's brother, James. Climb aboard the reproduction Ocean House omnibus for a nine-minute audio tour down turn-of-the-century Bellevue Avenue, accompanied by the clip-clops of horses' hooves.
Thames Street at foot of Washington Street. (401) 841-8770. Daily except Tuesday, 10 to 5, Sunday 1 to 5. Adults $5, children $3.

WALKING TOURS. The Newport Historical Society leads history-oriented walking tours of two neighborhoods from different eras, May-October and rest of year by appointment. You'll learn why Newport is home to twenty percent of the buildings listed on the National Register of Historic Places. Tours of Historic Hill, the city's oldest neighborhood, are offered Thursday-Saturday at 10 and 3; cost $5. The Cliff Walk/Bellevue Avenue tour is given Saturday at 10 and 3 for $7. For 1997, the society was installing signs for a self-guided walking tour past 27 sites in Historic Hill. Among them are the **Great Friends Meeting House,** corner of Farewell and Marlborough Streets, built in 1699 and the oldest surviving house of worship in Newport, and the 1675 **Wanton-Lyman-Hazard House,** 17 Broadway, Newport's earliest restored museum house and one of New England's first examples of Jacobean architecture. It's open for tours Friday and Saturday 10 to 4, mid-June through Labor Day; also Thursday 10 to 4 and Sunday 1 to 4 in July and August; adults $4.

Touro Synagogue. A home of worship for Congregation Jeshuat Israel, this is a National Historic Site, the oldest place of Jewish worship in the United States. Built in 1763 in classic Georgian style, the simple but beautifully proportioned exterior – cream brick with a trim of dark brown – hides an ornate interior in which twelve Ionic columns, representing the tribes of Israel, support a gallery where women in this Orthodox congregation sit. The Torah dates from 1658. The synagogue has a fascinating history, which you can learn from free guided tours.
27 Touro St. (401) 847-4794. Tours Sunday-Friday 10 to 4, late June to Labor Day; Sunday-Friday 1 to 3, mid-May to mid-June and Labor Day to mid-October; Sunday 1 to 3, rest of year. Free.

Trinity Church. Nicely framed by the spruced-up Queen Anne Square rising from America's Cup Avenue, Rhode Island's first Anglican church was built in 1726 from designs by Christopher Wren. Its graceful white spire is a Newport landmark. It has the second oldest organ in the country, two Tiffany windows and a triple-deck wineglass pulpit.
Corner of Church and Spring Streets. (401) 846-0660. Daily in summer, 10 to 4; weekdays, 10 to 4, through Columbus Day; weekdays 10 to 1, rest of year. Donation.

St. Mary's Church, corner of Spring Street and Memorial Boulevard, is the oldest Catholic parish in Rhode Island. Work was begun on the Gothic-style red stone church in 1848. The church is most famous as the site of the 1953 wedding of Jacqueline Bouvier to John F. Kennedy. The Kennedys summered in Newport in 1961, attending Mass on Sundays. A brass marker on the tenth pew, right side facing the altar, designates it as theirs. Open Monday-Friday 7 to 11:30.

Hunter House. Restored by the Preservation Society, Hunter House is an outstanding example of Georgian architecture and is considered one of the ten finest Colonial homes in America. Beside the harbor, it was built for a wealthy merchant family in 1748, and its collection of early Rhode Island furniture crafted by the famous Goddard and Townsend families in mahogany and walnut is priceless.
54 Washington St. (401) 847-1000. Daily 10 to 5, May-September; weekends in April and October. Adults $6.50, children $3.

Colony House. Built in 1739 in the style of an English manor house, this handsome brick building was the center of governmental affairs for 160 years.

Rhode Island was the first colony in 1776 to declare its independence and in May, the Declaration of Independence was read from its balcony. The building, still used for public ceremonies, displays the famous full-length portrait by Rhode Islander Gilbert Stuart of George Washington, who met here with Rochambeau during the Revolutionary War.

Washington Square. (401) 846-2980. Monday-Saturday 10 to 4 and Sunday noon to 4, mid-June to Labor Day; rest of year by appointment. Free.

Redwood Library and Atheneum, 50 Bellevue Ave., (401) 847-0292. Designed in 1748 by the architect who did Touro Synagogue, this is the nation's oldest lending library. It contains countless valuable books and a fine collection of early American paintings, including seven by Gilbert Stuart. Almost across the street in **Touro Park** is the **Old Stone Mill,** a 26-foot-high landmark that some think is a Viking church tower predating Columbus's voyage; others think it is the remains of Gov. Benedict Arnold's 17th-century windmill. Library open Monday-Saturday 9:30 to 5:30. Free.

International Tennis Hall of Fame. This place in the historic Newport Casino is one that tennis buffs won't want to miss. The casino, built in 1880 by Stanford White, is considered the cradle of American lawn tennis, and the National Men's Singles Championships were held here from 1881 to 1914. A gracious Victorian air lingers. This still is home to major tournaments played on the world's oldest grass courts in July. The world's largest tennis museum includes the Davis Cup Theater, where old tennis films are shown. Visitors can test their tennis trivia in new interactive video displays and, for a fee, play tennis on thirteen grass courts or three indoor courts.

194 Bellevue Ave. (401) 849-3990. Daily, 10 to 5. Adults $6, children $3, family $13.

Shopping

Although shops in Newport come and go, every year there seem to be more. You can have fun window-shopping, or you can be a big spender here. The main shopping areas are along Bellevue Avenue, where some of the more established stores cater to the descendants of the 400, Brick Market Place and Thames Street downtown, and the restored waterfront around Bowen's and Bannister's wharves. Increasingly, Lower Thames Street is populated by interesting shops all the way out to the new Wellington Square, and Spring Street is dotted with galleries and boutiques.

Along Bellevue Avenue you will find **Michael Hayes** for elegant clothing for adults and children, **On the Avenue** for distinctive gifts and home accessories (many with a sports theme), **Cadeaux du Monde** for art and handcrafts from around the world, the **Cole-Haan Company Store, The Linen Shop** and **Cabbages & Kings** for gifts and antiques of appeal to those who still live in Newport "cottages."

Brick Market Place is a complex of restaurants, condominiums and shops, among them **Dansk** and **Pier One Imports,** as the chain stores belatedly discover downtown Newport. Browse through **Si Lucia** for fine Italian pottery and imports, the **Mole Hole** and **Pleasant Surprise** for gifts, and **Beadworks** for beads from around the world. **Somethin' Else** is filled to the brim with gifts, gourmet goodies and home accessories.

Over at Bowen's and Bannister's wharves, the aroma drifting through the door may draw you into the **Cookie Jar** for chocolate chip, oatmeal raisin or gingersnap cookies. **Operculum** has a wondrous selection of shells. **Crabtree & Evelyn** offers its stock in trade. Quilts, pillows and prints are among the offerings at **Sarah Elizabeth's.** We like **Irish Imports Ltd.** for wools and linens, **Timberland** for rugged clothing, and **Marblehead Handprints** for colorful silk-screened prints. Occupying a prime location at the entrance to Bowen's Wharf is the large **Museum Store** of the Preservation Society of Newport County, where you'll find everything from mansion-inspired scarves and items with pineapples (the symbol of Newport) thereon to nautical memorabilia.

Check out lower Thames Street for gifty places like **The Wave, Euphoria** and **Out on a Whim.** Marine interests are appeased at the old-line **JT's Ship Chandlery** and the **Armchair Sailor** bookstore. **Tropical Gangsters** stocks ties we wonder whether anyone would wear and **Edna Mae Millinery** carries unique hats made exclusively for the owner. At **Thames Street Pottery,** we picked up a colorful clock shaped like a fish for a kitchen wall. **Pastabilities** purveys fifteen flavors of pasta, including rosemary and thyme. Colorful wind socks are available at **Flying Colors,** and avant-garde gifts at **Erica Zap Collection.** The native American and Western arts and crafts at **Tribal Pride** are fascinating. **Tea & Herb Essence** is the place for dozens of tea blends and herbal health-care products. At **Thames Glass,** you can watch glass blowers at work and see their output here as well as on Bowen's Wharf.

Newport also has many antiques shops, most in the Spring Street area around Queen Anne's Square. **Artifacts** specializes in hand-painted furniture, glassware and original art. **The Liberty Tree** sells good folk art. **MacDowell Pottery** carries the output of its own potter's wheel among its contemporary crafts. **Indesign** is an exceptional shop for glassware and home accessories. **Lily's of the Alley** carries cotton clothing, gifts and fragrances,

Where to Stay

Newport offers an enormous array of accommodations, from hotels to B&Bs. Lower-priced chain motels are located just north of the city in Middletown.

Big and Busy

Doubletree Islander Hotel. An island location and a variety of amenities are attributes of this renovated 253-room hotel, conference center and family resort (bring quarters for the kids, who like all the pinball machines and video games). Although it is unfortunately not quite within walking distance of the downtown area, its setting on Goat Island is magnificent and its architecture unusual (natives call it the grain elevator). A focal point is the huge indoor pool area, light and bright, with glass walls, high arched glass roof and a bar on an upper level where you can watch the swimmers. Try not to occupy a room opening onto the pool area as we once did, or you may have to endure the pool lights shining in your window all night (in desperation, we tacked the two bedspreads over the window, but that didn't help much). Much better are the deluxe rooms with whirlpool baths and waterfront balconies in the newer Captain's Quarters wing that we occupied during a conference a few years back. The Islander also has racquetball and tennis courts and an outdoor saltwater pool. For sustenance, there are the cheery **Sunset Cafe** coffee shop, where you can get meals and snacks at most times of the day, and the renovated **Windward Grille** dining room. The latter is well regarded locally, particularly for its lavish salad bar featuring shrimp and crab legs, which comes with dinner entrées ($14.95 to $21.95) or can be taken separately ($10.95 for all you can eat).

Goat Island, Newport 02840. (401) 849-2600. Fax (401) 846-7210. Doubles, $229 to $284; suites, $375 to $550.

Newport Marriott. Newport's biggest hotel was started as a Holiday Inn Crowne Plaza and finished by the Marriott, which accounts for the fact that the guest rooms are smaller than those the Marriott would have built. On Long Wharf, between the harbor and the new Gateway Visitors Center, this is billed as one of the Marriott chain's top ten resort hotels. The 317 guest rooms surround a five-story atrium, which often is used for parties and can get noisy. The indoor swimming pool has an outdoor sun deck. Health facilities include a whirlpool, sauna and exercise center and four racquetball courts. **J.W.'s Sea Grill** offers all-purpose dining all day, with dinner entrées priced from $13.95 for blackened chicken to $18.95 for baked stuffed shrimp. **Tickets Lounge** was designed to be Newport's liveliest disco.

25 America's Cup Ave., Newport 02840. (401) 849-1000 or (800) 458-3066. Fax (401) 849-3422. Doubles, $229 to $269.

Newport Harbor Hotel & Marina. The new ownership of the former Treadway hotel/motor inn has started phased renovations of all 133 rooms on four floors; the redone rooms on the third-floor command top dollar. About half the rooms face the harbor, but most do not open to the outside; the rest overlook the parking lot and the city. Each has a kingsize or two double beds. Decor is nicely nautical in blue and white, the stripes in the bedspreads being repeated in the draperies. Facilities include an indoor pool, saunas and a 60-slip marina. The location is one of Newport's best, beside the water and in the thick of the downtown action near Bowen's and Bannister's wharves. Three meals a day are served in **Waverleys,** a well regarded restaurant in several sections, with a few window tables and a canopied sidewalk terrace in summer. There's frequently live entertainment in the lounge.

49 America's Cup Ave., Newport 02840. (401) 847-9000 or (800) 955-2558. Fax (401) 849-6380. Doubles, $209 to $249.

The Newport Bay Club and Hotel. Probably the nicest of the many harborfront time-sharing resorts, this has 36 large and luxurious units, ranging from one-bedroom suites to two-bedroom townhouses. The old General Electric mill retains its high wood ceilings and paneling. Each condominium-style unit contains a kitchenette or full kitchen, a large living room with pullout bed and dining area, a queensize bedroom and a marble bathroom with jacuzzi tub. The fourth-floor townhouses have balconies upstairs and down, with side views of the harbor. Continental breakfast is served. Downstairs in the Perry Mill Marketplace are retail shops and **The Great American Pub** and **Thames Street Station,** a nightclub.

337 Thames St., Box 1440, Newport 02840. (401) 849-8600. Fax (401) 846-6857. One-bedroom suites, $199 to $279; two-bedroom suites and townhouses, $309 to $499.

Inn on Long Wharf. One in a group of time-sharing hotels, this offers 40 suites, all facing the harbor. Even the elevator, enclosed in a wall of glass, yields a water view. Most suites are entered through the bedroom; beyond are a kitchenette with refrigerator and microwave opposite a marble bathroom with double jacuzzi, and a living room with pullout queensize sofa. Corner suites are billed as superior in that you enter the living rooms first and both they and the bedrooms are larger and share water views. Although the rooms lack balconies, you can get outside on the rooftop sundeck. A casual steakhouse dinner menu is offered in the second-floor **Long Wharf Steak House,** a wraparound restaurant where you feel as if you're right out over the water.

142 Long Wharf, Newport 02840. (401) 847-7800 or (800) 225-3522. Doubles, $225 to $245.

— A 'Mansion-House Hotel'

Vanderbilt Hall. The first "mansion house hotel" of its kind in New England was scheduled to open in May 1997 in a former YMCA building in the heart of Newport's Historic Hill district. A $10 million renovation of the red-brick structure built by his son in memory of Cornelius Vanderbilt and a new wing were undertaken by the management team that opened the opulent Inn at Perry Cabin in Maryland and Keswick Hall in Virginia. The hotel has 50 guest rooms ranging from "cozy house rooms" to "state rooms" that measure up to their name to huge suites. All are appointed with period furnishings, unusual bed treatments (a couple draped in fabric in the middle of the room) and rich wallpapers, fabrics and linens. The main floor holds snug reading nooks, a carpeted music room, a board room and a morning room, plus a fireplaced dining room and a new greenhouse conservatory. Open to the public for three meals a day, the restaurant was to feature upscale international cuisine. Afternoon tea is served in the English tradition. Near the Y's restored indoor pool on the lower level are a fitness center and a billiards room.

41 Mary St., Box 840, Newport 02840. (401) 846-6200 or (888) 826-4255. Fax (401) 846-0701. Breakfast daily, 7:30 to 10; lunch, noon to 2:30; dinner, 6 to 9:30. Doubles, $195 to $395; suites, $395 to $650.

Mid-Size Yet Intimate

Castle Hill Inn & Resort. "The closest place to far away you'll ever find" is the new billing for this old inn, situated in a world of its own on a private peninsula jutting into Narragansett Bay. After refurbishing the main-floor restaurant (see Where to Eat) in 1996, the new management started a gradual upgrading of the accommodations. Finished first were the six outlying Harbor House units, duplexes that were winterized and given kingsize beds, whirlpool baths, televisions, fireplaces and french doors onto private decks overlooking the bay. Also refurbished was one of seven Victorian upstairs guest rooms and a suite with private baths. Upgrading of the others and the three small rooms sharing baths in the former servants' quarters awaited completion of renovations in 1998 of the side Chalet, where more kingsize beds and whirlpool tubs were planned. No changes were planned for the spartan little efficiency cottages beside the beach, rented by the week for $800 to $900.

Ocean Drive, Newport 02840. (401) 849-3800. Fax (401) 849-3838. Doubles, $145 to $250; suites, $275 to $325.

Mill Street Inn. Inn purists might find this inn austere, but we rather like its European atmosphere. A 19th-century brick mill restored in 1985 and now listed on the National Register of Historic Places, it has 23 deluxe guest suites. The vast expanses of white walls are fine backdrops for contemporary paintings and posters, modern sofas and chairs, industrial gray carpeting, vases filled with fresh flowers, wet bars and television sets. In a few rooms, original brick walls and beams tone down some of the white. Beds are queensize, fans whir on the ceilings, and baths are gleamingly white-tiled with pedestal sinks. Eight duplex townhouses on the second floor have living room down and bedroom above, opening onto decks raised just enough so you can sit on the chairs and still see the distant water and the Jamestown bridge. Innkeepers Bob and Paula Briskin are gradually replacing what she calls the high-tech look with something more colorful and luxurious. The rooftop deck has been made into a great spot where guests can enjoy continental-plus breakfast on summer mornings, along with a view of the harbor.

75 Mill St., Newport 02840. (401) 849-9500 or (800) 392-1316. Fax (401) 848-5131. Doubles, $255 to $285.

The InnTowne. This inn, built in 1980 after a fire destroyed the original structure, is aptly named. It couldn't be more in town, just off Thames Street, its side rooms facing the busy main street and those on the third and fourth floors catching a glimpse of the harbor. Built and furnished by Betty and Paul McEnroe, formerly of the famed Inn at Castle Hill, it was purchased by Carmella Gardner, who converted the old Restoration House annex at 20 Mary St. into time-sharing condos, which the inn rents as efficiency studios and suites. A suite and seventeen guest rooms with private baths in the main inn are nicely decorated in colorful and contemporary matching fabrics (right down to the shower curtains and wastebaskets), thick carpeting, canopy beds, upholstered wing chairs and wicker furniture. The inn has a delightful rooftop sun deck, and downstairs are a sitting room and a small dining room for afternoon tea and continental breakfast.

6 Mary St., Newport 02840. (401) 846-9200 or (800) 457-7803. Fax (401) 846-1534. Doubles, $139 to $179; condo suites, $189 to $375.

Small and Personal

The Francis Malbone House. Local investors have transformed a former physician's residence along Lower Thames Street into one of Newport's most elegant B&Bs. They started with eight stylish corner bedrooms on the second and third floors, each with private baths and antique queensize beds with monogrammed duvet covers, plus a sunken main-floor suite fashioned from the former doctor's office. Two main-floor guest parlors and a library/TV room, all with fireplaces, are unusually inviting. At our first spring visit, the rooms abounded with a profusion of colorful house plants, from African violets to hibiscus to hydrangeas. In 1996, a smashing nine-room addition at the rear was linked to the main house by a new breakfast room and a tiled and glass-walled corridor along a fountain courtyard. These rooms are larger and each has a kingsize bed, fireplace, jacuzzi and bigger vanities and closets – "all the things we wanted but couldn't have in the old house," according to innkeeper Will Dewey. Two rooms in the new wing have private garden courtyards, unexpectedly verdant retreats in downtown Newport, as is the larger courtyard between the buildings, where breakfast may be served in season. The handsome new breakfast room, with domed ceiling and shelves of

display china, seats up to 40 at four tables for fare that might include eg
or belgian waffles.

392 Thames St., Newport 02840. (401) 846-0392 or (800) 846-0392. Fax (401) 848-5956. Doubles, $160 to $250; suite, $295.

Cliffside Inn. Among the most alluring of Newport's upscale B&Bs is this Victorian charmer, beautifully upgraded and expanded by owner Winthrop Baker. A block above the ocean, the summer villa built in 1880 by a governor of Maryland offers fifteen rooms and suites, the nine largest of which Win considers "clearly room for room the best in Newport" with their jacuzzi baths, fireplaces and sumptuous sitting areas with TVs. The inn's many floor-to-ceiling and bay windows bathe the rooms with light, blending an airy Laura Ashley freshness with rich Victoriana. The Seaview Cottage below, a onetime ranch house, was transformed in 1996 into two suites, the Atlantic with a massive native stone fireplace and the Cliff with a two-sided fireplace visible from both the kingsize plantation bed and the plush living room. An elaborate Victorian tea is served in the late afternoon in a large fireplaced parlor or on the wide front veranda, from which the ocean can be glimpsed down the street. Innkeeper Stephan Nicolas prepares treats like walnut pancakes, strawberry crêpes or, in our case, eggs benedict, for a breakfast to remember.

2 Seaview Ave., Newport 02840. (401) 847-1811 or (800) 845-1811. Fax (401) 848-5850. Doubles, $165 to $205; suites, $255 to $325.

Elm Tree Cottage. Here is one beautiful "cottage," a shingle-style mansion built in 1882 a block from the water for the daughter of Unitarian clergyman William Ellery Channing. Guests enjoy an acre of landscaped grounds, a huge living room, a morning garden room and a bar room furnished in wicker. The five upstairs guest rooms are no slouches, either, particularly the 1,000-square-foot master bedroom with a canopied kingsize bed and two sitting areas, one in front of the fireplace. Almost as inviting is the main-floor library bedroom, lovely in wine and teal colors. Two plush chairs face a TV and guests have helped fill the room's shelves with favorite books. Personable innkeepers Priscilla and Tom Malone, who occupy the third floor with their three daughters, also design and execute stunning stained-glass pieces. Breakfast by candlelight in the pretty dining room is a special event. Ours started with juice and homemade oatmeal in a dish decorated with five varieties of dried leaves and culminated in delicious pumpkin waffles.

336 Gibbs Ave., Newport 02840. (401) 849-1610 or (888) 356-8733. Doubles, $175 to $325.

The Melville House. Typical but a cut above many of Newport's ubiquitous small B&Bs, this cozy 1750 Colonial has seven rooms with antique double beds, five with private bath and all decorated in Colonial style with stenciling done by a former innkeeper. New owners Vince DeRico and David Horan have added a suite with a fireplaced sitting room and a queensize bedroom, which they offer from November through April for $165, including champagne on arrival, liqueurs with turndown and breakfast in bed. Otherwise, guests come together in a small breakfast room for a full breakfast that might include ginger waffles, jonnycakes or the house specialty, eggs in mushroom-cheese sauce served over ham on an English muffin with a side of potato pancakes. Tea or sherry with homemade fruit breads and biscotti are served in the afternoon in the fireplaced sitting room. This is a place to immerse yourself in history, the location is good for walking to practically anywhere downtown, and there's off-street parking.

39 Clarke St., Newport 02840. (401) 847-0640. Fax (401) 847-0956. Doubles, $110 to $135.

The Victorian Ladies. These two Victorian beauties, one behind the other, are among the most comfortable of their genre. A prevailing pink and blue color scheme and striking window treatments characterize the eleven guest rooms, all with private baths, television sets and a light, uncluttered look. Innkeepers Helene and Donald O'Neill serve a full breakfast in the dining room of the front house, which also has a small parlor. The O'Neills added two deluxe suites upstairs in the rear caretaker's cottage. Both contain lavender carpeting with which Helene paired a pale yellow color scheme in one suite and dark green in the other. They have telephones, as well as the televisions common to all rooms. Don, a contractor, built a secluded garden courtyard and gazebo, pleasant places to relax on a nice day. Helene hoped to open a small gift shop in the carriage house.

63 Memorial Blvd., Newport 02840. (401) 849-9960. Doubles, $135 to $185.

The Old Beach Inn. Although not really near the beach, a residential location with a big back yard commends this romantic B&B opened in 1989 by Luke and Cyndi Murray. In the main house they offer five guest rooms with private baths, named after flowers and furnished with whimsy in various English country styles. Lately, the Murrays moved with their young sons to a rear carriage house, where they added two more guest rooms with private entrances. The room they vacated on the main floor was converted into a guest living room to supplement the small front parlor. A continental breakfast is served in the dining room or outside on a porch and brick patio overlooking the gazebo and lily pond in the back yard.

19 Old Beach Rd, Newport 02840. (401) 849-3479 or (888) 303-5033. Fax (401) 847-1236. Doubles, $135 to $165.

Stay in a Mansion

Wayside Guest House. If you want to stay in a Newport mansion, this beige brick summer cottage almost across from the Elms and just down the street from the homes of the Astors and Vanderbilts fits the bill. And the bill won't break your bankbook. Al and Dorothy Post and son Donald have converted the mansion into a low-key B&B with ten guest rooms, all with private baths and TVs. Lately they have updated the bathrooms and spiffed up the bedrooms, which are spacious and comfortable. Twelve-foot-high ceilings, queen canopy beds and crystal knobs on the doors are among the extravagant touches. Some rooms come with day beds to sleep a third person. The most prized accommodation is in the main-floor library, big enough for a kingsize bed, two sofas and a chair and now boasting two french doors that cost more than his first house, says Al. It's a steal for $140 a night. A continental-plus breakfast is served in the family dining room off a magnificent entry foyer with oak parquet floor, paneled walls and a fifteen-foot-high ceiling. There's a swimming pool out back for guests. Wayside welcomes children and accepts single-night reservations, which many Newport inns do not, on weekends.

Bellevue Avenue, Newport 02840. (401) 847-0302 or (800) 653-7678. Fax (401) 848-9374. Doubles, $125 to $140, from $95 in off-season.

Where to Eat

Newport is full of interesting dining. The best restaurants tend to be elegant, expensive and crowded; reservations and dressy attire are suggested for dinner. The town has many casual restaurants as well, with newcomers popping up like spring flowers.

Fine Dining

The Place. This wine bar and grill adjunct of Yesterday's, a pubby Washington Square institution, was opened by its owners as a showcase for their longtime chef, Alex Daglis. He obliges with the most exciting cuisine in Newport, served stylishly at white-clothed tables on two levels of a long, narrow dining room and accompanied by "flights" of wine (four samples of reds or whites for $13) or "schooners" of microbrews (four seven-ounce pilsener glasses ensconced in a hand-made wooden schooner for $6). Folks rave about the changing entrées, from the pork tenderloin with jalapeño-peach salsa to the grilled tenderloin stuffed with goat cheese. But we never got beyond the appetizers, so tempting that we shared and made a meal of five. The shrimp and corn tamales, the exquisite scallops with cranberries and ginger, the gratin of wild mushrooms, and raviolis of smoked chicken and goat cheese were mere warmups for a salad of smoked pheasant with poached pears and hazelnuts. Each was gorgeously presented on black octagonal plates. An apple crêpe with apple sorbet was a crowning finale. More casual fare is served day and night in Yesterday's, recently rechristened an Ale House to differentiate it from the wine bar and grill.
28 Washington Sq. (401) 847-0116. Entrées, $17.95 to $23.95. Dinner nightly, 5:30 to 10 or 11.

White Horse Tavern. The historic ambiance of the country's oldest operating tavern, carefully restored by the Preservation Society some years back, draws a well-heeled following who love the romantic, Colonial ambiance. Chef Brian Conners's food is equal to the elegant setting, which we find most appealing in the off-season when the fireplaces are lit, and a better value at lunch than at dinner. At noon, you can order a sandwich or a salad in the $9 to $11 range, although entrées go up to $17 for bouillabaisse or veal tenderloin over pasta. At night, expect main courses like an oriental sauté of shrimp and scallops, baked Atlantic salmon, grilled duck breast and confit, individual beef wellington or châteaubriand for two. Starters could be baked oysters or peking raviolis. For most, this is special-occasion dining, topped off by such masterful desserts as a three-cherry tart on a chocolate crust in a pool of vanilla cream sauce or triple silk torte on a bed of raspberry melba.
Marlborough and Farewell Streets. (401) 846-3600. Entrées, $23 to $33. Lunch, daily except Tuesday noon to 3; dinner nightly, 6 to 10; Sunday champagne brunch, noon to 3.

The Black Pearl. You can sit outside under the Cinzano umbrellas on Bannister's Wharf and watch the world go by while you enjoy some of the best clam chowder ever, thick and dill-laced ($2.75 a bowl). You also can enjoy a pearlburger ($6.25), served with mint salad in pita bread and good fries, plus a variety of other sandwiches, salads and desserts. Inside, the tavern is cozy, dark and noisy, usually with a line of people waiting for seats, and the fare is basically the same as outside, with a few heartier entrées available at lunch or dinner. Desserts are delectable, especially the Black Pearl cheesecake followed by cappuccino laced with kahlua and courvoisier. **The Commodore Room,** the adjacent highly rated formal dining room facing the harbor, serves contemporary cuisine, with dinner entrées like sautéed soft-shell crabs, gray sole meunière, salmon fillet with mustard-dill hollandaise, roast duckling with green peppercorn sauce, steak au poivre and rack of lamb. More than 1,500 meals a day in summer come forth from what must be one of the world's tiniest kitchens.

Bannister's Wharf. (401) 846-5264. Entrées, $16.50 to $26. Tavern, daily from 11; dinner in Commodore Room, 6 to 11. Closed six weeks in winter.

La Petite Auberge. On two floors in the historic Stephen Decatur House, Roger Putier serves classic French fare from an extensive menu in five small and elegant dining rooms where lace tablecloths are layered over pale blue or gold linen. There's also a rose-trellised courtyard where meals are served outdoors in season, plus a hidden bistro in the rear. The sauces are heavenly – from the escargots with cèpes, a house specialty, to our entrées of veal with morels and cream sauce and two tender pink lamb chops, also with cèpes and an intense brown sauce. Entrées range from frog's legs provençal to beef wellington. Most dishes are finished at tableside, even the tossed salad with choice of dressings. The excellent wine list is nicely priced, and desserts are mostly classics like crêpes suzette, cherries jubilee and, our happy choice, strawberries romanoff..

19 Charles St. (401) 849-6669. Entrées, $19.95 to $25.75. Dinner, Monday-Saturday 6 to 10, Sunday 5 to 9.

Castle Hill Inn & Resort. The dining experience has been upgraded here under new management, who refurbished our favorite Sunset Room, which, along with the rest of the main floor, has expansive windows jutting out toward the water. Chef Wayne Gibson features Northeastern regional cuisine with indigenous ingredients from Maine to the Chesapeake Bay – "you won't find artichokes here," advised general manager Leonard Panaggio. Instead find dinner appetizers like a sauté of lobster and "found mushrooms" with Sakonnet Vineyards vidal beurre blanc or seared foie gras with fresh peach jam. Main courses could be as basic as braised chicken breast with orzo or as exotic as steamed lobster with vanilla bean butter and lobster brandade. Desserts could be a pecan-walnut-pignoli tart or a baked chocolate terrine with a white chocolate grid. Lunch items range from $7 for a grilled turkey baguette sandwich to $12 for provimi calves liver with vidalia onions and caraway-shiraz glaze. Castle Hill's long-popular Sunday brunch, served inside, is followed by drinks, jazz and a barbecue on the lawn in the afternoon.

Ocean Drive. (401) 849-3800. Entrées, $19 to $30. Lunch, Tuesday-Saturday 11:30 to 3:30; dinner, Monday-Saturday 6 to 10; Sunday brunch, 11:30 to 3:30, afternoon barbecue with jazz on the lawn, 3 to 8.

More Casual Settings

The Mooring. The Mooring closed in early 1997 for renovations to enclose the upstairs deck, increasing the interior dining space by 50 percent. Happily, there's still plenty of outside dining on the downstairs brick patio, brightened by colorful geraniums and hailed by its owners for the best al fresco dining east of the Mississippi. The Mooring certainly has about the best water location around, thanks to its former incarnation as the New York Yacht Club station. The inside is all blue

Busy Bannister's Wharf waterfront scene embraces shops, restaurants and outdoor cafes.

and nautical, with a fireplace ablaze in the off-season. The lines for meals can get long (a very spicy bloody mary served in a pilsener glass may help). Or you could stop in during off-hours for a gin and tonic, a bowl of prize-winning clam chowder, or coffee and a piece of orange ambrosia pie. Our party of four had to wait only ten minutes for a table on the breezy patio as we eyed the "glacial" salads and hefty sandwiches (most $6.75 to $9.50) passing by. We sampled the warm salmon salad, the seafood quiche with coleslaw, steamed mussels with garlic bread and a terrific scallop chowder we deemed even better than the Mooring's award-winning clam chowder. Dinner choices include seafood paella, oriental fish stew, shrimp and scallops diablo, loin lamb chops and filet mignon with lobster tail. **The Smokehouse Cafe,** a new seasonal annex, attracts the family trade for its pulled pork sandwiches and "real barbecues."

Sayer's Wharf. (401) 846-2260. Entrées, $10.25 to $26. Lunch and dinner daily, from 11:30 or noon. Closed Monday and Tuesday in winter.

Asterix & Obelix. Young Danish restaurateur John Bach-Sorenson transformed an auto-repair garage into a European-style brasserie that has taken Newport by storm. He named it for two favorite French comic-strip characters, known for fighting the bureaucracy, which he had to do to win a wine and beer license. The colorful, high-ceilinged space has tables covered with white cloths and butcher paper, a semi-open rear kitchen, a handcrafted bar along one side, and garage doors that open to a sidewalk cafe in season. John calls his fare Mediterranean-Asian. The dinner menu is runs the gamut from mussels in tomato broth over linguini to filet mignon à la milanaise. Among the possibilities: tandoori chicken, sautéed swordfish in a Thai curry lobster sauce and rack of lamb with a Lebanese couscous. You might start with firecracker spring rolls with peanut dipping sauce or a salad of arugula and celery root with portobello mushroom. Finish with key lime pie or chocolate mousse. An exotic, lengthy lunch menu is priced from $6 for a burger to $17 for grilled swordfish; brunch items play a stronger role in summer.

599 Lower Thames St. (401) 841-8833. Entrées, $14 to $25. Daily, 11 a.m. to 11 p.m. or midnight. Closed Tuesday and Wednesday in winter.

The West Deck. Innovative bistro cuisine draws those in the know to this waterside hideaway beside the harbor. James Mitchell, who was chef at the Inn at Castle Hill in its heyday, took over an old, garage-like space that's one-third cooking area. He seats 60 people for candlelight dining in the main room and a new side sun porch, and more can be accommodated seasonally on an outside patio where there's a wood grill. For dinner, expect main dishes like almond-crusted mahi-mahi with Thai lobster curry sauce, salmon wrapped in potato crust with pinot noir sauce, roasted half chicken with creamed leeks and rack of lamb with bordelaise sauce. Start with cream of watercress soup or a warm goat cheese salad. Finish with a pear and raspberry crisp or the signature grand marnier soufflé. Barbecued chicken, spare ribs and grilled local seafood and lobster are featured for lunch and dinner on the outdoor patio in season. The wine and beer lists are affordably priced.
1 Waite's Wharf. (401) 847-3610. Entrées, $13.50 to $26.50. Lunch in summer, noon to 2:30; dinner nightly in summer, 6 to 10, Wednesday-Saturday in off-season; Sunday brunch in winter, noon to 3.

Cheeky Monkey Cafe. "Have a cheeky evening," advises the menu of this trendy new cafe and cigar lounge beside the waterfront. The name reflects the British expression of endearment for a fun-loving, devilish person, and owner Henry Kates chose it to reflect a cheeky point of view on foods and spirits. Dining is on two levels, facing an open kitchen amid a dark decor of black wood tables and faux-leopard skins on the benches and wainscoting. The menu is contemporary with a Southern accent. Typical starters are grilled chicken satay with a spicy peanut sauce, New Orleans-style barbecued shrimp with green onion popcorn rice, and a house-smoked salmon and goat cheese quesadilla. Expect main courses like skillet-seared chicken breast with creole tomato salsa, grilled pork chop with a spicy banana sauce and baked lobster with seafood and andouille sausage paella. Dessert could be bananas foster or chocolate suicide torte. Drinks are available in a separate bar across the hallway, or upstairs in a cigar lounge with a parlor-like ambiance of sofas, overstuffed chairs and floor lamps.
14 Perry Mill Wharf. (401) 845-9494. Entrées, $12.95 to $25. Dinner, Wednesday-Sunday 6 to 9 or 10.

Le Bistro. Stylish decor in the second- and third-floor dining rooms with glimpses of the harbor and creative French Provence-inspired cuisine recommend this bistro, now owned by James Beaulieu of the expanding Wharf Pub & Restaurant below. We've enjoyed a fine salade niçoise ($6.95) and a classic bouillabaisse ($9.95) from a luncheon menu on which everything looks good. Dinner entrées range from grilled chicken with lemon and garlic to rack of lamb with grilled eggplant and roasted tomato. We can vouch for the veal kidneys sauced with port and mushrooms and the roast duck in a red cream sauce with endives. Worthy desserts were a grape tart in puff pastry with whipped cream and creole bread pudding with bourbon sauce. Both the lunch and dinner menus are offered in the redecorated third-floor lounge. The new wine bar here is the dining choice of regulars.
Bowen's Wharf. (401) 849-7778. Entrées, $14.95 to $26.95. Lunch daily, 11:30 to 5; dinner nightly, 5 to 11; Sunday brunch, 11:30 to 2:30.

Scales and Shells. Almost as fast as seafood can be unloaded from the docks out back, retired sea captain Andy Ackerman and his staff cook up a storm in an open kitchen near the door of this casual "Southern Italian seafood" restaurant, a huge success since its opening in 1988. Plain and exotic seafood, simply prepared but presented with style, comes in many guises. The blackboard menu on the wall lists the offerings, from mussels marinara to shrimp fra diavolo. There are wood-grilled shrimp, tuna and bluefish with chipotle vinaigrette, but no non-seafood items beyond a couple of pasta dishes with vegetables. A raw bar offers fresh goodies near the entry, and there's a good wine list A second-floor addition called **Upscales,** a smaller and quieter room, is open from May-September.

527 Thames St. (401) 846-3474. Entrées, $10.95 to $17.95. Dinner, Monday-Saturday 5 to 9 or 10, Sunday 4 to 9. No credit cards.

Rhumb Line. A bistro-like place in the historic Point section of Newport, this has a cozy feeling, with oriental rugs dotted around the wide-plank floors, an old piano in one corner and a wood stove in another, old-fashioned lamps and woven tablecloths. Even the bar stools bear hooked rug cushions. Waitresses in bermuda shorts dart by with chowders, salads and burgers with huge steakfries. Prices are moderate, and many wines are available by the glass. Entrées like curried chicken madras, wiener schnitzel, scallops with pesto and filet mignon are listed on the dinner menu. Start with the smoked bluefish pâté; finish with chocolate bread pudding. Although there's an outdoor cafe, the Rhumb Line seems more appealing in the off-season than on a hot summer's day when you might rather be outdoors near the water.

62 Bridge St. (401) 849-6950. Entrées, $13.95 to $19.95. Lunch, 11:30 to 3, weekends to 5; dinner, 5 to 10 or 10:30; Sunday brunch, noon to 4.

A Pub for Fun

Brick Alley Pub & Restaurant. We don't know which is more dizzying: the bar with its mirrors and memorabilia, or the sixteen-page menu, which blows the mind. Not to mention the vintage red Chevy pickup truck beside the salad bar. Or the jungle of plants. Or, hanging from the ceiling, the tractors and wagons that owner Ralph Plumb says he's been collecting "since I was a kid." No matter. Everyone loves the place for its enormous variety of good food at pleasant prices. We can't begin to detail the fare; suffice to say that there's half a page for nachos and another half for potato skins, a full page for soup and salad buffet, two for sandwiches and two for dinner specials, from a couple of pastas to surf and turf. Sole vanderbilt (stuffed with scallops, crabmeat, mushrooms and cheese) is the house specialty.

140 Thames St. (401) 849-6334. Entrées, $11.95 to $19.95. Daily, 11 to 10 or 11.

Picnicking

Among many places to pick up picnic fare, we think the best is **The Market on the Boulevard,** 43 Memorial Blvd. A grocery store for the carriage trade, it has a terrific bakery, deli and "gourmet to go" section. With some of their great salads and sandwiches, head out Ocean Drive to Brenton Point State Park, where you can park and cross the street to your own perch along the rocky shoreline.

FOR MORE INFORMATION: Newport County Convention & Visitors Bureau, 23 America's Cup Ave., Newport. R.I. 02840. (401) 849-8048 or (800) 326-6030. Preservation Society of Newport County, 424 Bellevue Ave., Newport 02840, (401) 847-1000.

23 🌷 Spring

Brick sidewalk, iron fence and facade of 1789 house on Pleasant Street.

Restorations and Restaurants

Portsmouth, N.H.

For a small city (population, 23,000), Portsmouth packs a wallop. As New Hampshire's first settlement, it has a rich historic tradition and takes pride in its past. What it also has, and what makes it such fun for today's visitor, is a lively present. Waterfront redevelopment, the restoration of historic homes, interesting restaurants and good places to stay all make Portsmouth exciting.

The town's original name was Strawbery Banke, an impulsive and appropriate choice by English settlers who arrived in 1630 and found wild strawberries growing in profusion on the banks of the Piscataqua River. Twenty-three years later, the town was renamed Portsmouth.

The old name lives in a fine historic restoration in the city's South End. There a dilapidated but potentially rich neighborhood was saved from almost certain destruction in the 1950s. A few interested locals pleaded with the federal government not to raze buildings for the construction of subsidized rental apartments, but to help fund the restoration instead. The resulting Strawbery Banke celebrated its 30th anniversary in 1994.

"Adaptive re-use" is a phrase used by Strawbery Banke Inc. as it attempts to make this museum more than just a 9 to 5 affair – one where craftsmen and a few complementary businesses might also reside. There are a boat shop and a leather craftsman, for example.

Elsewhere in Portsmouth the same spirit of restoration exists. The entire city seems bent on the renovation and adaptation of its vintage houses and buildings, and it has plenty to work on. After all, the reason the city was settled so early was because of the deep-water port it offered, and those early sea captains built some great homes.

Several of Portsmouth's beautiful houses from the 18th and 19th centuries are open to the public as museums. The 1763 Moffatt-Ladd House, with its original formal English gardens out back, and the John Paul Jones House, built in 1758, are two of our favorites. Jones, whose ringing words, "I have not yet begun to fight," have inspired scores of schoolboys, rented rooms in town on two occasions while he oversaw the construction of vessels for the Revolutionary War.

Red tugboats, commercial fishing vessels, sightseeing boats, pleasure craft and the massive defense ships of the Portsmouth Naval Shipyard (located across the Piscataqua River in Kittery, Me.) ply Portsmouth's harbor. The river is the second fastest tidal river in the U.S. navigable by ship, with six knots the average current and a nine-foot tidal range. It is fun to sit outdoors on restaurant decks, or inside by windows in cooler weather, and check the action.

Portsmouth is cultural. Theater, chamber music, choral groups, artists and crafts-men lend their talents to the vibrancy of the city. While these aspects make Portsmouth a great place to visit, more and more people want to live here, too.

In the spring, this city by the sea is an especially good destination. That's the time when the idea of being near the water has special appeal, and yet a cozy bed and breakfast seems like the place to stay. Portsmouth can supply both experiences and more.

Getting There

Portsmouth is located at New Hampshire's most northerly seacoast point. It is easily reached by automobile via coastal Route 1 or Interstate 95. Greyhound buses stop in the center of town at Market Square. The closest major airport is Logan International in Boston; limousine service is provided frequently to Portsmouth.

Exploring the Area

Historic Restorations

Historic restorations abound in Portsmouth. More than 40 houses are open to the public in one way or another. The greatest concentration is in Strawbery Banke.

Strawbery Banke. Salvaged from demolition and urban renewal in the 1950s, this ten-acre site calls itself a museum in progress, and that is part of its appeal. Not only are there eight furnished houses of several time periods, but also on-site archaeological excavations, landscape reconstruction and building restorations as officials seek to renew the area piece by piece. Opened in 1990, for example, was the Rider-Wood House, built around 1800 and furnished to interpret the daily life of a widow around 1830. And there's now Abbott's Little Corner Store, restored to its 1943 wartime appearance, complete with familiar brand labels and wartime price controls. All but one house, the Goodwin Mansion, are on their original sites, which makes Strawbery Banke particularly authentic. Interpreters lead orientation tours a couple of times a day, but basically it's a do-it-yourself, walk-through deal, and with the museum's illustrated map in hand, you'll have no trouble finding everything. Take time to see the boat builder, the potter and the weaver. The annual heirloom heritage plant sale in May is one of several special events

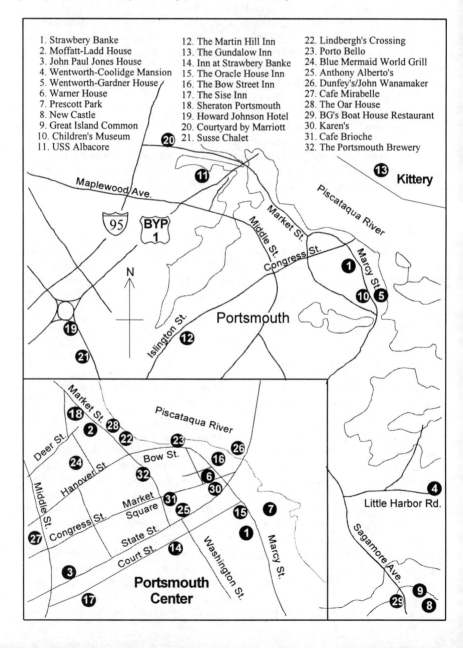

planned throughout the season. The Dunaway Store is a gift shop where you can pick up all sorts of quasi-historic items. If you're hungry, stop in at **The Washington Street Eatery,** a Colonial-style lunchroom where you can get home-baked muffins, soups, sandwiches and luscious desserts. Or tote your own lunch and picnic at Strawbery Banke.

Marcy Street. (603) 433-1100. Daily 10 to 5, April-November. Adults $10, children $7, family $25. Tickets may be used for two consecutive days.

1. Strawbery Banke
2. Moffatt-Ladd House
3. John Paul Jones House
4. Wentworth-Coolidge Mansion
5. Wentworth-Gardner House
6. Warner House
7. Prescott Park
8. New Castle
9. Great Island Common
10. Children's Museum
11. USS Albacore
12. The Martin Hill Inn
13. The Gundalow Inn
14. Inn at Strawbery Banke
15. The Oracle House Inn
16. The Bow Street Inn
17. The Sise Inn
18. Sheraton Portsmouth
19. Howard Johnson Hotel
20. Courtyard by Marriott
21. Susse Chalet
22. Lindbergh's Crossing
23. Porto Bello
24. Blue Mermaid World Grill
25. Anthony Alberto's
26. Dunfey's/John Wanamaker
27. Cafe Mirabelle
28. The Oar House
29. BG's Boat House Restaurant
30. Karen's
31. Cafe Brioche
32. The Portsmouth Brewery

Moffatt-Ladd House. If you can visit only one historic house while you are in Portsmouth, make it this. A copy of an English manor house, it is beautifully situated high on the banks of the Piscataqua River and it is not hard to imagine lawns extending to the water's edge, as they once did. Today, Market Street interrupts the line, but out back extensive English gardens remain much as they were. The gardens may be visited separately from the house. The house was built in 1763 as a wedding gift from John Moffatt, an English sea captain, to his son. Later it was the home of John's son-in-law, Gen. William Whipple, a signer of the Declaration of Independence. Visitors are treated to three floors of exceptional 18th-century furnishings. The design of the house is unusual, from the cellar with its great brick arches leading to a secret passageway that once went to the wharves, all the way up to rooms with extra-deep fireplaces allowing for spacious closets on each side (a novelty in their day). Next door is the 1823 Counting House where Moffatt and Ladd cargoes were laded; out back is an old-fashioned herb garden. A used-book sale is conducted on an ongoing basis in the Coach House.
154 Market St. (603) 436-8221. Monday-Saturday 10 to 4, Sunday 2 to 5, June 15 to Oct. 15. Adults $4, children $1. Gardens only, $1.

John Paul Jones House. John Paul Jones, the naval hero, was a bachelor who never owned a house. But he made this lovely yellow gambrel-roofed house his headquarters during two lengthy stays in Portsmouth. Sarah Wentworth Purcell, a widow, rented Jones a room in 1776-77 when he was in town to oversee construction of the sloop, Ranger, and again in 1781-82 when he returned for the building of the America. A handsome man (note the bust of Jones in the house), he is reputed to have turned a few pretty heads during his stay. The second-floor room he occupied is a memorial. The house, built in 1758, has been headquarters of the Portsmouth Historical Society for many years and contains rich local collections. You'll love the costumes, the collection of canes in which weapons are concealed and items from ships that were dismantled in Portsmouth. The kids will, too. On July 6, the anniversary of John Paul Jones's birth, the society hosts a birthday party.
43 Middle St. (603) 436-8240. Monday-Saturday 10 to 4, Sunday noon to 4, mid-May to mid-October. Adults $4, children $2.

Wentworth-Coolidge Mansion. This rambling yellow clapboard structure of 42 rooms is situated on a point of land with a great view of Portsmouth Harbor. It was originally the home of Benning Wentworth, New Hampshire's royal governor from 1741 to 1767, and contains the council chamber where the state's first provincial government conducted its affairs in the turbulent pre-Revolutionary War period. Today, the governor's council meets annually in the room, making the trek from Concord. It is a handsome space, with low corner cupboards, unique to the house, and a splendid table surrounded by beautiful walnut Queen Anne chairs. A glass chandelier hangs overhead. When Benning Wentworth died in 1770, his widow married Michael Wentworth, a retired British Army colonel. They made the mansion a hospitable social center, entertaining George Washington here in 1789. The house's many subsequent owners made changes and added rooms that contribute to its eclectic but not unattractive appearance. The grounds contain the oldest lilacs original to their property in the United States. A tour takes about an hour and is most interesting, although there's relatively little furniture in the house, which is viewed primarily for its construction and history.

Little Harbor Road. (603) 436-6607. Daily 10 to 5, June 20 to Labor Day; weekends only, Memorial Day to June 20. Adults $3.

Wentworth-Gardner House. Considered one of the most nearly perfect examples of Georgian architecture in America, this house had an interesting succession of owners, beginning with a member of the ubiquitous Wentworth family and including the Metropolitan Museum of Art, which at one time planned to move it to New York's Central Park. The carving throughout the interior required fourteen months to complete. Among items of interest are the great fireplace in the kitchen, original Dutch tiles and the spinning attic on the third floor.

Mechanic Street. (603) 436-4406. Tuesday-Sunday 1 to 4, June to mid-October. Adults $4, children $2.

Warner House. This house is considered the finest example in New England of a brick urban mansion of the early 18th century. Among its treasures: six mural paintings on the staircase wall, an early example of marbleization in the dining room and a lightning rod on the west wall, said to have been installed under the supervision of Benjamin Franklin in 1762. From 1748-54 it was the home of Gov. Benning Wentworth, who seems to have lived only in the best places. A guided tour takes 45 minutes to an hour.

150 Daniel St. (603) 436-5909. Tuesday-Saturday 10 to 4, mid-June to end of October. Adults $4, children $2.

Other historic houses include the **Gov. John Langdon House,** the **Rundlet-May House** and the **Jackson House,** oldest in New Hampshire, all operated by the Society for the Preservation of New England Antiquities, (603) 436-3205.

FORTS. Several forts are located along the Atlantic coast and the banks of the river. One of the most pleasant vistas of sea and coast is enjoyed from **Fort McClary** in nearby Kittery Point, Me. The site contains a six-sided blockhouse commanding impressive views of the coast and the river's mouth. The fort and grounds are maintained as a state park. Attractive paths lead to the edge of the bluff looking down on the sea. Picnicking is permitted. To reach the fort, take U.S. Route 1 to Kittery, then Route 103 or Kittery Point Road to the fort.

Fort Constitution on the island of New Castle fascinates young boys who like to climb around fortifications.

Walking

Portsmouth is a city for walkers. Its streets are narrow, its houses and shops easily viewable, and some of its sidewalks brick. One popular area for walking is the Market Street-Ceres Street area near the riverfront, where there are many shops and restaurants. Check out the red tugboats tied up by Ceres Street docks; they symbolize the city and are used to aid ships coming up the river. A map from the Chamber of Commerce is invaluable.

One walk we like begins at the Portsmouth Public Library on Islington Street (there's a public parking lot nearby). Walk along Middle Street to State Street and down State to Pleasant, passing the John Paul Jones House along the way. Follow

Pleasant Street all the way to Marcy. Pass a park to the right and follow it down to Mill Pond. Look at old houses, among them, at 346 Pleasant St., the **Gov. John Wentworth House,** the official residence of New Hampshire's last royal governor. Nearby is the Pleasant Street Cemetery dating from 1753. Turn left onto Marcy Street, which leads past Strawbery Banke on the left and Prescott Park on the right.

Prescott Park, 105 Marcy St., is located in an area that was once one of the seamiest in the city. Two civic-minded sisters, Mary and Josie Prescott, began to beautify the waterfront in the 1930s by establishing the oldest section of the park. They willed their fortunes for its further development. Formal gardens, with lighted fountains, have long been an attraction. One of two warehouses on the site now houses the **Folk Art Museum,** (603) 431-8748, with hand-carved mastheads and ship models. The Prescott Park Arts Festival operates all summer long with a variety of special events, musical, theatrical and otherwise. The gardens – a joint venture between the park and the University of New Hampshire's Cooperative Extension Service – are a place for trying new floral varieties, including annuals. Park open daily, 5 a.m. to midnight; museum, Wednesday-Sunday 10 to 7, June to Labor Day. Free.

Horse and Carriage Rides. If you're not up to all this walking, be advised that the Portsmouth Livery Co., (603) 427-0044, operates horse and carriage excursions in the downtown waterfront area and near Prescott Park. Day and evening sightseeing tours start at noon, May-October.

Boat Trips

Isles of Shoals. Ten miles off the coast of Portsmouth lie nine rocky islands first charted by Capt. John Smith when he sailed past in 1614. They were included on his now-famous map of the New England coast, and were subsequently used for many summers by European fishermen, who were attracted by the "shoals" or schools of fish. In the 1800s they became famous as summer resorts, especially the two largest, Appledore and Star islands. The most famous daughter of the islands was the poet Celia Thaxter, born in Portsmouth and raised out on the isles, where her father was the first innkeeper on Appledore. To his hotel, the Appledore House, Celia attracted many artistic and literary figures of the day, including Nathaniel Hawthorne, James Russell Lowell, Childe Hassam and Henry Ward Beecher.

Since early in this century, Star Island has operated as a religious conference center under the Congregational and Unitarian churches.

The Shoals Room at the Portsmouth Public Library on Islington Street is a great follow-up to a cruise through the islands. Ask the reference librarian to admit you to the upstairs room where the Shoals Collection is kept.

Isles of Shoals Steamship Co. The legends and lore of the barren islands are fascinating and you can hear about them aboard the cruise ships operated by the steamship company. Whale-watch cruises also are offered. While a regular Isles of Shoals cruise takes about three hours, we suggest the "Star Island Stopover," which leaves at 11 and returns before 5. This allows you to alight on Star Island

and spend a few hours exploring. Bring a picnic lunch or buy a snack on the island. Reservations are recommended, especially on weekends.

Steamship Dock at 315 Market St. (603) 431-5500 or (800) 441-4620. Cruises, May-October. Adults $14, children $8. Island Stopover, adults $20, children $12.

Portsmouth Harbor Cruises. The 90-minute narrated cruise down the Piscataqua River and around the island of New Castle is informative and amusing at times. Ours was particularly oriented to the importance of the Portsmouth Naval Shipyard, especially during World War II. You'll see what's left of the great resort, Wentworth-by-the-Sea, from the water. There are some cruises out to the Isles of Shoals, so check the itinerary before you depart.

64 Ceres St. (603) 436-8084 or (800) 776-0915. Cruises, Monday-Friday at noon, Saturday and Sunday at 10, noon and 3, mid-June through October. Adults $7 to $12; children $5 to $8.

New Castle

The town of **New Castle,** adjacent to Portsmouth, is very old and many of the houses sport dates from the 1700s. Driving or biking through offers visual treats. You can stop at **Great Island Common,** a large seacoast park with a vista of open ocean. Also in New Castle was the late, great Wentworth-by-the-Sea resort. The huge white hulk still towers, ghostlike, above the sea as a series of owners keeps coming up with plans, then discarding them. Its golf course is still in use.

For the Kids

The Children's Museum of Portsmouth. This special museum, just for the youngsters in your group, is not far from Strawbery Banke. Occupying the historic Old South Meeting House, it offers hands-on exhibits, workshops and demonstrations, and changing programs. "The Primary Place" is a great space for toddlers.

280 Marcy St. (603) 436-3853. Tuesday-Saturday 10 to 5, Sunday 1 to 5; also Monday in summer. Admission, $3.50.

USS Albacore. Now in permanent drydock, this 1,200-ton research vessel, built at the Portsmouth Naval Shipyard in 1952 and retired from service in 1972, was an experimental sub that carried a crew of 55. Its innovative hull design allowed it to set an underwater speed record in the 1960s. Following a brief film in the Visitor Center, visitors take guided tours of the cramped sleeping quarters, the engine room and the navigation station..

Albacore Park, Market Street. Exit 7 off I-95. (603) 436-3680. Daily, 9:30 to 5:30. Adults $4, children $2, family $10.

Shopping

People love to shop in Portsmouth's boutiques. Across the river in Kittery you'll find many discount outlets.

Market, Ceres and Bow streets contain most of the individualized small shops in Portsmouth. We like the **Cat House** with every kind of feline item imaginable, from stuffed cats to refrigerator magnets in the shape of cats. **Macro World** on Market Street offers all sorts of items for the ecology-minded; we especially liked stuffed and huggable globes, birds' nests and shower curtains showing the night sky.

Jester's Collectibles is filled with harlequin dolls, masks, marionettes, dolls and other items with a theatrical bent. **Fair Skies** on Market Street carries creatively designed clothes, both sportswear and dresses. Nearby, **Gallery 33** has imaginative pottery, things like papier maché sneakers, and more. **Les Cadeux** on Market Street stocks unusually nice tabletop appointments, stationery, games and painted furniture.

Randall Poquette, a small enterprise making moderately-priced women's clothing, has an outlet on Bow Street. The clothes, soft and swingy, range from dressy dresses to cozy fleece jackets.

The **Kumminz Gallery** on Daniel Street has particularly nice jewelry, clothing, accessories and watercolor paintings, all by respected New Hampshire artists and artisans. We loved the earring selection.

North of Kittery, Route 1 is lined with **factory outlet centers.** Among them are Boston Traders, Pfaltzgraff, Hickey Freeman, Reebok, Benetton, Crate & Barrel, J. Crew and Etienne Aigner.

Where to Stay

Accommodations are varied in Portsmouth. The city boasts several charming B&Bs in vintage homes and a larger Victorian-era inn that appeals to business people as well as travelers. A Sheraton hotel on the waterfront and several good motels at the Portsmouth Traffic Circle off I-95 provide more lodging choices. Rates in the motels change seasonally, and the Sheraton offers a weekend package.

Bed and Breakfasts

The Martin Hill Inn. What a charmer this place is! The first of Portsmouth's B&Bs, it is run with care by Jane and Paul Harnden, corporate dropouts who probably work as hard at innkeeping as they did in the business world. Seven air-conditioned rooms with private baths in two buildings are tastefully decorated with mostly period furnishings. The two yellow buildings are linked by an exquisite city garden, an oasis of coolness and color on a warm day, where the Harndens have also constructed a water garden. The inn is on a busy street, a couple of miles from the historic waterfront section of town, but once here, you're in a world of your own. Williamsburg wallpapers, oriental rugs and canopied beds strike the right note for Portsmouth. The Harndens furnish their own brand of wildflower and glycerine soaps, which can be purchased in gift packs as keepsakes. We like the suite with a greenhouse in the Guest House; for a change of pace, it features rattan furniture and lush plants. A first-floor room with pineapple-post twin beds is another special room. Breakfast, served in a dining room amid lovely Sheraton furniture, is delicious. Blueberry-pecan pancakes, omelets and baked apples are among the Harndens' most popular items.

404 Islington St., Portsmouth 03801. (603) 436-2287. Doubles, $85 to $115.

The Gundalow Inn. Although this inn is across the Piscataqua River in Kittery, it is just over Memorial Bridge from downtown Portsmouth and easily accessible to the action in town. The attractive red brick Victorian B&B was creatively transformed from a two-family house by Cevia and George Rosol. The large, rose-painted common room has a grand piano in the corner and all kinds of puzzles and books laid out on tables. Guests also enjoy a library area on the second floor. Four of the six guest rooms have river views, and all have private baths. They are named for gundalows, the special class of working boats used on the Piscataqua River for many years. Alice, a third-floor room with twin beds covered in crocheted spreads, is attractive with a pink striped floral wallpaper and a skylight that looks out over Memorial Bridge. Also on the third floor, the Royal George is cozy with blue carpeting, yellow walls, a wicker sitting area and a queen bed. Dido on the second floor is bright and private with four windows and an extra-long king bed. The Rosols serve breakfast at individual tables in a fireplaced breakfast room, or out-doors on a tree-shaded deck in warm weather. The fare includes fresh juice, scones, and an entrée like bread pudding incorporating homemade bread.

6 Water St., Kittery, Me. 03904. (207) 439-4040. Double, $110 and $125.

The Inn at Strawbery Banke. This B&B is conveniently located, right in the downtown section and a short walk to Strawbery Banke or the historic water-front and shopping area. Once you pull your car into the adjacent parking lot, you may not need it again. Sally O'Donnell, the innkeeper, works with a small staff to keep things shipshape. All seven guest rooms have private baths. Ours on the second floor was done in blue and white and was large and airy, with a queen and a single bed. Two first-floor rooms are located off the common area near the cheerful breakfast room. All have plain white bedspreads on the beds and interior shutters on the windows, original to the house, for a clean, uncluttered look. This is an old house, though, with narrow hallways and somewhat steep staircases. Guests enjoy the pleasant parlor with loads of books in floor-to-ceiling bookcases. Breakfast is served in a sunny breakfast room. Ours was juice, cantaloupe slices, bacon and eggs and the best homemade bread, toasted – plenty to fill us up for a day of touring. Other specialties are sourdough blueberry pancakes and sausage strata.

314 Court St., Portsmouth 03801. (603) 436-7242 or (800) 428-3933. Doubles, $95 and $100.

The Oracle House Inn. This salmon and cream colored structure built in 1709 was a restaurant before being converted into a three-or-four-room B&B in 1995. Owner Charles Godfrey of Kennebunk, Me., depends on resident managers to oversee the operation in Portsmouth, with mixed results. The house has a great location, across the street from the waterfront and Prescott Park and a short walk to Strawbery Banke and restaurants in the downtown area. Each bedroom – two on the first floor and two on the second – has a wood-burning fireplace but the two upstairs, with private baths, are preferable. Furnishings are spare but tasteful. We liked the second-floor room with a painted black floor and queen canopy bed dressed with red and white period print coverlet and checked dust ruffle. Its bath-room contains a large whirlpool tub. An extended continental breakfast is served in a little garden in good weather, or in a first-floor room in winter, which be-comes the fourth bedroom in summer.

Marcy Street, Portsmouth 03801. (603) 433-8827. Fax (603) 433-4309. Doubles, $135.

The Bow Street Inn. Claiming to be "Portsmouth's only waterfront inn," this establishment occupies the second floor of a brick building that is also home to the

Seacoast Repertory Theatre. Getting there means trekking up a flight of steps in front and then taking a small elevator one floor, but once you've arrived, the digs are quite attractive and comfortable. Two bedrooms offer harbor views, but all twelve are nicely decorated in pastels with Victorian touches. All have queensize beds, private baths, TVs and telephones. Parking is in a municipal garage nearby or, if you're lucky, on the street. Continental breakfast, served in a small but attractive breakfast room, includes home-baked breads.

121 Bow St., Portsmouth 03801. (603) 431-7760. Doubles, $89 to $130.

A Downtown Inn

The Sise Inn. This small luxury inn with 32 air-conditioned guest rooms is owned by Someplace Different Inc., a Canadian organization. Opened in 1986, it was the group's first in the United States. The house was built in 1881 by businessman John Sise as a family home. There are ten rooms in the original building and the rest are in an addition to the back. All have private baths, wall-to-wall carpeting and TVs hidden in armoires. The mood is Queen Anne Victorian and there are great oak beds, skylights, overhead fans and a different wallpaper (usually floral) in each room. Room 203 with a sitting area and a fireplace is particularly attractive; the fireplaces, however, are only to be looked at. A few bathrooms contain whirlpool tubs. The inn is notable for the amount of richly varnished butternut wood in the lobby. A Victorian-style parlor is comfortable and a cheerful breakfast room offers a continental-plus breakfast with yogurt, muffins, bagels, cereals and fruits. Newspapers are complimentary. We appreciated the weather report that is slipped under your door early in the morning so you can dress appropriately for the day ahead.

40 Court St., Portsmouth 03801. (603) 433-1200 or (800) 267-0525. Fax (603) 433-1200. Doubles, $110 to $150.

Hotels and Motels

Sheraton Portsmouth Hotel & Conference Center. Erected in 1988, this is one of the newest kids on a very good block. The brick hotel has been built high enough so that there's a view of the working waterfront and the Piscataqua River from the main lobby and the dining area, which is at the waterview end. While the building seems a bit imposing from the outside, inside the color scheme of green, peach and mauve is most restful and furnishings are traditional and comfortable. The 148 rooms with kingsize or two double beds offer cable TV and HBO. Several penthouse and townhouse suites with one or two bedrooms, kitchen and living room with fireplace are available for extended stays. There are an indoor pool and sauna and a fitness center. The restaurant is well-rated. Many weekend deals are offered.

250 Market St., Portsmouth 03801. (603) 431-2300 or (800) 325-3535. Fax (603) 433-5649. Doubles, $124 to $142; suites $150; townhouses, $225 to $350.

Howard Johnson Hotel. Located at the Portsmouth Traffic Circle right off I-95, this member of the national chain was in the process of redoing all its rooms in early 1997. An indoor pool and a new exercise room were recent additions; the motel/hotel has always had its own outdoor pool. Altogether there are 135 rooms, most furnished with one or two queen beds, lounge chairs and, in some cases, recliners for watching TV. The advertised 24-hour restaurant next door looked rather sorry to us, what with its vending machines and tired decor. But the lodging is just fine.

Interstate Traffic Circle, Portsmouth 03801. (603) 436-7600 or (800) 654-2000. Doubles, $80 to $145.

Courtyard by Marriott. New in 1996, this two-story motel offers 109 rooms and suites on a site not far from Interstate-95 and close to the USS Albacore museum. Rooms have kingsize beds or two doubles and decoration is in burgundy and green with contemporary furniture in dark wood. An indoor pool and jacuzzi plus a small exercise room are available. The main-floor bar/lounge turns into a breakfast room in the morning and a buffet breakfast plus full menu are offered for those who want it.

1000 Market St., Portsmouth 03801. (603) 436-2121. Doubles, $129 to $149.

A Budget Choice

Susse Chalet. We've been pleased with accommodations and service at this member of the national motel chain located close to the Portsmouth circle. There's a rather nice outdoor pool for warm-weather stays, and the motel is set back off a side road so that it seems quieter than some. Most of the 105 rooms contain two double beds. A continental breakfast is available in the lobby.

650 Borthwick Ave. Ext., Portsmouth 03801. (603) 436-6363. Doubles, $53.70 to $56.70 in spring, $85 in summer.

Where to Eat

Portsmouth has been known for its restaurants for some years. Here are a few of our favorites.

Classy Dining

Lindbergh's Crossing. This is the latest star in the restaurant firmament of Portsmouth. Located across from the waterfront in the restored ship's chandlery that once housed the famous restaurant, **The Blue Strawbery,** this successor in 1996 cut all ties with the previous prix-fixe dinner formula and struck out on its own. The restaurant's name, says the menu, is based on a shared spirit of "man with wings" and honors Charles Lindbergh. The connection is obscure, but perhaps unimportant. We felt lucky to snag the last table for two available at 8:45 on a Friday night and several other parties were kept waiting at the door. The atmosphere of the candlelit room is cozy and low-key, with old brick walls, bare-topped wood tables and mismatched chairs. Upstairs is a wine bar, where dinners are also served. The menu changes seasonally. Since we were there in late fall, hearty entrées included coq au vin (in a white, rather than the traditional red, wine sauce), braised lamb shanks with Moroccan curried vegetables, sautéed sea scallops served over lyonnaise potatoes, and pork medallions with sliced apples in a brandied cream sauce. Starters included calamari stew, french onion soup and hearty New England clam chowder. For dessert, our waitress pushed the "medium rare" chocolate cake, whose center is apparently the consistency of chocolate pudding. Also

Wentworth-Gardner House faces boats moored in Piscataqua River.

possible were crème brûlée and a stilton-crusted cheese cake. We were full and settled for coffee.

29 Ceres St. (603) 431-0887. Entrées, $11 to $18. Dinner, nightly, 5 to 9:30 or 10.

Porto Bello. This intimate second-floor, L-shaped dining room overlooking the water is given high marks for northern Italian cuisine. Yolanda Desario and her mother cook up authentic and traditional dishes in the kitchen. At lunchtime, main dishes ($9 to $13) might be panini alla Italiana (daily baked bread with prosciutto, fresh mozzarella, plum tomatoes, basil and olive oil), pasta with marinara sauce, ragu or al pesto, grilled fish of the day or veal milanese. In the evening, diners at white-clothed tables may start with a mixed salad or a grilled portobello mushroom topped with sautéed garlic. They might try a pasta such as linguini with clams, scallops, mussels and shrimp; spaghettia alla carbonara, or fettuccine bolognese. For a main course, possibilities include grilled sausages served with sweet peppers and roasted potatoes, a half chicken roasted with prosciutto, onions, mushrooms, peppers and fresh-diced tomatoes, all in white wine, and lamb chops served with sautéed garlic and rosemary. Cannoli, profiteroles and zuppa inglese are on the dessert menu.

67 Bow St. (603) 431-2989. Entrées, $13 to $18. Lunch, Wednesday-Saturday 11 to 2; dinner, Tuesday-Saturday 4:30 to 9:30.

Blue Mermaid World Grill. Young restaurateurs Jim Smith and Scott Logan team up to feature "world grill" cuisine in an historic house in the area known as The Hill in Portsmouth. The place attracts a youngish crowd for its foods of the Caribbean, the Southwest, South America and elsewhere, cooked on a wood-burning grill. The dining rooms are on the second floor - a long narrow space across the front of the building, and a smaller room toward the back. Live entertainment is booked Thursday through Saturday nights in the bar and lounge on the main floor. A few aquarium-style glass insets suggest the mermaid's environment in an otherwise simple decor with bare wood tables and white napkins. The drink of choice here is a margarita. The signature dinner dish is grilled Maine lobster with mango butter served with grilled vegetables and corn bread. Among other entrées are pan-seared haddock with coconut cream sauce, grilled boneless chicken breast with a sweet cranberry-ancho chile mustard, and a marinated lamb skewer with couscous and green beans. Pizzas and pastas include some unusual combinations. A southwestern pizza is topped with roasted corn, jack cheese, black beans and scallions. You can also get "small plates" like grilled black bean cakes or Jamaican jerk chicken wings. At lunch, wood-grilled burgers are offered along with pastas, pizzas and quesadillas.

The Hill. (603) 427-2583. Entrées, $10 to $16. Lunch daily, 11:30 to 5; dinner, 5 to 10 or 11.

Anthony Alberto's. Located in the cellar of the old Custom House, this romantic Italian restaurant is often chosen to celebrate a special event. The brick and stone walls are softened with Italian paintings and the gray slate floors are topped with small oriental rugs. A large Italian sculpture crowns the entry. Guests are served in several small, intimate dining rooms. Starters might be a grilled portobello mushroom over roasted pepper crostini, Maine lobster sautéed in a pistachio nut-brandy cream sauce, or baked oysters with lemon vodka-flavored sour cream. Pasta dishes include rigatoni with Italian sausage in a rich tomato sauce, ravioli with a smoked native shrimp filling served with grilled jumbo shrimp, and linguini with shrimp, scallops and clams in a spicy red sauce. Entrées could be pecan-encrusted chicken breast with whipped sweet potatoes, grilled swordfish served with a salad of white beans, caramelized fennel and sautéed peppers, cioppino or a veal chop prepared according to chef Kurt Holzweiss's whim. Crème brûlée is a signature dessert. Co-owners Tod Alberto and Massimo Morgia, who met in a Boston restaurant, are proud of their wine list of 140 choices.

Custom House Cellar, 59 Penhallow St. (603) 436-4000. Entrées, $13 to $23. Dinner, Monday-Saturday 5 to 9:30 or 10:30, Sunday 4 to 8:30.

Dunfey's Aboard the John Wanamaker. A restored tugboat with lots of wood and brass, making it look more like a yacht than a tugboat, is tied up to the Harbour Place Marina on the waterfront. It's a choice location for a restaurant, especially when you can eat outdoors on the upper deck in nice weather. Opened in 1996, the restaurant was being praised for its food, although service was said to be uneven. Preferred dining is in the elegant captain's dining room at the stern of the vessel, where white-clothed tables are pushed up against banquettes. Watching the lights dance across the harbor in the evening can be romantic. For starters, try fish chowder, a caesar or mesclun salad, or corn-fried oysters Napoleon in puff pastry. Entrées include pan-fried sole with lemon-caper butter, roasted quail with garlic-sausage stuffing and squash fritters, pork tenderloin stuffed with prosciutto, gruyère, olives and sundried tomatoes, and black angus steak with gorgonzola butter. At lunchtime, a chicken sandwich with sautéed mushrooms, a burger or pasta are among the possibilities.

Harbour Place Marina, foot of State Street. (603) 433-3111. Entrées, $15 to $20. Lunch daily in season, Thursday and Friday only in off-season; dinner, Monday-Saturday from 5:30; Sunday, 1 to 8.

Cafe Mirabelle. A French-born chef, Stephan Mayeux, and his wife operate this two-level dining spot. Upstairs is the main restaurant, serving dinner and Sunday brunch. Downstairs is **La Crêperie,** which offers crêpes and salads for lunch and dinner. The cafe atmosphere is pleasant with deep red tablecloths, straight-backed chairs and a wood-burning stove for cool weather. Warm crusty rolls wrapped in a napkin are brought to the table in a basket with a tiny crock of butter. Dinner appetizers include country pork pâté, escargots provençal and wild mushroom-stuffed raviolis. A house salad with herbs de provence vinaigrette accompanies the entrées. Among them are chicken française, steak au poivre and veal sautéed with lobster meat, prosciutto and spinach in a marsala wine sauce. One of us had a lamb special with shiitake mushrooms and goat cheese served with wonderful-tasting winter squash and polenta. The other chose a vegetable pasta dish with a rich cream sauce. A warm pear and almond tart was a good dessert.

64 Bridge St. (603) 430-9301. La Crêperie, lunch, Monday-Saturday, 11:30 to 2; dinner nightly at Cafe Mirabelle, starting at 5:15; Sunday brunch, 9:30 to 2. Entrées, $13 to $20.

The Oar House. A popular restaurant across the street from the waterfront draws crowds because of the location and the ambiance, as much as for the food. At our latest visit, a couple had arrived in a rainstorm and said they always had lunch here on their annual trip through Portsmouth. The restaurant is ensconced in what was once a warehouse for a local merchant. Brick walls, candles in hurricane lamps and eclectic furnishings – believe it or not, one table features the brass headboard and footboard of a bed – add charm. A small deck, across the street and overlooking the river, is crowded on warm days. Always on the menu are clam chowder and onion soup au gratin. Sandwiches and light entrées like seafood fettuccine are available at noon. For dinner, start with the signature bloody mary, then perhaps have steamed mussels, baked stuffed clams or scallops wrapped in bacon. Or head for the raw bar, where the shellfish is priced by the piece. As an entrée, try bouillabaisse, seafood-stuffed shrimp, baked haddock or the Oar House Delight (shrimp, scallops and fresh fish lightly sautéed and topped with sour cream and seasoned crumbs, then browned in the oven). For the non-seafood eater, there are roasted rack of lamb, pork tenderloin and chicken breast stuffed with Maine crabmeat.

55 Ceres St., (603) 436-4025. Entrées, $15 to $24. Lunch daily, 11:30 to 2:30; dinner, 5 to 9 or 10.

Seafood, Plain and Simple

BG's Boat House Restaurant. Lobster and down-home surroundings attract those in the know to this little restaurant with outdoor decks and a marina out past the Wentworth resort in New Castle. Windows look onto an ocean inlet officially known as Sagamore Creek. The walls are paneled, the floors bare and tables have captain's chairs and paper mats. It's a perfect backdrop for devouring the lobsters delivered to the back door by boat by BG's own lobstermen. Last we knew, the lobster dinner was going for $9.95 and a lobster roll with french fries for $7.25. A seafood platter commands top dollar at $13.95. BG's also offers sandwiches, hamburgers, potato skins and mozzarella sticks, but most people go here for lobster and seafood, plain and simple.

191 Wentworth Road. (603) 431-1074. Entrées, $7.95 to $13.95. Lunch, Monday-Friday 11 to 4; dinner nightly, 5 to 9. Closed Monday and Tuesday in spring and fall and December-February.

Lighter Fare

Karen's. First Karen Weiss taught school for a couple of years, then took a job making and selling ice cream during the summer vacation. That intrigued her so much that instead of returning to school, she stayed in the food business, soon opening her own little spot. It's been eighteen years and she's still at it. Locals and visitors, especially vegetarians, love Karen's for breakfast, lunch and dinner. In an old narrow building near the historic district, the restaurant has bare wood floors, stenciled walls, mismatched chairs and a blackboard menu above the fireplace. The tiny but well-organized kitchen whips up luncheon specialties ($4.50 to $7.50) like Karen's Favorite (sautéed red onion, tomato, mushrooms, artichoke hearts and spinach on pita bread with melted cheddar) and a wonderful Greek salad pita loaded with feta. The sandwiches come with a choice of potato salad or black bean salad; the black bean is out of this world. For breakfast, you can create your own omelet, or have buttermilk pancakes or french toast made with homemade cinnamon raisin bread. Grilled tuna with black peppercorns (served rare with sautéed apples, honey and smoked salmon), baked portobello mushroom with brown rice, apple, walnut and squash stuffing, and grilled vegetable and chèvre terrine are possibilities for dinner. Beer and wine are available.
105 Daniel St. (603) 431-1948. Breakfast and lunch daily, 7 or 8 to 2:30; dinner, Thursday-Saturday 6 to 9. Entrées, $9.95 to $10.95. No credit cards.

Cafe Brioche in Market Square has wondrous pastries and baked goods; you can sit at a little ice-cream table outside or indoors and enjoy a European-style repast. Now there's jazz on Saturday nights and the place has doubled to accommodate its loyal following. **The Portsmouth Brewery** on Market Street offers several different brews, which it makes right here, but its Weisenheimer Brown Dog is the signature ale. There's an all-day menu with pizzas, burgers, sandwiches and a couple of more serious items such as porterhouse steak and herb-rubbed game hen. It's a big place, with lots of booths and tables; next door is the retail store with a tee shirt to match each brew. The **Ceres Bakery** on Penhallow Street is always a good stop for fine pastries and delicious breads.

Picnicking is best on **Four Tree Island,** within walking distance from Prescott Park on the Portsmouth waterfront. You reach the little island via a short bridge that leads from Marcy Street to Pierce Island and then via causeway to the smaller island. There are sturdy picnic tables under shelters, all with views of riverfront activity. Other picnic spots are Prescott Park and the public beach in New Castle.

FOR MORE INFORMATION: Greater Portsmouth Chamber of Commerce, 500 Market St., Portsmouth, N.H. 03801, (603) 436-1118.

24 🌷 Spring

Tower of Casco Castle overlooks boats in South Freeport harbor.

Main Street and More

Freeport and the Harpswells, Maine

Every year, nearly four million people from around the world make the pilgrimage to the big, plain building with the canoes and kayaks out front in the center of Freeport. It's the famous 24-hour-a-day retail store of L.L. Bean, purveyors of goods for the outdoorsman and symbol to many of the Maine mystique. They may only have heard of Freeport from Bean's ubiquitous mail-order catalogs, but they're coming to mecca – many in search of nostalgia, of simpler times, of basic virtues and values. It's as much a draw in springtime for parents getting their youngsters outfitted for summer camp as it is for affluent urbanites seeking to get back to the earth, if only through a Bean jacket.

And what a shopping mecca it is. All those pilgrims have turned Bean's into the second most frequented tourist destination in the state (after Acadia National Park). In their wake in the last dozen years have popped up more than 125 outlet stores, two dozen inns and B&Bs, a dozen restaurants, and assorted peripheral services and attractions in Freeport.

Once a thriving shipbuilding center and later a mill town, 200-year-old Freeport had fallen on hard times in the mid-20th century. It harbored Bean's eccentric factory and mail-order house, where hunters would stop on their way to the woods, but that was about all. The Bean retail store emerged from relative obscurity only in the 1970s, and began inflating into its current gargantuan state in the 1980s.

Freeporters point to 1981 as the start of the town's latter-day tourism boom, which they consider a mixed blessing. Fire had destroyed Leighton's 5 & 10, and into its rebuilt quarters across from L.L. Bean moved a Dansk outlet center. More outlets were to follow. Their situation in Freeport, however, was determined by a two-year legal battle involving McDonald's, which sought to install golden arches in place of one of Freeport's finest remaining 19th-century mansions. Opponents, united in what they called a Mac Attack, forged a compromise: McDonald's could sell its hamburgers, but only if it restored the interior and retained the facade of the 1855 William Gore House. So it is that thousands of Big Macs are consumed in Freeport in a Colonial setting, that Banana Republic occupies a most un-Banana-Republic-like, two-story Federal brick edifice, and The Gap is located in a white contemporary colossus. Tight zoning and management helped the small town of 6,900 residents spurn the Kittery and Ellsworth strip looks in favor of a village downtown appearance patterned after that of Camden.

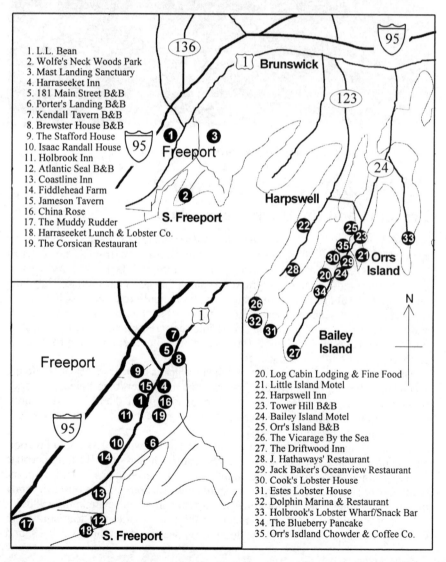

1. L.L. Bean
2. Wolfe's Neck Woods Park
3. Mast Landing Sanctuary
4. Harraseeket Inn
5. 181 Main Street B&B
6. Porter's Landing B&B
7. Kendall Tavern B&B
8. Brewster House B&B
9. The Stafford House
10. Isaac Randall House
11. Holbrook Inn
12. Atlantic Seal B&B
13. Coastline Inn
14. Fiddlehead Farm
15. Jameson Tavern
16. China Rose
17. The Muddy Rudder
18. Harraseeket Lunch & Lobster Co.
19. The Corsican Restaurant

20. Log Cabin Lodging & Fine Food
21. Little Island Motel
22. Harpswell Inn
23. Tower Hill B&B
24. Bailey Island Motel
25. Orr's Island B&B
26. The Vicarage By the Sea
27. The Driftwood Inn
28. J. Hathaways' Restaurant
29. Jack Baker's Oceanview Restaurant
30. Cook's Lobster House
31. Estes Lobster House
32. Dolphin Marina & Restaurant
33. Holbrook's Lobster Wharf/Snack Bar
34. The Blueberry Pancake
35. Orr's Isdland Chowder & Coffee Co.

Where shoppers converge, food and lodging are sure to follow. Jameson Tavern, where the papers were signed making Maine a separate state in 1820, was turned into a restaurant next door to L.L. Bean – a coincidence its owner likened to having the hot dog franchise at Boston's Fenway Park. Two native Maine sisters who had a thriving lodging operation in Connecticut recognized the opportunities in Freeport and eventually expanded a five-room B&B into the first-class Harraseeket Inn and restaurant. Small B&Bs emerged as well.

There's more to Freeport than Bean's and its expanding Main Street – a fact overlooked by most visitors bent on bargains. Head down to gracious South Freeport and a picturesque working harbor far removed in place and spirit from what the rest of us call Freeport and oldtimers know as Freeport Square or Freeport Corner. Explore the byways of Porter's Landing, Lower Mast Landing and the other settlements along Freeport's hidden coastline. Enjoy the waterside walking trails at Wolfe's Neck Woods State Park, the wildlife at Mast Landing Sanctuary, the swimming and camping at Winslow Memorial Park.

If that piques your interest, head a few miles east to the Harpswells, rural fingers of land stretching south from Brunswick into northern Casco Bay. Great, Orr's and Bailey islands, connected by bridges, make up one finger. Harpswell Neck forms another. This is the unspoiled Maine of old, the natural state you expect far Down East but not along the southwestern coast. Hidden coves, ocean vistas, quaint hamlets and lobster pounds portray the Maine you came for, the one you suspected lies far beyond the portals of L.L. Bean. But here it is, just outside.

Freeport and the Harpswells are at their best in spring, before the hordes arrive.

Getting There

Freeport straddles coastal Route 1 just off I-95, about eighteen miles east of Portland. The Harpswells extend south of Route 1 at Brunswick, a college town six miles northeast of Freeport.

A car is a necessity in both areas, although traffic and parking can be a problem in Freeport at peak shopping periods. Air service is available into Portland International Jetport. Greyhound buses serve Portland as well.

Freeport

Seeing and Doing

The draw for most visitors is shopping, specifically L.L. Bean. Be advised: beyond Main Street is another Freeport with often-bypassed attractions.

Shopping

L.L. Bean. Leon Leonwood Bean's legacy is the stuff of retailing legends. From his brother's clothing store across the street from what is now the Bean retail store, late-blooming outdoorsman "L.L." – as he was called – invented at age 40 the Maine hunting shoe, a practical boot with rubber bottoms and leather uppers that's still Bean's best-seller (about a quarter million pairs a year). Bean was a master at mail-order, promising unconditional guarantees and free delivery along with value, the assurance of personal testing and plenty of homespun charm. Bean designed many of the goods himself and tried them out personally on the trails.

Although mail-order remains the fastest-growing component of the business, it is retailing that is most evident in Freeport. The early factory/mail-order business located conveniently above the local post office developed a retail adjunct when sportsmen would stop for licenses and equipment at all hours. That prompted L.L. to throw away the key in 1951 and stay open for business 24 hours a day. Following his death in 1967, the Bean enterprise prospered under grandson Leon Gorman from sales of $4 million to $600 million a year. The original Bean building was removed in 1977 for parking space, but the various additions L.L. built over the decades comprise half of today's 125,000-square-foot, three-level structure that includes skylights, atriums and a stocked trout pond beneath the main staircase.

Although goods for the outdoorsman remain foremost, Bean's now carries 75,000 items – far more than are pictured in the 22 catalogs mailed annually to 114 million customers. Totes, books, Adirondack chairs, Maine foods, clothing, footwear, sports equipment, bicycles – you name it, and if it fits L.L.'s vision, Bean's carries it. Never more so than after Lisa Birnbach's *The Official Preppy Handbook* made L.L. Bean the bearer of preppy tidings. Bean's sales increased a record 42 percent in 1981. But as Leon Gorman noted, Bean's had suddenly become fashionable at the expense of function. While new customers were buying Bean's products, he said, they were buying them for the wrong reasons. Threatened with being passed by as last year's fashion house, Bean rededicated itself to the family and to the outdoors. In 1997, it was planning to build a children's store at the rear and a large addition to the main store.

98 Main St., Freeport. (800) 341-4341. Open 24 hours a day, 365 days a year.

OTHER RETAILING. Freeport's recent advertising as Maine's answer to Rodeo Drive is somewhat far-fetched; more credible is its claim to be "the Maine village quality goods made famous." Downtown Freeport avoided the strip mentality of Kittery, Ellsworth and North Conway, though a bit of that is evident on the outskirts along Route 1 south.

It also shunned the outlet image of its counterparts. Twenty percent of the 125 (and growing) retailers here aren't factory outlets at all; these include **Abacus** for outstanding crafts, **Edgecomb Potters** for fine pottery and the **Claire Murray Store's** fabulous hand-hooked rugs. Most of the others feature first-quality items (no seconds) at prices that aren't particular bargains. Some have outlet corners or floors (Bean's factory store is tucked away off Depot Street). Ten to fifteen new retailers enter the Freeport market every year and five to ten leave as the merchandising mix evolves.

Freeport considers itself unique in having the first **Laura Ashley** outlet. A **Brooks Brothers** factory store occupies a prime space along Bow Street. Among the biggest along Main Street are **The Gap, Benetton, Banana Republic** and **Mikasa,** which has three floors crammed full of china, silver and more. We also liked the **Patagonia, Foreside Company, Denby** china and **Burberrys Ltd.** stores. The new **Mangy Moose** has more items with moose on them than we knew existed, from swizzle sticks to tea towels to Christmas cards to coasters and, of course, T-shirts for the entire family.

And, sign of the times, **Rocky Mountain Chocolate Factory** and **Gloria Jean's Gourmet Coffee** are juxtaposed in close proximity to a new **Arby's.** There seem to be as many sidewalk food vendors per corner as in midtown Manhattan; the hot dog cart across the street from Bean's is managed and operated by students from

Freeport High School. The best deal we saw was two hot dogs for $1.85 at Depot Street Caboose.

If you suffer from crowds, avoid Freeport at peak hours on busy shopping days. We happened by on a cloudy, non-beach weekday in early August to find ourselves embroiled in what until then was Freeport's biggest day ever – an estimated 25,000 people. Vehicles were bumper-to-bumper along Main Street between exits from I-95. Cars cruised for parking spaces blocks away from downtown. Pedestrians, who have the right of way in crosswalks, kept traffic at a standstill and made negotiating the sidewalks difficult. A new Bean parking lot behind its store has eased congestion a bit.

Other Attractions

South Freeport. The focal point of a 19th-century boom in shipbuilding and still a working harbor, this is now a fashionable residential area and yachting center. We first discovered there was more to Freeport than Main Street a few years ago when we set out for a lobster roll at Harraseeket Lunch & Lobster Co. The surprises yielded by the rural route there were exceeded only by the sights of the gracious homes and the picturesque harbor at the end. One of our visits coincided with the South Freeport Summer Festival, three days of art shows, craft sales and feasting (lobster dinner, $8; chicken barbecue, $7) inside and out at the South Freeport United Church of Christ. Other than the harbor, the town's best known landmark is Casco Castle, a 100-foot-high stone tower – all that remains of a large summer hotel destroyed by fire in 1914.

Atlantic Seal Cruises. An old, 28-passenger Coast Guard cruiser departs from the town wharf on a variety of daily excursions. Most popular are three-hour tours at 9 and 1:30 out seven miles to Eagle Island, a state park where the boat pauses for an hour to let passengers explore the seventeen-acre island and visit the museum/home of Admiral Robert E. Peary, the first man to reach the North Pole. Photos and artifacts from his Arctic explorations are displayed in his summer home along with a collection of mounted Arctic and Maine birds. The state of Maine and the National Geographic Society restored the home's library. Capt. Tom Ring hauls his lobster traps on the return voyage. The Atlantic Seal also offers seal and osprey watches and dinner cruises to Chebeague Island on various summer evenings.
25 Main St., South Freeport. (207) 865-6112. Adults $20, children $15.

Also leaving from the wharf on several trips daily is a mail boat to Bustin's Island (passengers, $5). Capt. Sharon Renk-Greenlaw of **Freeport Sailing Adventures,** (207) 865-9225, offers half-day and day cruises for $35 on her 44-foot yacht.

Wolfe's Neck Woods State Park. Five miles of hiking trails and secluded picnic sites are the attractions of this 200-acre property along the Harraseeket River and Casco Bay. "To the uninitiated, all of this may appear as nothing more than a collection of trees and brush," notes the display board. You learn that the forests of Wolfe's Neck represent a unique collection of ecological and local climatic conditions. Some of the white pine trees are thought to have been used by the British Navy as masts for their sailing ships. That led to the name for nearby Mast Landing and gave the unusual shape to Freeport Square, the triangle opposite L.L. Bean, where the logs were given extra turning room as they were hauled to the waterfront. People can swim off the Casco Bay trail, spot the pair of osprey that make the Googins Island sanctuary their home, and dig up to a peck of clams from the salt marsh when the tide is out. The park is open daily from 9 to sunset, Memorial Day through Labor Day; fee for parking. Upon leaving, drive farther down Wolfe's Neck Road through huge pines that resemble a redwood forest to the University of Southern Maine's working farm and Smith Stone House, whose landscaped grounds yield a view of Casco Bay on one side and South Freeport's Casco Castle on the other.

Wolfe's Neck Road, Freeport. (207) 865-4465.

Mast Landing Sanctuary. The Maine Audubon Society operates this 140-acre sanctuary amid fields and streams. A favorite attraction is a mill stream cascading over a dam into the tidal salt marshes of the Harraseeket River estuary. Visitors see shorebirds, minks, deer and porcupines from two miles of marked trails.

Upper Mast Landing Road, Freeport. (207) 781-2330. Daily, dawn to dusk; donation.

Other choice spots include **Winslow Memorial Park,** Staples Point Road, South Freeport, a 90-acre municipal park with a good sandy beach (the area's nine-foot tides are such that there's swimming at high tide only), a grassy picnicking area and a campground.

The Freeport Historical Society operates the **Harrington House Museum Store** at 45 Main St., an 1830 house museum in which the contents are displayed for purchase. Personnel there can give directions for a scenic walk out to the society's **Pettingill Farm,** an old saltbox farmhouse on a saltwater farm.

Good Earth Farm at 55 Pleasant Hill Road, Freeport, purveys all kinds of dried flowers and herbs.

Commercial attractions are the **North American Wildlife Expo,** Route 1 south of Freeport, billed as the largest wildlife museum of its kind on the East Coast, and **Desert of Maine,** 100 acres of sand dunes that evolved from pastureland that lost its topsoil.

A short excursion takes visitors just across the town line to **Lower Falls Landing,** a commercial complex and marina beside the Royal River in Yarmouth. Here are a handful of stores and The Cannery, a good seafood restaurant run by the owners of the Waterfront restaurant in Camden and much recommended by Freeport innkeepers.

Where to Stay

Harraseeket Inn. Nancy Gray and Jody Dyer, two sisters from South Portland who built the thriving Inn at Mystic complex in Connecticut, saw what was happening back in their home state and began assembling property for a full-service inn and gathering spot in the center of Freeport. They started with an elegant five-room B&B in 1984 and, in 1989, added a three-story, 49-room inn and restaurant. Such was the response that the Harraseeket was expanding its tavern and adding an enclosed swimming pool and 30 more guest rooms in 1997. Standard accommodations offer one queensize or two double beds with blue and white fabric half-canopies, wing chairs and baskets of Lord & Mayfair toiletries in the bathrooms. Deluxe rooms contain fireplaces and jacuzzis, wet bars and TVs hidden in armoires. Chocolates come with turndown service at night. Excellent meals are available in the **Maine Dining Room** and the **Broad Arrow Tavern** (see Where to Eat). A full breakfast buffet and an elaborate afternoon tea in the inn's attractive living room are included in the rates.

162 Main St., Freeport 04032. (207) 865-9377 or (800) 342-6423. Fax (207) 865-1684. Doubles, $145 to $220; suites, $235.

181 Main Street Bed & Breakfast. David Cates and Ed Hasset renovated this 1840 Greek Revival House into a B&B in 1986. Theirs was the first along an outer Main Street stretch that is now full of B&Bs. They offer seven upstairs guest rooms with private baths, all attractively furnished but rather small, as rooms in some historic homes are apt to be. Guests spread out in twin front parlors, one containing quite a collection of ceramic animals in a sideboard and a long coffee table made of glass atop an old ship's rope bed. The other is more like a library with a TV. The partners serve a breakfast to remember in two dining rooms dressed with calico tablecloths and Hitchcock chairs. The day we visited, it included a choice of juices, a poached pear with pureed strawberries and blueberries on a bed of vanilla yogurt, and blueberry pancakes with sausage. An asset here is the secluded swimming pool in the long back yard.

181 Main St., Freeport 04032. (207) 865-1226 or (800) 235-9750. Doubles, $85 to $100.

Porter's Landing Bed & Breakfast. A rural location and suave accommodations recommend this B&B on five shady acres. Peter and Barbara Griffin, parents of three young children, turned the carriage house attached to their classic 1830 Greek Revival home into three guest rooms, a spiffy living/dining room and a library loft. The soaring space gave their architect lots of room and angles; witness the stairway and landing leading to the skylit, third-floor library hideaway. All three rooms on the second floor have private baths. They are furnished simply but elegantly and contain interesting art. Lemonade and banana bread might be served in the afternoon. Breakfast involves fresh fruit, homemade granola and perhaps belgian waffles, egg ramekins or cheese omelets.

70 South St., Freeport 04032. (207) 865-4488. Doubles, $95.

The Kendall Tavern Bed & Breakfast. Big bucks went into the renovation of this old farmhouse by three California men in 1991. The landscaped grounds and the attractive yellow house with white trim are welcoming, as are the two small fireplaced living rooms, one with a Steinway piano and the other with a TV. Wonderful paintings adorn a breakfast room set with seven tables for two, where innkeeper Jim Whitley serves a fruit course, muffins and pancakes or a mushroom omelet. Upstairs are five fairly small bedrooms with queensize beds and two with twins, each with private bath and most with attractive bed coverings. At the rear of the main floor is a large indoor whirlpool tub for guests' use.

213 Main St., Freeport 04032. (207) 865-1338 or (800) 341-9572. Doubles, $100 to $125.

Brewster House Bed & Breakfast. A restored Queen Anne house was converted from three-family apartment status in 1994 by a young Connecticut couple who met in the kitchen of an Appalachian Mountain Club camp, where he was the cook. Amy and Matthew Cartmell put their restaurant backgrounds to use here, she as waitress and he as short-order cook. They offer guests a choice of omelets, waffles, pancakes or french toast to go along with the fruit course, muffins and cereal. Breakfast is served at individual tables dressed with woven blue mats, blueberry pottery and blue-handled silverware in a dining room with deep blue walls and a pressed-tin ceiling. The dining room opens into a soft pink parlor with fireplace, TV and piano. The main floor also has a guest room with twin beds and the second floor adds four bedrooms with queen beds and private baths. New on the third floor are two family suites, each consisting of a master bedroom with king or queen bed connected via a bathroom to a smaller room with double bed. Rooms are carpeted and fresh-looking with floral fabrics and comforters. The Cartmells, parents of two youngsters, welcome children over 8.

180 Main St., Freeport 04032. (207) 865-4121 or (800) 865-0822. Fax (207) 865-42211. Doubles, $100 to $110; suites, $150.

The Stafford House. You don't expect to find so substantial a house just off Freeport's busy Main Street, let alone a gracious English Tudor set up a hill on nearly three acres of lawns and gardens. Then you learn that this "oasis" at the edge of downtown was built in 1941 for the son of L.L. Bean. Freeport natives Margaret and Nelson Soule, he a retired train agent, and their daughter Judi, who works at Bean's, bought the house in 1994 with the idea of renovating it to share as a B&B. Judi, who did the decorating, is on hand in the morning and at night to help her parents. The house is true to Maine, from the formal living room with grand piano and TV to the paneled den on the second floor, fully outfitted with Bean memorabilia. Three substantial bedrooms come with private baths, queen beds, antique furnishings, and Maine paintings and artifacts. The skylit attic room also contains a day bed. The canopied four-poster bed in the front room looks traditional until Nelson shows how its novel air mattress can be pumped into a hard or soft surface. Breakfast is served in the dining room at a long English table beneath a crystal chandelier from Austria. The fare might be baked pancakes with strawberries or eggs and bacon with hash browns.

24 Elm St., Freeport 04032. (207) 865-4490. Doubles, $95.

Isaac Randall House. Spirited conversation is the norm in the beamed country kitchen of this rambling 1823 farmhouse, once a stop on the Underground Railroad as slaves made their way to Canada. Here is where owners Glynrose and Jim Friedlander prepare breakfast for guests around a large table above a rug painted on the floor. Quiche, huevos rancheros or orange-almond french toast could be the fare. Opened as Freeport's first B&B in 1984, the house has eight homey guest rooms, all with private baths, two with gas fireplaces and several outfitted with day beds that make them good for families. The two nicest are in the rear. The Pine Room offers a queen bed and an antique copper tub. Above is the large Loft, with sloping ceiling, skylights, a draped kingsize bed, TV, oriental rattan furniture and an enormous, two-section bathroom with a rattan chair. Besides the kitchen focal point, there's a Victorian sitting room with TV on the second floor, plus a kitchenette where soft drinks, cheese and crackers are kept for guests. The B&B is located on five rural acres, with a parked train caboose and a pond out back. Guests are scarcely aware of the presence of the sprawling L.L. Bean office and distribution center across the street.

5 Independence Drive, Freeport 04032. (207) 865-9295 or (800) 865-9295. Fax (207) 865-9003. Doubles, $90 to $125.

Holbrook Inn. Only one house separates the 100-year-old Victorian home of new owners Sue and Mark Trottier from the busy Main Street shopping area. But the side yard is turned the other way and the three spotless guest rooms are air conditioned and equipped with TVs, queensize four-poster beds and private baths. Lest the amenities mislead: this is not a typical B&B layout. The two main rooms on the second floor amount to a two-bedroom suite with a living room and a kitchen attesting to its former status as an apartment. The other room at the rear has a small wicker sitting room downstairs off the office and a bedroom with two stenciled rockers and a shower bath upstairs. At a polished round table in an airy breakfast room, Sue serves a hearty breakfast that might include eggs, pancakes or french toast. She had plans to add a side deck and eventually a gazebo.

7 Holbrook St., Freeport 04032. (207) 865-6693. Doubles, $75.

Atlantic Seal Bed & Breakfast. Freeport's only B&B on the water, this is the lifelong home of Tom Ring, a tugboat captain by trade. His is a house full of nautical memorabilia and antiques, among them an ancient sextant, an original clipper ship painting over the fireplace and old ship models made by his grandfather and showcased in a lighted corner cabinet. Tom offers three bedrooms, all with private baths and views of the Harraseeket River and Harbor. Largest is the Dash, with windows on three sides, a queensize and a double bed, TV and a private bath with a deep, oversize jacuzzi and a separate shower. The old-fashioned Heart's Desire room has a kingsize cannonball bed and a Rumford fireplace., while the cozy Glen has a double bed and a hall bath. The rear deck overlooking the water holds some of the striking modern wood slat chairs made by Tom's father. Tom lets guests use a rowboat at high tide, and offers a discount on his morning Atlantic Seal excursions to Eagle Island. He traps the lobsters that go into the trademark lobster omelets for breakfast.

25 Main St., Box 1046, South Freeport 04078. (207) 865-6112. Doubles, $85 to $135.

A Budget Motel

Coastline Inn. One of a small Maine motel chain, this has 109 rooms with two double, one double or one kingsize bed and standard motel furnishings. The rooms are air-conditioned, have no balconies and the windows unfortunately don't open. (In the off-season, these would be quite adequate but in summer, we wonder who wants to be in Maine in a place where you can't sit outside or open the windows?) At least the room configuration puts guests away from the highway, which is more than we can say for the Super 8 squashed between Route 1 and I-95 across the street. Continental breakfast is included in the rates.

209 Route 1 South, Freeport 04032. (207) 865-3777 or (800) 470-9494. Fax (207) 865-4678. Doubles, $83.

Where to Eat

Harraseeket Inn. Chris Toole, chef de cuisine here for six years, continued the culinary tradition launched by Sam Hayward (who left to open his own restaurant in Portland) when he succeeded him as executive chef in 1996. Creative fare featuring Maine ingredients is offered, both in the three elegant rooms of the Maine Dining Room and in the relocated and expanded Broad Arrow Tavern. The changing dinner menu ranges widely, from a heart-healthy grilled vegetable platter with root vegetable gratin to local saddle of venison with saffron risotto and ratatouille. The farm-raised salmon might be teamed with potato risotto and asparagus; the grilled lamb sirloin with red lentils, eggplant and oregano. Fettuccine with grilled portobello mushrooms, rack of lamb and châteaubriand are prepared tableside for two. You might start with sherried lobster stew, chilled Pemaquid oysters or foie gras on a toasted brioche. Finish with a flourish: warm chocolate cake flamed with grand marnier, Jamaican bananas, or a sampling of the homemade ice creams and sorbets. In the enlarged tavern, you can order sandwiches, salads and entrées priced from $9.95 for fish and chips to $15.905 for grilled sirloin steak. The $10.95 luncheon buffet spread in the dining room is quite a cut above the norm.

162 Main St., Freeport. (207) 865-9377. Entrées, $14 to $26. Lunch daily, 11:30 to 2:30; dinner nightly, 6 to 9 or 9:30.

Fiddlehead Farm. This rural homestead across from the L.L. Bean distribution center offers some of Freeport's most highly touted cuisine. Chef-owners Chris and Laura Washburn acquired their culinary skills at restaurants across the country before returning to her native Maine to acquire the former Sebastian's, renaming it and adding a country cafe out back. The farmhouse interior is cozy and properly historic; for lunch, we're partial to the small, canopied outdoor deck, somewhat dwarfed lately by the cafe. Here at one visit we enjoyed fish chowder and the Fiddlehead Farm salad ($7.95), spinach with dried cranberries, feta cheese and turkey, and the restaurant's "famous grilled turkey club" ($7.50), which turned out not to be a three-decker club but simply a regular sandwich, albeit excellent, on toasted potato bread. You also can order Maine crab cakes, sautéed chicken with cranberry chutney or quiche and salad in the $6.96 to $8.95 range. The traditional dinner service at Fiddlehead Farm was discontinued in 1996, and future hours were uncertain. Basic breakfasts and lunches are served in the intimate Country Cafe.

15 Independence Drive, Freeport. (207) 865-0466. Lunch daily, 11:30 to 2; cafe, daily 7 to 2.

Jameson Tavern. With a location next to L.L. Bean and an historic setting proclaimed as the birthplace of Maine, how could this place miss? A plaque outside denotes it as the site in 1820 of the signing of the papers that separated Maine from Massachusetts. A selection of menus steers hundreds of patrons on a busy day to the dark and intimate dining rooms, the rear tap room and the large outdoor deck alongside. This is not a place for leisurely dining, and the menu encourages turnover of tables by limiting appetizers and desserts. Dinner entrées run from baked haddock to filet mignon topped with crabmeat. Salmon oscar, roast duckling and steak au poivre reflect a continental bent. Burgers and lighter fare are offered in the tap room, where shrimp stew is a highlight and you might order the grilled jerk chicken quesadilla for $6.95.

115 Main St., Freeport. (207) 865-4196. Entrées, $14.95 to $20.95. Tap room daily, 11:30 to 10 or 11. Dining room, lunch or Sunday brunch, 11:30 to 2:30; dinner, 5 to 10.

China Rose. Leave it to Freeport to turn up a Chinese restaurant that earned 4½ stars for food from the Maine Sunday Telegram reviewer shortly after it opened. Unusual dishes, attractively presented, are served in a serene, two-level dining room pretty in pink and black. Among them are a seafood hot and sour soup, shrimp and scallops sautéed in mala sauce, sizzling seafood wor bar and lobster with ginger and scallions. Prices are moderate, except for Peking duck ($23.95).

10 School St., Freeport. (207) 865-6886. Entrées, $7.95 to $13.95. Lunch daily, 11 to 3; dinner to 9:30 or 10.

The Muddy Rudder. Just across the narrow Cousins River from Freeport is this large and spiffy restaurant and lounge where the first-thing-you-see bar gives little hint of the cut-above food to come. We like the jaunty outdoor deck overlooking the Great Salt Marsh and the dining room with large windows beside. The menu is one of those something-for-everyone encyclopedias, offering for dinner a range from broiled scrod with a blackened mayonnaise and shrimp creole over pasta to grilled halibut, swordfish kabob and fisherman platter. Chicken and broccoli carbonara with prosciutto and the house alfredo sauce were being touted at our latest visit. There are some good-sounding salads and sandwiches for lunch, and seafood benedict is a highlight of the weekend brunch. Live piano music is played in the bar at night.

Route 1, Yarmouth. (207) 846-3082. Entrées, $10.95 to $14.95. Daily, 11 to midnight.

A Budget Choice

The Corsican Restaurant. Plain as plain can be but ever-popular is this offshoot of a Brunswick pizza and vegetarian eatery. For lunch, you might choose a veggie and avocado sub for $4.95, a lobster pizza for $9.95 or any number of salads or sandwiches. Dinnertime adds such entrées as broiled salmon, sautéed scallops in garlic butter, and chicken and lobster marsala. There are no beef dishes beyond a meatball sub. Beer and wine are available.

9 Mechanic St., Freeport. (207) 865-9421. Entrées, $10.95 to $15.95. Daily, 11 to 9.

Seafood by the Shore

Harraseeket Lunch & Lobster Company. Family-run and astride the fishing pier, this serves typical lobster-pound and seafood fare inside and out. It's at its best for lunch, when you can sit outside and watch the harbor goings-on (though you might have to wait in a long line for a table); nighttime is apt to get buggy. Our latest lunch included a delicious clam chowder, a clam roll on a toasted bun and a clam burger for under $10. The two weighty lobsters we took home for dinner in a special icebox cost an additional $22. Last we knew, hot dogs were going for $1.25, lobster rolls for $9.95 and the specialty basket of fried clams for $11.25.

Town Wharf, South Freeport. (207) 865-4888. Open daily, 11 to 9. BYOB. No credit cards.

The Harpswells

Diametrically opposed to Freeport's Main Street and what it represents are the Harpswells, the collective name for the fingers of land stretching into Casco Bay south of Brunswick and embracing Great Island, Orr's Island, Bailey Island and Harpswell Neck. The three islands are attached one to the other and the mainland by short bridges and, because of their narrowness, cast a thoroughly watery aspect. Bailey, the most seaward of the islands, is said to be the most popular of Casco Bay's 365 Calendar Islands because of its accessibility, though relatively few venture down there. Harpswell Neck is a peninsula leading from Brunswick and, because it is wider, has less of a watery feeling except at the ends of roads leading off Route 123 or at the neck's far end near South Harpswell.

The Harpswells – with their solitude, their scenery and their stability reflecting Maine as it used to be – are the perfect antidote to the frenzy of Freeport. Anyone partial to being near the water should make them their base for exploring the area.

Seeing and Doing

What's there to do? Not much, which is precisely the lure for those in the know. A few inns, motels and B&Bs of the old school offer lodging, the lobster houses provide sustenance, the fishing villages and working harbors add charm, the seaside air is exhilarating, and rockbound coves and inlets pop up at almost every turn.

The Casco Bay Lines out of Portland runs a six-hour cruise to Bailey Island; as round-trip passengers lay over here, others board for a 90-minute **nature cruise** past nearby islands (noon daily from Cook's Marina; adults $7, children $3).

Explore the shoreline, dig clams, walk or bike along the back roads, browse at one of the Harpswell Craft Guild's member galleries or shop for seasonal produce at the Vegetable Corner in North Harpswell, a rustic stand that seems to be the busiest enterprise along Harpswell Neck. If you want more, the shops of Freeport are less than 45 minutes' drive away. Where Freeport has action, the Harpswells have, well, character.

You'll notice that during an early-morning walk, many others are out walking, too. Folks exchange pleasantries, and even wave to the occasional motorist with out-of-state license plates who happens by. You marvel at the piles of lobster traps, some stunning seaside homes interspersed between the prevailing weatherbeaten cottages, the old fishing boats that give Mackerel Cove the look of Nova Scotia, and the passing lobster boats hauling in their bounty.

You stop outside All Saints By the Sea, a tiny Episcopal chapel that is most un-chapel-like, a shingled cottage without so much as a steeple. A sign points the way to **Giant Stairs,** a five-minute walk past wild rose and bayberry bushes along a bluff like that of Ogunquit's Marginal Way. Just when you think you won't find the stairs, a family who preceded say that you've arrived. Their youngsters are scrambling on the massive stone steps that march down to the ocean. A plaque at the top relates that these were given to their native town in 1910 by Capt. William Henry Sinnett and his wife Joanna. The preceding family, who have summered for years on Bailey Island, point out the jagged Pinnacle Rock, advise of Thunder Hole and Pirate's Cove and Land's End beyond, and tell how the locals go out by small boat to trade with Russian fishermen on trawlers just beyond the lighthouse.

Fishing shack at Mackerel Cove, Bailey Island.

You drive down to **Land's End,** where a statue of a lobsterman rises outside an unlikely-looking gift shop.

All this is a genuine Maine experience for you.

Where to Stay

Log Cabin Lodging & Fine Food. This may have started as a log cabin, but the new lodgings upstairs and in a former garage beside are anything but rustic. Downsizing their restaurant to add fine lodging in 1996, Sue and Neal Favreau offer six of the Harpswells' top accommodations, each with its own water-view deck. We liked the looks of the bright and airy York Room with queen bed, TV and telephone, kitchenette, jacuzzi tub and separate shower. The other rooms are similar, although three have full kitchens and two have none at all. The Mount Washington suite atop a former garage comes with a full kitchen, separate kingsize bedroom, two TVs, stereo and deck with private hot tub, from which you can see New England's tallest peak 90 miles away. "The sun sets right behind the mountain in summer," says Sue. Her guests also were able to see four July Fourth fireworks displays at once, stretching from Bath to Portland. The summery lounge chairs on the decks and in the rooms are display models for the line she carries in her gift shop. Guests enjoy a complimentary breakfast of eggs or french toast with meats and home fries.

Route 24, Box 41, Bailey Island 04003. (207) 833-5546. Fax (207) 833-7858. Doubles, $99 to $109; suite, $150.

Little Island Motel. "Please drive slowly – duck crossing," advises the sign at the entrance to the spit of land jutting into the water off Lowell's Cove Road. Beyond is an inviting small complex billed by owner Jo Atlass as "the intimate resort." It includes a seven-room, chalet-style motel with decks right over the water and two more private units at either end of her house opposite. A carved duck and a lobster trap are outside each door. The rooms we saw had small sitting areas with cable TV and mini-refrigerators, but most appealing were the decks, given privacy by canvas screens between each unit. Ducks emerged from under the trees and waddled up to a shady sitting area with a barbecue and picnic tables beside the water. Jo puts out a complimentary continental buffet breakfast in her home: lots of fresh fruits, muffins, croissants, jams, cereals, and ham and cheese biscuits. She also operates a small shop called the Gull's Nest, which stocks Maine handcrafts and rather suave gifts.

RD 1, Box 15, Orr's Island 04066. (207) 833-2392. Doubles, $110 to $114.

Harpswell Inn. A handsome 1761 structure that once served as the cookhouse for the famed Lookout Point Shipyard has been renovated into an up-and-coming B&B. Bill and Susan Menz, Connecticut natives who tired of corporate life in Houston, acquired the old Lookout Point House in 1991 and set about its restoration; visiting when we first were there was a woman who had grown up in the house and couldn't believe the changes. The inn has twelve bedrooms, six with private baths; the others have sinks in the rooms and shared baths. Rooms are stylishly outfitted and decorated. The prized main-floor Rackliffe Room is all blue and yellow with peacock wallpaper. A smaller favorite is the rear Bowdoin Room, resembling a college dorm room and bearing all sorts of memorabilia from Bill's days at Bowdoin College in Brunswick. The Texas Room on the third floor sports a queensize bed with longhorns above. Youngsters like to pull the chain at the top of the staircase to ring the rooftop bell that summoned hungry shipbuilders to their meals back in the 1860s. New in 1996 was an expanded carriage house that Bill was rebuilding himself. He produced three light and airy luxury units with kitchen facilities, gas-fired stoves, queen beds and decks with water views. In the carriage house, the downstairs room comes with a jacuzzi tub; the larger upstairs suite is on two floors. A third suite was created when the Menzes vacated their space at the back of the inn for new quarters in the rear of the carriage house. Much of the main floor in the inn is given over to a "great" room, which has a huge fieldstone fireplace, a grand piano, comfortable seating and windows almost to the floor. Breakfast in a large dining room might bring Swedish pancakes, waffles with caramelized strawberry sauce, french toast triage (regular, orange and caramelized fruit), omelets or sausage and cheese casserole.

141 Lookout Point Road, RR1, Box 141, South Harpswell 04079. (207) 833-5509 or (800) 843-5509. Doubles, $59 to $116; luxury units, $135 and $150.

Tower Hill Bed & Breakfast. The stone foundation of what had been a 1,000-gallon water and observation tower greets visitors to this farmhouse built in the early 19th century and claiming several subsequent additions. Bill Whiteside, a retired Bowdoin history professor, and his wife Susan share their home with guests in four rooms that Susan calls demi-suites. Theirs is a much-lived in house – "a work in progress," Susan calls it – full of the couple's collections. Hats take over part of the living room and stunning Western Chinese ceremonial costumes line the walls of a stairway. Bill's scholar's gown from his years in China is displayed in the sitting area of the Fan Room. Feminine and frilly and decorated with oriental fans, it is one of two bedrooms that share a bath. The East Room is masculine, paneled in bead board and yellow pine, its queen bed outfitted with an array of sheets that change depending on the guests and the whim of the hostess. Both the East and the Iris Suite have private baths, the latter containing a clawfoot tub and all kinds of iris prints, including iris on the tiles of the vanity's backsplash. The Iris also includes a sitting room with day bed and rattan chairs and a paneled bedroom with kingsize bed, colorful quilt and big TV. Lilacs are the decorative theme in the dining room, where Bill might serve his specialty pancakes, strata, quiche or eggs at a table for eight. Breakfast also can be taken in the rear "green-house," if you can find a place to sit amid all the plants and what-not.

Route 24, RD 1, Box 688, Orr's Island 04066. (207) 833-2311. Fax (207) 833-6256. Doubles, $65 to $100; suite, $125.

Bailey Island Motel. Route 24, Box 4, Bailey Island 04003. (207) 844-2886. Idyllically located on a grassy, shady waterside property beside the last cribstone bridge in existence at the entrance to Bailey Island, this two-story motel has ten rooms. Ralph Black Jr., a lifelong island resident, has upgraded the rooms since he took over in 1992 and added helpful books of visitor information in each room. There are several places from which to enjoy the views of Casco Bay: from the balcony off the second-floor rooms, on a new brick terrace off the ground-floor rooms, or on chairs right beside the water. We like to take the complimentary breakfast of coffee, juice and homemade strawberry muffins to a picnic table on a shady knoll affording views of both bay and Harpswell Sound beyond the cribstone bridge. The bridge was built with granite blocks laid in honeycomb fashion without cement to let the area's nine-foot tides flow through.

Route 24, RD 1, Box 688, Orr's Island 04066, (207) 833-2311. Fax (207) 833-6256. Doubles, $85. Closed late October to early May.

Orr's Island Bed & Breakfast. Lovely landscaped grounds and gardens that slope down to Long Cove, a huge raised sun deck and a rambling contemporary house. These attributes draw overnight guests to the home of Sandy and Colin Robinson, who opened in 1991 when "the rooms became available and I needed something to do," in Sandy's words. Two upstairs bedrooms vacated by their offspring share a large bath and a cathedral-ceilinged family room with a TV. Guests sometimes join the Robinsons in their modern living room, and eat a full breakfast in a skylit kitchen-dining area or on the deck. You can swim from the dock in Long Cove when the tide's in; otherwise, as is the case with shallow places in the area when the water disappears, the mud flats are good for clamming.

Route 24, Box 561, Orr's Island 04066. (207) 833-2940 or (800) 550-2940. Doubles, $75 to $85.

A Budget B&B

The Vicarage By the Sea. An avid gardener is obviously at work on the shady grounds of this three-room B&B in an attractive house off by itself beside Curtis Cove. There's a pleasant deck and a rope hammock, although the foliage of all the trees obscures much of the water view in summer. Inside, owner Joan Peterson-Moulton offers three bedrooms, one downstairs with a queen bed, private bath and glimpse of the cove. Two upstairs rooms with twins or double bed share a bath. Joan says she'll cook whatever guests like – eggs or pancakes, perhaps a casserole – for breakfast.

Route 1, Box 368B, South Harpswell 04079. (207) 833-5480. Doubles, $65 to $80.

An Inn from Yesteryear

The Driftwood Inn. A simple, old-fashioned place, this complex of shingled buildings perched beside the water at Land's End has been around for more than 80 years. The Conrad family offer five housekeeping cabins and 26 double and single guest rooms in three houses, most sharing one bathroom per floor. Four rooms in one house contain half-baths. Each house includes a common room and a porch that takes full advantage of the view toward the open ocean. A saltwater swimming pool set in the rocks is popular with children. Meals are served at a single seating in an open-timbered dining room with windows onto the water on two sides. Outside diners may come for breakfast ($4.50) at 8 or dinner ($10) at 6. The single-choice menu may offer roast pork on Monday, lamb on Wednesday, steak or lobster on Friday and turkey dinner on Sunday.

Bailey Island 04003. (207) 833-5461. Doubles, $65 to $70, EP. No credit cards. Closed mid-October to May.

Where to Eat

Log Cabin Lodging & Fine Food. Original owner Sue Favreau took back the cavernous Log Cabin in 1992 after leasing it for four years to Jack Baker (see below). She and her family did some modest upgrading, but the high-ceilinged interior that looks like a log cabin remains, complete with a moosehead over the fireplace. Additional seating is in a cozy front bar, as well as in enclosed porches with water views. In downsizing the restaurant operation by two-thirds, the upstairs function rooms have been converted into rooms for overnight guests. Sue, who has been in the restaurant business since she was 13, oversees the kitchen, assisted by her baker, Sue Bear, who has been with her for 22 years. The extensive menu changes nightly and ranges widely, from $12.95 for orange chicken and rice to $19.95 for black angus filet mignon. Seafood is featured: three versions of haddock, shrimp scampi over pasta, scallops fried or honey glazed, grilled salmon provençal. Lobster comes boiled or stuffed or in stew. A complete shore dinner, served in courses, goes for $26.95. Start with the seafood sampler: gulf shrimp, scallops in bacon, lobster, seafood dip and crackers. Finish with one of the delectable desserts, perhaps rhubarb custard pie, peach pie with crumb topping, sugar-free blueberry crisp or cheesecake with strawberries.

Route 24, Bailey Island. (207) 833-5546. Lunch daily, 11:30 to 2; dinner, 5 to 8 or 9. Closed November to mid-March.

Jack Baker's Oceanview Restaurant. Our favorite Rock Ovens restaurant, long a beacon of culinary creativity beside the cribstone bridge, has given way to the Oceanview. The decor remains the same, and oil lamps flickered and Vivaldi played as we watched the moonlight dance on the waves of Casco Bay. The menu is mostly seafood, from $8.95 for three homemade fish cakes to $21.95 for a shore dinner. Homemade meat lasagna, chicken pot pie, steak and fettuccine alfredo are the only non-fish dishes. The house salad is a cut above the norm, as are the rolls and corn fritters. The garlic shrimp on a bed of fettuccine, billed on the menu as something special for $12.95, turned out to be just that. The grilled swordfish was standard and the broiled flounder plainer than plain. The only real

disappointment was Maine crab cakes ($10.95) that were deep-fried rather than sautéed and were much too overdone. Boiled red potatoes and sautéed summer squashes came with. A bottle of Entre Deux Mers cost $13.50. Desserts tend to the heavy side, but we enjoyed rum raisin ice cream one evening and raspberry sorbet another. Much the same fare is available for lunch, inside or on the adjacent dock.
Route 24, Bailey Island. (207) 833-5366. Lunch, 11:30 to 4; dinner, 4 to 9 or 10.

J. Hathaways' Restaurant & Tavern. In an area where seafood and lobster houses reign, this chef-owned restaurant in a Maine farmhouse has stood out since 1984. Jeff Hathaway offers dinners priced from $9.95 for charbroiled ham steak with a side of stewed apples and raisins to $13.95 for pork spareribs, a full rack slowly cooked in the house barbecue sauce. Other possibilities include haddock with herbed meringue, baked scallops, sautéed honey-mustard chicken and sirloin steak. Prime rib is available on Saturdays, and fish and chips every night. Crackers with cheese dip precede the meal. Among desserts are apple crisp, lime mousse pie and brownie sundae. You can eat at nicely spaced tables amid dark Colonial decor in the main dining room, or more casually in the tavern.
Route 123, Harpswell Center. (207) 833-5305. Dinner, Tuesday-Saturday 5 to 9, Sunday 4 to 8. Closed January and February.

Seafood by the Shore

Cook's Lobster House. Folks come from all over the Harpswells for the fresh seafood and lobster at this oldtimer in a marina on a point surrounded by water. With windows on three sides, the main dining room is an expanse of low pine booths with a lamp on every table. Outside is Moby's Deck, a raw bar serving light food and drinks. The dinner menu is priced from $12.95 for fried haddock to $19.95 for sautéed lobster. Four shore dinners are $24.95 to $27.95. Blackboard specials when we were there were grilled swordfish and fried oysters. A lobster roll was $9.95 and boiled lobster, $13.95.
Bailey Island. (207) 833-2818. Daily, 11:30 to 9. Closed in January.

Estes Lobster House. Here is a huge, two-story barn of a place on a spit of land with water on both sides. You order at a large counter near the entrance, pick up your meal served on paper plates with wimpy plastic implements, and take a seat in a couple of long, nondescript dining rooms or, our choice, at picnic tables outside. The mosquitoes were fierce only for ten minutes around dusk, and the manager obliged by providing a couple of citronella candles (well, we *were* the only ones outside on a slow night and the inside was nearly empty). Estes was pushing its original triple lobster plate for $23.95, but we stuck with the lobster pie (lots of lobster, topped with stuffing) and a really good seafood medley (broiled halibut, swordfish, salmon and scallops), both with french fries and $14.95. A bottle of wine, candlelight and a gorgeous sunset made for quite a picnic, but next time we'll bring our own cutlery.
Route 123, South Harpswell. (207) 833-6340. Daily, 11:30 to 9. Closed mid-October to mid-April.

Dolphin Marina and Restaurant. Local folks pour in for three meals a day at this small, pine-paneled restaurant with a counter, eight tables, two booths, an attempt at a store and the best fish chowder around. We can vouch for the chowder, absolutely delectable and containing more fish than chowder. Also great for lunch was the lobster stew ($9.95), accompanied, rather strangely, by a blueberry muffin that we took home for breakfast the next day. Although it was lunchtime, the value enticed one of us to try the complete dinner ($9.95) of clam strips, chowder, salad (with pepper-parmesan dressing on the side), french fries, rainbow sherbet and coffee, ending up thoroughly sated. No wonder the oldtimers come here for their midday meal. At night, dinners are priced from $10.95 to $16.95 (for boiled lobster). There's no liquor, and iced tea seems to be the beverage of choice. The windows also don't open, and one of us found the air so stifling she thought she was going to faint.

Basin Point, South Harpswell. (207) 833-6000. Open daily, 8 to 8. Seasonal.

Budget Choices

Holbrook's Lobster Wharf & Snack Bar. A favorite haunt of Brunswick restaurateurs and others in the know is this seasonal spot beside Cundy's Harbor. You sit at picnic tables on the wharf and see everybody you know, says our local informant who thinks it's the best place going. Concert pianist Martin Perry and Broadway stage dancer Henry D'Allessandris came up to be part of the Maine State Theater and decided to stay. They run a quality, summery lunch place and their lobsters, salads and desserts are first-rate, particularly the steamed chocolate pudding. A lobster roll sells for $7.25; the baked haddock or scallop dinner for $7.95.

Cundy's Harbor. (207) 725-0708. Daily, 11 to 8. Closed October-April.

Orr's Island Chowder & Coffee Co. Located next to the cribstone bridge to Bailey Island, this neat little place that's part of a store and kayak complex is known for its all-natural seafood chowder, a thick and ultra creamy brew of haddock, scallops, clams and shrimp for $3.50 a bowl. Penny Michaud also offers lobster rolls ($6.50), vegetarian soups, pies and homemade muffins. The last go well with the Caravali coffees from Seattle.

Route 24, Orr's Island. Daily in summer, 11 to 6.

Just for Breakfast

The Blueberry Pancake. The sign outside says "breakfast restaurant," and geraniums are painted on the door. The little house is owned by Aleesa Baker Coffin, daughter of local restaurateur Jack Baker and herself owner of the Great Impasta restaurant, which serves lunch and dinner in Brunswick. Here, she and her staff whip up fancy-for-the-area breakfasts, from apple and cheddar omelets with fruit chutney to eggs benedict and filled crêpes, in our case one with ricotta, eggs, artichoke hearts and scallions, served with home fries, quite a plateful for $5.95. If you think that won't fill you up, opt for the fisherman's breakfast, yielding two each of eggs, bacon and pancakes, plus toast, juice and coffee for $5.95. Fresh flowers decorate the tables, inside and out on a small covered deck.

Route 24, Bailey Island. (207) 833-6808. Breakfast daily, 7:30 to 11, weekends to noon. Seasonal.

FOR MORE INFORMATION: The Freeport Merchants Association, Box 452, Freeport, Me. (04032, (207) 865-1212 or (800) 865-1994. It operates a small visitor center at the foot of Mill Street in downtown Freeport. The state-run Yarmouth Information Center along Route 1 at Exit 17 off I-95 has considerable information on Freeport and environs.

Index

A

B

Also by Wood Pond Press

Waterside Escapes in the Northeast. This new edition by Betsy Wittemann and Nancy Woodworth relates the best lodging, dining, attractions and activities in 36 great waterside vacation spots from the Chesapeake Bay to Cape Breton Island, from the Thousand Islands to Martha's Vineyard. Everything you need to know for a day trip, a weekend or a week near the water is told the way you want to know it. First published in 1987; revised and expanded in 1996. 474 pages to discover and enjoy. $15.95.

The Fireside Guide to New England Inns and Restaurants. This book by Betsy and Ross Wittemann details romantic places to stay and dine by the warmth of a crackling fire. The perfect off-season companion to *Waterside Escapes,* it tells which inns to go to for in-room fireplaces and which restaurants to seek out for tables beside the hearth. Published in 1995. 282 pages of warm information. $14.95.

Getaways for Gourmets in the Northeast. The first book by Nancy and Richard Woodworth appeals to the gourmet in all of us. It guides you to the best dining, lodging, specialty food shops and culinary attractions in 22 areas from the Brandywine Valley to Montreal, the Finger Lakes to Nantucket. First published in 1984; fully revised and expanded in 1997. 538 pages to read and savor. $18.95.

Inn Spots & Special Places in New England. Much more than an inn guide, this guide by Nancy and Richard Woodworth tells you where to go, stay, eat and enjoy in the region's choicest places. Focusing on 32 special destination areas, it details the best inns and B&Bs, restaurants, sights to see and things to do. First published in 1986; revised and expanded in 1995. 488 pages of timely ideas. $16.95.

Inn Spots & Special Places/New York and Mid-Atlantic. The second volume in the series, the newest book by Nancy and Richard Woodworth guides you to the best in 32 of the Mid-Atlantic region's choicest areas, from New York to Virginia. First published in 1992; revised and expanded in 1995. 504 pages of fresh ideas. $16.95.

The Restaurants of New England. This book by Nancy and Richard Woodworth is the most comprehensive guide to restaurants throughout New England. The authors detail menu offerings, atmosphere, hours and prices for more than 1,200 restaurants. First published in 1990; revised and expanded edition in 1994. 490 pages of thorough information. $14.95.

The Originals in Their Fields

These books may be ordered from your local bookstore or direct from the publisher, pre-paid, plus $2 handling for each book. Connecticut residents add sales tax.

Wood Pond Press
365 Ridgewood Road
West Hartford, Conn. 06107

Tel: (860) 521-0389
Fax: (860) 313-0185

E-Mail: woodpond@pop.ntplx.net
Web Site: http://www.ntplx.net/~woodpond/